# Alan Roge

# FRANCE
## 2003

**Quality Camping and Caravanning Sites**

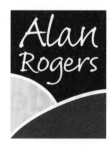

Compiled by: Alan Rogers Guides Ltd

Cover design: Paul Effenberg, Vine Cottage Design
Maps created by Customised Mapping (01985 844092)
contain background data provided by GisDATA Ltd.
Maps are © Alan Rogers Guides and GisDATA Ltd 2002

Clive Edwards, Lois Edwards & Sue Smart have asserted
their rights to be identified as the authors of this work.

First published in this format 2002

**© Alan Rogers Guides Ltd 2002**

Published by: Alan Rogers Guides Ltd, Burton Bradstock, Bridport, Dorset DT6 4QA


British Library Cataloguing-in-Publication Data:
A catalogue record for this book is available from the British Library.

**ISBN: 0 901586 88 9**

Printed in Great Britain by J H Haynes & Co Ltd

# Contents

# Introduction

It is thirty-five years since Alan Rogers, now sadly no longer with us, published the first campsite guide that bore his name, so we have been indulging in a little nostalgia and celebrating our 35th anniversary most notably by moving into new larger offices, by having our guides published in Dutch as well as in English, and by opening new offices in the Netherlands at Amersfoort. Apart from all this we have added a record number of new campsites to our France guide for 2003 - in fact we are featuring almost 100 new sites.

When Alan published the first of his guides in 1968 he introduced it with the words "I would like to stress that the camps which are included in this book have been chosen entirely on merit, and no payment of any sort is made by them for their inclusion". As campers and caravanners ourselves it was this objective approach that attracted us to become regular readers of his Guides, and which eventually lead to our taking over the editing and publishing of the Guides when Alan retired in 1986.

Whilst the content and scope of the Guides have expanded considerably in the 15 years since we took over, mainly due to the huge growth in the number of campsites throughout the UK, France and the rest of Europe during those years, our selection of sites to be featured still employs exactly the same philosophy as Alan defined 35 years ago.

## The Alan Rogers' Approach to Selecting Sites

Firstly, and most importantly, our selection is based entirely on our own rigorous inspection. Parks cannot buy their way into our guides - indeed the extensive Site Report which is written by us, not by the site owner, is provided free of charge so we are free to say what we think and to provide an honest description. This is written in plain English and without the use of icons or symbols.

The criteria which we use when selecting sites are numerous, but the most important by far is the question of good quality and standards. Whatever the size of the site, whether it's part of a campsite chain, or even a local authority site, makes no difference in terms of it being required to meet our exacting standards in terms of its quality. In other words, irrespective of the size of the site, or the number of facilities offered, the essentials (the welcome, the pitches, the sanitary facilities, the cleanliness and the general maintenance) must all be of a high standard.

Our selection of sites is designed to cater for a wide variety of preferences, from those seeking a small peaceful campsite in the heart of the countryside, to those looking for an 'all singing, all dancing' site in a popular seaside resort, and for those with more specific needs such as sports facilities, cultural or historical attractions, even sites for naturism.

We rely on our small, dedicated team of Site Assessors, all of whom are experienced campers, caravanners or motorcaravanners, to visit and recommend sites, following which our Sites Director makes the final decision on those to be included in the following year's guide. Once a site is included, it will be regularly inspected to ensure that standards are being maintained.

We also appreciate the feedback we receive from many of our readers, and we always make a point of following up complaints, suggestions or recommendations for possible new sites. Given the occasion of our 35th anniversary we felt we might include a selection of some of the comments we've had from readers during the past year:

*'Very useful - excellent guide! Wouldn't go without it.'*

*'Totally brilliant! As a first timer to camping abroad it has become my bible.'*

*'I like the honest reviews and assessments.'*

*'A pleasure to use and very reliable.'*

*'Makes it a lot easier to find a campsite that suits you, especially when you have two toddlers like us... good reading - keep writing!'*

*'A wealth of information you can't find anywhere else.'*

Of course we get a few grumbles too - but it really is a few, and those we do get usually arrive at the end of the high season and relate mainly to overcrowding or to poor maintenance during the peak school holiday period. The most frustrating complaints we get are from readers who have been using a guide that's several years out of date. We don't necessarily expect readers to buy a new guide every year, but it can be galling to receive a complaint about a campsite which hasn't been featured in our guides for the past several years!

Please bear in mind that although we are interested to hear about any complaints, we have no contractual relationship with the sites featured in our guides and are therefore not in a position to intervene in any dispute between a reader and a campsite. If you have a complaint about a campsite featured in our Guides the first step should be to take the matter up with the site owner or manager, preferably at the time as in most cases we'd expect any of the professional owners or managers of sites featured in our guides to do their best to address any justifiable complaint positively and quickly.

This year our dedicated team of site assessors has been very busy in France and achieved a record number of visits. Our thanks are due to them for the many miles they travel, their patience with our detailed site report forms and their commitment to the philosophy of the guides. As a result of all these visits, our 2003 edition includes 100 'new' sites (featured for the first time), but at the same time we have removed nearly 30 sites that, for one reason or another, failed to meet our inspection criteria.

During our own visits to France visiting sites, talking to owners, attending exhibitions, etc. we have also undertaken some research into tourist attractions and for the first time we include some information about these increasingly popular attractions - see page 368.

## Hints on using the Alan Rogers Guides

Being written in plain English, our guides are exceptionally easy to use, but a few words of explanation regarding the layout, etc. may be helpful. Regular readers will see that our Site Reports are grouped into eighteen 'tourist regions' and then by the various départements in each of these regions in numerical order.

### Regions and départements

For administrative purposes France is actually divided into 23 official Regions covering the 95 'départements' (similar to our counties). However, these do not always coincide with the needs of tourists (for example the area we think of as 'The Dordogne' is split between two of the official regions. We have, therefore, opted to feature our campsites within unofficial 'tourist regions', including in our introduction to each region the relevant départements with their official number (e.g. the département of Manche is number 50). We use these département numbers as the first two digits of our campsite numbers, so any campsite in the Manche département will start with the number 50.

### Indexes

Our three indexes allow you to find sites by site number and name, by region and site name or by the town or village where the site is situated.

### Campsite Maps

The maps relate to our tourist regions and will help you to identify the approximate position of each campsite.

The Site Reports
Example of an entry:

number

## Tourist Region
# Site name
Postal address

### Site report
*A description of the site in which we try to give an idea its general features - its size, its situation, its strengths and weaknesses. This column should provide a picture of the site itself with reference to the facilities provided if they impact on its appearence or character. We retain reference to pitch numbers, electricity (with amperage), hardstandings etc. in this section as pitch design, planning and terracing affects the site's overall appearence. Similarly we continue to include reference to mobile homes, chalets, etc. but no longer indicate if they are available to let (this type of information will appear in our new 'Mobile Homes and Chalets' guide). Importantly at the end of this column we indicate if there are any restrictions, e.g. no tents, naturist sites, etc.*

### Facilities:
*The second column in smaller print contains all the more specific information on the site facilities.*

*Please see the notes below.*

### Charges

| | |
|---|---|
| *Given in Euros!* | €1 = Ffrancs 6.56 |

### Tel/Fax/E-mail:
### Reservations:
### Open:
### Directions:
*Separated from the main text in order that they may be read and assimilated more easily by a navigator en-route. Bear in mind that road improvement schemes can result in some road numbers being altered.*

### Facilities:

**Toilet blocks:** are covered in less detail than in previous editions. We assume that toilet blocks will be equipped with at least some British style WCs, washbasins with hot and cold water and hot showers with dividers or curtains, and will have all necessary shelves, hooks, plugs and mirrors. We assume that there will be an identified chemical toilet disposal point, and that the campsite will provide water and waste water points and bin areas. If not the case, we comment. We continue to mention certain features that some readers find important: washbasins in cubicles, facilities for babies, facilities for those with disabilities and motorcaravan service points. Disabled readers are advised to telephone the site of their choice to ensure that facilities are appropriate to their needs.

**Shop:** basic or full supplies, and opening dates.

**Bars, restaurants, takeaway facilities and entertainment:** we try hard to supply opening and closing dates if other than the campsite opening dates and to identify if there are discos or other noisy entertainment.

**Children's play areas:** fenced and with safety surface (e.g. sand, bark or pea-gravel).

**Swimming pools:** if particularly special, we cover in detail in the first column but reference is always included in the second column. Opening dates, charges and levels of supervision are provided where we have been notified.

**Leisure facilities:** e.g. playing fields, bicycle hire, organised activities and entertainment.

**Dogs:** If dogs are not accepted or restrictions apply, we state it here. Check the quick reference list on page 343.

**Off site:** This briefly covers leisure facilities, tourist attractions, restaurants etc nearby. Geographical tourist information is more likely to be in the first column.

**Charges:** are the latest provided by the sites. In those few cases where 2002 or 2003 prices are not given, we try to give a general guide. All prices shown are in Euros per night (see page 356). Be aware that some sites, including many municipal sites, probably won't accept credit cards.

**Telephone numbers:** All numbers assume that you are 'phoning from within France. To phone France from outside that country, prefix the number shown with the relevant International Code (00 33) and drop the first 0, shown as (0) in the numbers indicated.

**Opening dates:** are those advised to us during the early autumn of the previous year -

site owners can, and sometimes do, alter these dates before the start of the following season - often for good reasons - so if you intend to visit shortly after a published opening date, or shortly before the closing date, it is wise to check that it will actually be open at the time required. Similarly some sites operate a restricted service during the low season, only opening some of their facilities (e.g. swimming pools) during the main season - where we know about this, and have the relevant dates, we indicate it, but if you are at all doubtful again it is wise to check.

**Reservations:** Necessary for high season (roughly mid-July to mid-August) in popular holiday areas (i.e beach areas). You can reserve via our own Travel Service or through tour operators (see adverts). Or be wholly independent and contact the campsite(s) of your choice direct, using the phone, fax or e-mail numbers shown in the site reports, but please bear in mind that many sites are closed all winter.

**Directions:** Given last, with a coloured background, in order that they may be read and assimilated more easily by a navigator en route.

### Points to bear in mind

Some French site owners are very laid back when it comes to opening and closing dates. They may not be fully ready by their opening date - grass and hedges may not all be cut and perhaps only limited sanitary facilities open. At the end of the season they also tend to close down some facilities and generally wind down prior to the closing date. Bear this mind if you are travelling early or late in the season - it is worth ringing ahead.

The 'Camping Cheque' system goes some way to addressing this in that participating campsites are advised to have all facilities open and running by the opening date and to remain fully operational until the closing date. Participating sites are marked in this guide with the Camping Cheque logo.

Another area which has caused readers problems is the regulations which exist in some regions whereby Bermuda shorts may not be worn in swimming pools (for health reasons). It is worth ensuring the you do take 'proper' swimming trunks with you.

Whether you're an 'old hand' in terms of camping or caravanning in France, or contemplating your first caravan holiday abroad, a regular reader of our Guides or a new reader, we hope you will find that this latest, full colour edition with over 100 new sites has plenty to interest you and to help you make your choices for your holiday. Bonnes Vacances!

Lois Edwards MAEd, FTS
Clive Edwards BEd, FTS
Sue Smart    Editors

## The Alan Rogers' Travel Service

**the travel service**

**TO BOOK**

| | |
|---|---|
| Ferry | ✓ |
| Pitch | ✓ |
| Accommodation | ✓ |

**01892 55 98 98**

The unique Alan Rogers Travel Service enables our readers to book at over 200 of the best sites in this guide, along with assistance with ferry crossings and comprehensive insurance cover, all at extremely competitive rates.

One simple telephone call to our Travel Service on 01892 55 98 98 is all that is needed to make all the arrangements. Why not take advantage of our years of experience of camping and caravanning in France. We would be delighted to discuss your holiday plans with you, and offer advice and recommendations.

All the sites included in the special Travel Service programme have been carefully selected and we believe that we are able to offer the widest selection of sites in France, ranging from the most sophisticated 'Les Castels' sites to delightful rural municipals.

In establishing our programme, we have ensured a selection of sites in eery corner of France and, as well as offering sites in well known areas and well established resorts, we have also sought to include some smaller sites in little known areas, but which are very well worth a visit. A brief summary follows by region of what we are able to offer for 2003:

Brittany - 30 sites in the four Breton départements. Many are placed close to charming seaside resorts, ideal for taking advantage of super sandy beaches, others offer the opportunity to discover the wooded valleys and sleepy villages of the less known hinterland.

Normandy - a good choice of 6 sites ranging from the superb beaches of the Cotentin peninsula to the stylish resorts of the Côte Fleurie, as well as sites surrounded by the cider and calvados producing orchards for which the region is justly famous.

Northern France - 6 sites in a relatively little known region embracing the sandy beaches of Picardy and the often over-looked Pas-de-Calais, which, as well as having the advantage of being close to Calais, has very much else of interest.

Paris / Ile de France - Paris needs no introduction but there is much else to discover in the Ile de France - magnificent chateaux, hidden valleys and, very much more recently, the late 20th century monuments of Disneyland Paris and Parc Asterix. 4 sites.

Eastern France - 7 sites in another often overlooked region. Why not visit the great champagne vineyards around Reims or the wooded valleys and rolling hills further east, leading up to the German border.

Vendée Charente - 26 sites in one of France's best loved holiday regions. It's hard to beat the fine sandy beaches of this region, often backed by fragrant pines and lively resorts. Inland, world-class vineyards extend to the horizon.

Loire Valley - a choice of 14 sites scattered throughout this celebrated region with many of France's finest chateaux, most picturesque villages and elegant cities. Known as the Garden of France, the region is bisected by the great River Loire as it makes its 1000 km course to the sea.

Burgundy - 5 sites in this region which can justifiably claim to be the heartland of France. Best known for some of the world's finest wines, the region also boasts an array of magnificent architecture and evocative mediaeval towns and villages.

Franche - Comté - less well-known than its Alpine neighbours, this region nevertheless boasts the rugged mountain ranges and dense forests of the Jura, as well as renowned spa towns such as Besançon and Salin-les -Bains. 4 sites.

Savoy / Dauphiny Alps - 6 excellent sites in this region of superlatives. One the world's foremost wintersports areas, the region has much to offer in the summer, with a wide range of outdoor activities and major spa towns like Annecy and Aix-les -Bains on hand for relaxation.

Atlantic Coast - a good choice of 17 sites in a diverse region of endless sandy beaches, backed by one of Europe's largest forests, and with the Pyrénées rising spectacularly to the south.

Dordogne - Aveyron - 14 sites nestling within the beautiful valleys and honey-coloured villages of this magnificent region, descending to the spectacular gorges of the Tarn and Truyere.

Limousin / Auvergne - 3 sites in this thinly populated rugged region which has much the same appeal as the Dordogne but with the overriding sense of much still to be discovered, including awe-inspiring extinct volcanoes, lakes, rivers and forests. The mountains hide a number of winter sport resorts and some of France's most important thermal spas.

Rhone Valley - one of France's most varied regions ; from the dramatic gorges of the Ardèche and the mountains of the Vercors, to the vineyards of Beaujolais, by way of Lyon, the nation's second city. 4 sites.

Provence - 5 sites in a magnificent region of lavender fields, dramatic mountains and glittering coastline. Set back from the coast, there are innumerable sleepy villages and ancient remains to discover, such as the Roman amphitheatres of Arles and Orange.

Midi-Pyrénées - 5 sites in France's largest region. Many of the sleepy villages seem unchanged from the Middle Ages, but the region also boasts great cities such as Toulouse, as well as Lourdes, the world's most visited pilgrimage site, with the Pyrénées rising to the south.

Mediterranean - 29 sites in a region boasting one of Europe's best loved coastlines, from the Spanish border, by way of the vineyards of Corbieres and Minervois through the mountains and gorges of the Cevennes to the glittering coastline of the Côte d'Azur. Better known as the French Riviera, this is a spectacular coastline stretching to the Italian border and boasting world -class resorts such as Cannes, Monte Carlo and Nice.

*Get the site you want - Get the dates you want*
*Get the ferry you want - Get the price you want*

**01892 55 98 98**     **www.alanrogers.com**

**Save Money, and Take It Easy!**

● *No more trying to contact foreign sites direct*
● *No more doubt as to whether your pitch really is booked*
● *No more ringing round the ferry companies for the best price*
● *No more foreign currency booking fees*

# Brittany

Map 1

Major cities: Rennes, Brest

Départements: 22 Côtes d'Armor, 29 Finistère,
35 Ille-et-Vilaine, 56 Morbihan, 44 Loire Atlantique

Strong Celtic roots provide this region with its own distinctive traditions, evident in the local Breton costume and music, the religious festivals and the cuisine, featuring crêpes and cider. Brittany offers 800 miles of rocky coastline with numerous bays, busy little fishing villages and broad sandy beaches dotted with charming seaside resorts. Inland you find wooded valleys, rolling fields, moors and giant granite boulders, but most impressive is the wealth of prehistoric sites, notably the Carnac standing stones. Many castles and manor houses, countless chapels and old villages provide evidence of Brittany's eventful history and wealth of traditions. The Bretons are proud of their culture, very different from the rest of France, and are determined to keep it so. If you are able to attend a 'Pardon' (a religious procession), you will understand some of the Breton history and piety, and see some beautiful traditional costumes. Brittany is a popular destination for families with young children or for those visiting France for the first time. Note: the site reports are laid out by département, in numerical order.

## Cuisine of the region

Fish and shellfish are commonplace – lobsters, huitres, langoustes, various sorts of crabs, moules, prawns, shrimps, coquilles St Jacques, for example

Traditional 'crêperies' abound and welcome visitors with a cup of local cider

Other specialties are wafer biscuits and butter biscuits

*Agneau de pré-salé* – leg of lamb from animals pastured in the salt marshes and meadows

*Beurre blanc* – sauce for fish dishes made fron a reduction of shallots, wine vinegar and the finest butter (sometimes with dry white wine)

*Cotriade* – fish soup with potatoes, onions, garlic and butter

*Crêpes Bretonnes* – the thinnest of pancakes with a variety of sweet fillings

*Galette* – can be a biscuit, cake or pancake; the latter usually with fillings of mushrooms or ham or cheese or seafood, and called a Galette de blé noir (buckwheat flour)

*Gâteau Breton* – rich cake with butter, egg yolks and sugar

*Poulet blanc Breton* – free-range, fine quality, white Breton chicken

## Wine

This is cider country! Crêperies serve cider in pottery type cups

## Places of interest

*Cancale* – small fishing port famous for oysters

*Carnac* – 3,000 standing stones (menhirs), the last erected in 2,000 BC

*Concarneau* – fishing port, old walled town surrounded by ramparts

*Dinan* – historical walled town high above the River Rance

*La Baule* – resort with lovely, sandy bay and beach

*Le Croisic* – fishing port, Naval museum

*Guérande* – historic walled town

*Perros-Guirec* – leading resort of the 'Pink Granite Coast'

*Quiberon* – boat service to three islands: Belle Ile (largest of the Breton islands), Houat, Hoedic

*Rennes* – capital of Brittany, medieval streets, half timbered houses; Brittany Museum

*St Malo* – historical walled city, fishing port and yachting harbour

*Tréguier* – former Episcopal city, 13th-19th centuary St Tugdual cathedral

## Brittany
### Camping Château de Galinée
La Galinée, 22380 Saint-Cast-le-Guildo

Situated a few kilometers back from St Cast and owned and managed by the Vervel family, Galinée is in a parkland setting on level grass with numerous and varied mature trees. It has 273 pitches, all with electricity, water and drainage and separated by many mature shrubs and bushes. The top section is mostly for mobile homes. An attractive pool complex has swimming and paddling pools, two new pools with a water slide and a 'magic stream'. Entertainment is organised during peak season featuring traditional Breton music at times or weekly discos. Gate is locked 23.00-07.00 hrs.

**Facilities:** The main tiled, modern sanitary block includes washbasins in private cabins, facilities for babies and a good unit for disabled people. Dishwashing under cover. Laundry room. Shop for basics, bar and excellent takeaway menu (both 1/7-2/9). Attractive, heated pool complex (26/5-2/9) with swimming and paddling pools, two new pools with water slide and 'magic stream'. Three tennis courts. Fishing. Children's play area and field for ball games. **Off site:** Riding 6 km, golf 3.5 km.

**Charges** 2002

| | | |
|---|---|---|
| Per pitch incl. water and drainage | € 8.40 - | € 5.50 |
| adult | € 3.85 - | € 5.30 |
| child (under 7 yrs) | € 2.30 - | € 3.60 |
| animal | | € 3.00 |
| electricity (10A) | | € 4.20 |
| local tax | | € 0.31 |

**Tel:** 02 96 41 10 56. Fax: 02 96 41 03 72. E-mail: chateaugalinee@wanadoo.fr. **Reservations:** Made with deposit (€ 31) and fee (€ 15,24); min. 1 week July/Aug. **Open** 15 May - 8 September.

**Directions:** From D168 Ploubalay-Plancoet road turn on D786 towards Matignon and St Cast. Site is well signed 1 km. after Notre Dame de Guildo.

## Brittany
### Camping Le Vieux Moulin
14 rue des Moulins, 22430 Erquy

Le Vieux Moulin is a well established and busy site, fully operational from 15 May, and it becomes full with much activity in July and August. It is situated approximately 1.5 - 2 km from a beach of sand and shingle, accessed by an unmade track which can get dusty. There is, however, a good pool complex on site with a children's pool and water slides. There are 173 pitches, of which 150 have electricity and 87 have electricity, water and waste water. A further newer section of 39 pitches is arranged around a pond. Most of the pitches are of fair size in square boxes with trees giving shade. Discos are arranged in high season said to finish at midnight so expect some noise. It si perhaps a site more suited to those with teenage children. About 50 tour operator pitches add to the busy atmosphere.

**Facilities:** Two good quality toilet blocks have mostly British toilets and plenty of individual basins, facilities for disabled people and for babies. A further small block provides toilets and dishwashing only. Washing machines and dryer. Motorcaravan service point. Shop. Smart pizzeria and takeaway. Attractive bar and terrace overlooking the good heated pool complex. Two playgrounds. Free tennis, free power gym. TV room (with satellite) and games room with table tennis. **Off site:** Bicycle hire 1 km, fishing 1.2 km, riding 9 km, golf 7 km.

**Charges** 2003

| | | |
|---|---|---|
| Per pitch | | 11.00 |
| person | | 4.90 |
| child (under 7 yrs) | | 3.90 |
| electricity 6-9A | 4.20 - | 4.50 |
| local tax (July/Aug) | | 0.38 |

No credit cards. **Tel:** 02 96 72 34 23. Fax: 02 96 72 36 63. E-mail: camp.vieux.moulin@wanadoo.fr. **Reservations:** Made for a min. of 1 week. **Open** 15 May - 15 September.

**Directions:** Site is 2 km. east of Erquy. Take minor road towards Les Hôpitaux and site is signed from junction of D786 and D34 roads.

## Camping Le Châtelet

rue des Nouettes, 22380 St-Cast-le-Guildo

Carefully developed over the years from a former quarry, Le Châtelet is pleasantly and quietly situated with views over the estuary from many pitches. It is well laid out, mainly in terraces, with 219 individual pitches of good size marked out by hedge separator. All have electrical points and 30 also have water and drainage. The narrow gravel access roads can make life awkward for larger units and make the site dusty in breezy weather. Some pitches are around a little lake (unfenced) which can be used for fishing. A 'green' walking area is a nice feature around the lower edge of the site and a path leads from the site directly down to a beach (about 150 m. but including steps). St Cast, 1 km. away to the centre, has a very long beach with many opportunities for sail-boarding and other watersports. Used by four different tour operators (109 pitches).

**Facilities:** Three toilet blocks with access at different levels and a new block include plentiful washbasins in cabins and small sized toilets and showers for children. Motorcaravan services. Heated swimming pool and children's pool. Shop for basics, takeaway service, bar lounge and general room with satellite TV and pool table. Games room with table tennis, amusement machines. Small play area. Organised games and activities in season. **Off site:** Bicycle hire, riding and golf within 1.5 km.

**Charges** 2002

| | | |
|---|---:|---:|
| Per person | 3.51 - | 4.88 |
| child (under 7 yrs) | 2.13 - | 3.35 |
| pitch | 9.60 - | 16.00 |
| electricity (6-10A) | 3.05 - | 3.51 |
| local tax (high season only) | | 0.30 |

Credit cards only accepted in low season. **Tel:** 02 96 41 96 33. Fax: 02 96 41 97 99. E-mail: chateletcp@aol.com. **Reservations:** Necessary for July/Aug. and made (min. 1 week) with deposit ( 60) and booking fee ( 19,82). **Open** 1 May - 8 September.

**Directions:** Best approach is to turn off D786 road at Matignon towards St Cast; just inside St Cast limits turn left at sign for 'campings' and follow camp signs on C90.

LE CHATELET
CAMPING-CARAVANING ★ ★ ★ ★

Rue des Nouettes
22380 Saint-Cast-Le-Guildo
Tel: 0033 296.41.96.33
Fax: 0033 296.41.97.99
E-mail: chateletcp@aol.com
Website: www.lechatelet.com

COTE D'EMERAUDE

## Camping des Vallées

chemin des Vallées, Parc de Brézillet, 22000 Saint-Brieuc

Previously run by the municipality, this site is now privately managed. Neat and tidy, it has 106 good size pitches, 70 with electrical connections (10A), set mainly on flat terraced grass and separated by shrubs and bushes. There are 14 pitches with hardstanding and electricity, water and sewage connections. Mature trees are plentiful, providing shade if required, and a small stream winds through the middle of the site creating a quiet, peaceful atmosphere. A key system operates the access gate (closed 22.30-07.00 hrs). Saint Brieuc's pedestrianised centre is filled with small shops and boutiques and several speciality food emporia. The old quarter of the town and the excellent street markets on Wednesday and Saturday mornings are worth a visit. There are no tour operators.

**Facilities:** The two main toilet blocks include some washbasins in cabins, facilities for disabled people and a well equipped baby room. Laundry with washing machines and dryer. Motorcaravan services. Two further smaller blocks are at the bottom of the site. Shop with basic provisions. Compact bar with snacks (1/7-26/8). Children's play area, volley and basketball, arcade games. Bicycle hire. Animation organised in peak season, also weekly pony days for children. Barbecues are not permitted. **Off site:** A superb new aquatic centre, gym and fitness centre is part of a holiday village near the site and campers may use these facilities. Saint Brieuc 800 m.

**Charges** 2002

| | | |
|---|---:|---:|
| Per pitch incl. car and 1 adult | 7.60 - | 9.50 |
| extra adult | 3.00 - | 3.80 |
| child (under 7 yrs) | 1.60 - | 2.50 |
| electricity (10A) | | 3.50 |
| animal | 1.60 - | 2.00 |

**Tel:** 02 96 94 05 05. Fax: 02 96 94 05 05. **Reservations:** Contact site. **Open** Easter - 15 October.

**Directions:** From the east, on entering St Brieuc, look for the sign to the railway station and from there, signs for Brézillet or site.

## Camping Municipal La Hallerais

6 Bourg de Taden, 22100 Taden

2206M

As well as being an attractive old medieval town, Dinan is quite a short run from the resorts of the Côte d'Armor. This useful municipal site, open for a long season, is just outside Dinan, beyond and above the little harbour on the Rance estuary. There is a pleasant riverside walk where the site slopes down towards the Rance. The 223 pitches, all with electricity (5/6A) and most with water and drainaway, are mainly on level, shallow terraces connected by tarmac roads, with trees and hedges giving a park-like atmosphere. This is an efficiently run and well organised site.

**Facilities:** Three traditional toilet blocks, of good quality and heated in cool seasons, have some private cabins with shower and washbasin. Unit for disabled people. Laundry room. Shop. Attractive bar/restaurant with outside terrace and takeaway (all season). Small swimming pool and children's pool (20/5-15/9). Tennis courts, minigolf, games room with table tennis and TV room. Playground. Fishing.

**Charges** guide

| | |
|---|---|
| Per person over 7 yrs | € 2.90 - € 3.51 |
| child (under 7 yrs) | € 1.22 - € 1.52 |
| pitch incl. electricity | € 6.40 - € 10.98 |

Plus local tax. **Tel:** 02 96 39 15 93. Fax: 02 96 39 94 64. **Reservations:** Made for high season only (min. 1 week) with deposit. **Open** 15 March - 31 October.

**Directions:** Taden is northeast of Dinan; on leaving Dinan on D766, turn right to Taden and site before large bridge and N176 junction. From N176 take Taden/Dinan exit and follow Taden and site signs.

## Camping L'Abri Côtier

Ville Es Rouxel, 22680 Etables-sur-Mer

2210

L'Abri Cotier is a well-cared-for, friendly, family run site 500 m. from a sandy beach. Small and tranquil, it is arranged in two sections separated by a lane. The pitches are marked out on part level, part sloping grass, divided by mature trees and shrubs with some in a charming walled area with a quaint, old-world atmosphere. The second section has an orchard type setting. Tim Lee and his French wife are busy with ideas to improve this very popular, friendly site. In total there are 130 pitches, all with electrical connections (6/10A, long leads useful) and 35 fully serviced. Beach within walking distance. There are restaurants in the village.

**Facilities:** Good clean sanitary facilities, heated in low season, include some washbasins in cabins, two units for disabled visitors and a baby bath/shower. Dishwashing under cover. Laundry room. Well stocked shop, set menu and simple takeaway service. Bar (with TV) and terrace. Sheltered, heated swimming pool with children's pool and jacuzzi. Playground. Games room. Some entertainment in peak season. Gates locked at 11 pm. **Off site:** Beach within walking distance. Fishing 2 km, bicycle hire 1 km, riding 3 km, golf 5 km.

**Charges** 2002

| | |
|---|---|
| Per person | € 4.00 - € 4.50 |
| child (1-7 yrs) | € 2.50 - € 3.00 |
| pitch | € 6.00 - € 8.00 |
| electricity (6/10A) | € 3.00 - € 4.00 |
| animal | € 1.50 |

**Tel:** 02 96 70 61 57. Fax: 02 96 70 65 23. E-mail: camping.abricotier@wanadoo.fr. **Reservations:** Made with deposit (€ 39, sterling cheque acceptable £25). **Open** 12 April - 8 September.

**Directions:** From N12 after St Brieuc take D786; site is well signed before St Quay Portrieux.

## Camping-Caravaning Les Madières

Le Vau Madec, 22590 Pordic

2215

The welcoming Camio family are proud of this small friendly, rather unsophisticated site for families. It is 800 metres from good beaches and is convenient for the coastal resorts of the Baie de St Brieuc. There are 83 large grassy pitches separated by small hedges, mostly level but some on an incline and there is plenty of shade from numerous mature trees. The narrow road ends at the campsite which has no other passing traffic. Horse riding features here and musical entertainment two or three times a week is provided by the family and friends. A heated swimming pool is in Spanish style. This is a quiet site in a natural setting for those who like traditional camping.

**Facilities:** The rather old fashioned toilet block has British style toilets for women, Turkish for men. Large room for families or disabled visitors. Covered dishwashing and laundry sinks. Washing machine. Small shop and bar (15/5-15/9). Snacks (limited June). Restaurant (15/5-15/9). Swimming pool. No double axle units are accepted. **Off site:** Supermarket 3 km.

**Charges** 2002

| | |
|---|---|
| Per person | € 3.35 |
| child (0-7 yrs) | € 2.31 |
| pitch | € 4.75 |
| car | € 2.59 |
| motorcaravan | € 7.17 |
| animal | € 1.54 |
| electricity | € 2.90 |

**Tel:** 02 96 79 02 48. Fax: 02 96 79 46 67. E-mail: campinglesmadieres@wanadoo.fr. **Reservations:** Advised for July/Aug. **Open** 1 May - 30 September.

**Directions:** From St Briuex bypass take D786 `Paimpol by the coast`. At Pordic look for camp signs (well signed).

# Camping de Port La Chaîne

22610 Pleubian

**2214**

the travel service
TO BOOK
Ferry ✓
Pitch ✓
Accommodation ✗
01892 55 98 98

The Palvadeau family own Camping de Port La Chaîne and are working hard to establish it as a comfortable, quiet, family site in a beautiful location on the 'Untamed Peninsula' between Paimpol and Perros Guirec. Attractive trees and shrubs provide a balance of sun and shade, edging the central roadway and grassy bays or fields which branch off on the gradual decline towards the bay and the sea (a sandy bay with rocks). To the right are mostly French mobile homes, quite discreet, with the left side for independent units. Most of the bays have a slight slope, so those with motorcaravans will need to choose their pitch carefully. More open, level pitches nearer the sea are useful for tents. In all there are 200 pitches with 6A electricity said to be available everywhere (a long lead may be useful). Essentially a quiet site for families, there are good opportunities for walking and cycling, with a way-marked footpath running along the coast to the Sillon du Talbert that juts out into the sea opposite the Island of Bréhat

**Facilities:** Two traditional style toilet blocks are comfortable and fully equipped, both now completely renovated. There are washbasins in cabins, British and Turkish style toilets. Cabins for families or disabled visitors. Plentiful dishwashing sinks (H&C). Laundry sinks with cold water only. Washing machines and dryer. Bar and terrace (1/7-1/9) overlooking a heated pool (2/6-15/9), play area and petanque pitch. Children's animator July/Aug. **Off site:** Village 2 km. for tennis, market, shops and restaurants. Good fishing and diving.

**Charges** 2002

| | |
|---|---|
| Per person | 4.80 |
| child (under 7 yrs) | 3.00 |
| pitch | 8.00 |
| electricity | 3.00 |
| dog | 1.50 |

Less 10-20% in low seasons. **Tel:** 02 96 22 92 38. Fax: 02 96 22 87 92. E-mail: ptchaine@club-internet.fr. **Reservations:** Contact site. **Open** 1 May - 15 September.

**Directions:** Leave D786 between Lézardrieux and Tréguier to go north to the village of Pleubian (approx. 8 km). Continue on D20 towards Larmor Pleubian and site signed on left, approx. 2 km. from Pleubian.

---

# Camping de Port L'Epine

Venelle de Pors Garo, 22660 Trélévern

**2213**

the travel service
TO BOOK
Ferry ✓
Pitch ✓
Accommodation ✗
01892 55 98 98

Port L'Epine is a pretty little site in a unique situation on a promontory. There is access to the sea, therefore, on the south side of the site, with views across to Perros Guirec, and just outside the entrance on the north side is a further sandy bay with little boats moored and facing out to an archipelago of seven small islands. It is charming - you can sail or swim from both sides. However, in spite of this, the site has its own small heated pool. The area covered by the site is not large but there are 160 grass pitches divided by pretty hedging and trees, some of which are used for mobile homes. Access is a little tight in parts. Electricity (16A) is available but a long lead may be useful. This site is ideal for families with young children (probably not for teenagers). The site is used by tour operators.

**Facilities:** The original toilet block is well equipped and a second block has been refurbished in modern style (the showers lack hooks), including facilities for disabled visitors. Unusual dishwashing sinks in open air stone units. Shop and bar/restaurant with take-away facility (both 1/7-31/8). Small heated swimming pool and paddling pool (lifeguard July/Aug). Fenced children's play area beside exit road (no gate). Table tennis and video games. Bicycle hire. Site's own beach has rock pools, jetty and slipway for small boats or fishing. Barrier closed 23.00-07.00 hrs. **Off site:** Riding or golf 15 km. Useful small supermarket up-hill from the site. Many coastal paths to enjoy.

**Charges** 2002

| | |
|---|---|
| Per pitch incl. 2 persons, electricity | € 14.50 - € 22.00 |
| extra person | € 5.00 |
| extra child (2-7 yrs) | € 2.50 |
| animal | € 2.50 |
| serviced pitch | € 2.30 |

**Tel:** 02 96 23 71 94. Fax: 02 96 23 77 83. E-mail: camping-de-port-lepine@wanadoo.fr. **Reservations:** Made with deposit (€ 90, or € 45 for stay of less than 3 nights). **Open** 26 April - 13 October.

**Directions:** From roundabout south of Perros Guirec take D6 towards Tréguier. After passing through Louannec, take left turn at crossroads for Trélévern. Go through village following camp signs - Port L'Epine is clearly marked as distinct from the municipal site.

## Camping Les Capucines

2201

Kervourdon, 22300 Tredrez-Locquémeau

A warm welcome awaits at Les Capucines which is quietly situated 1 km. from the village of St Michel with its good, sandy beach and also very near Locquémeau, a pretty fishing village. This attractive, family run site has 100 pitches on flat or slightly sloping ground. All are well marked out by hedges, with mature trees and with more recently planted. There are 70 with electricity, water and drainage, including 10 for larger units. All the amenities are open all season. A good value restaurant/crêperie is at Trédrez, others at St Michel. A Sites et Paysages member.

**Facilities:** Two modern toilet blocks include washbasins mainly in cabins, facilities for babies and disabled people. Laundry with washing machines and dryer. Small shop for essentials (bread to order). Takeaway, bar with TV and a general room with table tennis and table football. Swimming and paddling pools. Children's playground. Tennis, minigolf and bicycle hire. Dogs are not accepted. **Off site:** Fishing 1 km, riding 2 km, golf 15 km.

**Charges** 2002

| | |
|---|---|
| Per person | € 3.50 - € 4.60 |
| child | € 2.30 - € 3.10 |
| pitch | € 5.50 - € 10.50 |
| electricity (4/7A) | € 2.30 - € 3.05 |
| local tax (over 18 yrs) | € 0.30 |

**Tel:** 02 96 35 72 28. Fax: 02 96 35 78 98. E-mail: les.capucines@wanadoo.fr. **Reservations:** Advised for high season, made for any length with deposit (€ 62) and fee (€ 8). **Open** 4 May - 8 September.

**Directions:** Turn off main D786 road northeast of St Michel where signed and 1 km. to site.

## Camping Municipal Bois de la Palud

2921M

29250 Plougoulm

This delightful, small municipal site is on the edge of the little village of Plougoulm, about 10 km. southwest of Roscoff. It sits on the brow of a hill with lovely views across the Guillec valley and the sandy bay and estuary to which there is access by footpath. There are 34 reasonably level, numbered pitches grouped in small hedged bays and most have access to 6A electricity (although long leads may be necessary). A small building near the entrance houses reception and sanitary facilities. The season is short - only 15 June - 15 September.

**Facilities:** All necessary toilet facilities are provided. Children's play area. **Off site:** Fishing, bicycle hire, riding and golf, all within 4 km.

**Charges** 2002

| | |
|---|---|
| Per adult | € 2.90 |
| child (under 7 yrs) | € 1.83 |
| pitch | € 3.05 |
| electricity | € 2.59 |

No credit cards. **Tel:** 02 98 29 81 82. **Reservations:** Advised in high season. When closed contact the Mairie: (0)2.98.29.90.76. **Open** 15 June - 15 September.

**Directions:** On leaving Roscoff, follow signs for Morlaix. After 6 km. take D10 (westward) signed Plouescat and after 3 km. watch for clear camp signs in the village of Plougoulm.

## Camping de la Côte des Légendes

2934

Keravezan, BP36, 29890 Brignogan-Plages

Located just behind the sandy beach and adjacent to a Centre Nautique (sailing, windsurfing, kayak), this site is ideal for a family seaside holiday or as a base to discover the history behind the fables of the Côte des Légendes. Visit the nearby preserved fishing village of Meneham, set amongst spectacular random granite outcrops and boulders, and learn of its history of coastal defence from the English. Less than 40 km. from Roscoff ferry port, Brignogan is ideal if you do not want to drive too far in France. With energetic owners this site is being comprehensively updated. It has around 130 flat pitches arranged in rows and protected by hedges (these include young fruit bushes - you may help yourself to fruit in season). There are a few mobile homes for rent but at present most pitches are for touring units. The beach of fine sand can be reached directly from the site.

**Facilities:** The main toilet facilities are at the rear of the site in a large block (completely refitted for 2001) that provides washbasins in cubicles, baby baths and facilities for disabled visitors. Dishwashing and laundry sinks. Motorcaravan service point. The upper floor provides a games room with views of the sea. Further toilet facilities are at the reception building, also a laundry (2 washing machines and a dryer). Small shop. Playground and play field. Table tennis. **Off site:** Watersports centre. Village services 700 m.

**Charges** guide

| | |
|---|---|
| Per pitch | € 3.35 |
| person | € 2.44 |
| child (under 7 yrs) | € 1.83 |
| electricity 5/10A | € 1.83 - € 3.20 |
| dog | € 0.76 |

**Tel:** 02 98 83 41 65. Fax: 02 98 83 59 94. E-mail: camping-cote-des-legendes@wanadoo.fr. **Reservations:** Advised for high season. **Open** 30 March - 3 November.

**Directions:** From Roscoff take D10 towards Lesneven, then D770 to Brignogan-Plages. In the main street (Général de Gaulle) go straight on following signs for 'Le Menhir' and 'Le Phare'. At the menhir follow camping signs to Keravezan and site.

## Brittany
# Camping Les Mouettes
La Grande Grève, 29660 Carantec

**2900**

Les Mouettes is less than 15 km. from the Roscoff ferry port, so is well situated when heading to or from home, although it also provides many facilities for a longer family holiday. For those who do not want to drive too far, the area has plenty to offer with beautiful bays and many places of interest within easy reach. Les Mouettes is a sheltered site on the edge of an attractive bay with access to the sea at the front of the site. In a wooded setting with many attractive trees and shrubs, the 273 pitches, some sloping, include just 70 for touring units, the remainder being taken by tour operators and around 60 site-owned mobile homes and tents (located together at the top of the site). The touring pitches, mostly arranged in hedged areas in the lower areas of the site, are of a good size and all have electricity connections (6A). The focal point of the site is an impressive heated swimming pool complex comprising a water slide pool and three water slides, 'tropical river', swimming pool and children's pool, a jacuzzi and new sauna.

**Facilities:** Three clean unisex sanitary blocks include washbasins in cabins, mainly British toilets and baby bathrooms. Facilities for disabled people. Laundry facilities. Motorcaravan services. Shop (23/5-13/9, limited hours outside the main season). Takeaway. Centrally located bar (20/5-13/9) overlooking pool complex. Sauna. Games and TV rooms. Play area. Volleyball, two half-courts for tennis, minigolf and archery (July/Aug). Table tennis. Good childrens' club. Discos and other entertainment organised in main season - can be noisy. **Off site:** Bicycle hire 10 km. Riding 6 km. Golf 2 km.

**Charges** guide

| | | |
|---|---:|---:|
| Per pitch | 9.45 - | 14.64 |
| person | 3.35 - | 5.18 |
| child (under 7 yrs) | 2.13 - | 3.20 |
| electricity (6A) | | 3.05 |
| water and waste water connection | 0.76 - | 1.52 |
| local tax | | 0.15 |
| dog | 1.68 - | 2.74 |

**Tel:** 02 98 67 02 46. Fax: 02 98 78 31 46. E-mail: camping@les-mouettes.com. **Reservations:** Write to site with deposit (  46) and fee (  18,29). **Open** 1 May - 13 September.

**Directions:** From D58 Roscoff - Morlaix road, turn to Carantec on D173. Site is approx. 4 km. from here on the outskirts of the village, signed to the left at roundabout immediately after passing supermarket on right.

## Brittany
# Camping-Caravaning Le Grand Large
Lambezen, 29570 Camaret sur Mer

**2930**

This is a good quality site catering for families and the very friendly owners, M. Senechal and his family give everyone a great welcome. The site is close to the popular seaside resort of Camaret-sur-Mer (2 km) and a rural footpath leads down to the local beach (450 m). There are 123 large, partly shaded pitches (100 for touring units). Most are separated by hedges, some having wonderful sea views, and they are easily accessible for all types of unit. All pitches have electricity (5/10A), water and drainage close by. There are plenty of restaurants, activities, etc. close by in Camaret and the surrounding district and this is a good walking and cycling area.

**Facilities:** There are two well maintained, clean toilet blocks, one quite new and only one open in low season. Most washbasins are in cabins. Two baby rooms (only available on request in low season) and good facilities for disabled visitors. Ample facilities for washing clothes and dishes. Laundry room (free iron). Motorcaravan service point. Small shop, bar, takeaway (all 15/6-15/9). Heated swimming pool (no bermuda style shorts), attractively situated close to the bar with good sea views. New play area for children (2-12 yrs). Table tennis and pool table.

**Charges** 2002

| | |
|---|---:|
| Per person | € 4.70 |
| child (under 7 yrs) | € 3.00 |
| pitch | € 11.00 |
| electricity (5A) | € 2.74 |
| local tax | € 0.11 - € 0.23 |
| dog | € 1.83 |

**Tel:** 02 98 27 91 41. Fax: 02 98 27 93 72. E-mail: lglca@club-internet.fr. **Reservations:** Made for min. 15 days with deposit (€ 38) and fee (€ 15,24). **Open** 1 April - 30 September.

**Directions:** On entering Camaret-sur-Mer turn right at roundabout onto D355 signed Pointe des Espagnols. Site is well signed and is just over 2 km.

# Camping des Abers

Dunes de Ste Marguerite, 29870 Landéda

This delightful 12 acre site is beautifully situated almost at the tip of the Sainte Marguerite peninsula on the north-western shores of Brittany in a wide bay formed between the mouths (abers) of two rivers, L`Aber Wrac`h and L`Aber Benoit. With soft, white sandy beaches and rocky outcrops and islands at high tide, the setting is ideal for those with younger children and this quiet, rural area provides a wonderful, tranquil escape from the busier areas of France, even in high season. Camping des Abers is set just back from the beach, the lower pitches sheltered from the wind by high hedges or with panoramic views of the bay from the higher places. There are 180 pitches arranged in distinct areas, partly shaded and sheltered by mature hedges, trees and flowering shrubs, all planted and carefully tended over 30 years by the Le Cuff family. Landscaping and terracing where appropriate on the different levels avoids any regimentation or crowding. Easily accessed by good internal roads, electricity is available to all (5A, long leads may be needed). Speaking several languages, the family who own and run this site with `TLC` will make you very welcome.

**Facilities:** Three toilet blocks (one part of the reception building and all recently refurbished) are very clean, providing washbasins in cubicles and roomy showers (token from reception). Good new facilities for disabled visitors and babies have been added at the reception block. Dishwashing sinks. Fully equipped laundry. Motorcaravan service point. Mini-market stocks essentials (1/5-15/9). Simple takeaway dishes (1/7-31/8). Pizzeria and restaurant next door. Table tennis. Good play area (on sand). Indoor TV and games room. Live music, Breton dancing and Breton cooking classes, and guided walks arranged. Splendid beach reached direct from the site with good bathing (best at high tide), fishing, windsurfing and other watersports. Miles of superb coastal walks. Torch useful. Gates locked 22.30-07.00 hrs.
**Off site:** Tennis and riding close. The nearby town of L`Aber Wrac`h, a well known yachting centre, has many memorable restaurants

**Charges** 2003

| | |
|---|---|
| Per person | € 3.10 |
| child (-17 yrs) | € 1.70 |
| pitch | € 4.70 |
| car | € 1.40 |
| electricity | € 2.20 |
| dog | € 1.50 |

Less 20% until 15 June and Sept. **Tel:** 02 98 04 93 35. Fax: 02 98 04 84 35. E-mail: camping-des-abers@wanadoo.fr. **Reservations:** Write to site. **Open** 18 April - 28 September.

**Directions:** From Roscoff (D10, then D13), cross river bridge (L'Aber Wrac'h) to Lannilis. Go through town taking road to Landéda and from there signs for Dunes de Ste Marguerite, 'camping' and des Abers.

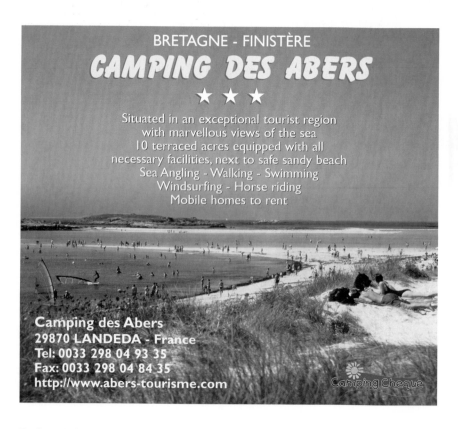

## Camping Le Panoramic

route de la Plage Penker, 29560 Telgruc-sur-Mer

**2908**

This medium sized, ten acre site is situated on quite a steep hillside, with fine views along the coast. It is well tended and personally run by M. Jacq and his family who all speak good English. The site is in two parts, divided by a fairly quiet road leading to a good beach. The main upper site is where most of the facilities are situated, with the swimming pool, terrace and a playground located with the lower pitches across the road. Some up-and-down walking is therefore necessary, but this is a small price to pay for such pleasant and comfortable surroundings. The 220 pitches are arranged on flat, shady terraces, mostly in small groups with hedges and flowering shrubs and 20 pitches have services for motorcaravans. A good area for lovely coastal footpaths. Used by tour operators (20 pitches). A `Sites et Paysages` member.

**Facilities:** The main site has two well kept toilet blocks with another good block across the road. All three include British and Turkish style WCs, wash-basins in cubicles, facilities for disabled people, baby baths, dishwashing, plus washing machines and dryers. Motorcaravan services. Small shop (1/7-31/8). Bar/restaurant with good value takeaway (1/7-31/8). Barbecue area. Heated swimming pool, children`s pool and jacuzzi (all 15/5-7/9). Playground. Games and TV rooms. Children`s club in season. Tennis courts, volleyball. Bicycle hire. **Off site:** Riding 6 km, golf 14 km. Sailing school nearby. Good sandy beach 700 m. downhill by road, bit less on foot.

**Charges** 2003

| | | |
|---|---|---|
| Per person | | 5.00 |
| child (under 7 yrs) | | 3.00 |
| pitch | | 10.00 |
| electricity (6-10A) | 3.10 - | 4.50 |
| water and drainage connection | | 2.50 |
| dog | | 1.60 |
| local tax (over 10 yrs) | | 0.40 |

Less 20% outside July/Aug. No credit cards. **Tel:** 02 98 27 78 41. Fax: 02 98 27 36 10. **Reservations:** Made for any period; contact site. **Open** 15 June- 10 September.

**Directions:** Site is just south of Telgruc-sur-Mer. On D887 pass through Ste Marie du Ménez Horn. In 11 km. turn left on D208 signed Telgruc-sur-Mer. Continue straight on through the town and site is on right within 1 km.

## Camping La Corniche

29710 Plozévet

**2933**

A well presented site, La Corniche is conveniently placed for both coast - with some sandy beaches - and the delights of in inland Brittany. The owners speak mini-mal English, but are good at sign language. Large level fields are divided into smaller areas by mature hedging and there is some shade from trees. There are120 grass pitches with 6A electricity available to touring units, with some static vans as well. The season is quite short (early April to 30 September) and some of the facilities are only open during high season. The town of Plozévet is a ten minute stroll away. There are several restaurants, most specialising in galettes and other Breton food, bars and a small supermarket.

**Facilities:** Toilet facilities are excellent, one block having being completely rebuilt. Comprehensively equipped, they include individual wash cubicles. Roof lights create a light and airy feel. Provision for those with disabilities. Small shop. Bar and take-away. Swimming pool and paddling pool. **Off site:** Village within walking distance. Beach 2 km.

**Charges** 2002

| | |
|---|---|
| Per pitch | € 5.03 |
| vehicle | € 1.52 |
| adult | € 3.96 |
| child under 7 yrs | € 2.44 |
| electricity (6A) | € 2.74 |

**Tel:** (0)2 98 91 33 94. Fax: (0)2 98 91 41 53. **Reservations:** Contact site. **Open** 1 April - 30 September.

**Directions:** Head west from Quimper and pick up D784 towards Landudec and Plozévet. After 26 km, where road makes a sharp right in centre of Plozévet, turn left (site sign partially obscured on corner) towards the coast. Site on right after 1 km.

## La Pointe Superbe Camping

route de St Coulitz, 29150 Châteaulin

**2928**

La Pointe, just outside Châteaulin, has been lovingly and impressively brought back to life by its delightful English owners Colin Grewer and Sue Dodds who provide a warm welcome. Châteaulin is a bustling market town, 15 km. from the beach at Pentrez and within easy reach of Quimper, mediaeval Locronan and the Crozon peninsula. Although not endowed with a great deal in terms of amenities, this very tranquil site does boast particularly large, grassy pitches in a quiet valley leading down to the River Aulne, which makes up part of the Nantes - Brest canal. The 60 pitches all have electricity (6/10A) with water close by. This small site is well suited to those who like peace and quiet.

**Facilities:** The first-class toilet block, kept very clean at all times, has many washbasins in cubicles. Shower cubicles are somewhat small but have full adjustable hot and cold taps. Large room with facilities for disabled visitors. Baby bathroom. Motorcaravan service point. Play area. Table tennis, volleyball and large activity room with basketball, badminton and children's corner. **Off site:** Châteaulin has a wide range of shops (700 m), as well as plenty of restaurants and bars. Riding and tennis nearby. Woodland walks and fishing possible in the Aulne (permit needed).

**Charges** 2002

| Per unit incl. 2 persons | € 9.00 - € 11.00 |
| --- | --- |
| extra person | € 2.00 - € 3.00 |
| child (under 7 yrs) | € 1.20 - € 1.70 |
| electricity (10A) | € 2.00 - € 3.00 |
| animal | € 1.00 |

No credit cards. **Tel:** 02 98 86 51 53. Fax: 02 98 86 51 53. **Reservations:** Advised for high season and made with deposit ( 15,24). **Open** 15 March - 15 October.

**Directions:** Site is just southeast of Châteaulin. From the bridge over the river in town centre follow signs for St Coulitz and Quimper. Shortly turn left signed St Coulitz. Site is clearly signed at this point and is a further 100 m. on the right.

## Camping Village La Plage

rue de Men-Meur BP 9, 29730 Le Guilvinec

**2911**

| the travel service | |
| --- | --- |
| TO BOOK | |
| Ferry | ✓ |
| Pitch | ✓ |
| Accommodation | ✗ |
| 01892 55 98 98 | |

La Plage is a friendly site located beside a long sandy beach between the fishing town of Le Guilvinec and the watersports beaches of Penmarc'h on the southwest tip of Brittany. It is spacious and surrounded by tall trees, which provide shelter, and is made up of several flat, sandy meadows. The 410 pitches (189 for touring units) are arranged on either side of sandy access roads, mostly not separated but all numbered. There is less shade in the newer areas. Electricity is available on most pitches (2, 6 or 10A). Like all beachside sites, the facilities receive heavy usage. There is plenty to occupy one at this friendly site but the bustling fishing harbour at Le Guilvinec and the watersports of Penmarc'h and Pointe de la Torche are within easy travelling distance. Used by tour operators (89 pitches). A Yelloh Village member.

**Facilities:** Five sanitary blocks are of differing designs but all provide modern, bright facilities including washbasins in cabins, good facilities for children and toilets for disabled people. Laundry facilities. Motorcaravan service point. Shop with gas supplies. Bright, airy well furnished bar, crêperie and takeaway. Heated swimming pool with paddling pool and water slide. Sauna. Children's play area. TV room. Tennis courts. Volleyball, basketball, minigolf, badminton, petanque, table tennis, giant chess/draughts. Bicycle hire. **Off site:** Fishing and watersports near. Riding 5 km. Golf 20 km.

**Charges** 2002

| Per unit incl. 2 persons | |
| --- | --- |
| incl. 5A electricity | € 17.00 - € 31.00 |
| extra person | € 3.00 - € 5.00 |
| child (under 7 yrs) | € 2.00 - € 3.00 |
| electricity (10A) | € 0.70 |
| local tax (over 16 yrs) | € 0.15 |
| dog | € 2.00 - € 3.00 |

**Tel:** 02 98 58 61 90. Fax: 02 98 58 89 06. E-mail: info@campingsbretagnesud.com. **Reservations:** Advised and accepted until 15/6 with deposit (25%) and fee (€ 19). **Open** 4 May - 8 September, with all facilities.

**Directions:** Site is west of Guilvinec. From Pont l'Abbé, take the D785 road towards Penmarc'h. In Plomeur, turn left on D57 signed Guilvinec. On entering Guilvinec fork right signed Port and camping. Follow road along coast to site on left.

*see advertisement on page 21*

# Camping-Caravaning Le Pil-Koad

route de Douarnenez, Poullan-sur-Mer, 29100 Douarnenez

**2906**

Pil Koad is an attractive, family run site just back from the sea near Douarnenez in Finistère. It has 190 pitches on fairly flat ground, marked out by separating hedges and of quite good, though varying, size and shape. The site also has a number of mobile homes and chalets. Nearly all pitches have electrical connections (10A) and original trees provide shade in some areas. A large room, the 'Woodpecker Bar', is used for entertainment with discos and cabaret in July and August. The gates are closed 10.30 - 07.00 hrs. A variety of beaches is within easy reach, with the coast offering some wonderful scenery and good for walking.

**Facilities:** Two main toilet blocks in modern style include mainly British style WCs and washbasins mostly in cabins. Laundry facilities. Motorcaravan service point. Gas supplies. Small shop for basics (16/6-8/9). Takeaway (23/6-1/9). Heated swimming pool and paddling pool (no bermuda-style shorts). Tennis court. Table tennis, minigolf and volleyball. Fishing. Bicycle hire. Playground. Weekly outings and clubs for children (30/6-30/8) with charge included in tariff. **Off site:** Riding 4 km. Restaurants in village 500 m. Nearest sandy beach 4 km. Douarnenez 6 km.

**Charges** 2002

| | |
|---|---|
| Per person | € 3.00 - € 5.00 |
| child (under 7 yrs) | € 1.50 - € 3.00 |
| pitch | € 6.00 - € 12.00 |
| electricity (10A) | € 3.50 |
| dog | € 1.50 - € 2.50 |
| local tax (over 16 yrs from 1/7-31/8) | € 0.15 |

**Tel:** 02 98 74 26 39. Fax: 02 98 74 55 97. E-mail: camping.pil.koad@wanadoo.fr. **Reservations:** Made for min. 1 week with 25% deposit and fee (€ 19). **Open** 1 May - 15 September.

**Directions:** Site is 500 m. east from the centre of Poullan on D7 road towards Douarnenez. From Douarnenez take circular bypass route towards Audierne; if you see road for Poullan sign at round about, take it, otherwise there is camping sign at turning to Poullan from the D765 road.

## Camping Village Le Manoir de Kerlut

**2912** 29740 Plobannalec-Lesconil

Le Manoir de Kerlut is a comfortable site in the grounds of a manor house on a river estuary near Pont l'Abbe. The old 'manoir' is not open to the public, but is used occasionally for weddings and private functions. Opened in '89, the campsite has neat, modern buildings and is laid out on flat grass providing 240 pitches (90 for touring units). All have electricity connections (5, 6 or 10A), some also have water and drainage and around ten pitches have hardstanding. One area is rather open with separating hedges planted, the other part being amongst more mature bushes and some trees which provide shade. Site amenities are of good quality. Used by tour operators (38 pitches). A Yelloh Village member.

**Facilities:** Toilet facilities in two good blocks, each with several rooms (not all open outside July/Aug), include washbasins all in cabins, and facilities for babies and disabled people. Laundry. Small shop. Takeaway. Large modern bar with TV (satellite) and entertainment all season. Bar in the Manoir. Two heated swimming pools, children's pool and water slide. Sauna, solarium and small gym. Play area. Tennis, volleyball, badminton and petanque. Games room. Bicycle hire. Gates closed 22.30 - 7.30 hrs. **Off site:** Fishing 2 km, riding 5 km, golf 15 km.

**Charges** 2002

| | |
|---|---|
| Per unit incl. 2 persons and 5A electricity | € 17.00 - € 31.00 |
| extra person | € 3.00 - € 5.00 |
| child (under 7 yrs) | € 2.00 - € 3.00 |
| electricity (10A) | € 0.70 |
| dog | € 2.00 - € 3.00 |
| local tax (over 16 yrs) | € 0.15 |

**Tel:** 02 98 82 23 89. **Fax:** 02 98 82 26 49. **E-mail:** info@campingsbretagnesud.com. **Reservations:** Write to site with deposit (€ 45) and fee (€ 19). **Open** 1 May - 9 September, with all services.

**Directions:** From Pont l'Abbé, on D785, take D102 road towards Lesconil. Site is signed on the left, shortly after the village of Plobannalec.

## Camping Village Le Grand Large

**2929** 48 route du Grand Large, Mousterlin, 29170 Fouesnant

Le Grand Large is a beach-side site situated on the Pointe de Mousterlin in natural surroundings. The site is separated from the beach by the road that follows the coast around the point. It is also protected from the wind by an earth bank with trees and a fence. The beach itself looks over the bay towards the Isles de Glénan. There are 300 level grass pitches of average size and rather sandy in places with some shrubs and mature trees. Tour operators take 44 places and the site itself has 96 tents and mobile homes to rent. Electricity is available everywhere (long leads useful) and some pitches have drainage. A small river runs through the site but it is fenced. Benodet (7 km) and Fouesnant (5 km) are near in different directions and the sandy beach is just up the steps and across the road. A family site, would also suit walkers and nature lovers in the low seasons as it is adjacent to a large tract of protected land, Marais de Mousterlin, ideal for walking, cycling and birdwatching.

**Facilities:** Two neat, new sanitary blocks include plenty of washbasins in cabins (warm water only). Two baby baths in the larger block with children's shower and toilet and facilities for disabled people in both blocks. Two washing machines, two dryers and plenty of laundry and washing up sinks (hot water only). Bar overlooks the sea with attractive terrace and a crêperie/grill restaurant that also provides takeaway food. Swimming pool with paddling pool, water slides in a separate pool. Tennis court and multi-sport court where it is possible to play 5-a-side football, badminton, volleyball, handball or basketball. Small play area. TV room and games room with table tennis and billiards.

**Charges** 2002

| | |
|---|---|
| Per unit incl. 2 persons and 5A electricity | € 17.00 - € 31.00 |
| extra person | € 3.00 - € 5.00 |
| child (under 7 yrs) | € 2.00 - € 3.00 |
| electricity (10A) | € 0.70 |
| local tax (over 16 yrs) | € 0.15 |
| dog | € 2.00 - € 3.00 |

**Tel:** 02 98 56 04 06. **Fax:** 02 98 56 58 26. **E-mail:** info@campingsbretagnesud.com. **Reservations:** Made with deposit (€ 45) and non-refundable fee (€ 19). **Open** 4 May (may be later for 2003) - 8 September.

**Directions:** Site is 7 km. south of Fouesnant. Turn off N165 expressway at Coat Conq, signed Concarneau and Fouesnant. At Fouesnant take A45 signed Beg Meil, then follow signs to Mousterlin. In Mousterlin turn left and follow camping signs.

Campings Villages *coloured holidays*

Southern Brittany

CAMPING PLUS BRETAGNE

## ★★★★ Manoir de Kerlut

29740 Plobannalec - Lesconil
Tél : 33 (0)2 98 82 23 89
Fax : 33 (0)2 98 82 26 49

### At the seaside

## ★★★★ Le Grand Large

Mousterlin - 29170 Fouesnant
Tél : 33 (0)2 98 56 04 06
Fax : 33 (0)2 98 56 58 26

### Direct access to the beach

## ★★★ La Plage

29730 Le Guilvinec
Tél : 33 (0)2 98 58 61 90
Fax : 33 (0)2 98 58 89 06

Réalisation *i comme...* 33 (0)2 98 10 19 20

### Activities for everyone

### Childrens' paradise...

### ... parents' peace of mind

www.campingsbretagnesud.com
Email : info@campingsbretagnesud.com

yelloh! VILLAGE

## Camping Club du Saint-Laurent

Kerleven, 29940 La Forêt-Fouesnant

**2902**

Saint-Laurent is a well established site, situated on a sheltered wooded slope bordering one of the many attractive little inlets that typify the Brittany coastline. There is direct access from the site to two small sandy bays, which empty at low tide to reveal numerous rockpools (ideal for children to explore), and the site is on the coastal footpath that leads from Kerleven to Concarneau. The 260 pitches are on levelled terraces, under tall trees. All pitches are divided by hedging, have electrical connections (6A), are partly shaded and are of average size (100 sq.m.). Pitches with the best sea views tend to be adjacent to the cliff edge, and may not be suitable for families with young children. Access to some pitches can also be a little difficult, but the friendly site owners ensure that this is not a problem by offering to site any caravan using their own 4 x 4 vehicle. The swimming pool (complete with paddling pool and two water slides) is overlooked by the bar terrace. With organised activities and entertainment in high season, this site is an ideal choice for a lively family holiday, particularly for older children. Around 50% of the pitches are occupied by tour operators or site owned mobile homes.

**Facilities:** Two sanitary blocks provide combined shower and washbasin cubicles, separate washbasin cubicles, baby changing and facilities for disabled people. Laundry and dishwashing sinks. Washing machines, dryers and ironing facilities in newly refurbished room. Small shop at reception provides essentials. Bar, snack bar and takeaway (all 12/5-10/9). Swimming pools. Gym and sauna. Canoe hire. Basketball, two tennis courts (no charge), and table tennis. Children's play area. During July and August daily children's clubs and adult entertainments are organised (in English as well as in French), with discos in the bar each evening.

**Charges** 2002

| | |
|---|---|
| Per unit incl. 1 or 2 persons, electricity and water | € 15.24 - € 23.63 |
| extra person over 7 yrs | € 2.29 - € 4.27 |
| child 2-7 yrs | € 1.52 - € 3.05 |
| dog | free - € 1.83 |
| extra car | € 1.52 - € 3.05 |

**Tel:** 02 98 56 97 65. Fax: 02 98 56 92 51.
**Reservations:** Advised for July/Aug. and made with deposit (€ 77) and fee (€ 22,87). **Open** 3 May - 13 September.

**Directions:** From N165 take D70 Concarneau exit. At first roundabout take first exit D44 (Fouesnant). After 2.5 km. turn right at T junction, follow for 2.5 km, then turn left (Port La Forêt - take care - 200 m. before the junction is a sign that implies Port La Forêt is straight on, and it isn't). Continue to round about, straight ahead (Port La Forêt) and after 1 km. turn left (site signed here). In 400 m left turn to site at end of this road.

# Camping du Letty

29950 Bénodet

**2903**

Built around their former farm, the Guyader family have ensured that this excellent and attractive site, with direct beach access, has plenty to offer for all the family. The site on the outskirts of the popular resort of Bénodet spreads over 22 acres with 493 pitches, all for touring units. Groups of eight to ten pitches are set in cul-de-sacs with mature hedging and trees to divide each cul-de-sac. Markers indicate the limits of each pitch which are slightly smaller than average (none more than about 80 sq.m), although they do not feel too small since they are not hedged or fenced. Most pitches have electricity (up to 10A), fresh and waste water connections. At the attractive floral entrance, former farm buildings provide a host of facilities including an extensively equipped fitness room. There is also a modern, purpose built nightclub and bar providing high quality live entertainment most evenings (situated well away from most pitches to avoid disturbance). Although there is no swimming pool here, the site has direct access to a small sandy beach, and has provided a floating pontoon with diving platform and water slides into the sea (safe bathing depends on the tides).

**Facilities:** Six well placed toilet blocks around the site, are of good quality with modern fittings. They include mixed style WCs, washbasins in large cabins and controllable hot showers (charged). Laundry and dishwashing sinks. Three well equipped baby changing rooms. Separate facility for disabled visitors. Launderette. Hairdressing room. Motorcaravan service points. Well stocked and reasonably priced minimarket, including butchery counter. Extensive snack bar and takeaway (22/6-30/8). Bar with games room and night club. Library/reading room. Games lounge with billiard and card tables and entertainment room with satellite TV. Fitness centre (no charge). Saunas, jacuzzis and solarium (all on payment). Table tennis. Two tennis and two squash courts (charged). Boules, volleyball, basketball and archery. Well equipped children's play area. In July/Aug. entertainment and activities organised for the whole family.

**Charges** 2003

| | |
|---|---|
| Per adult | € 4.50 |
| child (under 7 yrs) | € 2.25 |
| pitch | € 7.00 |
| car or motorcaravan | € 1.70 |
| m/cycle | € 1.20 |
| electricity (1, 2, 5 or 10A) | € 1.50 - € 4.00 |
| dog | € 2.30 |
| local tax | € 0.23 - € 0.46 |

**Tel:** 02 98 57 04 69. **Fax:** 02 98 66 22 56. E-mail: reception@campingduletty.com. **Reservations:** Not made. **Open** 15 June - 6 September.

**Directions:** From N165 take D70 Concarneau exit. At first roundabout take D44 to Fouesnant. Turn right at T junction. After about 2 km. turn left to Fouesnant (still D44). Continue through La Forêt Fouesnant and Fouesnant, picking up signs for Bénodet. Shortly before Benodet at roundabout turn left (signed Le Letty). Turn right at next mini round about and site is 500 m. on left.

---

# Camping de la Piscine

Kerleya, B.P.12, Beg-Meil, 29170 Fouesnant

**2917**

the travel service
TO BOOK

| | |
|---|---|
| Ferry | ✓ |
| Pitch | ✓ |
| Accommodation | ✗ |

01892 55 98 98

There are many campsites in this area but La Piscine is notable for the care and attention to detail that contributes to the well-being of its guests. Created by the Caradec family from an apple orchard, the 185 level, grass pitches are of generous size and are separated by an interesting variety of hedges and trees. Water, waste and electricity points are provided, normally one stand between two pitches. The nearby towns of Beg-Meil and Fouesnant, and (a little further) Quimper, are well worth a visit if only to taste the local cider and crêpes which are specialities of the area. A quiet site, set back from the sea, La Piscine will appeal to families looking for good quality without too many on site activities.

**Facilities:** Two refurbished toilet units of differing design and size include British and Turkish style toilets and washbasins in cabins. Facilities for disabled people. Dishwashing and laundry sinks, washing machines and dryers. Motorcaravan service point. Shop well stocked with basic provisions (1/7-15/9). Takeaway (high season). Swimming pool with separate flume (from 1/7, no bermuda style shorts), sauna and solarium. Play area. BMX track. Football pitch, volleyball, half-court tennis and table tennis. TV room. Entertainment organised in high season. Caravan storage. **Off site:** Bicycle hire, fishing and riding within 4 km. Golf 7 km. The sea is 15 minutes walk.

**Charges** 2002

| | | |
|---|---|---|
| Per person | 3.15 - | 4.50 |
| child (under 7 yrs) | 1.57 - | 2.25 |
| pitch incl. vehicle | 6.30 - | 9.00 |
| dog | 1.19 - | 1.70 |
| electricity (3-10A) | 2.60 - | 4.00 |
| local tax (child 0-16 yrs, adult) | 0.18 - | 0.36 |

**Tel:** 02 98 56 56 06. **Fax:** 02 98 56 57 64. E-mail: campingdelapiscine@altica.com. **Reservations:** made with 25% deposit and 19 fee. **Open** 15 May - 15 September.

**Directions:** Site is 5 km. south of Fouesnant. Turn off N165 expressway at Coat Conq signed Concarnau and Fouesnant. At Fouesnant join D45 signed Beg Meil and shortly turn left onto D145 signed Mousterlin. In 1 km. turn left and follow signs to site.

# Camping Municipal de Mariano

29720 Plonéour-Lanvern

This well kept municipal campsite, with attractive flower beds and planters around the site, is 7 km. from Pont L'Abbe, 18 km from the historic town of Quimper, and only a 15 minute drive from the sandy beaches of the Audierne bay. It makes an ideal inexpensive base from which to explore the region. There are 59 large, level grass pitches, all with electrical connections. The majority are divided by mature hedging, although 14 newer pitches are more open, but afford beautiful views over the surrounding countryside. Well signed local walks start from the rear entrance.

**Facilities:** Two fully equipped toilet blocks include laundry and dishwashing sinks, washing machines, dryers and freezers. Play area for young children and table tennis. **Off site:** Bars, restaurants and small supermarket within easy walking distance in town.

**Charges** 2002

| | |
|---|---|
| Per person | € 3.00 |
| child (-17 yrs) | € 1.60 |
| pitch | € 4.50 |
| car | € 1.30 |
| electricity | € 2.20 |

**Tel:** 02 98 82 66 00. Fax: 02 98 82 66 09.
**Reservations:** Advised for high season. **Open** 15 June - 15 September.

**Directions:** From D785 around Pont L'Abbe take D2 to Plonéour-Lanvern. On entering Plonéour-Lanvern turn right at church in town square. Follow for about 500 m, then turn left following signs.

# Camping de Kéranterec

route de Port la Forêt, 29940 La Forêt Fouesnant

The area around La Forêt Fouesnant is very much picture postcard Brittany - plenty of enticing crêperies and seafood restaurants, enchanting villages and towns and delightful hidden coves. For these and many other reasons, there are plenty of campsites to choose from and Camping de Kéranterec is well worth considering. A well established family run site with a French ambience (unlike some neighbouring sites with a much higher UK presence), Kéranterec has 265 grassy pitches in two distinct areas. The upper part of the site is more open and has little shade, and is also largely taken up by private mobile homes. The lower and more mature area is predominantly for tourers, with terraced pitches set in a former orchard (the trees still provide fruit for the cider produced on site, which we can highly recommend!). Some of these pitches have shade from the many trees on this part of the site, and some also overlook the little cove at the rear of the site. Spacious and divided by mature hedging, all have electrical connections (25 m. cable advised) and most also offer water and drainage.

**Facilities:** Two modern, fully equipped toilet blocks kept very clean include washbasins in cubicles, baby baths and facilities for disabled visitors. Washing machines, dryers and ironing boards. Small shop and bar (15/6-7/9) and takeaway (1/7-31/8). TV room with satellite. Heated swimming pool (15/5-7/9) with paddling pool, jacuzzi and three new water slides. Tennis court, boules, volleyball and basketball, table tennis (some indoors). Play area. In July/Aug. organised daily events and activities for all the family, and a free children`s club. **Off site:** Attractive sandy beach of Kerleven 10 minutes walk. Golf 1 km. Riding 3 km.

**Charges** 2002

| | |
|---|---|
| Per pitch | € 5.50 - € 7.40 |
| person | € 4.50 - € 5.80 |
| child (under 7 yrs) | € 2.10 - € 2.90 |
| dog | € 1.14 - € 1.70 |
| electricity | € 3.05 - € 3.10 |
| local tax (15/6-15/9) | € 0.30 |

**Tel:** 02 98 56 98 11. Fax: 02 98 56 81 73. E-mail: info@camping-keranterec.com. **Reservations:** Advised in high season and made with deposit (€ 77) and fee (€ 22). **Open** 5 April - 21 September.

**Directions:** From N165 take D70 Concarneau exit. At first roundabout take D44 signed Fouesnant. After 2.5 km. turn right at T junction, and follow for 2.5 km. and turn left (Port La Forêt - take care, 200 m. before junction a sign implies Port La Forêt is straight on - it isn`t). Continue to roundabout and take second exit (straight ahead), signed Port La Forêt. After 1 km. turn left (site signed), then in 400 m. turn left to site on left.

# Camping des Dunes

**2927** 67 rue Paul Langevin, 29740 Lesconil

On the edge of the sand dunes near the village of Lesconil, this campsite has the great advantage of providing direct access to an excellent sandy beach. The 120 sandy and grassy pitches have little shade, but are quite spacious and all have electricity (6A). The site is only 800 m from the village of Lesconil, a delightfully unspoiled fishing port where you can still see the little fishing fleet return each day, which offers a good choice of restaurants and cafes, and a 'Centre Nautique' offering range of watersports.

**Facilities:** Two central, unisex toilet blocks have mainly British style toilets and washbasins, both open and in cubicles. Baby area. Two toilet/shower rooms for disabled people. Laundry and dishwashing sinks. Washing machine and dryer. Baker visits each morning in high season. Play area for young children. Two trampolines, volleyball and table tennis.

**Charges** 2003

| | |
|---|---|
| Per unit incl. 2 adults | € 17.10 |
| extra adult | € 4.00 |
| child (under 7 yrs) | € 2.30 |
| electricity | € 3.05 |
| local tax (over 16 yrs) | € 0.15 |
| dog | € 1.50 |

**Tel:** 02 98 87 81 78. Fax: 02 98 82 27 05.
**Reservations:** Essential for high season and made with deposit (€ 61). **Open** 1 June - 15 September.

**Directions:** From Pont L'Abbe follow D102 to Lesconil. Just before the village a sports stadium is on the right - site signed just past stadium (look carefully - the sign is small). Site approx. 1.5 km. on right, just past Camping de la Grande Plage.

# Camping La Roche Percée

**2931** Hent Kerveltrec, Beg-Meil, 29170 Fouesnant

Close to the beautiful Brittany coastline, La Roche Percée combines a tranquil setting with a friendly and active family environment, only 400 metres from the beach. The site is English/French owned with 123 pitches, of which 80 are available for touring units, the rest being for privately owned or site owned mobile homes. Pitches are arranged in cul-de-sacs off a central area, and are of good size, grassy and flat, all with electrical connections (some may require a long lead). All pitches are separated by mature hedging, and some benefit from the shade of the variety of trees planted around the site. The bar terrace overlooks the swimming and paddling pools, and there is a waterslide into the main pool. During high season the owners organise a variety of entertainment activities, including boules, table tennis, pool and darts tournaments, barbecues, and live music in the bar.

**Facilities:** The clean central toilet block has mostly British style toilets, washbasins in cubicles, dish-washing and laundry sinks. Baby area. Wheelchair access provided on request. Motorcaravan service point. Small shop, snack bar and bar, 15/05 - 15/09, with bread to order outside these dates (dates can be flexible if busy.) Swimming pools (all season). Two play areas. Football and volleyball. Large trampoline (parental supervision essential!) Bicycle hire. **Off site:** Sailing school, golf and riding nearby.

**Charges** 2003

| | | |
|---|---|---|
| Per pitch | 8.50 - | 11.50 |
| adult | 3.00 - | 4.50 |
| child (under 7 yrs) | 1.50 - | 2.50 |
| electricity (6/10A) | | 3.00 |
| local tax (15/6-15/9) | 0.20 - | 0.40 |
| dog | 1.50 - | 2.00 |

**Tel:** (0)2 98 94 94 15. Fax: (0)2 98 94 48 05. E-mail: info@campingbrittany.com. **Reservations:** Accepted with deposit ( 80) and booking fee ( 16). **Open** 17 April - 28 September.

**Directions:** From N165 take D70 Concarneau exit, at first roundabout take first exit onto D44 (signed Fouesnant and Benodet). Following D44, turning right at T junction, after approx. 2 km turn left and follow through village of Forêt Fouesnant. Approx. 2 km. after village are two roundabouts. Go straight over first (smaller) one, and turn left at second on D45 to Beg Meil. After 3 km. site signed on left. Turn left, entrance just past 'Auberge la Roche Percée'.

# Castel Camping L'Orangerie de Lanniron

Château de Lanniron, 29336 Quimper

L'Orangerie is a beautiful and peaceful, family site in 10 acres of a XVIIth century, 42 acre country estate on the banks of the Odet river. It is just to the south of Quimper and about 15 km. from the sea and beaches at Bénodet. The family have a five year programme to restore and rehabilitate the park, the original canal, fountains, ornamental Lake of Neptune, the boathouse and the gardens and avenues. The original outbuildings have been attractively converted around a walled courtyard. The site has 200 grassy pitches, 149 for touring units, of three types (varying in size and services) on fairly flat ground laid out in rows alongside access roads. Most have electricity and 32 have all three services, with shrubs and bushes providing pleasant pitches. The restaurant in the beautiful XVIIth century Orangerie, and the Gardens are both open to the public and in Spring the rhododendrons and azaleas are magnificent, with lovely walks within the grounds and a riverside walk to town. Used by tour operators (45 pitches). All facilities are available when the site is open.

**Facilities:** The main heated block in the courtyard has been totally refurbished and is excellent. A second modern block serves the newer pitches at the top of the site and includes facilities for disabled people and babies. Washing machines and dryers. Motorcaravan service point. Shop (all season), Gas supplies. Bar, snacks and takeaway, plus restaurant (open daily from 20/5, reasonably priced with children's menu). Heated swimming pool (144 sq.m.) with children's pool. New pool planned. Small play area. Tennis. Minigolf, attractively set among mature trees. Table tennis. Fishing. Archery. Bicycle hire. General reading, games and billiards rooms. TV/video room (cable and satellite). Karaoke. Animation provided including outdoor activities with large room for indoor activities. **Off site:** Sea 15 km. Historic town of Quimper under 3 km. Two hypermarkets 1 km.

**Charges** 2002

| | |
|---|---:|
| Per adult | 5.40 |
| child (2-7 yrs) | 3.50 |
| pitch (100 sq.m.) | 12.50 |
| with electricity (10A) | 16.20 |
| special pitch (120/150sq.m.) | |
| with water and electricity | 19.00 |
| animal | 3.50 |

Less 15% outside July/Aug. **Tel:** 02 98 90 62 02. Fax: 02 98 52 15 56. E-mail: camping@lanniron.com. **Reservations:** Made with deposit ( 61) and fee ( 19). **Open** 15 May - 15 September.

**Directions:** From Quimper follow 'Quimper Sud' signs, then 'Toutes Directions' and general camping signs, finally signs for Lanniron.

## Camping du Manoir de Pen-ar-Steir

2910 | 29940 La Forêt-Fouesnant

This campsite will appeal to those who prefer a quiet place to stay at any time of the year, away from the noise and bustle of busier sites, even in high season. Situated on terraces up the steep sides of a valley in the grounds of an old Breton house, the site has a picturesque, garden-like quality. Beautifully kept, the entrance is a mass of planted flower displays, with a pond, stream and a small aviary next to the reception, and carefully tended trees and plants throughout the site itself. There are 105 pitches, of which about half are for touring units (the remainder used for mobile homes). Pitches vary in size (80-100 sq.m) and some are accessed by steep slopes, but all are on flat, grassy terraces, with low hedging around them, and all have electricity (3-10A), water and drainage.The main village is easily reached on foot which makes the site ideal for those with motorcaravans.

**Facilities:** Two sanitary blocks, refurbished to a high standard, include mixed British and Turkish style toilets, cabins with washbasins and showers, baby areas and children's toilets. The small block at rear of the old house contains washing machines and dryers, along with sanitary facilities (including those for disabled people) that are heated for winter use. Children's play area. Tennis court and volleyball. Barrier with card (deposit 15,24). **Off site:** Baker 50 m. Village with all amenities 150 m. Golf.

**Charges** 2002

| | | |
|---|---|---|
| Per adult | | 4.42 |
| child (under 7 yrs) | | 2.74 |
| pitch incl. car | | 7.32 |
| electricity 3-10A | 2.13 - | 3.05 |
| local tax | | 0.32 |

No credit cards. Less 20 % outside 1/7-26/8. **Tel:** 02 98 56 97 75. Fax: 02 98 56 80 49. E-mail: info@ camping-penarsteir.com. **Reservations:** Write for details. **Open** all year.

**Directions:** From N165 take D70 Concarneau exit. At first roundabout take D44 (signed Forêt Fouesnant). Follow to T-junction and turn right on D783. After 2 km. turn left back onto D44 to Forêt Fouesnant. In village take first exit right at round about to site 150 m. on left.

## Camping Les Prés Verts

2919 | Kernous-Plage, 29900 Concarneau

What sets this family site apart from the many others in this region are its more unusual features - its stylish pool complex with Romanesque style columns and statue, and its plants and flower tubs. The 150 pitches are mostly arranged on long, open, grassy areas either side of main access roads. Specimen trees, shrubs or hedges divide the site into smaller areas. There are a few individual pitches and an area towards the rear of the site where the pitches have sea views. Concarneau is just 2.5 km. and there are numerous marked coastal walks to enjoy in the area, plus watersports or boat and fishing trips available nearby. A 'Sites et Paysages' member.

**Facilities:** Two toilet blocks provide unisex WCs, but separate washing facilities for ladies and men. Pre-set hot showers and washbasins in cabins for ladies, both closed 21.00 - 08.00 hrs. Some child size toilets. Dishwashing and laundry sinks, washing machine and dryer. Pizza service twice weekly. Swimming pool (1/6-31/8; around 18 x 11 m.) and children's pool. Playground (0-5 yrs only). Minigolf. Path to sandy/rocky beach (300 m.) and coastal path. **Off site:** Supermarket 2 km. Riding 1 km, bicycle hire 3 km, golf 5 km.

**Charges** 2003

| | | |
|---|---|---|
| Per unit incl. 2 adults | 16.48 - | 20.60 |
| extra adult | 4.76 - | 5.95 |
| child (2-7 yrs) | 3.12 - | 3.90 |
| dog | 1.16 - | 1.45 |
| electricity (2-6A) | 2.90 - | 4.43 |
| local tax | | 0.25 |

**Tel:** 02 98 97 09 74. Fax: 02 98 97 32 06. E-mail: info@pres-verts.com. **Reservations:** Contact site for details. **Open** 1 May - 22 September.

**Directions:** Turn off C7 road, 2.5 km. north of Concarneau, where site is signed. Take third left after Hotel de l'Océan.

# Haven Camping Domaine de Kerlann

Land Rosted, 29930 Pont-Aven

**2914**

Starting with a small original site, Haven Europe have, with careful and imaginative planning, ensured that mobile homes blend naturally into the environment. The remaining 20% of around 140 touring pitches (some 80 sq.m, some 120 sq.m) have been left in a more natural situation on rough grass with a small stream flowing through and with some of the mature trees providing shade. Electricity is available to all pitches. Land drainage may be poor due to the park being on low lying ground. The 'piece de resistance' of the site is the amazing pool complex comprising three outdoor pools with separate toboggan, attractively landscaped with sunbathing terraces, and an indoor tropical style complex complete with jacuzzi and its own toboggan. Much evening holiday camp style entertainment (with a French flavour) takes place. on the bar terrace with its raised stage which overlooks the complex.

**Facilities:** The main large toilet block on the edge of the mobile home area offers a good provision including washbasins in cubicles, outside dishwashing and laundry sinks. Good laundry. A second block in the touring section opens in high season. Shop. French style restaurant, snack restaurant, takeaway and bar. Impressive pool complex including indoor and outdoor pools with lifeguards. Well equipped play areas. All weather multti-sports court, tennis courts, minigolf. Video games room, pool tables and satellite TV in the bar. Three children's clubs for different age groups. Gas barbecues are not permitted. **Off site:** Pont-Aven with its Gauguin connection, art galleries and museums is well worth visiting. A range of safe beaches and small ports and villages are nearby.

**Charges** 2002
| Per pitch incl. up to 2 persons | |
|---|---|
| with electricity | € 10.67 - € 30.34 |
| extra person | € 2.29 - € 5.34 |

**Tel:** 02 98 06 01 77. Fax: 02 98 06 18 50. E-mail: havenres@bourne-leisure.co.uk. **Reservations:** Accepted at any time for min. 4 days; no booking fee. Contact site or Haven Europe in the UK on 0870 242 7777 for information or reservation. **Open** 10 April - 24 September.

**Directions:** From Tregunc - Pont-Aven road, turn south towards Névez and site is on right.

**Enjoy the relaxed atmosphere at the beautiful Domaine de Kerlann - a lovely wooded parc in a perfect location for making the most of Southern Brittany.**

- Good size pitches grouped together in a grassy area
- Fabulous indoor pool complex with waterslide and spa bath
- Heated outdoor pools with new splash zone & waterslide
- Scattered play areas, multi-sport pitch & tennis courts
- 3 children's clubs for all ages
- Restaurant, takeaway, bar & entertainment's room
- Bilingual staff on parc
- Superb low season prices
- Site open from: 10 April - 24 October

**Domaine de Kerlann** ★★★★
Pont Aven

Domaine de Kerlann, Land Rosted, 29930 Pont Aven, France
Tel:00 33 298 06 01 77  Fax:00 33 298 06 18 50
To book please call the number above, quoting code FAR03

ABTA
V2819

# Camping du Domaine de Pendruc

Hameau de Penanguer, 29910 Tregunc

**2932**

Domaine de Pendruc is a quiet, traditional site which is welcoming, friendly and family-oriented. It is set in beautiful countryside less than one kilometre from the coast and wonderful beaches. The site has 160 grassy, level pitches, all divided by mature hedging which provide privacy without claustrophobia. All pitches have electricity (6A) and are of a good size, with a balance between sunny open pitches and those benefiting from shade from the tall trees. The owner, Madame Beau, keeps the campsite with its abundance of flowers and shrubs, very clean and tidy. Coastal walks, sailing, watersports, boat and fishing trips, golf, tennis and riding are all possible locally.

**Facilities:** Although relatively old, the central toilet block is kept very clean. British and Turkish style toilets, most washbasins in cubicles and sinks for dishwashing and laundry. Laundry room with washing machines and dryer. Motorcaravan service point. Small shop (1/7-31/8). Heated pool (1/6-15/9). Modern play area for younger children. TV room. Large field for volleyball, basketball and football.

**Charges** 2002
| Per pitch and vehicle | € 8.60 |
|---|---|
| person | € 4.75 |
| child (under 7 yrs) | € 2.08 |
| electricity (6A) | € 2.70 |
| local tax (over 18 yrs 1/6-30/9) | € 0.30 |

Less 20 % in low season. **Tel:** 02 98 97 66 28. Fax: 02 98 50 24 30. E-mail: domdependruc@wanadoo.fr. **Reservations:** Accepted with deposit (€ 87) and booking fee (€ 7,62). **Open** 1 June - 30 September.

**Directions:** From N165 take D70 Concarneau exit, (which becomes the D783) follow Tregunc signs. About 2 km. before Tregunc off roundabout signed Pendruc and Lambell (very small site sign). Follow for 1.5 km. and turn right (large site sign on corner). Site about 900 m. down on your left.

Brittany

# Camping Ty-Nadan

route d'Arzano, 29310 Locunolé

**2901**

the travel service
TO BOOK

| Ferry | ✔ |
| Pitch | ✔ |
| Accommodation | ✔ |

01892 55 98 98

Ty Nadan is a well organised site set amongst wooded countryside along the bank of the River Elle. The 183 pitches for touring units are grassy, many with shade and 152 with 10A electricity. An exciting and varied programme of activities is offered throughout the season - canoeing, rock climbing, mountain biking, aqua-gym, riding or walking - all supervised by qualified staff. A full programme of entertainment for all ages is provided in high season including concerts, Breton evenings with pig roasts, dancing, etc. (be warned, you will be actively encouraged to join in!) Recent developments include a new toilet block and extensions to the shop and bar. The swimming pool complex with its slides and paddling pool is very popular and now has an attractive viewing platform. Several tour operators use the site (90 pitches).

**Facilities:** Two older, split-level toilet blocks are of fair quality and unusual design. They include washbasins in cabins, and baby rooms. A new, impressively equipped block was opened in 2002 which provides easier access for disabled people. Dishwashing facilities in two attractive gazebo style units. Laundry room with washing machines and dryers. Good sized restaurant, takeaway, bar and well stocked shop (all open all season). Heated swimming pool (17 x 8 m), pool with water slides and paddling pool. Small beach on the river (unfenced). Tennis courts, table tennis, pool tables, archery and trampolines. Exciting adventure play park. Riding. Small roller skating rink. Bicycle hire. Skateboards, roller skates and boat hire. Fishing. Canoe expeditions. High season entertainment.

**Charges** 2002

| | |
|---|---|
| Per person | € 5.70 |
| child (under 7 yrs) | € 3.60 |
| pitch | € 12.20 |
| electricity | € 4.60 |
| water/drainage | € 6.50 |
| animal | € 3.00 |

Less 15-30% outside July/Aug. **Tel:** 02 98 71 75 47. Fax: 02 98 71 77 31. E-mail: TY-NADAN@wanadoo.fr.
**Reservations:** Made for exact dates with deposit (€ 50) and fee (€ 25). **Open** 15 May - 5 September.

**Directions:** Make for Arzano which is northeast of Quimperlé on the Pontivy road and turn off D22 just west of village at camp sign. Site is approx. 3 km.

Camping ★★★★ "Le Ty Nadan"

the only campsite where you can do this...

LE TY NADAN

*i comme...* 33(2) 98 10 19 20

www.camping-ty-nadan.fr

# Camping Municipal du Bois de Pleuven

Bois de Pleuven, 29140 Saint-Yvi

**2920M**

Set in 17 ha. of forest surroundings, this large municipal site has 280 pitches (177 for touring units, plus campsite owned mobile homes) set amongst the shady woodland of the Bois de Pleuven. Pitches vary in size but are all spacious, making this an ideal site for larger caravans. Most pitches have electricity, and the cul-de-sac layout combined with the mature trees and bushes provides a good degree of privacy. The site's leisure facilities including the pool complex are also open to the public. Situated between the historic towns of Quimper and Concarneau, and only 8 km. from the coast, this campsite makes an ideal base from which to explore this beautiful region.

**Facilities:** Two main toilet blocks, rather old fashioned, but clean, include washbasins in cubicles, British and Turkish style toilets, and laundry and dishwashing sinks. Two smaller blocks provide toilet facilities only. Washing machine and dryer. Small shop, takeaway, bar and TV room (all 20/6-31/8). Swimming pools. Bicycle hire. Tennis. Minigolf. Football, volleyball. Play areas. Torches useful. **Off site:** Fishing 7 km, riding 1 km, golf 4 km.

**Charges** guide

| | |
|---|---:|
| Per unit incl. up to 2 people | 12.20 |
| 3 persons | 15.24 |
| local tax (1/06-30/9) | 0.30 |

Small charges for amenities (not open in winter). **Tel:** 02 98 94 70 47. Fax: 02 98 94 76 92. **Reservations:** Advised for July/Aug. and made with fee ( 9,15). **Open** Easter - September.

**Directions:** From N165 take exit 'Quimper Sud - Troyalac'h" D765' and follow signs for St Yvi. After 4 km. turn right, signed Bois de Pleuven and site. At roundabout follow sign to campings and 'maison de repos'. Site is second campsite on right.

# Camping Le Raguénès-Plage

19 rue des Iles, Raguénéz, 29920 Névez

**2909**

the travel service
TO BOOK
Ferry ✓
Pitch ✓
Accommodation ✗
01892 55 98 98

Mme Guyader and her family will ensure you receive a warm welcome on arrival at this well kept and pleasant site. Although the entrance could best be described as more functional than beautiful, once you have passed the reception block you find yourself in an attractive and well laid out campsite with many shrubs and trees. The 287 pitches are a good size, flat and grassy, separated by trees and hedges. All have electricity (2/6A), water and drainage. The site is used by one tour operator (63 pitches), and has 27 mobile homes of its own. A new pool complex is planned for 2003 complete with a water toboggan. From the far end of the campsite a five minute walk along a path takes you down to a pleasant, sandy beach.

**Facilities:** Three clean, well maintained sanitary blocks include mixed style toilets, washbasins in cabins, baby baths and facilities for disabled visitors. Laundry and dishwashing sinks. Laundry room. Motorcaravan service point. Small shop (from 15/5). Bar and restaurant (from 1/6) with terrace and takeaway. Reading and TV room, internet point. Heated pool with sun terrace and children's pool. Sauna (charged). Play areas, table tennis, games room and volleyball. Activities organised in July/Aug. **Off site:** Supermarket 3 km. Fishing 300 m, riding 4 km.

**Charges** 2002

| | | |
|---|---:|---:|
| Per unit incl. 2 persons | 13.75 - | 21.07 |
| extra person | 3.72 - | 5.10 |
| child (under 7 yrs) | 2.20 - | 2.75 |
| electricity 2/6A | 2.45 - | 3.05 |
| local tax (over 18 yrs) | € | 0.40 |
| dog | free - € | 1.60 |

No credit cards. **Tel:** 02 98 06 80 69. Fax: 02 98 06 89 05. **Reservations:** Advised for high season, min. 7 days preferred for July/Aug. Write with deposit (€ 100). **Open** 18 April - 1 October.

**Directions:** From N165 take D24 Kerampaou exit. After 3 km turn right towards Nizon and bear right at church in village following signs to Névez (D77). Continue straight over roundabout through Névez, following signs to Raguénès. Continue for about 3 km. to site entrance on left (take care - entrance is quite small and easy to miss.)

Direct access to the beach 300 meters

*Le Raguenès*

Airotel *Plage* ★★★★

19, rue des Îles
29920 RAGUENÈZ EN NÉVEZ
Tel : 0033 298 06 80 69
Fax : 0033 298 06 89 05

✓ Heated swimming pool
✓ New water slide
✓ Direct and private access to the beach
✓ Renting of mobil-homes

Low season : 40% reduction

## Camping Les Genets d'Or

**2916**

Kermerour, Pont Kereon, 29380 Bannalec

A jewel of a small site, Les Genets d'Or is situated in a tiny country hamlet at the end of a road from Bannalec, 12 km. from Pont-Aven in Finistère. The spacious surroundings offer a safe haven for young children and a rural, tranquil environment for adults. The gently sloping, grassy site is edged with mature trees and divided into hedged glades with the odd apple tree providing shade. There are only 52 pitches (46 for touring units), all of a good size - some over 100 sq.m. - and most have electricity (6A), each glade having a water point. Alan and Judy, the English owners, ensure a friendly welcome and are proud of their site, keeping it in pristine condition. A play area and pond are planned.

**Facilities:** The good quality toilet block provides all the necessary amenities and washing facilities. Small bar/drinks service. Bread delivered in season. Reception has a small library and an indoor room provides snooker and table tennis. Bicycle hire. Caravan storage. **Off site:** Riding 3 km. The village is 15 minutes walk with bars, shop, baker, etc.

**Charges** 2002

| | | |
|---|---|---|
| Per pitch (incl. vehicle) | € | 5.50 |
| person | € | 2.50 |
| child under 6 yrs | € | 1.70 |
| electricity (6A) | € | 2.90 |
| animal | € | 1.00 |

Less 10% for over 7 nights. **Tel:** 02 98 39 54 35. **Fax:** 02 98 39 54 35. **E-mail:** enquiries@holidaybrittany.com. **Reservations:** Contact site. **Open** Easter/1 April - 30 September.

**Directions:** Take exit D4 from N165 towards Bannalec. In Bannalec turn right into Rue Lorec (signed Quimperlé) and follow camp signs for 1 km.

---

## Camping Les Embruns

**2918**

rue du Philosophe Alain, Le Pouldu, 29360 Clohars-Carnoët

This site is unusual in that it is located in the heart of a village, yet is only 250 metres from a sandy cove. It is also close to beautiful countryside and the Carnoët Forest. The entrance with its card operated barrier and superb floral displays, is the first indication that this is a well tended and well organised site, and the owners have won numerous regional and national awards for its superb presentation. The 180 pitches (80 occupied by mobile homes) are separated by trees, shrubs and bushes, and most have electricity (3/5A), water and waste water facilities. There is a covered, heated swimming pool, a circular paddling pool, and a new water play pool. It is only a short walk to the village centre, with all its attractions and services.

**Facilities:** Two modern sanitary blocks include mainly British style toilets, some washbasins in cubicles, baby baths and good facilities for disabled people. Dishwashing and laundry sinks under cover. Washing, drying and ironing facilities. Motorcaravan service point. Small shop. Bar and terrace (1/7-31/8) overlooking a covered, heated swimming pool (1/4-10/9) and paddling pool. Games hall with pinball machines and table tennis. Play area. Football field, volleyball and minigolf. Communal barbecue area. Activities organised in July/Aug. **Off site:** Bicycle hire 50 m, riding 2 km.

**Charges** 2002

| | | |
|---|---|---|
| Per unit incl. 2 persons | € 11.00 - € | 19.00 |
| extra person | € 3.50 - € | 4.30 |
| child (under 7 yrs) | € 2.30 - € | 2.60 |
| electricity | € | 3.00 |
| animal | free - € | 1.00 |
| local tax (June-Sept) | € | 0.30 |

Less in low seasons. Use of motorcaravan services € 1,83. **Tel:** 02 98 39 91 07. **Fax:** 02 98 39 97 87. **E-mail:** camping-les-embruns@wanadoo.fr. **Reservations:** Advised for high season. **Open** 6 April - 15 September.

**Directions:** From N165 take either 'Kervidanou, Quimperlé Ouest' exit or 'Kergostiou, Quimperlé Centre, Clohars Carnoët' exit and follow D16 to Clohars Carnoët. Then take D24 for Le Pouldu and follow site signs in village.

## Camping Municipal de Kerisole

Kerisole, 29390 Scaer

**2922M**

Within walking distance of the pleasant little town of Scaër, Camping Kerisole is an attractive and well kept site, ideal for exploring inland Brittany and yet only 32 km. from the coast. There are 83 mostly level, grass pitches, not hedged, but individually numbered. Most have electricity (10A). At the back of the site is access to a marked woodland footpath, which also has a range of 'assault course' obstacles along the way. All season the campsite in conjunction with the local council organises walks, local visits and activities. With its delightful park-like setting, reasonable charges, and proximity to both town facilities and countryside walks, this site makes an ideal base.

**Facilities:** Central, clean and tidy sanitary blocks include washbasins in cubicles and separate men's and ladies' disabled facilities. Laundry and dishwashing sinks. Bread to order. Adjacent children's play area in large grassy field. **Off site:** Nearby tennis, basketball and petanque courts, and indoor swimming pool. Shops, bars and restaurants a few minutes walk away in the centre of Scaër.

**Charges** 2002

| | |
|---|---|
| Per pitch | € 2.35 |
| adult | € 1.30 - € 2.00 |
| child (under 7 yrs) | € 1.91 - € 1.30 |
| vehicle | € 1.10 - € 1.30 |
| electricity | € 2.35 |

**Tel:** 02 98 57 60 91. **Fax:** 02 98 57 66 89.
**Reservations:** contact site. **Open** 15 June - 15 Sept.

**Directions:** From N165 take D70 to Rosporden, then D782 to Scaër. Drive through town centre, following signs for Faouet, and site is on left at traffic lights on leaving town centre.

## Camping Bois des Ecureuils

29300 Guilligomarc'h

**2925**

Situated in beautiful countryside between the rivers Scorff and Elle, this two star site provides camping `au natural` for those seeking an ideal base from which to explore southern and central Brittany. The site is set in 4 acres of natural woodland, with oak, chestnut, birch and beech trees providing shade for many of the 40 pitches. Of reasonable size, the owners say that `electricity is possible everywhere`. Those pitching tents may need to avoid protruding tree roots, etc. The British owners, David and Barbara Reed, can provide a wealth of information on things to do, including walking, cycling, canoeing and fishing. Although by no means a luxurious site, the tranquillity and peacefulness of this rural setting, combined with the friendly reception make it ideal for anyone seeking a `back to nature` style holiday.

**Facilities:** Small toilet block with hot showers, washbasins, British and Turkish style WCs, dishwashing and laundry sinks. Reception also provides basic groceries and bread to order. Small playground for children. Large grass area with boules pitch, table tennis, badminton net and TV tent. Bicycle hire.

**Charges** 2003

| | |
|---|---|
| Per person | € 2.40 |
| child (under 7 yrs) | € 1.30 |
| pitch | € 4.00 |
| electricity (5A) | € 2.20 |

**Tel:** 02 98 71 70 98. **Fax:** 02 98 71 70 98. E-mail: price.reed@wanadoo.fr. **Reservations:** Made with deposit (€ 15.24 or £10). **Open** 15 May - 15 September.

**Directions:** From south on N165 take Quimperlé D765 exit. Before entering Quimperlé turn right on D22 to Arzano. On leaving Arzano turn left on D222 to Guilligomarc'h. After 3 km. turn right and follow road into village (site signed). In the village follow one way system around the church and take C2 to Meslan. Site is 3 km. on right. From north take D769 Carhaix-Plouguer - Lorient road and, 39 km. past Carhaix-Plouguer turn right on D6 to Arzano, then left on C2 to Guilligomarc'h to site 3 km on left.

## Camping Municipal de Fougères

Rte. de la Chapelle Janson, 35300 Fougères

**3503M**

Fougères boasts the oldest medieval castle in Brittany. Its well presented campsite has 90 good-sized pitches, secluded by rows of shrubs. Most are on flat grass, with 18 level hardstandings available and all have electricity and water adjacent. This is a useful overnight stop.

**Facilities:** A good toilet block provides washbasins in cabins and large showers (hot water 7-10am, 12-2pm, 7-10pm). Washing machines and dryers. No shop but baker tours the site approx. 8 am. Office open 9-11am, 5-8 pm. American motorhomes are not accepted. **Off site:** Tennis and minigolf nearby

**Charges** guide

| | |
|---|---|
| Per adult | € 2.00 |
| pitch | € 2.50 |
| electricity (5/10A) | € 2.40 - € 3.00 |

**Tel:** 02 99 99 40 81. **Fax:** 02 99 94 27 94.
**Reservations:** Write to Service des Sports et de la Vie Associative, 22 rue du Tribunal, 35300 Fougères. **Open** 1 March - 30 November.

**Directions:** The approach is signed from a round about on the eastern ring road near the Formula 1 hotel and Gendarmerie. Take small road to Le Chapelle-Janson (D17) and site is 300 m. on right.

# Camping Le Vieux Chêne

Baguer-Pican, 35120 Dol-de-Bretagne

This attractive, family owned site is situated between St Malo and Mont St Michel. Developed in the grounds of a country farmhouse dating from 1638, its young and enthusiastic owner has created a really pleasant, traditional atmosphere with a very personal feel. It offers 200 good sized pitches, most with electricity, water tap and light, in spacious rural surroundings on gently sloping grass. They are separated by bushes and flowers, with mature trees for shade. A very attractive tenting area (without electricity) is in the orchard. There are three lakes in the grounds and centrally located leisure facilities include an attractive pool complex. Some entertainment is provided in high season, free for children. Used by a Dutch tour operator (10 pitches).

**Facilities:** Three very good, unisex toilet blocks include washbasins in cabins, a baby room and facilities for disabled people. All recently been refurbished and can be heated. Small laundry with washing machine, dryer and iron. Motorcaravan services. Shop. Takeaway. Café with terrace overlooking the pools (all season). Medium sized, heated swimming pool, children's pool, toboggans, slides, etc. (17/5-14/9; lifeguard July/Aug). TV (satellite) and games rooms. Tennis court, minigolf, giant chess. Play area. Riding in July/Aug. Fishing is possible in two of the three lakes. **Off site:** Supermarket 3 km. Golf 12 km.

**Charges** 2002

| | |
|---|---|
| Per unit | € 7.00 - € 13.50 |
| adult | € 4.50 |
| child (under 10 yrs) | € 3.00 |
| electricity (5A) | € 3.50 |
| dog | free |

**Tel:** 02 99 48 09 55. Fax: 02 99 48 13 37. E-mail: vieux.chene@wanadoo.fr. **Reservations:** Made with deposit (€ 30) and fee (€ 15). **Open** 1 April - 1 October.

**Directions:** Site is by the D576 Dol-de-Bretagne - Pontorson road, just east of Baguer-Pican. It can be reached from the new N176 taking exit for Dol-Est and Baguer-Pican.

*BRITTANY*

★★★★
Camping - Caravaning
**le Vieux Chêne**

Baguer Pican
35120 Dol de Bretagne
Tél. 0033 2 99 48 09 55
Fax 0033 2 99 48 13 37
Website: www.camping-vieuxchene.fr

- *200 pitches,*
- *Tennis,*
- *Aquatic Park,*
- *Fishing ponds,*
- *Mini-golf,*
- *Mini-club,*
- *Snack-bar, Shop,*
- *Ponies...*

# Camping La Touesse

35800 Saint-Lunaire

This family campsite was purpose built and has been developed since 1987 by Alain Clement who is keen to welcome more British visitors. Set just back from the coast road, 300 m. from a sandy beach it is in a semi-residential area. It is, nevertheless, an attractive sheltered site with a range of trees and shrubs. The 142 level, grass pitches in bays (95 for touring units) have electricity and are accessed by circular tarmac roads. The plus factor of this site, besides its proximity to Dinard, is the fine sandy beach which is sheltered - so useful in early season - and safe for children. The friendly owners speak English.

**Facilities:** The central toilet block is well maintained, heated in low season and provides all modern facilities. Part of it may not be open outside July/Aug. Baby bath and toilet for disabled people. Laundry and dishwashing sinks, and two washing machines and a dryer. Motorcaravan service point. Shop for basics (1/4-15/9). Pleasant bar/restaurant (or clubhouse as it is called) with TV. Volleyball, table tennis and video games for children. Sauna. **Off site:** Bicycle hire 1 km. Fishing 300 m. Riding 500 m. Golf 2 km. Sandy beach 4 minutes walk.

**Charges** 2003

| | |
|---|---|
| Per pitch | € 4.20 - € 5.70 |
| adult | € 3.40 - € 4.40 |
| child (under 7 yrs) | € 1.90 - € 2.40 |
| electricity 5/10A | € 2.90 - € 3.10 |
| local tax (child 4-10 yrs, others) | € 0.10 - € 0.25 |

No credit cards. **Tel:** 02 99 46 61 13. Fax: 02 99 16 02 58. E-mail: camping.la.touesse@wanadoo.fr. **Reservations:** 1 April - 30 September. **Open** 1 April - 30 September.

**Directions:** From Dinard take D786 coast road towards St Lunaire; watch for site signs to the left.

## Brittany

# Castel Camping des Ormes
Epiniac, 35120 Dol-de-Bretagne

3502

the travel service
TO BOOK
Ferry ☑
Pitch ☑
Accommodation ☑
01892 55 98 98

This impressive site is in the northern part of Brittany, about 30 kilometres from the old town of St Malo, in the grounds of the Château des Ormes. In an estate of wooded parkland and lakes it has a pleasant atmosphere, busy in high season, almost a holiday village, but peaceful at other times, with a wide range of facilities. The 700 pitches, of which only 150 are for touring units, are divided into a series of different sections, each with its own distinctive character. They offer a choice of terrain - flat or gently sloping, wooded or open - and mixed with the range of tour operator units. There are electrical connections (3/6A) on 200 pitches. A marvellous `Aqua Park' with pink stone and palms and a variety of pools, toboggans, waterfalls and jacuzzi (free) is set just above the small lake with pedaloes and canoes for hire. A pleasant bar and terrace overlooks the pools and a grass sunbathing area surrounds them - almost a touch of the Caribbean! The original pools are sheltered by the restaurant building, parts of which are developed from the 600 year old water-mill. A particular feature is an 18 hole golf course; also a golf practice range and a beginners 5 hole course. A hotel with pool and restaurant is now part of the complex. A popular site with British visitors, with some 80% of the pitches occupied by tour operators and seasonal units and consequently very busy with much organised entertainment and lots for children to do.

**Facilities:** Sanitary installations are of fair standard, including washbasins in cabins and ample facilities for disabled people. Motorcaravan services. Shop, bar, restaurant and takeaway. Games room, bar and disco. Two traditional heated swimming pool and Aqua park. Golf. Bicycle hire. Fishing. Riding. Minigolf, two tennis courts, sports ground with volleyball, etc, paintball, archery and a cricket club.

**Charges** guide

| | |
|---|---|
| Per person | € 5.34 |
| child (under 7 yrs) | € 3.05 |
| pitch incl. vehicle | € 18.29 |
| electricity 3/6A | € 3.05 - € 3.51 |
| water and drainage | € 1.07 |
| animal | € 1.07 |
| local tax (over 10 yrs) | € 0.08 |

Less 10% outside July/Aug. **Tel:** 02 99 73 50 00. Fax: 02 99 73 53 55. E-mail: info@lesormes.com. **Reservations:** Made for min. 3 nights; details from site. **Open** 15 May - 10 September.

**Directions:** Access road leads off main D795 about 7 km. south of Dol-de-Bretagne, north of Combourg.

## Camping Le P'tit Bois

3504

St-Jouan-des-Guerets, 35430 St Malo

the travel service
TO BOOK
Ferry ✓
Pitch ✓
Accommodation ✓
01892 55 98 98

On the outskirts of St Malo, this neat, family oriented site is very popular with British visitors, being ideal for one night stops or for longer stays in this interesting area. Le P'tit Bois is a busy site providing 274 large level pitches (around 140 for touring units) which are divided into groups by mature hedges and trees, separated by shrubs and flowers and with access from tarmac roads. Nearly all have electrical hook-ups and over half have water taps. Behind reception, an attractive, sheltered terraced area around the pools provides a focus during the day with the bar and snack bar. There are site-owned mobile homes and chalets but this does mean that the facilities are open over a long season (but possibly for limited hours).

**Facilities:** Two fully equipped toilet blocks, one in the newer area across the lane, include washbasins in cabins, baby baths and laundry facilities. Simple facilities for disabled people. Motorcaravan service point. Small shop (from 15/5). Bar where entertainment and discos are organised. Snack bar with take-away, small bar, TV room (large screen for sports events) and games rooms. Swimming pool complex with standard pool, two paddling pools and two water slides (from 15/5). Indoor pool planned. Playground and multi-sports court. Tennis court, minigolf, table tennis, and outdoor chess. Charcoal barbecues are not permitted. Card operated security gates (deposit). **Off site:** Fishing 1.5 km, bicycle hire or riding 5 km, golf 7 km.

**Charges** 2003

| | |
|---|---|
| Per person | € 6.00 - € 7.00 |
| child (under 7 yrs) | € 4.00 |
| pitch and car | € 10.00 - € 16.00 |
| dog | € 4.00 |
| electricity (6A) | € 4.00 |

**Tel:** 02 99 21 14 30. **Fax:** 02 99 81 74 14. **E-mail:** camping.ptitbois@wanadoo.fr. **Reservations:** Made on receipt of 25% of total cost, plus fee (€ 18,29) for July/Aug. **Open** 30 April - 13 September.

**Directions:** St Jouan is west off the St Malo - Rennes road (N137) just outside St Malo. Site is signed from the N137 (exit St Jouan or Quelmer).

## Camping Municipal du Moulin

4402M

route de Nantes, 44190 Clisson

This good value, small site is conveniently located on one of the main north - south routes on the edge of the interesting old town of Clisson. A typical municipal site, it is useful for short stays. The site has 47 good sized, marked and level pitches with electricity (6A) and divided by hedges and trees giving a good degree of privacy; also an unmarked area for small tents. A barbecue and camp fire area (with free wood) is to the rear of the site above the river where one can fish or canoe (via a steep path). The warden lives on site in high season. The attractive old town is within walking distance.

**Facilities:** The fully equipped unisex toilet block includes some washbasins in cabins and others in a separate large room, with hot and cold water. Unit for disabled people. Dishwashing and laundry sinks. Cleaning can be a bit haphazard. Bread delivered daily. Table tennis, volleyball and small playground. No double axle or commercial vehicles accepted. **Off site:** Supermarket with cheap fuel across the road.

**Charges** 2002

| | |
|---|---|
| Per unit incl. 1 adult and electricity | € 8.30 |
| extra adult | € 2.35 |
| child (0-7 yrs) | € 1.55 |

**Tel:** 02 40 54 44 48. **Fax:** 02 40 80 17 66. **Reservations:** Contact site. **Open** 1 March - 31 October.

**Directions:** Entering Clisson from the north on N249 (Nantes - Poitiers) road, turn right at round about after passing Leclerc supermarket on your left. Site access is directly off roundabout.

## Camping Municipal Henri Dubourg

4414M

route de Rennes, 44170 Nozay

This good, small site is ideal for short stays or as an overnight stop, being situated in the northern outskirts of Nozay with easy access from the N137 Rennes - Nantes road. There are 25 well hedged, level, grassy pitches with electricity (6A) and a more open area at the rear of the site. Tourist information and an ice pack service are available at reception, there is a barbecue area and a baker calls each morning. Reception opens 07.30-09.00 and 18.00-20.30 hrs. A small lake with a playground and minigolf is five minutes walk.

**Facilities:** A neat, modern and very clean toilet block has plenty of hot water, roomy showers and includes an odd Turkish style toilet. Facilities for disabled visitors. Dishwashing area under cover, laundry sinks inside. **Off site:** Fishing or golf 400 m.

**Charges** 2002

| | |
|---|---|
| Per pitch and car | € 3.35 |
| person | € 0.91 - € 1.83 |
| electricity | € 1.83 |
| animal | € 0.91 |

**Tel:** 02 40 87 94 33. **Fax:** 02 40 79 35 64. **Reservations:** Contact site. **Open** 15 May - 15 September.

**Directions:** From N137 take N171 Chateaubriant exit, then take first right D121 for Nozay. Site is on right after the lake (approx. 1 km).

## Camping L'Hermitage

**4413** 36 ave du Paradis, 44290 Guemene-Penfao

L'Hermitage is a pretty wooded site, useful for en-route or longer stays. The enthusiastic staff, even though their English is a little limited, provide a warm welcome and maintain this reasonably priced site to high standards. There are 110 pitches of which 80 are a good size for touring and camping. Some are formally arranged on open, level grass pitches, whereas others are informal amongst light woodland. Electricity (6A) is available to all (a long lead may be useful). A fairly small swimming pool is nicely maintained and carefully fenced.

**Facilities:** A clean, old style and well serviced toilet block includes some washbasins in cabins with warm water. Laundry and dishwashing sinks under cover (cold water but a hot tap is provided. Smallish pool and paddling pool. Small play area. Table tennis, petanque and games room with video games. **Off site:** Leisure complex with an indoor pool opposite. Village 1 km. for all facilities. Fishing 500 m. Riding 2 km. Many walking trails.

**Charges** 2002

| | |
|---|---|
| Per unit incl. 2 adults | € 7.65 - € 9.00 |
| extra adult | € 2.75 |
| child (under 10 yrs) | € 1.55 |
| dog | € 1.00 |
| electricity | € 2.30 |

**Tel:** 02 40 79 23 48. Fax: 02 40 51 11 87. E-mail: contact@campinglhermitage.com. **Reservations:** Contact site. **Open** 1 April - 31 October.

**Directions:** Exit N137 at Derval (signed Châteaubriant) but take D775 for Redon. Guémené-Penfao is approx. 13 km. Watch for site signs before village centre. Site is in the outskirts in a semi-residential area to the northeast.

CAMPING • GÎTE D'ÉTAPE
L'HERMITAGE ★★★
*Sun, calm and uncovered*

36 avenue du Paradis
[4]4290 GUÉMÉNÉ-PENFAO
Tél. : 02 40 79 23 48
Fax : 02 40 51 11 87
contact@campinglhermitage.com
**www.campinglhermitage.com**

## Camping du Petit Port

**4401M** 21 bvd. du Petit Port, 44300 Nantes

This modern site, which is within the town limits in a park-like area with mature trees, is well maintained and of good quality. It has 120 flat good-sized, hedged hardstandings for caravans, all with electricity (10A), water and drainaway (awning pegs possibly a problem). From Easter - 30 Sept. it also takes about 80 tents on separate grass areas. At certain times the caravan pitches become full with those working in the town or visiting for commercial reasons. However, in the holiday season, it is said that about half are available for tourists and one should usually find a space. The tram system within the town is cheap and reliable (tickets available from reception) and the site is easily reached by bus or tram from the railway station.

**Facilities:** Four good sanitary blocks (code-controlled access) can be heated and include washbasins in cubicles (a little cramped) and facilities for disabled people. Launderette. Motorcaravan service point open to all (free for those staying on the site). Shop for basics (1/6-30/8). Play area. TV room. Bicycle hire. **Off site:** Swimming pool (free for campers), ice rink (discount), bowling alley and café very close, bakery 100 m. and restaurant opposite. Golf course easily accessible via tramway.

**Charges** 2002

| | |
|---|---|
| Per caravan incl. car or motorcaravan | € 6.10 - € 7.62 |
| tent | € 3.23 - € 5.75 |
| person | € 2.24 - € 2.80 |
| child (under 10 yrs) | € 1.49 - € 1.87 |
| double axle caravan | € 1.44 - € 14.31 |
| electricity (10A) | € 2.80 |
| local tax | € 0.15 |

Less 20% for stays over 3 days. **Tel:** 02 40 74 47 94. Fax: 02 40 74 23 06. E-mail: camping-petit-port@mge-mantes.fr. **Reservations:** Not made, but you could phone the previous day. **Open** all year.

**Directions:** Site is on northern edge of the town on Bvd. Petit Port, near the university (ring road east). From express road use exit signed for Porte de la Chapelle and follow signs for Petit Port and university. Alternatively follow signs 'Porte de Rennes'.

# Castel Camping Château du Deffay

BP 18 Le Deffay, Ste Reine de Bretagne, 44160 Pontchâteau

A family owned site, Château de Deffay is a refreshing departure from the usual Castel formula in that it is not over organised or supervised and has no tour operator units. The landscape is natural to encourage wildlife, right down to the mole-hills, and the site blends well with the rural environment of the estate, lake and farmland which surround it. For these reasons it is enjoyed by many. However, with the temptation of free pedaloes and the fairly deep, unfenced lake, parents should ensure that children are supervised. The 120 good sized, somewhat uneven pitches have pleasant views and are either on open grass, on shallow terraces divided by hedges, or informally arranged in a central, slightly sloping wooded area. Most have 6A electricity. The facilities are situated within the old courtyard area of the smaller château (that dates from before 1400). The larger château (built 1880) and another lake stand away from this area providing pleasant walking. The reception has been built separately to contain the camping area. Alpine type chalets overlook the lake and fit well with the environment.

**Facilities:** The main sanitary unit, housed in a converted barn, is well equipped including wash-basins in cabins, provision for disabled people and a baby bathroom. Washing machines, and dryer. Maintenance can be variable and, with the boiler located at one end of the block, hot water can take time to reach the other in low season. Extra facilities are in the courtyard area where the well stocked shop, bar, small restaurant with takeaway and solar heated swimming pool and paddling pool are located (all 15/5-15/9). Play area for children. TV in the bar, separate room for table tennis. English language animation in season including children's mini club. Torches useful. **Off site:** Golf 5 km. Close to the Brière Regional Park, the Guérande Peninsula, and La Baule with its magnificent beach.

**Charges** guide

| | |
|---|---|
| Per pitch | € 5.95 - € 8.99 |
| with electricity (6A) | € 9.15 - € 12.20 |
| with 3 services | € 10.52 - € 13.72 |
| per adult | € 2.44 - € 3.90 |
| child (2-12 yrs) | € 1.68 - € 2.59 |

**Tel:** 02 40 88 00 57. Fax: 02 40 01 66 55. E-mail: info@camping-le-deffay.com. **Reservations:** Accepted with deposit (€ 10 per day) and fee (€ 16). **Open** 1 May - 21 September.

**Directions:** Site is signed from D33 Pontchâteau - Herbignac road near Ste. Reine. Also signed from the D773 and N165.

## Camping Armor-Héol

Route de Guérande, 44420 Piriac-sur-Mer

**4416**

Situated only 700 metres from Piriac town and beach and 14 km. from Guérande this site makes an ideal base for a beach holiday or for touring the Breton countryside and coastline. With considerable recent investment, the site now offers excellent facilities for visitors of all ages. There are 250 good sized (120 sq.m) level pitches all with 5A electricity. Although site owned mobiles and chalets take 160 pitches, they do not feel intrusive. In 2002 a new facility was completed providing an outdoor swimming pool, a paddling pool and 70 m. of water slides, together with a bar and restaurant with a large terrace. For 2003 an indoor pool is planned with water movement where you swim and stay stationary! This is a friendly site with English spoken.

**Facilities:** Two clean and well maintained toilet blocks include washbasins in cabins, baby rooms, family rooms, dishwashing and laundries. Dishwashing, washing machines and dryers. Super bar and restaurant (1/6-15/9). Most activities are in one part of the site with heated pools and water slides ((1/6-15/9). Multi sports area, tennis courts, volleyball. Playground. **Off site:** Beach and town, fishing, boat launching, surfing and bicycle hire 700 m. Golf 2 km.

**Charges** 2002

| | |
|---|---|
| Per unit incl. 2 persons, electricity | € 11.43 - € 24.39 |
| extra person | € 1.83 - € 3.81 |
| child under 4 yrs | € 1.68 - € 2.74 |
| animal | € 3.05 |
| local tax | € 0.23 - € 0.46 |

**Tel:** (0)2 40 23 57 80. Fax: (0)2 40 23 59 42. E-mail: armor.heol@wanadoo.fr. **Reservations:** Contact site. **Open** 15 April - 29 September.

**Directions:** From N165 Vannes - Nantes road, take D774 southwest at Guérande. Follow D333 signed Piriac sur Mer. Site is on left 0.5 km. before Piriac sur Mer, 4 km. from Guérande.

## Camping Parc Sainte-Brigitte

Domaine de Bréhet, 44420 La Turballe

**4404**

Sainte-Brigitte is a well established site in the grounds of a manor housr, three kilometres from the beaches. It is a spacious site with 150 pitches, 106 with electricity (6A) and 25 also with water and waste water. Some are in a circular, park-like setting near the entrance, more are in wooded areas under tall trees and others are on more open grass in an unmarked area near the pool. One can walk around many of the areas of the estate not used for camping, there are farm animals to see and a fishing lake is very popular. A quiet place to stay outside the main season, with few facilities open; in high season, however, it is mainly used by families with its full share of British visitors and it can become very busy. Used by a tour operator (20 pitches).

**Facilities:** The main toilet block is of fair quality, supplemented by a second block next to it. Washbasins in cabins, with bidets for women, and two bathrooms. Washing machines and dryer (no washing on pitches, lines provided). Motorcaravan services. Small shop for basics, baker calls. Little restaurant/bar with takeaway (both 15/5-15/9). Heated swimming pool and children's pool (all season). Playground. Bicycle hire. Boules, volleyball, pool and 'baby-foot' and table tennis room. TV room and traditional 'salle de reunion' in renovated outbuildings of the manor house. **Off site:** Nearest beach 3 km. Riding 2 km, golf 15 km.

**Charges** 2003

| | |
|---|---|
| Per person | € 5.00 |
| child (under 7) | € 3.30 |
| pitch | € 5.20 |
| with water and electricity | € 10.50 |
| car | 42.70 |
| dog | € 1.50 |
| local tax | € 0.15 |

No credit cards. **Tel:** 02 40 24 88 91. Fax: 02 40 23 30 42. **Reservations:** Made for any length with exact dates and recommended for July/Aug, with deposit (€ 77) plus fee (€ 15,24). **Open** 1 April - 1 October.

**Directions:** Entrance is off the busy D99 La Turballe - Guérande road, 3 km. east of La Turballe. A one-way system operates.

# PARC SAINTE-BRIGITTE
★ ★ ★ ★ N.N.
De Luxe Camping Site

**HEATED SWIMMING POOL**

Close to the fishing village of LaTurballe and neighbouring beaches. 10 km from the well-known resort of La Baule. The charm of the countryside with the pleasures of the seaside. Sanitary facilities as in a first class hotel. Heated and covered swimming pool (approximately 200 m² water and 200 m² covered terrace around it). The cover can be retracted during warm weather. Childrens pool.

campingsaintebrigitte@wanadoo.fr
www.campingsaintebrigitte.com

## Castel Camping Le Pré du Château de Careil

33 rue du Château, Careil, 44350 Guérande

**4403**

This site is totally different from the more usual Castel sites. It is the smallest site in the group and has few of the facilities or activities usually associated with these sites. It has a quiet atmosphere and is very popular with couples, retired people and those with young children (it is not really recommended for families with older children or teenagers). In the grounds of the Château de Careil, a building dating from the 14th century which may be visited, this small site, shaded by mature trees, contains just 50 good sized pitches. All are equipped with electricity (6/10A) and water, some with drainage also.

**Facilities:** The main refurbished toilet facilities in the main building include four unisex shower and wash-basin rooms. En-suite facilities for disabled people, baby room and washing machine. In season (15/6-5/9) some emergency provisions are kept and bread can be ordered. Small pool (11 x 5 m. open 15/6-5/9). Playground. TV room. Volleyball and table tennis. Archery occasionally. **Off site:** Supermarket near. Fishing or golf 10 km, bicycle hire 2 km, riding 5 km. In July/Aug. tours of the Château are possible.

**Charges** 2002

| | |
|---|---|
| Per unit incl. 2 persons, electricity | € 17.00 - € 20.00 |
| extra person | € 4.50 |
| extra child (under 10 yrs) | € 3.00 |
| electricity (10A) | € 1.60 |
| local tax | € 0.23 - € 0.46 |

No credit cards. **Tel:** 02 40 60 22 99. Fax: 02 40 60 22 99. E-mail: chateau.careil@free.fr. **Reservations:** Possible with deposit (€ 21,34) and booking fee (€ 15,24). **Open** 1 May - 30 September.

**Directions:** Take D92 from Guérande to La Baule and turn east to Careil before the town. From D99 Guérande - St Nazaire road, turn onto D92, follow ing signs to `Intermarche' and for Château de Careil. Take care as site entrance gate is fairly narrow and located between two bends making access a little awkward.

## Camping Les Ajoncs d'Or

chemin du Rocher, 44500 La Baule

**4417**

This site is situated in pine woods, 1.5 km. on the inland side of La Baule and its beautiful bay. It can be difficult to find an informal campsite close to an exciting seaside resort that retains its touring and camping identity. Les Ajoncs d'Or does this. A well maintained, natural woodland setting provides a wide variety of pitch types, some level and bordered with hedges and tall trees to provide shade and many others that maintain the natural characteristics of the woodland. Most pitches have electricity (6A) and water nearby and are usually of a larger size. A central building provides a shop and open friendly bar that serve snacks and takeaways. The English speaking Bazillails family (the owners) who live on site will welcome you to their campsite. There are only just over 200 pitches, so large areas of woodland have been retained for quiet and recreational purposes and are safe for children to roam. Enjoy the gentle breezes off the sea that constantly rustle the trees. The family are justifiably proud of their site.

**Facilities:** Two good quality sanitary blocks are clean and well maintained providing plenty of facilities including a baby room Washing machines and dryers. Shop and bar (July/Aug). Good size swimming pool and paddling pool (1/6-5/9). Sports and playground areas. Reception with security barrier (closed 22.30 - 7.30 hrs). **Off site:** Everything for an enjoyable holiday can be found in nearby La Baule.

**Charges** 2002

| | |
|---|---|
| Per unit incl. 2 persons | € 18.00 |
| with electricity | € 21.00 |
| with water and drainage | € 23.00 |
| extra person | € 4.60 |
| child 2-7 yrs | € 3.00 |
| dog | € 0.95 |
| local tax (July/Aug; over 18 yrs) | € 0.46 |

Less 15-25% outside July/Aug. **Tel:** (0)2 40 60 33 29. Fax: (0)2 40 24 44 37. E-mail: contact@ajoncs.com. **Reservations:** Contact site. **Open** 1 April - 30 September.

**Directions:** From N171 take exit for La Baule les Pins. Site is well signed from the village.

## Camping La Tabardière

4415 44770 La Plaine-sur-Mer

Owned and managed by the Barre family, this campsite lies next to the family farm. Pleasant, peaceful and immaculate, this site will suit those who want to enjoy the local coast and towns but return to an 'oasis' for relaxation. It still, however, provides activities and fun for those with energy remaining. The pitches are mostly terraced either side of a narrow valley and care needs to be taken in manoeuvring caravans into position - although the effort is well worth it. Most pitches have access to electricity (3/6A) and water taps are conveniently situated. Whilst this is a rural site, its amenities are excellent with a swimming pool, paddling pool and water toboggan slide, table tennis, volleyball, tennis, boules and a very challenging 18 hole minigolf to keep you occupied, plus a friendly bar. The beautiful beaches are 3 km distant, with the fishing harbour town, Pomic, some 5 km, ideal for cafes, restaurants and the evening strolls.

**Facilities:** The good, clean sanitary block is well equipped and includes laundry facilities. Bar. Shop. Snacks and takeaway. Good sized swimming pool, paddling pool and slides (supervised). Playground. Minigolf. Table tennis. Volleyball and basketball. Half size tennis courts. Boules. **Off site:** Sea fishing, golf, riding all 5 km. Beach 3 km.

**Charges** 2002

| | |
|---|---|
| Per unit incl. 1 or 2 persons | € 10.50 - € 14.10 |
| extra person | € 3.60 - € 4.60 |
| child 2-6 yrs | € 3.10 - € 3.70 |
| animal | € 1.60 |
| electricity | € 3.10 |

**Tel:** (0)2 40 21 58 83. Fax: (0)2 40 21 02 68. E-mail: info@camping-la-tabardiere.com. **Reservations:** Made with 20% deposit and € 13 fee. **Open** 1 April - 30 September.

**Directions:** Site is well signed, situated inland off the D13 Pornic - La Plaine sur Mer road.

## Camping de la Boutinardière

4418 Rue de la Plage de la Boutinardière, 44210 Pornic

This campsite has it all - two kilometres from the beautiful harbour town of Pornic and 200 metres from the sea, together with the very best of amenities and facilities (unusually all open and functioning from 1 May - 22 September). This is truly a holiday site to suit all the family whatever their age. The site has 250 individual good sized pitches, 100-120 sq.m. in size, many bordered by three metre high, well maintained hedges for shade and privacy. All pitches have electricity available (3, 6 or 10A). This is a family owned site and English is spoken by the helpful, obliging reception staff. Beside reception is the site shop which is excellent in size, range and quantity of goods for the holidaymaker. Across the road is a new complex of indoor and outdoor swimming pools, paddling pool and a twin toboggan water slide. Facing the water complex, the bar, restaurant and terraces are also new and serve excellent food, be it a snack or in the restaurant or perhaps a takeaway. On site there are also sports and entertainment areas. This site is difficult to better in the South Brittany, Loire Atlantic area.

**Facilities:** Toilet facilities are in three good blocks, one large and centrally situated and two supporting blocks. Whilst the blocks are of traditional build the quality, maintenance and cleanliness is amongst the best you will experience. Washbasins are in cabins, dishwashing is under cover. Laundry room with sinks, washing machines and dryers. Excellent shop. New complex of bar, restaurant, terraces. Three heated swimming pools, one indoors, a paddling pool and water slides. Games room. Sports and activity area. Playground. Minigolf. Table tennis. **Off site:** Sandy cove 200 m. Golf, riding, sea fishing, restaurants, cafes, fishing harbour, boat trips, sailing and windsurfing, all within 5 km. of site.

**Charges** 2002

| | |
|---|---|
| Per unit incl. 2 persons | € 11.00 - € 21.00 |
| extra person | € 3.00 - € 5.50 |
| child (2-10 yrs) | € 2.00 - € 4.00 |
| electricity 3-10A | € 2.50 - € 5.00 |
| animal | € 2.00 |
| local tax (over 10 yrs) | € 0.35 |

**Tel:** (0)2 40 82 05 68. Fax: (0)2 40 82 49 01. E-mail: info@laboutinardiere.com. **Reservations:** Made with deposit (€ 60) and fee (€ 15). **Open** 30 March - 29 September.

**Directions:** From north or south on D213, take Nantes D751 exit. At roundabout (with McDonalds) take D13 signed Bemerie-en-Retz. After 4 km. site is signed to right. Note: do NOT exit from D213 at Pomic Ouest or Centre.

## Brittany
# Sunêlia Le Patisseau
29 rue du Patisseau, 44210 Pornic

**4410**

Le Patisseau is situated 2.5 km. from the sea. It is a relaxed site which can be very busy and even a little noisy in high season due to its popularity with young families and teenagers from the large number of mobile homes and chalets. On the left of the campsite there are some attractive touring pitches, all with electrical connections (4, 6 or 10A) and water supply near. On the field area at the bottom of the site pitches are close to the site's mobile homes and tend to be noisier. The pitches are connected by mostly unmade roads which can become quite muddy in wet weather. A railway line runs along the bottom half of the site with trains two or three times a day, but they do finish at 22.30 hrs and the noise is minimal. The site's restaurant and bar overlook the indoor pool. This is a busy site and the Morice family work very hard to maintain a friendly atmosphere, but don't expect it to be too neat and tidy with everything run like clockwork. They plan to convert all the touring pitches to hard accommodation in the future and are not spending money on maintaining the toilet blocks.

**Facilities:** There are three sanitary blocks, one of reasonable quality, but the other two dating from the '80s are very poor. They include washbasins in private cabins, child-size toilets, baby baths, fully equipped laundry rooms and dishwashing facilities. Maintenance can be variable so do not expect too much. Shop (main season). New bar, restaurant and takeaway (1/4-30/8). Indoor heated pool (with sauna, jacuzzi and spa) and outdoor pools with water slides (1/5-30/8). Play area. Volleyball and table tennis. Bicycle hire. **Off site:** Fishing 1.5 km, golf 5 km.

**Charges** 2002

| | |
|---|---|
| Per unit incl. 2 persons | € 15.02 - € 24.70 |
| extra adult | € 5.51 |
| child (1-7 yrs) | € 3.67 |
| electricity 4-10A | € 4.17 - € 5.84 |
| animal | € 4.17 |
| local tax | € 0.13 - € 0.26 |

**Tel:** 02 40 82 10 39. **Fax:** 02 40 82 22 81. **E-mail:** contact@lepatisseau.com. **Reservations:** Made with deposit (€ 46) and fee (€ 16); contact site by letter, phone or fax. **Open** 1 April - 15 September.

**Directions:** Site signed at roundabout junction of D751 (Pornic - Nantes) road, and from the town centre.

## Brittany
# Camping de Moulin Neuf
56220 Rochefort en Terre

**5610**

This quiet family site is in wooded countryside, 600 m. from the small medieval town. Ian and Norma Hetherington have worked hard over the last few years to develop Moulin Neuf into a neat, tidy and organised site. There is provision for 72 pitches (60 for tourers, 44 with 10A electricity) of good size (120 sq.m.) on neat grass, laid out on two levels. The top level, with a limited number of electrical hook-ups, is flat and pitches are divided by young shrubs. The entrance to the site is here and reception is located just beyond the security gate. The lower level is partly sloping but offers mature trees, shade and electricity on all the pitches. Rochefort en Terre itself is a marvellous medieval town, beautifully preserved and only ten minutes walk from the site, with a wealth of art and craft workshops, antique shops and art galleries.

**Facilities:** The modern heated sanitary block is on the lower level but convenient for both. Facilities are kept very clean and include large, comfortable showers, cabins with washbasins and British and Turkish style WCs. Provision for disabled people. Baby changing room. Dishwashing area and laundry room with sinks. Washing machine, dryer and washing lines. Bread delivered each morning. Heated swimming pool (15/6-31/8). Tennis court, table tennis, basketball, football area and two boules pitches. Two children's play areas. Weekly barbecues organised in the season. **Off site:** Shop 600 m. Riding and golf locally. Lake within 500 m. with watersports. Vannes is a 30 minute drive and the beaches of Golfe du Morbihan.

**Charges** 2002

| | |
|---|---|
| Per pitch | € 6.90 - € 7.70 |
| adult | € 3.90 - € 4.60 |
| child (under 8 yrs) | € 2.40 - € 3.10 |
| electricity | € 4.00 |
| local tax | € 0.30 |

**Tel:** 02 97 43 37 52. **Fax:** 02 97 43 35 45.
**Reservations:** Made with deposit (€ 70) and fee (€ 8); contact site for booking form. **Open** 15 May - 16 September.

**Directions:** From Redon take D775 Vannes road west for 25 km. Branch north on D774 signed Rochefort en Terre. Follow road past the lake on left, in 800 m. Turn left and follow sign to site.

# Camping La Grande Métairie

route des Alignements de Kermario, BP 85, 56342 Carnac Cedex

**5601**

La Grande Métairie is a good quality site quietly situated a little back from the sea, close to the impressive rows of the famous 'menhirs' (giant prehistoric standing stones). It has a great deal to offer on site and is lively and busy over a long season. There is a feeling of spaciousness with a wide entrance and access road, with 574 individual pitches (140 for touring units), surrounded by hedges and trees. All have electricity (30 m. cables are needed in parts). Paddocks with ponds are home for ducks, goats and ponies to watch and feed. A super swimming pool complex comprises heated pools, water slides and toboggans, a flowing river, jacuzzi and a covered pool. The site, although large and not cheap, is well known and popular. Services are limited before late May. It has many British visitors with 320 pitches taken by several tour operators, plus site-owned mobile homes and many British touring caravanners and campers.

**Facilities:** Three large toilet blocks are good and well maintained, with washbasins in cabins, and facilities for babies and disabled people. Laundry room in each block. Motorcaravan service points. Shop and boutique. Restaurant, good takeaway. Bar lounge and terrace, and adjoining TV and games rooms. Pool complex with poolside bar and terrace. Two playgrounds and large playing field with football posts. Two tennis courts. Volleyball and basketball. Minigolf. BMX track. Bicycle hire. Table tennis. Fishing (on permit). Pony rides around the site. Outside amphitheatre for musical evenings and barbecues. Organised events daytime and evening. Occasional dances (pitches near these facilities may be noisy late at night - the bar closes at midnight). American motorhomes accepted up to 30 ft. Dogs and other pets only accepted by arrangement. **Off site:** Riding 1 km, golf 12 km. Nearest beach 3 km. by road. Local market at Carnac on Wednesdays and Sundays.

**Charges** 2002

| | |
| --- | --- |
| Per person | € 3.35 - € 5.60 |
| child (under 7 yrs) | € 2.40 - € 4.00 |
| pitch incl. car | € 13.45 - € 22.40 |
| with 6A electricity | € 15.35 - € 25.60 |
| water and drainage | € 3.20 |
| local tax | € 0.35 |

Less 20% 26/5-29/6 and after 25/8, 40% before 26/5. **Tel:** 02 97 52 24 01. Fax: 02 97 52 83 58. E-mail: info@lagrandemetairie.com. **Reservations:** Made (min. 1 week) with deposit (€ 3,20 per person, per day, no fee). English is spoken - office open from 2 Jan. **Open** 5 April - 13 September (all services form 24/5).

**Directions:** From N165 take Quiberon/Carnac exit onto the D768. After 5 km. turn left on D119 towards Carnac and after 4 km. turn left at traffic lights onto D196 to the site.

La Grande Métairie

★★★★

LES CASTELS

CAMPING PLUS BRETAGNE

" EXCEPTIONAL HOLIDAYS! "

Route des Alignements de Kermario
B.P. 85 - 56342 CARNAC Cedex
Bretagne-Sud - France
Tél.33 (0)2 97 52 2401 -Fax.(0)2 97 52 83 58
www.lagrandemetairie.com

# Camping Moulin de Kermaux

56340 Carnac

**5609**

Only 100 metres from the famous Carnac megaliths, Le Moulin de Kermaux is an excellent base from which to see these ancient stones as they portray their ever changing mood, colour and profile. The family run site has 150 pitches (120 with 6-10A electricity) and its compact nature offers a safe environment for parents and children alike. The 70 pitches for touring units are mostly separated by hedges and numerous mature trees offer welcome shade. Keen distance walkers and families with young children alike, will enjoy the numerous footpaths in the area. Carnac town provides an assortment of boutiques, crêperies, restaurants and night clubs. Used by tour operators (11 pitches).

**Facilities:** The fully equipped toilet block has high standards of cleanliness and washbasins in cabins. Toilets are a mix of (mainly) British and (a few) Turkish types. Facilities for disabled visitors. Baby bath. Laundry and dishwashing sinks. Washing machine and dryer - washing line provided. Motorcaravan service point. Well stocked shop (20/5-7/9). Bar (20/5-7/9) evenings in low season, all day in high season. Swimming pool and paddling pool. Sauna and jacuzzi. Challenging adventure playground. Volleyball and basketball, minigolf and table tennis. Organised activities in July/Aug. including a variety of competitions during the day and a weekly disco and karaoke in the evening. **Off site:** Fishing, bicycle hire and riding within 2 km. Sandy beaches and rocky coves within 3 km. Large supermarkets 3 km.

**Charges** 2002

| | |
|---|---|
| Per person | € 4.00 |
| child (under 7 yrs) | € 3.00 |
| pitch and car | € 12.00 |
| electricity 3A/6A | € 3.00 |
| dog | € 2.00 |
| local tax | € 0.35 |

Less 10-40% outside high season. **Tel:** 02 97 52 15 90. Fax: 02 97 52 83 85. **Reservations:** Contact site. **Open** 30 March - 15 September.

**Directions:** From N165 take Quiberon/Carnac exit onto D768. After 5 km. turn left on D781 to Carnac and following camp signs, turn left at traffic lights to site.

# Camping du Moustoir

route du Moustoir, 56340 Carnac

**5611**

the **travel service**
TO BOOK

| | |
|---|---|
| Ferry | ✔ |
| Pitch | ✔ |
| Accommodation | ✔ |

01892 55 98 98

Camping du Moustoir is a friendly, family run site situated about three kilometres inland from the many beaches of the area and close to the famous 'alignments' of standing stones. Pitches are grassy and separated by shrubs and hedges, with several shaded by tall pine trees. There is a popular pool area with slides, a separate swimming pool and a paddling pool with 'mushroom' fountain. The bar and terrace adjoining the pool become the social centre of the site in the evenings. A high season programme includes family entertainment and a daily 'Kid's club' which attracts children of several nationalities. Several small tour operators use the site.

**Facilities:** The substantial, traditional style toilet block is well maintained and clean (outside peak season some sections may be closed). Motorcaravan service facilities. Shop, bar and takeaway (all from 20/5, hours vary). Heated swimming pool (21 x 8 m), water slides with landing pool, and paddling pool (from 15/5). Adventure style playground. Tennis. Boules. Volleyball, football and basketball. Table tennis and pool table. Kids Club' daily in high season. **Off site:** Easy access to water sports at Carnac Plage. Fishing, bicycle hire or riding 2 km, golf 5 km.

**Charges** 2002

| | | |
|---|---|---|
| Per pitch | € 7.20 - € 12.00 |
| person | € 2.50 - € 4.00 |
| child (under 7 yrs) | € 1.70 - € 2.75 |
| animal | € 1.00 - € 1.50 |
| electricity | € 2.00 - € 3.00 |
| local tax (over 15 yrs) | € 0.35 |

No credit cards. **Tel:** 02 97 52 16 18. Fax: 02 97 52 88 37. E-mail: info@lemoustoir.com. **Reservations:** Made with deposit (€ 75). **Open** 1 May - 10 September.

**Directions:** From N165, take exit to D768 (Carnac and Quiberon). At second crossroads after 5 km. take left hand junction (D119) towards Carnac. After 3 km. turn left (oblique turning) after a hotel, and site is 500 m. on your left.

## Camping de La Plage

5602 Plage de Kervilaine, 56470 La Trinité-sur-Mer

The area of Carnac/La Trinité is popular with holiday makers and the two La Trinité sites of La Plage and La Baie have the great advantage of direct access to a good sandy beach. Both sites are owned by the same family, and each is very well maintained, both having a small (12 m.) heated pool with a slide. The grassy pitches, which have electricity (6/10A) and water (70% with drainage also), are separated by hedges and shrubs and at La Plage there are attractive flower beds. Situated on a low cliff, the terrace with its views across the bay is a very popular place for a meal or a drink. Reception areas are welcoming and friendly with tourist information on display. Both sites have a number of tour operator pitches.

**Facilities:** The sanitary blocks have washbasins in cubicles, facilities for disabled visitors and small children. Washing machines and dryers. Well provided shop with bakery. Bar, restaurant, crêperie, takeaway. Lively entertainment programme in high season that caters for all ages and some evening entertainment in nearby disco. Good play areas including ball pool. Tennis, basketball, minigolf, table tennis. Large TV screen. Hire of sailboards and bikes. Guided tours on foot or bicycle. Internet access available. Small communal barbecue areas, otherwise only gas ones are allowed. **Off site:** The village of La Trinité is about an hours walk away along the cliff path and ten minutes (approx) by car.

**Charges 2002**

| | |
|---|---|
| Per pitch incl. 2 persons | € 15.60 - € 27.60 |
| extra adult | € 4.00 |
| child (2-18 yrs) | € 2.00 |
| electricity (6/10A) | € 1.80 - € 3.25 |
| dog | free - 1.05 |

**Tel:** 02 97 55 73 28. Fax: 02 97 55 88 31. E-mail: laplage@club-internet.fr. **Reservations:** Contact site. **Open** 8 May - 15 September.

**Directions:** Site is signed in different places from D186 coast road from La Trinité to Carnac-Plage.

# Direct access to the beach

CAMPING DE LA PLAGE ★★★★
Plage de Kervillen
F-56470 LA TRINITE SUR MER
TEL : 33(0)297 557 328
FAX : 33(0)297 558 831
e-mail : laplage@club-internet.fr
http : www.camping-plage.com
Swimming pool - Waterslides
Restaurant - Bar - Shop
Tennis - Mini Golf - Jacuzzi
Mobil-homes for hire

"In 2003 : New Waterslides"

## Camping de Kervilor

5605 56470 La Trinité-sur-Mer

the travel service
TO BOOK
Ferry ✓
Pitch ✓
Accommodation ✗
01892 55 98 98

Kervilor may be a good alternative for those who find the beach-side sites in La Trinité too busy and lively. In a village on the outskirts of the town, it has 230 pitches on flat grass and is attractively landscaped with trees (silver birches) and flowers. The pitches are in groups divided by hedges, separated by shrubs and trees and 200 have electricity (3/6A). There is a feeling of spaciousness. Used by tour operators (28 pitches).

**Facilities:** Two modern toilet blocks are of a good standard with further facilities in an older block by the entrance. Many washbasins in cabins, facilities for disabled people and babies. Dishwashing under cover. Small laundry. Small shop and takeaway in season. Bar (20/5-9/9). Medium sized pool, children's pool and water slides. Play area. Minigolf, pétanque, tennis and volleyball. Table tennis. Bicycle hire. **Off site:** Fishing or riding 2 km, golf 12 km. Sandy beach 2 km. Town facilities 1.5 km by car.

**Charges 2003**

| | |
|---|---|
| Per person | € 4.50 |
| child (under 7 yrs) | € 3.00 |
| pitch | € 15.70 |
| electricity | € 2.10 - € 3.50 |
| dog | € 2.00 |

Less 25% outside high season. 7 days for the price of 6 outside July/Aug. **Tel:** 02 97 55 76 75. Fax: 02 97 55 87 26. E-mail: ebideau@camping-kervilor.com. **Reservations:** Made with deposit (€ 46) and fee (€ 18,30). **Open** 9 May - 15 September.

**Directions:** Site is north of La Trinité-sur-Mer and is signed in the town. From Auray take D186 Quiberon road; turn left at camp sign at Kergroix on D186 to La Trinité, and left again at outskirts of town.

## Camping de Penboch

9, chemin de Penboch, 56610 Arradon

Penboch is 200 metres by footpath from the shores of the Golfe du Morbihan with its many islands, where there is plenty to do including watersports, fishing and boat trips. There are also old towns with weekly markets nearby and it is 30 minutes walk to Arradon which has a good range of shops and restaurants. The site in a peaceful, rural area is divided into two parts - one in woodland with lots of shade and used mainly for mobile homes and youth groups (which can be very noisy at times) and the other main part, across a minor road on more open ground with hedges and young trees. Penboch offers 175 pitches on flat grass, mostly divided into groups; electricity is available on most pitches (6/10A) and there are plenty of water points. Popular with British tour operators (40 pitches). A `Sites et Paysages' member.

**Facilities:** Three fully equipped toilet blocks, two on the main part of the site and one on the annex, include washbasins in cabins. Facilities can be under considerable pressure in peak season. Washing machines and dryers. Motorcaravan service point. Friendly bar with satellite TV, snacks and takeaway, where basic food supplies kept (all 24/5-9/9) and further TV room. Heated swimming pool with water slide, toboggan and children's pool with mushroom fountain (1/5-15/9). Good children's playground, visible from reception, with interesting play equipment. Games room. Caravan storage. American motorhomes accepted in low season. **Off site:** Fishing 200 m, bicycle hire 6 km, golf or riding 6 km. Sailing and windsurfing 2 km.

**Charges** 2002

| | |
|---|---|
| Per unit incl. 2 persons | € 9.95 - € 24.90 |
| extra person over 7 yrs | € 2.95 - € 4.60 |
| child (2-7 yrs) | € 2.30 - € 3.50 |
| dog | free - € 1.52 |
| electricity 6A/10A | € 2.80 - € 3.80 |
| local tax (over 18 yrs) | € 0.46 |

**Tel:** 02 97 44 71 29. Fax: 02 97 44 79 10. E-mail: camping.penboch@wanadoo.fr. **Reservations:** Advised for high season (min. 7 days 10/7-18/8). **Open** 5 April - 27 September.

**Directions:** From N165 at Auray or Vannes, take D101 along northern shores of the Golfe du Morbihan; or leave N165 at D127 signed Ploeren and Arradon. Take turn to Arradon and site is signed.

## Camping Municipal Le Pâtis

3 chemin du Pâtis, 56130 La Roche Bernard

This is another of those excellent municipal sites one comes across in France. Situated beside the River Vilaine, just below the very attractive old town of La Roche Bernard and beside the port and marina, it provides 60 level grass, part-hedged pitches in bays of four, with 10A electricity and water. Next door is a sailing school, boats to hire, fishing, tennis, archery, etc. A restaurant and bar are on the quayside, with others uphill in the town.

**Facilities:** There are two fully equipped sanitary blocks, one new and very modern, the other fully refurbished. New laundry room behind reception with washing machine and dryer. Small play area. **Off site:** Bicycle hire 500 m, riding 5 km, golf 15 km.

**Charges** guide

| | |
|---|---|
| Per pitch | € 3.05 |
| adult | € 2.44 |
| child (under 9 yrs) | € 1.22 |
| vehicle | € 1.06 |
| electricity | € 2.13 |
| animal | € 0.76 |

No credit cards. **Tel:** 02 99 90 60 13. Fax: 02 99 90 88 28. **Reservations:** Contact site. **Open** Easter/April - 30 September.

**Directions:** Go into town centre and follow signs for the Port around a one-way system and then a sharp turn down hill.

# Camping Les Iles

La Pointe du Bile, 56760 Penestin-sur-Mer

You are assured of a warm and friendly welcome at this family run campsite where the owners, M. and Mme. Communal, encourage everyone to make the most of this beautiful region. The 124 pitches are mostly of a reasonable size (although larger caravans and American motorhomes are advised to book) and all have electricity (6A). All services are fully open 14/5-16/9, with a limited service at other times. There is direct access from the site to clifftop walks and local beaches (you can even walk to small off-shore islands at low tide). Used by one tour operator (20 pitches).

**Facilities:** The large central toilet block has mostly British style WCs and washbasins in cabins. Dishwashing and laundry sinks. Facilities for disabled people and two baby baths. Motorcaravan service point across the road at `Parc des Iles`, the mobile home section of the site. Shop. Bar with takeaway overlooking swimming and paddling pools (14/5-16/9). Modern multi-sports pitch for football, basketball and volleyball. Tennis court across the road. Bicycle hire. Riding. Full range of activities and entertainment for adults and children in July/Aug. **Off site:** Windsurfing (500 m), sailing school 3 km.

**Charges** guide

| | |
|---|---|
| Per unit incl. 2 adults | € 17.00 - € 26.00 |
| extra person (over 10 yrs) | € 3.00 - € 4.00 |
| child (under 7 yrs) | € 1.50 - € 2.00 |
| electricity (6A) | € 2.50 |
| animal | € 1.00 - € 1.50 |

**Tel:** 02 99 90 30 24. Fax: 02 99 90 44 55. E-mail: contact@camping-des-iles.fr. **Reservations:** Made with deposit (€ 92) and fee (€ 18). **Open** 1 April - 4 October.

**Directions:** From Pénestin take D201 south, taking a right fork to Pointe du Bile after 2 km. Turn right at crossroads just before beach and site is on left. Take care on arrival - the barrier is fairly close to the entrance, but there is some parking along the road outside.

CAMPING & PARC
DES ILES

La Pointe du Bile
56760 PENESTIN
Tél. **02 99 90 30 24**
Fax 02 99 90 44 55
www.camping-des-iles.com
E mail : accueil@camping-des-iles.com

# Camping Mané Guernehué

56870 Baden

Located close to the Morbihan Gulf, Mané Guernehué is a smart, modern site offering a variety of pitches. Some are terraced beneath pine trees, others in a former orchard with delightful views of the surrounding countryside. The 277 pitches are generally large, 65 being occupied by mobile homes and chalets. All pitches have electricity and a few are also equipped with water and drainage. Many are level but others, particularly those in the centre of the site, slope to varying degrees. There are plenty of excellent amenities. A fitness track runs through the site, with a well stocked fishing lake on the edge. Used by tour operators (around 45 pitches).

**Facilities:** Three modern toilet blocks include washbasins in cabins. In high season, the maintenance of the blocks does seem to be under some pressure. Facilities for disabled visitors. Washing machines and dryers. Small shop, bar and takeaway. Heated swimming pool, waterslide, jacuzzi and gym. Fishing. Teenagers' room with table tennis, pool, billiards and TV. Varied entertainment programme in high season, based around a large purpose built hall. **Off site:** Beach 3 km. Golf 3 km.

**Charges** 2002

| | |
|---|---|
| Per pitch and car | € 9.60 - € 14.30 |
| adult | € 2.75 - € 5.10 |
| child (2-7 yrs) | € 1.85 - € 3.70 |
| electricity (6/10A) | € 3.00 - € 4.00 |
| dog | € 1.50 - € 3.00 |

**Tel:** 02 97 57 02 06. Fax: 02 97 57 15 43. E-mail: mane-guernehue@wanadoo.fr. **Reservations:** Advised for high season and made with deposit (€ 61) and fee (€ 19,82). **Open** Easter - 30 September.

**Directions:** From Auray or Vannes use the D101 to Baden and watch for signs to site.

# Camping-Caravaning Le Cénic

56760 Pénestin-sur-Mer

5618

the travel service
TO BOOK

| Ferry | ✓ |
| Pitch | ✓ |
| Accommodation | ✗ |

01892 55 98 98

Le Cénic is attractively set amidst trees and flowers, providing activities for all tastes. An attractive covered aquatic complex has water slides, bridges, rivers and a jacuzzi, whilst the outdoor pool comes complete with water slide, 'magic mushroom' fountain and sunbathing areas. You may fish in the pretty lake or use inflatables, watched by the geese, and yes, the peacock and turkeys. Unusually there is also a covered sports hall for ball games. A range of accommodation is on offer from tent and caravan pitches to static caravans and chalets and bungalows to rent. There are 90 pitches in total with electricity (6A) available.

**Facilities:** Fully equipped toilet facilities include laundry and dishwashing sinks. Washing machines and dryers. Bar, restaurant, shop, TV and games room. Indoor and outdoor swimming pools. Children's play area. Indoor ball area. Fishing. **Off site:** The area has much to offer from the beaches of La Mine d'Or, the harbour at Trébiguier-Pénestin, La Baule with its magnificent beach and the medieval city of Guérande to the unique Brière nature reserve.

**Charges** 2002

| | |
| --- | --- |
| Per pitch | € 4.50 - € 7.50 |
| adult | € 3.40 - € 5.00 |
| child under 7 yrs. | € 1.70 - € 2.50 |
| electricity | € 2.80 |
| dog | € 1.00 |
| local tax over 10 yrs. | € 0.31 |

**Tel:** 02 99 90 33 14. Fax: 02 99 90 45 65.
**Reservations:** Necessary for high season. **Open** 1 May - 30 September.

**Directions:** Site is 300 m. from the D34, and 1 km. from the town, to the southwest.

# Camping La Vallée du Ninian

Le Rocher, 56800 Taupont

5616

M. and Mme. Joubaud developed this peaceful family run site in central Brittany from a farm area in the eighties and take care to ensure that everyone has an enjoyable holiday. The level site falls into the three areas - the orchard with 32 large, hedged pitches with electricity, the wood with about 13 pitches more suited to tents, and the meadow by the river providing a further 35 pitches delineated by small trees and shrubs, some with electricity. The shop has, as a centre-piece, a working cider press with which M. Joubaud makes his own 'potion magique'. The adjoining covered bar area is the venue for song and dance evenings with a Breton flavour and occasional sing-songs are organised.

**Facilities:** The central building houses unisex toilet facilities including washbasins in cubicles, large cubicle with facilities for disabled visitors and laundry area with washing machines, dryer and ironing board. Covered dishwashing area. Shop. Small (7 x 12 m) heated pool. Swings and slides.

**Charges** 2002

| | |
| --- | --- |
| Per pitch incl. vehicle | € 5.00 |
| adult | € 3.10 |
| child (under 7 yrs) | € 2.30 |
| electricity 3/6A | € 1.60 - € 3.10 |
| local tax | € 0.08 - € 0.15 |

**Tel:** 02 97 93 53 01. Fax: 02 97 93 57 27.
**Reservations:** Contact site. **Open** 1 May - 30 September.

**Directions:** From Ploërmel centre follow signs to Taupont north on the N8. Continue through village of Taupont and turn left (east) signed Vallée du Ninian. Follow road until 1 km. before Hellean. From Josselin follow signs for Hellean. Go through village and turn sharp right after the bridge over the river Ninian. Site is 400 m. on the right.

# Camping Municipal Kergouguec

56400 Plougoumelen

5617M

This well run, basic municipal site is adjacent to the village sports stadium with which it shares shower and toilet facilities. However, since very few sporting events take place at the stadium during the camping season, this is not a problem and the facilities are always clean with plenty of hot water, the 'home' and 'away' changing rooms being designated 'ladies' and 'gents'. There are 80 good size level grassy pitches mostly separated in pairs by mature hedges and some trees. The 44 pitches in the central area have electrical connections (5A). A peaceful, no frills and good value site, it is well situated for exploring the Golfe du Morbihan, close to the towns of Auray and Vannes.

**Facilities:** The fully equipped toilets are a mixture of Turkish and British style with some washbasins in cubicles. A key is available at the office for facilities with wheelchair access. Indoor washing area with separate sinks for dishes and laundry. Ironing board on request. Table tennis, basketball and sand pit. Badminton (free). Two tennis courts (charged). **Off site:** No shop on site but the village of Plougoumelen is short walk (350 m.) for bread and basic provisions.

**Charges** 2002

| | |
| --- | --- |
| Per pitch | € 2.00 |
| adult | € 1.52 |
| child (under 7 yrs) | € 0.76 |
| electricity | € 1.83 |

**Tel:** (0)2 97 57 88 74. **Reservations:** Contact site. **Open** 15 June - 15 September

**Directions:** From centre of Plougoumelen take C3 heading south, signed to Baden. Site is on right through the sports stadium.

# Normandy

Map 2

Major cities: Caen, Rouen

Départements: 14 Calvados, 27 Eure, 50 Manche, 61 Orme, 76 Seine Maritime

Normandy is a pastoral region – or, in fact, the dairy of France providing rich cream, butter, and fine cheeses such as Camembert and 'Pont l'Evêque'. Contented cows graze the apple orchards – the apples are used in producing cider and the well known 'Calvados', Normandy's apple brandy. Normandy also has a superb coast line including the Cotentin Peninsula, the cliffs of the Côte d'Albâtre and the fine beaches and fashionable resorts of the Côte Fleurie.

The history of Normandy is closely linked with our own as in 1066 the Norman Duke William defeated the Saxon King Harold in the battle of Hastings and was crowned King of England, his exploits well chronicled on the famous Bayeux Tapestry. In more recent times, June 1944, the Allied Forces landed on the Normandy coast. Many museums, exhibitions, sites and monuments, including the Caen Memorial Museum, commemorate operations that took place between 6 June and August of 1944.

Note: the site reports are laid out by département in numerical order not by region.

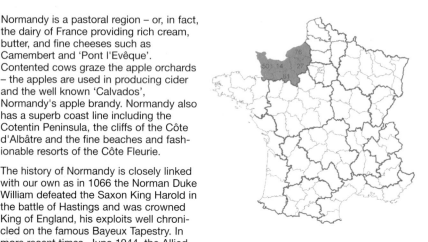

## Cuisine of the region

*Andouillette de Vire* – small chitterling (tripe) sausage

*Barbue au cidre* – brill cooked in cider and Calvados

*Douillons de pommes à la Normande* – baked apples in pastry

*Escalope (Vallée d'Auge)* – veal sautéed and flamed in Calvados and served with cream and apples

*Ficelle Normande* – pancake with ham, mushrooms and cheese

*Marnite Dieppoisse* – fish soup with some or all of the following: sole, turbot, rouget, moules, crevettes, onions, white wine, butter and cream

*Poulet (Vallée d'Auge)* – chicken cooked in the same way as Escalope Vallée d'Auge

*Tripes à la Mode de Caen* – stewed beef tripe with onions, carrots, leeks, garlic, cider and Calvados

## Wine

Cider usually accompanies a meal

*Trou Normand Calvados* – a 'dram' drunk in one gulp, between courses; claimed to restore the appetite

## Places of interest

*Alençon* – famous for lace, fine art museum, birthplace of Ste Thérèse

*Bagnoles-de-l'Orne* – spa resort and casino, guided tours of Arthurian land of Lancelot

*Bayeux* – home to the famous tapestry; 15th-18th century houses, cathedral, museums

*Caen* – feudal castle, Museum of Normandy, Museum for Peace

*Omaha Beach* – D-Day beaches, Landing site monuments commemorating the Allied Forces, American Cemetery

*Deauville* – internationally famous seaside resort and horse racing centre

*Giverny* – home of impressionist painter Claude Monet, Monet Museum

*Honfleur* – picturesque port city with old town and bridge

*Lisieux* – pilgrimage site, shrine of Ste Thérèse, Basilic and Carmelite convent

*Mont St Michel* – world famous abbey on island which becomes isolated by incoming tide

*Rouen* – Joan of Arc Museum; Gothic churches, cathedrals, abbey, clock tower

## Camping Le Puits

La Groudière, 14350 St Martin des Besaces

**1408**

This traditional little site in the heart of historic Normandy is becoming very popular. Situated on the edge of the village, it only has 30 pitches in two areas, either individual ones divided by flowers and shrubs, or marked out on an open grassy field. All have electricity (6A) and are slightly sloping. The Ashworth family are gradually upgrading the facilities on what was originally an 'á la ferme' site. The site has its own newsletter to keep guests informed and a comprehensive stock of tourist information in reception. A museum with a difference is close to the site featuring a unique account of the Battle of Normandy with displays, sound and light presentations, artefacts and personal memorabilia (some belonging to regular visitors to the campsite).

**Facilities:** Simple, basic toilet facilities at the rear of the farmhouse are being upgraded with additional toilets and showers. Sinks for dishwashing and laundry, plus washing machine and dryer. Motorcaravan services. In renovated barns are a small shop, bar with a snack bar serving pizzas, chips and quiches to order with a café style eating area outside. Bread, croissants or breakfast can be ordered. One barn provides a function room and games room. Minigolf, table tennis, billiards, volleyball and fishing in pond. Tyres, logs and planks provide children with a DIY play park. Activities organised in season - barbecues, murder mysteries, quizzes and visits to local cider makers - even bungee jumping! **Off site:** Bicycle hire 5 km, riding 10 km. Market in St Martin des Besaces Saturday morning.

**Charges** 2002

| | |
|---|---|
| Per pitch | € 6.00 |
| small tent and bicycle | € 3.00 |
| adult | € 3.00 |
| child (3-9 yrs) | € 1.50 |
| electricity (6A) | € 3.00 |

**Tel:** 02 31 67 80 02. Fax: 02 31 67 80 02. E-mail: camping.le.puits@wanadoo.fr. **Reservations:** Advised in season and made with deposit of 1 nights fees. **Open** 1 February - 31 October.

**Directions:** From Caen take A84 at Porte de Bretagne towards Avranches to St Martin des Besaces (exit 41). Follow signs to village on D53. At lights turn right on N175 and site is signed to left at far end of village. From Cherbourg follow N13 and after Carentan (approx. 50 km) take N174 signed St Lô. In St Lô follow signs for Vire, then Torigni-sur-Vire. After Torigni in 9 km. take N175 (not A84) turn left towards St Martin des Besaces and site is signed to right at entrance to village.

## Castel Camping du Brévedent

Le Brévedent, 14130 Pont-l'Evêque

**1409**

the **travel service**
TO BOOK

| | |
|---|---|
| Ferry | ✔ |
| Pitch | ✔ |
| Accommodation | ✗ |

01892 55 98 98

Le Brévedent is a well established, traditional site with 140 pitches (100 for tourists) set in the grounds of an elegant 18th century hunting pavilion. Level pitches are set around the fishing lake or in the lower gardens, others are in the old orchard. All have electricity (10A). The new reception provides a vast amount of tourist information, with organised tours in the main season to Paris, Disney, a cider farm and a local distillery. This is an excellent holiday destination within easy reach of the Channel ports. The peaceful, friendly environment make it ideal for mature campers or families with younger children (note: the lake is unfenced). Particularly popular are the Saturday evening talks, the Sunday countryside rambles and the evening family meal. Attractions in the area include cheese factories, Pont L'Evêque (14 km.) and its market (Sunday and Monday) and the Château de Betteville with its motor museum. There are market days in Cormeilles (Friday), Lisieux and Honfleur (Thursday). The site is used by a tour operator (40 pitches).

**Facilities:** Three sanitary units of varying ages (one new), include washbasins in cubicles, dishwashing and laundry sinks, and new facilities for babies and disabled people. Good motorcaravan service point. Laundries with washing machines and dryers. Well stocked shop. Baker calls each morning. Small bar. New restaurant including snacks, breakfasts and tradtional Normandy cuisine (12/5-20/9). Takeaway. Clubroom with TV and library. Swimming pool and children's pool (unsupervised), heated and in separate enclosures. Two playgrounds. Table tennis tables in open fronted barns. Minigolf, boules, volleyball, games room with games machines, and a pool table. Fishing is free (but put the fish back). Rowing boats (with lifejackets). Bicycle and buggy hire. Organised activities for children including pony lessons. Dogs are not accepted. **Off site:** Discounts arranged for riding (1 km), St Julien golf club and tennis on the local court.

**Charges** 2002

| | |
|---|---|
| Per pitch | € 8.00 |
| adult | € 5.00 |
| child 1-6 yrs | € 2.30 |
| child 7-12 yrs | € 3.80 |
| electricity | € 3.00 |

Less 10% in low season (excl. electricity). **Tel:** 02 31 64 72 88. Fax: 02 31 64 33 41. E-mail: castelcamp. lebrevedent@mangeos.com. **Reservations:** Advised for the main season; contact site. **Open** 12 May - 20 September.

**Directions:** From Pont L'Evêque take D579 toward Lisieux for 4 km. then D51 towards Moyaux. At Blangy le Château turn right (still on D51) to Le Brévedent.

## Normandy
# Camping Le Château de Martragny
14740 Martragny

Martragny is an attractive site in a parkland setting adjoining the château and close to D-Day beaches. It is particularly convenient for both Caen and Cherbourg, and has the facilities and charm to encourage both long stays and stopovers. The pleasant lawns surrounding and approaching the château take 160 units, with electricity connections for 140. The majority of the pitches are divided by either a small hedge or a couple of trees, only a few not marked out. Bed and breakfast are available in the château all year (reservation essential). Madame de Chassey takes great pride in the site and takes care that the peace and quiet is preserved. This is a perfect place for a quiet relaxing holiday yet only 12 km. from the sea, the wartime landing beaches or the Bayeux tapestry.

**Facilities:** Two recently modernised sanitary blocks include washbasins in cabins, sinks for dishes and clothes and two baby baths. Disabled people are well catered for. Good laundry. Well stocked shop and takeaway food bar open 15/5-15/9. Bar. Swimming pool (20 x 6 m.) and children's paddling pool heated in poor weather. Play areas, one new. Minigolf, games and TV room, table tennis and billiards. Fishing. Bicycle hire. **Off site:** Riding 1 km.

**Charges** 2003

| | | |
|---|---|---|
| Per person | € 3.90 - € | 4.50 |
| child (under 7 yrs) | € 2.30 - € | 2.70 |
| tent pitch | € 7.70 - € | 9.00 |
| pitch for caravan or motorcaravan | € 8.30 - € | 9.80 |
| electricity (6A) | € 2.50 - € | 2.80 |
| local tax | € | 0.15 |

Less 15% outside 16/6-31/8. **Tel:** 02 31 80 21 40. Fax: 02 31 08 14 91. E-mail: chateau.martragny@wanadoo.fr. **Reservations:** Made for min. 3 nights; deposit and small fee required. **Open** 1 May - 15 September.

**Directions:** Site is off N13, 8 km. southeast of Bayeux. Take Martragny exit from dual carriageway.

## Normandy
# Camping Municipal du Bayeux
boulevard Eindhoven, 14400 Bayeux

Whether or not you want to see the tapestry, this site makes a very useful night stop on the way to or from Cherbourg, and in addition it is only a few kilometres from the coast and the landing beaches. Pleasantly laid out with grassy lawns and bushes, its neat, cared for appearance make a good impression. The 140 pitches are in two areas. In the main area 27 hardstanding pitches have been created, with the other pitches well marked, generally of good size and with electricity. The site is busy over a long season - early arrival is advised as reservations are not taken. There is a full time site warden from 15/6-15/9, otherwise reception is only open for one hour in the morning and two in the evening.

**Facilities:** The two good quality toilet blocks have British style WCs, washbasins in cabins in the main block, and units for disabled people. Laundry room. Takeaway snacks. Two playgrounds. Reading room with TV. Games room. **Off site:** Large public indoor pool adjoins site. Supermarket very close (closes 8 pm). Bicycle hire 1 km, riding 5 km, golf 8 km.

**Charges** 2003

| | |
|---|---|
| Per person | € 2.91 |
| child (under 7 yrs) | € 1.56 |
| pitch and car | € 3.60 |
| electricity | € 2.90 |

Less 10% for stay over 5 days. **Tel:** 02 31 92 08 43. Fax: 02 31 92 08 43. **Reservations:** Not made. **Open** 1 May - 30 September.

**Directions:** Site is on the south side of northern ring road to town.

## Normandy
# Camping Municipal du Château
3 rue du Val d'Ante, 14700 Falaise

The location of this site is really quite spectacular, lying in the shadow of the Château de Falaise, in the old part of the town, in the 'coeur de Normandie'. The site itself is small, with only 66 pitches (all with 5A electricity). It has a rather intimate `up-market` feel about it, rather different from the average municipal site. With good shade, tarmac roads and easy access, it was well recommended by the British campers we met there. Whatever this site lacks in size and facilities it makes up for in its situation, close to the town centre, the swimming pool and tennis club and near to the river for fishing. The charges are reasonable and the reception friendly.

**Facilities:** The sanitary facilities could be insufficient in terms of quantity when the site is full - perhaps it never is. The quality is good and they are clean. Unit for disabled visitors. Access to showers, laundry and dishwashing closed 22.00-07.30. Playground. Table tennis. TV room.

**Charges** 2003

| | |
|---|---|
| Per adult | € 3.00 |
| child (under 10 yrs) | € 2.00 |
| pitch | € 2.50 |
| dog | € 1.00 |
| electricity | € 2.50 |

No credit cards. **Tel:** 02 31 90 16 55. Fax: 02 31 90 53 38. **Reservations:** Advised for July/Aug. **Open** 1 May - 30 September.

**Directions:** Site is on western side of town, well signed from the ring road. From N158 heading south take first roundabout into Falaise (site signed), then pass through residential suburb to site.

## Camping de la Vallée

88 rue de la Vallée, 14510 Houlgate

Camping de la Vallée is an attractive site with good, well maintained facilities. Situated on a grassy hillside overlooking Houlgate, the 278 pitches (180 for touring units) are large and open. Hedges have been planted and all have electricity. Part of the site is sloping, the rest level, with gravel or tarmac roads. An old farmhouse has been converted to house a new bar and comfortable TV lounge and billiards room. English is spoken in season. Used by tour operators (55 pitches). Very busy in high season, maintenance and cleaning could be variable at that time. The town is 900 m, the beach 1 km.

**Facilities:** Three good toilet blocks include wash-basins in cabins, mainly British style toilets, facilities for disabled people and baby room. Dishwashing, laundry with machines, dryers and ironing boards (no washing lines allowed). Motorcaravan services. Shop (from 1/5). Bar. Snack bar with takeaway in season (from 15/5). Heated pool (from 15/5; no shorts). Playground. Bicycle hire. Volleyball, football field, tennis, petanque. Entertainment in July/Aug. **Off site:** Fishing 1 km. Riding 500 m. Golf 2 km.

**Charges** 2002

| | |
|---|---|
| Per unit incl. 2 persons, electricity € | 16.00 - € 25.00 |
| extra adult | € 5.00 - € 6.00 |
| child (under 7 yrs) | € 2.50 - € 3.00 |
| dog | € 3.00 |

Credit card minimum € 76. **Tel:** 02 31 24 40 69. Fax: 02 31 24 42 42. E-mail: camping.lavallee@wanadoo.fr. **Reservations:** Made with deposit and fee. **Open** 1 April - 30 September.

**Directions:** From A13 take exit for Cabourg and follow signs for Dives/Houlgate going straight on at roundabout. Follow road straight on at next round about, and then four sets of traffic lights. Turn left along seafront. After 1 km. at lights turn right, carry on for about 1 km. and over mini-roundabout - look for site sign and flag poles on right.

CAMPING CARAVANING

LA VALLÉE
★★★★

88, Rue de la Vallée
14510 Houlgate
Tel: 0033 231.24.40.69
Fax: 0033 231.28.08.29

❏ SHOP ❏ BAR ❏ GAMES ROOM
❏ TENNIS ❏ HEATED SWIMMING POOL
❏ CHILDREN'S POOL ❏ ENTERTAINMENT

## Camping Les Hautes Coutures

route de Ouistreham, 14970 Bénouville

Les Hautes Coutures is a useful, neat and tidy site near the Caen-Portsmouth ferry terminal, for overnight or longer stays. It is beside the Caen ship canal, 2 km. from the sea (and ferry port) and 10 km. from Caen - the gates are opened at 6 am. for early ferries. There are 110 well drained, touring pitches of 100 sq.m, clearly marked by mature hedges formed from flowering shrubs, with tarmac roads. All pitches have electricity (up to 10A). An area close to the canal is being developed to provide further pitches. There are also over 150 mobile homes. Ouistreham is within walking distance along the canal (fishing free) and the Pegasus Bridge Airborne Division Museum. A pedestrian gate leads on to the towpath (a code is needed for re-entry).

**Facilities:** Two good sanitary blocks, both recently refurbished, include good showers, washbasins in cabins (warm water only). Dishwashing and laundry facilities with washing machine and dryer. Motorcaravan service point. Small shop keeps basic items. Bar and takeaway. Small heated swimming pool (from May) - ask for access. Small lounge/TV area and games room. Play area on sand. Two tennis courts. Volleyball. Minigolf. Boules. Table tennis. **Off site:** Golf 4 km. Riding 2 km. Beach 2 km.

**Charges** 2002

| | |
|---|---|
| Per person | € 5.80 |
| child (under 7 yrs) | € 4.00 |
| pitch incl. car and tent/caravan | € 6.50 |
| electricity (6/10A) | € 3.20 |

**Tel:** 02 31 44 73 08. Fax: 02 31 95 30 80. E-mail: camping-hautes-coutures@wanadoo.fr. **Reservations:** Contact site. **Open** 1 April - 30 September.

**Directions:** Site is just off D514 dual-carriageway, north of Benouville. From Caen, follow Ouistreham ferry signs and take first exit after Benouville.

## Château Camping Le Colombier

Le Val Sery, 14590 Moyaux

**1405**

Le Colombier is a quality site in an attractive landscaped setting of formal French gardens, between the Normandy manor house and the 'Colombier' (a circular building now housing the bar and library). Reception is in a newly restored building and the staff are efficient and friendly. The site has 180 large pitches, all with electricity (12A) and marked out by trees at the corners, but with no dividing hedges. You do pay for the quality here, and there are no off-peak reductions, but the site's main amenities are open all season and the château and its surroundings do have a certain elegance. Used by a tour operator (5 pitches).

**Facilities:** Two good toilet blocks include private cabins, and a good unit for disabled visitors. Motorcaravan service point. Washing machine and dryer. Bar, shop, crêperie and takeaway (all season). Special dinners (limited numbers) are served some days in the château (baby sitting service for these dinners). Free heated swimming pool (25 x 12 m). Large general room for reading, cards, etc. with TV. Tennis, minigolf and volleyball. Bicycle hire. Free fishing on a nearby lake. **Off site:** Riding 8 km, golf 20 km. Lisieux is 16 km. and places on the coast such as Deauville and Honfleur 30 to 40 km.

**Charges** guide

| | |
|---|---|
| Per person | € 5.34 |
| child (under 7 yrs) | € 2.29 |
| pitch | € 10.67 |
| electricity (12A) | € 2.29 |

Reductions for long stays. **Tel:** 02 31 63 63 08. Fax: 02 31 63 15 97. E-mail: chateau@camping-lecolombier.com. **Reservations:** Advised for main season; made for min. 3 days with deposit and fee. **Open** 1 May - 15 September, with all services.

**Directions:** Site is 3 km. northeast of Moyaux on the D143, well signed from Cormeilles - Lisieux road.

## Camping du Traspy

rue du Pont Benoit, 14220 Thury-Harcourt

**1411**

Somewhat akin to a tiny nature park, close to a lake (reputedly excellent for fishing) and with a small stream running through it, this secluded, former municipal site is resplendent with mature tall trees. The 92 pitches are on two levels, both flat, with a choice of 6A or 10A electrical connections. Close to the popular leisure park of the Valley of Traspy, it is a useful site for night stops or for longer stays for keen anglers!

**Facilities:** Toilet facilities include both British and Turkish type WCs, and some washbasins in cabins. External dishwashing facilities and laundry room. **Off site:** Village facilities 500 m. Leisure park 200 m.

**Charges** guide

| | |
|---|---|
| Per pitch | € 3.81 |
| adult | € 3.81 |
| child (under 16 yrs) | € 2.29 |
| electricity (10A) | € 3.05 |

**Tel:** 02 31 79 61 80. Fax: 02 31 84 76 19. **Reservations:** Advised July/Aug; made with deposit (€ 18,29). **Open** 30 April - 12 September.

**Directions:** Site is signed in the town of Thury-Harcourt on D562 Caen - Vire road, 26 km. from Caen.

## Camping Municipal Saint-Nicolas

27800 Le Bec-Hellouin

**2703M**

This lovely, sheltered, floral site with resident wardens is located on a forested hillside above the interesting and attractive small town of Le Bec-Hellouin. There are 90 marked grassy pitches, 30 used for seasonal units, leaving about 60 for tourists all with 10A hook-ups and some with water taps. There is some shade from mature trees. A rather steep footpath leads down to the town and the imposing Abbey of Bec. This is still a working monastery, which was founded in 1034, at the time of William the Conqueror, and has links to the archbishops of Canterbury. It is well worth a visit. The town itself is quite photogenic, has the usual tourist shops, several bars and restaurants and horse drawn carriage rides. The surrounding area is very popular with artists and photographers.

**Facilities:** A modern heated unit has good showers, British style WCs, open and cubicled washbasins, and a dishwashing area. Extra facilities in the old unit by reception. Washing machine and dryer. Baker calls each morning. Playing field and tennis courts. **Off site:** Fishing 1.5 km. Riding 2 km. Golf 20 km.

**Charges** 2002

| | |
|---|---|
| Per unit incl. 2 persons | € 6.71 |
| extra person | € 2.44 |
| child under 7 yrs | € 1.22 |
| electricity | € 2.44 |
| first dog free, extra dog | € 0.76 |

No credit cards. **Tel:** (0)2 32 44 83 55. Fax: (0)2 32 44 83 55. **Reservations:** Contact site. **Open** 1 April - 30 September.

**Directions:** Le Bec-Hellouin is 24 km. southeast of Pont Audemer. From Pont Audemer take D130 southeast for 20 km to Pont Authou. Turn left onto D39 to Le Bec-Hellouin, pass slowly through town and at far end of one-way system, turn left on minor road (site signed) for 1 km. Take left fork, and carry on for about 500 m. to site entrance on right.

## Camping du Domaine Catinière

**2702**

Route de Honfleur, 27210 Fiquefleur-Equainville

A peaceful, friendly site, convenient for Le Havre ferries, this is a developing site with new owners (1998) who are intent on improving this countryside site which lies in the middle of a very long village. The site is steadily achieving a modern look, whilst retaining its original French flavour. There some privately owned mobile homes, but there should be around 85 pitches for tourists including a large open field for tents and units not needing electricity. Caravan pitches are separated, some with shade, others are more open and all have electricity hook-ups (4, 6, or 10A). The site is divided by well fenced streams, popular with young anglers. The site is a good base for a short break to visit this part of Normandy, the pretty harbour town of Honfleur less than 5 km., and the nearby Vallée de la Risle. It is only a short distance from the ferry terminal, and makes every effort to meet the demands of ferry users.

**Facilities:** Already modernised, the toilet facilities include some washbasins in cubicles, and facilities for disabled people and babies. Reception with shop. Small bar/restaurant with regional dishes and snacks. Heated swimming pool (mid-June - end Aug). Two children's playgrounds, trampoline, table tennis, and boules court. New barrier (card deposit). **Off site:** Large supermarket is also close to the southern end of the bridge.

**Charges** 2003

| | |
|---|---|
| Per adult | € 4.20 |
| child (under 7 yrs) | € 2.50 |
| pitch | € 5.00 |
| electricity (4/10A) | € 3.50 - € 4.70 |
| dog | € 2.00 |

**Tel:** (0)2 32 57 63 51. Fax: (0)2 32 42 12 57. E-mail: info@camping-catiniere.com. **Reservations:** Advisable for high season, made with deposit of € 39 per week. **Open** 1 April - 30 September.

**Directions:** From Le Havre ferry terminal follow signs to the Pont de Normandie. From the southern end of the bridge, take D580 / D180 towards Toutainville for 2.5 km., then take D22 (right) towards Beuzeville for 1 km., and site is on right.

# Domaine de la Catinière

Is situated 5 km from Honfleur and 25 km from le Havre
in a quiet and green valley.

You are welcome from the 1st April till the 30th september.

MOBILE HOMES FOR HIRE

**Route d'Honfleur D22
27210 Fiquefleur Equainville
Tel: 0033 232 576 351 - Fax: 0033 232 421 257
E-mail: info@camping-catiniere.com
Website: www.camping-catiniere.com**

## Camping Jean-Louis Bougourd

**5002M**

Le Pré de la Rose, 50800 Villedieu-les-Poêles

Villedieu is 28 km. inland on a route followed by many who use the port of Cherbourg, and to a lesser extent Le Havre. Camping Jean-Louis Bougourd, also known as Pré de la Rose, is a small, well kept site taking some 100 units on individual pitches. These are of good size, marked out and separated by low hedges. A small river, La Sienne, runs alongside the site (fenced off) with fishing. Electricity is available in all parts from very modern connection points. The site has a cared-for look - it becomes full in main season but there are departures each day providing places for early arrivals.

**Facilities:** One good sized toilet block with Turkish style WCs for men and British for women (plus bidets), and smaller one with British WCs for all, make a good provision. Few washbasins in private cabins., the others are open with cold water only. Children's playground table tennis and volleyball. **Off site:** Tennis adjacent. Shops 400 m. in town centre, with a Tuesday market.

**Charges** 2002

| | |
|---|---|
| Per adult | € 2.50 |
| child | € 1.40 |
| pitch | € 2.50 |
| car | € 1.00 |
| electricity | € 2.50 |

No credit cards. **Tel:** 02 33 61 02 44. Fax: 02 33 61 18 58 (Mairie). E-mail: camping-bougourd@wanadoo.fr. **Reservations:** Made for about a week without deposit. **Open** Easter - 30 September.

**Directions:** Site is an easy walk from the town centre; entrance is past market place car park.

## Camping L'Etang des Haizes

43 rue Cauticotte, La Haye du Puits, 50250 St-Symphorien-le-Valois

This already appealing and friendly site has added a new swimming pool complex with four lane slides, jacuzzi and a paddling pool. L'Etang des Haizes provides 98 good size pitches, of which 60 are for touring units, on fairly level ground and all with electricity (6/10A). They are set in a mixture of conifers, orchard and shrubbery, with some very attractive slightly smaller pitches overlooking the lake and 34 mobile homes inconspicuously sited. The fenced lake offers good coarse fishing for huge carp (we are told!), pedaloes, a small beach, ducks and, believe it or not, a turtle can sometimes be seen on a fine day! Gate locked 22.00 - 07.00 hrs.

**Facilities:** Two well kept toilet blocks are of modern construction, open plan and unisex. They have washbasins in cabins and units for disabled people. Dishwashing under cover, small laundry. Motorcaravan services. Milk, bread and takeaway snacks are available on site (no gas). Bar with TV and terrace overlooking the lake and pool complex (all 20/5-10/9).Two children's play areas. Bicycle hire. Table tennis, pool table, petanque and volleyball. Entertainment and activities organised for all ages, including treasure hunts, archery and food tasting (10/7-25/8). **Off site:** La Haye-du-Puits (1 km) has two supermarkets, good restaurants and a market on Wednesdays. Good sandy beach 8 km. Normandy landing beaches 25 km.

**Charges** 2002

| | |
|---|---|
| Per unit incl. 2 adults | € 13.00 - € 19.00 |
| incl. 10A electricity | € 15.00 - € 24.25 |
| extra person over 3 yrs | € 1.50 - € 4.00 |
| dog | € 2.00 |
| electricity (6A) | € 1.00 - € 3.75 |

**Tel:** 02 33 46 01 16. Fax: 02 33 47 23 80. E-mail: etang.des.haizes@wanadoo.fr. **Reservations:** Made with 25% deposit. **Open** 1 April - 15 October.

**Directions:** From Cherbourg follow N13 (Mont St Michel) road as far as Valognes, then the D2 to St Sauveur-le-Vicomte. Continue on the D900 for La Haye-du-Puits, go straight on at new roundabout on the outskirts of town and site is signed almost immediately on the right.

# Camping Le Grand Large

50340 Les Pieux

5006

Le Grand Large is a well established, quality family site with direct access to a long sandy beach and within a 20 km. drive of Cherbourg. A neat, tidy site with both touring and mobile home pitches which are divided and separated by hedging, which gives an orderly well laid out appearance. At the entrance, alongside the security barrier, stands the modern reception area. Decorating the forecourt are low brick walls with sunken flower beds, the toilet blocks also having their share of flower troughs. To the rear of the site and laid out in the sand-hills is an excellent play area for children, with swings, slides and climbing frame. However, the sandy beach is the big attraction. Roads around the site are tarmac and there are pleasant views across the bay to the tip of the Cherbourg peninsula.

**Facilities:** The two toilet blocks are well maintained, the main one modern and colourful including washbasins in cubicles. WCs are mostly to the outside of the building. Provision for people with disabilities is good. Baby bathroom, dishwashing sinks, laundry area, and motorcaravan services. Shop for basic groceries. Bar/café and takeaway (snacks 15/6-31/8). Swimming pool and children's pool. Children's play area. Tennis, table tennis, volleyball and boules. Animation in July/Aug. **Off site:** Bicycle hire or riding 5 km, golf 15 km.

**Charges** 2003

| | |
|---|---|
| Per unit incl. 2 persons | € 22.00 |
| extra person | € 5.00 |
| child (under 7 yrs) | € 3.00 |
| electricity (6A) | € 3.50 |

Less 20% in low seasons (excl. electricity). Motorcaravan services € 6,10 - 7,62 (free to guests). **Tel:** 02 33 52 40 75. **Fax:** 02 33 52 58 20. **E-mail:** le-grand-large@wanadoo.fr. **Reservations:** Made with deposit (€ 77). **Open** 5 April - 21 September.

**Directions:** From Cherbourg port take N13 south for approx. 2 km. Branch right on D650 road (previously D904) signed Cartaret. Continue for 18 km to Les Pieux and follow camp signs via D117/517.

F - 50340 LES PIEUX — Le Grand Large — CAMPING

Tél. : 02 33 52 40 75 - Fax : 02 33 52 58 20 - Site internet : Legrandlarge.com

# Camping La Gerfleur

Rue Guillaume Le Conquérant, 50270 Barneville-Carteret

5009

La Gerfleur is a very pleasant little site with a warm welcome from the new owners (1999), a new heated pool, a fishing lake and reasonable sanitary facilities. There are 26 mobile homes, but these are separated from 55 individual tourist pitches. On grass with small dividing hedges, these all have electric hook-ups (6A) and some shade from mature trees. A few are in a newly created, more open area adjacent to the lake, and will need more time to fully mature. The new outdoor, heated pool has a separate circular paddling pool. An excellent long ramp gives access for disabled people. La Gerfleur makes a good holiday base, being an easy cycle ride from the large sandy beach at Barneville Plage, or from the harbour and the smaller coves at Carteret (both only 1.5 km). Day trips to the Channel Islands are also possible. A little English is spoken.

**Facilities:** Clean facilities include British style WCs, chain operated showers and some washbasins, all in modern cubicles, units for the disabled, laundry and dishwashing sinks. Washing machine and dryer. Basic motorcaravan service point. Swimming pool (6.5 x 14 m). Fishing lake. Table tennis, boules, games room with snooker and table football. Small playground. In July/Aug. services include a bar, a visit by a 'frites' van and a daily visit from a baker. **Off site:** Barneville town centre 550 m, sandy beach at Barneville Plage (1.5 km). Golf 4 km. Riding 7 km.

**Charges** 2002

| | |
|---|---|
| Per pitch | € 4.30 |
| adult | € 3.80 |
| child under 10 yrs | € 2.70 |
| electricity | € 3.20 |

**Tel:** (0)2 33 04 38 41. **Fax:** (0)2 33 04 38 41. **Reservations:** Advisable for July/August and made with deposit (€ 76). **Open** 1 April - 31 October.

**Directions:** Barneville-Carteret is approx. 37 km. SSW of Cherbourg. From north on D904 turn off the Barneville-Carteret by-pass, and use the old road to the town. After 1 km. at 'figure of eight' roundabout, continue on D903E towards Barneville town centre, and site entrance is immediately on your right.

# Camping L'Anse du Brick

route du Val de Saire, 50330 Maupertus-sur-Mer

5007

the **travel service**
TO BOOK

| | |
|---|---|
| Ferry | ✓ |
| Pitch | ✓ |
| Accommodation | ✗ |

01892 55 98 98

A friendly, family site, L'Anse du Brick overlooks a picturesque bay on the northern tip of the Contentin peninsula, 8 km. east of Cherbourg Port. This quality site makes a pleasant night halt, or an ideal longer stay destination for those not wishing to travel too far. Its pleasing location offers access to a small sandy beach, also to a woodland walk where only the noise of a cascading stream disturbs the peace. Beyond the site lies miles of walking tracks through the gorse-covered hills which, together with a stark rock face, cluster around the site and make it a sheltered sun-trap. This is a mature, terraced site with magnificent sea and hill views from certain pitches. Tarmac roads climb gradually to the pitches which are level, separated and mostly well shaded by the many trees, bushes and shrubs.

**Facilities:** Two sanitary blocks, although not ultra-modern, are kept spotlessly clean and are maintained to a satisfactory standard. They include provision for disabled visitors, laundry and dishwashing areas and a motorcaravan service point. Swimming pool complex. Simple restaurant and popular bar/pizzeria. Tennis court. Children's play area. Organised entertainment in season. Mini-club for children (6-12 yrs). Bicycle and kayak hire.

**Charges** 2003

| | |
|---|---|
| Per person | € 3.60 - € 4.80 |
| child (3-10 yrs) | € 2.10 - € 2.80 |
| pitch | € 7.80 - € 10.90 |
| electricity (10A) | € 3.50 |
| dog | € 1.60 - € 1.80 |

**Tel:** 02 33 54 33 57. Fax: 02 33 54 49 66. E-mail: welcome@anse-du-brick.com. **Reservations:** Advised for July/Aug. **Open** 1 April - 15 September.

**Directions:** From Cherbourg port turn left at crossroads (where site is signed) onto D116 coast road towards Barfleur. Continue for 8 km. and site is signed on right.

Beach at 100 m

L'Anse du Brick ★★★★

50330 MAUPERTUS/MER
Tel : 33 (0) 233 543 357
Fax :33 (0) 233 544 966.
Internet : www.anse-du-brick.com
Mail : welcome@anse-du-brick.com

Mobile home and chalets to rent

# Camping Municipal Le Pont-Roulland

50370 Brécey

5010M

Comfortable and good value, this little site is set in an old orchard of apple and cherry trees. The 50 numbered tourist pitches are on lush grass, with electric hook-ups (6A) for all, although some may need long leads. The entire site has a slight slope, so motorcaravans will probably need levelling blocks. There is good site lighting and tarmac roads. Although off-ground barbecues are allowed on the pitch, a large communal barbecue is provided in a traditional style "storehouse". The guardienne lives on site and reception is open from 1700-2200 hours daily- just choose your pitch and pay later if you arrive outside these hours. The usual small country town hustle and bustle and swimming pool noise during the day gives way to quiet nights after 8 pm.

**Facilities:** A traditional Normandy stone building houses the toilet facilities with modern fittings including spacious hot showers, some basins in cubicles, dishwashing and laundry sinks, and a washing machine, but no dedicated facilities for disabled persons. Table tennis. Playground for young children. **Off site:** Town centre and shops 1 km. Reception issues vouchers for free admission to adjacent municipal swimming pool. (June 16.30-19.00, July/Aug 14.00-19.00). Tennis and small park with paddling pool also adjacent. River fishing nearby.

**Charges** 2002

| | |
|---|---|
| Per pitch | € 2.20 |
| adult | € 2.35 |
| child under 7 yrs | € 1.20 |
| dog | € 0.45 |
| electricity | € 2.00 |

No credit cards. **Tel:** (0)2 33 48 60 60. Fax: (0)2 33 89 21 09. E-mail: tourisme-brecey@wanadoo.fr. **Reservations:** Contact site. **Open** 1 April - 30 September.

**Directions:** Brécey is 16 km. northeast of Avranches. Site is 1 km. east of town centre just off D911. Turn south on D79 towards Les Cresnays (site is signed). Site entrance adjacent to the swimming pool and off public car park.

## Normandy

# Camping Le Cormoran

Ravenoville-Plage, 50480 Sainte-Mère-Eglise

the travel service
TO BOOK
Ferry ✓
Pitch ✓
Accommodation ✓
01892 55 98 98

5005

Set in a flat and open landscape and only separated from the beach by the coast road, Le Cormoran is ideal for a holiday or short break quite near to Cherbourg (33 km), with the Landing Beaches close by. Holiday mobile homes, many privately owned, take 146 places but the remaining 80 are comfortable touring pitches sheltered from the wind by neat hedges and with 6A electricity available. With a narrow frontage, decorated with flags and a fountain, it is a fairly long site with most of the amenities at the entrance. This is a well run, family managed site with many regular visitors. A Sites et Paysages' member.

**Facilities:** Four toilet blocks are of varying styles but all clean and tidy. Improvements continue including extra cabins with shower, WC and washbasin. Washbasins are in cabins. Dishwashing sinks. Washing machine and dryer in three blocks. The smallest block is of the mobile type and serves 15 extra large pitches (150 sq.m.) at the back of the site. Small shop, bar with snacks (all season) and takeaway. Communal barbecue. Heated swimming pool (1/5-15/9, unsupervised). Three small play areas. Tennis court. Boules pitch. Entertainment and games room. Bicycle and shrimp net hire. **Off site:** Archery, riding and day trips to the Channel Islands can be organised. Golf 5 km. Utah Beach 5 km. Sports field and storage for up to 60 boats adjacent to the site.

**Charges 2003**

| | |
|---|---|
| Per unit incl. 1 or 2 persons | € 15.00 - € 20.00 |
| extra person | € 4.20 - € 5.50 |
| child (3- 7 yrs) | € 1.70 - € 2.10 |
| dog | € 2.50 - € 3.00 |
| electricity (6A) | € 3.70 |

Overnight (18.00-10.00 hrs) rate for motorcaravans € 11.00. Local tax included. **Tel:** 02 33 41 33 94. Fax: 02 33 95 16 08. E-mail: lecormoran@wanadoo.fr. **Reservations:** Advised for July/Aug. and made with 25% deposit. **Open** 1 April - 21 September.

**Directions:** From N13 take Ste Mère Eglise exit and in centre of town take road to Ravenoville (6 km), then Ravenoville-Plage (3 km). Just before beach turn right and site is 500 m.

## Normandy

# Camping Lez-Eaux

Saint Aubin des Préaux, 50380 St-Pair-sur-Mer

the travel service
TO BOOK
Ferry ✓
Pitch ✓
Accommodation ✗
01892 55 98 98

5003

Set in the spacious grounds of a château, Lez Eaux lies in a rural situation just off the main route south, under two hours from Cherbourg. It is a very pleasant situation from which to explore this corner of the Cotentin peninsula, with swimming pools on site and beaches nearby. However, because of its location Lez Eaux receives much en-route trade, both from tour operator clients and independent campers on their way further south and at times this can put heavy pressure on the facilities (it is a good idea to book for peak season visits, or for single nights arrive early). There are 229 pitches, nearly 50% taken by British and some Dutch tour operators. Most pitches are of a very good size, partly separated by trees and shrubs on either flat or very slightly sloping, grassy ground overlooking Normandy farmland and on either side of a small lake (with carp and other fish). All pitches have electrical connections (5/10A) and some have drainage.

**Facilities:** Three modern toilet blocks (cleaned three times daily) include washbasins in cabins, good facilities for children and babies, and full provision for disabled people. Shop, small bar, snacks and takeaway with set meal each night to order in advance (all from 15/5). Small heated swimming pool (12 x 6 m.) and attractive, indoor tropical style fun pool with slides and a glass roof (from 15/5, no T-shirts or Bermuda style shorts). Jacuzzi. Adventure play area. Good tennis court. Football, volleyball. Games room with table tennis, and TV room. Bicycle hire. Lake fishing. Torches required at night. Only one dog per pitch is accepted. Note: facilities not fully open until 15/5. **Off site:** Riding 5 km, golf 7 km. Nearest beach is 3 km, St Pair is 4 km. and Granville 7.

**Charges 2002**

| | |
|---|---|
| Per pitch incl. 2 persons | € 15.00 - € 26.00 |
| all services | € 8.50 |
| extra person | € 7.00 |
| child (under 7 yrs) | € 5.00 |
| electricity (5A) | € 5.00 |

**Tel:** 02 33 51 66 09. Fax: 02 33 51 92 02. E-mail: lez.eaux@wanadoo.fr. **Reservations:** Advisable for high season and made with 25% deposit. **Open** 1 May - 15 September.

**Directions:** Site access is signed west about 7 km. southeast of Granville on main D973 road to Avranches.

For latest information visit www.alanrogers.com **57**

## Camping Haliotis

Chemin des Soupirs, 50170 Pontorson

**5008**

Formerly Camping Municipal les Rives du Couesnon, this site is now privately owned and is undergoing considerable redevelopment. Currently with 110 pitches all for tourists (55 with 6A electricity) and a separate area for tents, the owner intends to extend the site with more touring pitches and new mobile home accommodation. A new leisure complex incorporating indoor and outdoor pools is planned. Despite the renovation work in reception and the toilet block, all was clean and tidy when we visited. We will visit again next season but anticipate that it will become a really good site. Mont-Saint-Michel is within walking, cycling and canoeing distance.

**Facilities:** The single sanitary unit is being completely renovated. It has British and Turkish style WCs, washbasins in cubicles, dishwashing and laundry sinks, and limited facilities for disabled people. Small children's playground. Free fishing in the River Couesnon. **Off site:** Local services in Pontorson within walking distance. Riding or golf 3 km. Tennis 800 m.

**Charges** 2002

| | |
|---|---|
| Per adult | € 2.00 - € 2.70 |
| child (under 7 yrs) | € 1.25 - € 1.50 |
| caravan and car | € 3.20 - € 3.90 |
| tent and car | € 2.90 - € 3.70 |
| motorcaravan | € 3.00 - € 3.60 |
| electricity | € 2.00 - € 2.10 |
| local tax | € 0.19 |
| dog | € 0.50 |

No credit cards. **Tel:** (0)2 33 68 11 59. Fax: (0)2 33 68 11 59. **Reservations:** Contact site. **Open** 1 May - 15 October.

**Directions:** Site is 300 m. from the town centre, west of D976, alongside the river, and is well signed from the town.

## Camping La Campière

bvd. du Docteur Dentu, 61120 Vimoutiers

**6101M**

This small, well kept site is situated in a valley to the north of the town, which is on both the Normandy Cheese and Cider routes. Indeed the town is famous for its cheese and has a Camembert Museum, five minutes walk away in the town centre. The 40 pitches here are flat and grassy, separated by laurel hedging and laid out amongst attractive and well maintained flower and shrub beds. There is some shade around the perimeter and all pitches have electricity (6/10A).

**Facilities:** The single central sanitary block is clean and heated, providing open washbasins and a bathroom for disabled visitors. Dishwashing and laundry facilities under cover. **Off site:** No shop but a large supermarket is 300 m. Tennis courts and a park are adjacent. Water sports facilities or riding 2 km.

**Charges** 2002

| | |
|---|---|
| Per person | € 2.53 |
| child (under 10 yrs) | € 1.26 |
| pitch | € 1.75 |
| car | € 1.43 |
| electricity | € 1.73 - € 2.79 |
| animal | € 0.84 |

Reductions for 7th and subsequent days. **Tel:** 02 33 39 18 86. Fax: 02 33 36 51 43. E-mail: mairie. vimoutiers@wanadoo.fr. **Reservations:** Not normally necessary. **Open:** March - October.

**Directions:** Site is on northern edge of town, signed from main Lisieux-Argentan road next to large sports complex.

## Camping Municipal du Champ Passais

61700 Domfront

6104M

Situated on the edge of the old fortified town of Domfront, this small site has 34 individual pitches on a series of level terraces and a separate open grassy area for tents. The nine pitches nearest the entrance are all hardstandings separated by grass and are supplied with a 10A electricity connection. Grass pitches on the lower levels, divided by well tended shrubs and hedges, have a 5A electricity connection and most have water and waste water points.

**Facilities:** Excellent sanitary facilities, housed in a modern building, include some washbasins in cubicles, facilities for disabled people, dishwashing and laundry sinks plus a washing machine. No separate chemical waste disposal point, but a notice tells visitors where to empty toilet cassettes. Motorcaravan service point planned. Boules. Play area. Double axle caravans are not accepte. **Off site:** Fishing 1 km. Supermarket, with cheap fuel 800 m. Sports centre adjacent to site.

**Charges** 2002

| | |
|---|---|
| Per unit incl. 1 adult | € 3.70 |
| adult | € 2.00 |
| child (under 10 yrs) | € 1.00 |
| electricity (5/10A) | € 1.80 - € 3.00 |
| dog | € 0.60 |

No credit cards. **Tel:** 02 33 37 37 66. **Reservations:** Not normally necessary. **Open** 1 April - 5 October.

**Directions:** Site is well signed from the town.

## Camping Municipal Parc du Château d'Eu

76260 Eu

7605M

In the grounds of the Château d'Eu, the setting for this site is quite lovely, even with the main town of Eu only minutes away. On entering the site, there is a long woodland area and park providing excellent picnic opportunities with lots of shade. The main building on a bank to one side of the site houses reception, recreation rooms and thesanitary unit. Of the 75 pitches, around 55 are used for touring units and there is an area of hardstanding for inclement weather. Most pitches are on grass under tall trees and all have access to electricity (6A). Previously the property of the Princes of Orleans, the Château houses the Town Hall and a museum, and some of the rooms and the gardens are open to the public. The park gates are closed 10 pm. - 7 am.

**Facilities:** The toilet unit is fairly elderly but is kept clean and can be heated. Some facilities are unisex including laundry and dishwashing facilities. Showers are of good quality with an adequate provision for the size of the site which is quite small despite its initial appearance. Playground. Volleyball, basketball and boules courts. **Off site:** Fishing 500 m. Town shops and services within walking distance.

**Charges** 2002

| | |
|---|---|
| Per person | € 1.80 |
| child (2-10 yrs) | € 0.90 |
| motorcaravan | € 2.50 |
| car or motorcycle | € 1.80 |
| tent or caravan | € 1.80 |
| electricity (6A) | € 3.20 |

**Tel:** 02 35 86 20 04. **Reservations:** Contact site. **Open** 1 April - 31 October.

**Directions:** From the D925, turn into Eu town centre where the Château and site are signed.

## Camping Municipal Les Boucaniers

Rue Pierre Mendès-France, 76470 Le Tréport

7611M

This large, good quality, municipal site has an attractive entrance and some floral displays, tarmac roads and site lighting. The 320 pitches are on level grass, some with dividing hedges, and a variety of trees to provide a little shade. There are 16 good quality wooden chalets for rent, and some privately owned mobile homes, which leaves around 276 pitches for tourists, all with electric hook-ups (5A). A small shop, bar and takeaway operates all season, the baker calls daily in high season, and every day except Monday in low season. The town centre is within walking distance with many good seafood restaurants to choose from.

**Facilities:** Three well equipped sanitary blocks (one can be heated) provide mainly British style WCs, washbasins in cubicles, pre-set hot showers, with facilities for small children and disabled persons at block three (furthest from entrance). Shop, bar and takeaway (1/4-31/10). Multicourt, minigolf, boules court. **Off site:** Tennis, football and gymnasium nearby. Fishing, golf or beach 2km. Markets at Le Tréport Monday and Saturday.

**Charges** 2002

| | |
|---|---|
| Per pitch | € 2.40 |
| with electricity | € 5.80 |
| adult | € 2.50 |
| child 2-10 yrs | € 1.40 |
| local tax (May-Sept) | € 0.30 |

**Tel:** (0)2 35 86 35 47. **Reservations:** Contact site. **Open** 1 April - 30 September.

**Directions:** From Eu on D1915, on entering town of Le Tréport, at first set of traffic lights on a multi-way junction, turn right into Rue Pierre Mendès-France, and site entrance is on right (signed).

## Camping Municipal du Colombier

7608M

453 rue Loucheur, 76550 Offranville

Approaching through the town, the work of the parks department is immediately evident with many floral displays, and this dedication extends to the site itself. The 103 individual pitches are divided by hedges and shrubs with well tended grass, and hardstanding for vehicles. Many are taken by seasonal units, with only 33 for tourers. Electricity is available to all pitches (6/10A) and the site is well lit. From reception one passes through the barrier and down an attractive drive through a park to the site. In the park adjacent to the site there is minigolf, tennis, children's playgrounds, horse and pony riding lessons and lovely gardens. The park also has a beautifully restored building 'La Maison du Parc' with a tea-room and a museum.

**Facilities:** A modern, spotlessly clean sanitary building provides single sex facilities with both British and Turkish style WCs, open and cubicled washbasins, roomy showers and good facilities for disabled people. Dishwashing and laundry sinks under cover. Caravan storage. **Off site:** Golf 8 km, fishing 10 km. The town is an easy walk.

**Charges** 2002

| | |
|---|---|
| Per person | € 3.50 |
| child (under 7 yrs) | € 2.00 |
| pitch | € 3.50 |
| vehicle | € 2.00 |
| electricity (6/10A) | € 2.00 - € 2.50 |

No credit cards. **Tel:** 02 35 85 21 14. Fax: 02 35 04 52 67. **Reservations:** Advised for high season. **Open** 1 April - 15 October.

**Directions:** Site is well signed from all major roads into the town.

## Camping Municipal d'Etennemare

7609M

Hameau d'Etennemare, 76460 Saint-Valery-en-Caux

This comfortable, neat municipal site is 2 km. from the harbour and town, 30 km. west of Dieppe. Quietly located, it has 116 pitches of which 50% are available for touring units. The grassy pitches are all on a slight slope, all with electricity (6A), water and drain, but there is very little shade. Reception is open daily from June - mid-Sept. but is closed on Wednesdays in low season and there is now a card operated security barrier. The site is close to the municipal sports complex with tennis and football field, and there are shops and restaurants in the town.

**Facilities:** Two modern, clean and well maintained sanitary buildings are side by side, one containing showers and the other, more recently refitted, has toilets, both open and cubicled washbasins and facilities for disabled people. Both blocks can be heated in winter. Dishwashing and laundry sinks. Washing machines. Small shop (July/Aug). Play area. Table tennis. **Off site:** Supermarket 1 km.

**Charges** 2002

| | |
|---|---|
| Per unit incl. 2 adults and electricity | € 12.50 |
| extra adult | € 2.55 |
| child (under 10 yrs) | € 1.60 |
| local tax | € 0.15 |

**Tel:** 02 35 97 15 79. Fax: 02 35 97 15 79. **Reservations:** Essential for July/Aug; contact site. **Open** all year.

**Directions:** Site is southwest of town centre and is signed from the D925 (Fécamp) road, just west of the railway station. Follow signs to site or 'terrain de sports'.

## Camping Municipal Veulettes-seu-Mer

7612M

8 Rue de Greenock, 76450 Veulettes-seu-Mer

A good value, well kept municipal site in an attractive coastal town, just 500m. from the beach and all town services. There are 116 marked pitches on open level grass, 40 of which are seasonal pitches, which leaves around 76 multi-service pitches for tourists, all with electric hook-ups (10A), water and waste water drain. Reception keeps soft drinks and ices during July/August. Also on site is an attractive 'salle' (open all day in July/August) with a library and TV, a games area with electronic game, table tennis, babyfoot and further toilet facilities.

**Facilities:** Three good modern sanitary units in traditional style buildings are of varying ages (one can be heated). Pre-set showers, washbasins in cubicles. Facilities for disabled people in the small unit on the far side of the site. Washing machine. Playground. Boules. TV, library and table tennis. **Off site:** Park with tennis, large playground, beach (pebble), watersports centre and all shops and services are within 500 m. level walk.

**Charges** 2002

| | |
|---|---|
| Per pitch | € 2.15 |
| adult | € 2.50 |
| child (4-10 yrs) | € 1.25 |
| car | € 1.00 |
| electricity | € 2.50 |

**Tel:** (0)2 35 97 53 44. Fax: (0)2 35 97 90 09. **Reservations:** Contact site. **Open** 1 April - 31 October.

**Directions:** Veulettes-sur-Mer is on the coast about 45 km. WSW of Dieppe. Site is central in town, about 500 m. back from the main promenade.

## Camping La Source

**76604**

Petit Appeville, 76550 Hautot-sur-Mer

This attractive, friendly site is just four kilometres from Dieppe and is useful for those using the Newhaven - Dieppe ferry crossing. The 120 pitches are flat and shady, and the site is quietly located in a valley with the only disturbance the occasional passing train. A fast-flowing small river flows along one border (not protected for young children), with opportunities for eel fishing, rowing or canoeing. There are hardstandings for motorcaravans and 6A electricity is available. The site is well lit and stays open for late night ferries (so there could be some noise late at night).

**Facilities:** A good, clean single toilet block (men to the left, ladies to the right) includes washbasins in cubicles and mainly British style WCs. Well equipped en-suite unit for disabled people but the unmade gravel roads may cause problems. Dishwashing under cover and laundry. Small bar and terrace with snack meals (15/3-15/10) and open late for ferries. Small play field. TV room and room for young people with table tennis and amusement machines. Small gym with modern fitness machines, free for campers. Volleyball, basketball and badminton. Fishing. **Off site:** Riding 2 km, bicycle hire 1 km, golf 4 km.

**Charges 2002**

| | |
|---|---|
| Per pitch | € 4.80 - € 7.70 |
| person | € 3.70 |
| child (under 7 yrs) | € 2.30 |
| electricity | € 2.60 |
| dog | € 1.00 |

**Tel:** 02 35 84 27 04. **Reservations:** Write to site. **Open** 15 March - 15 October.

**Directions:** From dock, follow one way system bearing left at Canadian War memorial, below the castle. Follow signs to Paris and Rouen and, after long hill, at large roundabout, take first exit to right on D925, Av. St Jaures. After 2 km. turn left at traffic lights on D153 (Pourville sur Mer to right). Just past railway station turn left under bridge (3.10 m.) into narrow road with stream on right. Site is a short distance on the left.

## Camping Municipal Cany-Barville

**7610M**

76450 Cany-Barville

This good quality site, first opened in 1997 adjacent to the municipal sports stadium, has a floral entrance and tarmac roads. Of the 100 individual hedged pitches around 74 are available for tourists. There are around 40 concrete hardstandings and the remainder are on grass, all are fully serviced with water, drain and electric hook-ups (10A). As yet, there is not very much shade from the young specimen trees. Cany-Barville is a bustling small town with a traditional Normandy market on Monday mornings. There is a Château and an Eco-museum (1/4-30/10), and the Durdent valley has numerous other châteaux, mills, churches and 'colombiers'.

**Facilities:** The modern, centrally located, sanitary unit can be heated and has some washbasins in cubicles. Dishwashing and laundry sinks. Separate suites for disabled people. Motorcaravan service point with chemical disposal facility. Table tennis, volleyball, boules. **Off site:** Sailing and windsurfing centre 2 km. Beach 10 km. Supermarket 1 km.

**Charges 2002**

| | |
|---|---|
| Per adult | € 2.20 |
| child (under 14 yrs) | € 0.95 |
| pitch | € 2.40 |
| animal | € 0.80 |
| electricity | € 2.40 |

**Tel:** 02 35 97 70 37. **Reservations:** Advisable in July and August. **Open** all year.

**Directions:** From traffic lights on eastern side of town turn off D925 on to D268 towards Yvetot. Go under railway arch and continue straight on. Site is 600 m. from town centre adjacent to sports field.

Camping Municipal Cany-Barville

76450 Cany-Barville - Tél : 0033 235.97.70.37

# Northern France

Map 3

## Nord / Pas de Calais

Major City: Lille
Ports: Calais and Boulogne
Departements: 59 Nord
62 Pas-de-Calais

## Picardy

Major City: Amiens
Departements: 02 Aisne,
60 Oise, 80 Somme

This is an area where centuries of invaders from the north as well as Britain have left their mark. Evidence of this is visible in the 17th century defensive citadels designed by Vauban at the end of a long period of conquests by English kings and Burgundian dukes; and from a more recent age the area around Flanders and the Somme is imprinted with the battles of two Great Wars with acres of immaculately tended war graves. At Vimy Ridge near Arras, First World War trenches have been preserved intact, a most poignant sight: while almost every village between Arras and Amiens has its memorial. On the other hand, it is the birthplace of Gothic architecture with six cathedrals, Amiens, Laon, and Beauvais the better known and Amiens arguably the grandest in France.

The area is however predominately rural with forests of mature beech and oak, though in Maritime Flanders the landscape is of polders and copses, a contrast to the industrial cities such as Lille now sporting a futuristic image with the development of Eurolille. The coastline has sandy beaches, dunes and ports. Le Touquet combines the modernity of its sports facilities with an old world charm. Boulogne and its ramparts is home to Nausicaa, the world's largest sea-life centre and from Cap Griz-Nez you may be able to see the White Cliffs of Dover. Perhaps though for some of us it is the huge hypermarkets which have grown up in this area that interest us as we stock up with wine, beer and cheese, etc. on our way home via ferry or the Tunnel.

Note: the site reports are laid out by département in numerical order not by region.

### Cuisine of the region

*Carbonnade de Boeuf à la Flamande* – braised beef with beer, onions and bacon

*Caudière (Chaudière, Caudrée)* – versions of fish and potato soup

*Ficelles Picardes* – ham pancakes with mushroom sauce

*Flamiche aux poireaux* – puff pastry tart with cream and leeks

*Hochepot* – a thick Flemish soup with virtu-ally everything in it but the kitchen sink

*Soupe courquignoise* – soup with white wine, fish, moules, leeks and Gruyère cheese

*Tarte aux Maroilles* – a hot creamy tart based on Maroilles cheese

*Waterzooï* – a cross between soup and stew, usually of fish or chicken

### Places of Interest

*Amiens* – Notre Dame cathedral, impressive for its size and the richly sculpted facade and the wood and stone carvings of the choir; monument to 1918 Battle of the Somme, also known for its remarkable 'hortillonnages' (water gardens) and inter-linking canals

*Chantilly* – the Château of Chantilly now houses the Musée Condé with impressive Baroque gardens to walk around, as well as a 17th century stable with a 'live' Horse museum.

*Compiègne* – Seven miles east of the town is Clairière de l'Armistice. The railway coach here is a replica of the one in which the 1918 Armistice was signed and in which Hitler received the French surrender in 1942

*Laon* – 12th century cathedral, WW1 trenches, Vauclair Abbey

*Marquesterre* – at the mouth of the Somme, one of Europe's most important bird sanc-tuaries

# Camping-Caravaning du Vivier aux Carpes

10 rue Charles Voyeux, 02790 Seraucourt-le-Grand

Vivier aux Carpes is a small quiet site, close to the A26, two hours from Calais, so it is ideal for an overnight stop but is also worthy of a longer stay. A neat, purpose designed site is imaginatively set out taking full benefit of large ponds which are well stocked for fishing. There is also abundant wild life. The 60 well spaced pitches, are at least 100 sq.m. on flat grass with dividing hedges. The 45 for touring units all have electricity (6A), some also with water points, and there are special pitches for motorcaravans. This peaceful site has a comfortable feel and is close to the village centre. The enthusiastic owners and the manager speak excellent English and are keen to welcome British visitors. The cathedral cities of St Quentin, Reims, Amiens and Laon are close, Disneyland just over an hour away, Compiegne and the WW1 battlefields are near and Paris easily reached by train (1 hr 15 mins from St Quentin). This site is good for couples or fishing enthusiasts.

**Facilities:** The spacious, clean toilet block has separate, heated facilities for disabled visitors, which are made available to other campers in the winter months. Laundry facilities. Motorcaravan service point (fresh water for large vans is charged). Above the toilet block is a large TV/games room with table tennis and snooker. Small children's play area. Bicycle hire. Petanque. Fishing (about € 5,50 p/day). Gates close 22.00 hrs, office open 09.00-21.30. Rallies welcome. **Off site:** Village has post office, doctor, chemist and small supermarket. Riding 500 m. Golf 12 km.

**Charges 2003**

| | |
|---|---|
| Per unit incl. 2 persons and electricity | € 15.00 |
| extra person | € 2.80 |
| child (under 10 yrs) | € 2.00 |
| pet | € 0.60 |

Monthly, weekly or weekend rates available. Discounts for students with tents. No credit cards. **Tel:** 03 23 60 50 10. Fax: 03 23 60 51 69. E-mail: camping.du.vivier@wanadoo.fr. **Reservations:** Advised for peak season. **Open** 1 March - 30 October.

**Directions:** Leave A26 (Calais - Reims) road at exit 11 and take D1 left towards Soissons for 4 km. Take D8 and on entering Essigny-la-Grand (4 km.) turn sharp right on D72 signed Seraucourt-le-Grand (5 km). Site is clearly signed - it is in the centre of the village.

# Camping Municipal Guignicourt

02190 Guignicourt

This very pleasant little municipal site has 100 pitches, 50 for long stay units and 50 for tourists. The manager takes great pride in his site, which is clean and tidy with many floral displays. Pitches are generally large and level, although you might need an extra long electric lead for some, but there are few dividing hedges. Pitches along the river bank have most shade, with a few specimen trees providing a little shade to some of the more open pitches. The town is quite attractive and is worthy of an evening stroll. At the junction of the N44 and D925, 7 km. west of the town, is the Chemin des Dames, Monument des Chars d'Assaut - a memorial to the WW1 tank campaign at Berry-au-Bac.

**Facilities:** The modern sanitary unit has British and Turkish style Toilets, washbasins (cold only except for the one in a cubicle), push-button hot showers, dishwashing and laundry sinks. Playground, tennis and boules courts, and fishing. **Off site:** The town has all services including a supermarket and bank. You may notice a low level hum from the nearby Generale Sucrière factory, a major industry of the town. Golf nearby.

**Charges 2002**

| | |
|---|---|
| Per adult | € 1.80 |
| child (2-10 yrs) | € 1.00 |
| pitch | € 2.00 - € 3.10 |
| animal | € 1.15 |
| electricity (6/10A) | € 2.75 - € 4.60 |

**Tel:** 03 23 79 74 58. **Reservations:** Contact site for details. **Open** 1 April - 30 September.

**Directions:** Guignicourt is about 20 km. north of Reims, just east of the A26, junction 14. The site is well signed from D925 in the village.

## Northern France
# Camping-Caravaning La Chaumière

**5901** 529 langhemast Straete, 59285 Buysscheure

This is a very friendly, pleasant site, tucked away in the département du Nord with a strong Flanders influence, well worth considering for those using the local Channel crossings. There is a real welcome from the owners, Guy and Bernadette. Set just behind the village of Buysscheure (with a shop and two cafés), the site has just 22 pitches separated by young trees and bushes. With 16 for touring units, mostly quite large and with some slope, they are on grass with a gravel hardstanding area for the car. Each pair of pitches shares a brick-built unit, decorated with flowers, incorporating a light, 6A electricity connections, water points and rubbish container. A small, fenced fishing lake contains some large carp (seen!) and ducks will help you eat your baguettes. A bonus is that Bernadette works for the local vet and can arrange all the documentation for British visitors' pets. English is spoken.

**Facilities:** Although modern, the unisex toilet facilities are simple with two WCs, one shower and one washbasin cabin. Facilities provided for disabled visitors may also be used (a toilet and separate washbasin/shower room). Dishwashing room. Laundry room. Motorcaravan services. Bar (daily) and restaurant (weekends only, all day, all season). Dog exercise area - with jumps etc. **Off site:** Interesting local market (Monday) at Bergues. Shop and café/restaurants in the village.

**Charges 2003**

| | |
|---|---|
| Per unit incl. 2 persons, electricity | € 14.00 |
| extra person | € 7.00 |
| child (under 7 yrs) | € 3.50 |
| dog | € 1.00 |

**Tel:** 03 28 43 03 57. E-mail: camping.lachaumiere@wanadoo.fr. **Reservations:** Contact site. **Open** 1 April - 31 October.

**Directions:** From Calais take N43 towards St Omer for 25 km. Just beyond Nordausques take D221 left to Watten. In Watten turn left for the centre, then right onto D26 towards Cassel. Soon after Lederzeele the site is signed to the right (just before railway bridge). When you reach Buysscheure turn left and then right from where the site is signed again.

## Northern France
# Camping Domaine de la Sablière

**5907** Mont-Noir, 59270 St-Jans-Cappel

This site offers spacious pitches and modern clean sanitary facilities. Mont-Noir, which straddles the France/Belgium border, enjoys an elevated, rural situation approximately 40 km. southeast of Dunkirk and 25 km. northwest of Lille. Entry to the site is on the brow of a hill, but not difficult. The site, which is terraced, is laid out in avenues shaded by mature trees and shrubs. The 100 pitches are level and separated by hedging with water, drainage and electricity (6A). There are many seasonal caravans but 10 pitches are allocated for touring units. Care is needed for larger units negotiating sharp bends and a steep descent if sited at the lower level.

**Facilities:** A central toilet block is fully equipped and of a modern design, clean and attractively sited on a high level approached by paved walkway and tiled forecourt. Facilities include washbasins in private cabins. On a lower level another block of older construction. Dishwashing sinks,and laundry facilities. Bar and café. Games room. Baker calls each morning. **Off site:** Restaurant across the road offers excellent value snacks and meals.

**Charges 2002**

| | |
|---|---|
| Per adult | € 2.30 |
| child (under 7 yrs) | € 1.20 |
| pitch and car | € 4.20 |
| electricity | 2.30 |

**Tel:** 03 28 49 46 34. **Reservations:** Contact site. **Open** 1 April - 31 October.

**Directions:** Leave A25 Lille - Dunkerque autoroute at Bailleul exit 10 on D10. Continue through Bailleul and follow camp signs to St-Jans-Cappel - through village and turn right at crossroads to Mont-Noir. Site is on right at top of hill opposite restaurant.

## Northern France
# Camping Municipal Mauberge

**5905M** route de Mons, 59600 Maubeuge

This is an attractive site convenient for a night-stop or for longer stays close to the RN2 road. It is a neat and tidy municipal site with 92 marked pitches of fair size. Mainly on level ground and separated by trim hedges, most have electrical connections (3, 6 or 10A) and some have hardstanding. A variety of broadleaf trees provides shade when needed. When inspected, reception staff were friendly and helpful. Although there are few amenities on the site, the interesting town centre of Maubeuge itself is only about 1 km.

**Facilities:** Two circular sanitary blocks provide good modern facilities. Dishwashing sinks under cover and washing machines. The block used in winter can be heated. Small adventure-style playground.

**Charges 2002**

| | |
|---|---|
| Per person | € 3.05 |
| child (4-7 yrs) | € 1.68 |
| pitch | € 3.05 - € 4.12 |
| electricity (3/10A) | € 2.59 - € 5.03 |

**Tel:** 03 27 62 25 48. **Reservations:** Not normally made or necessary, but if in doubt phone site. **Open** all year.

**Directions:** Site is on the RN2 road (known as the N6 in Belgium) north of the town, on the right going towards Mons.

## Camping Campix

6001

BP 37, 60340 St-Leu-d'Esserent

Opened in 1991, this informal site has been unusually developed in a former sandstone quarry on the outskirts of the small town. The quarry walls provide very different boundaries to most of the site, giving it a sheltered, peaceful environment. Trees have grown to soften the slopes. Not a neat, manicured site, the 160 pitches are arranged in small groups on the different levels with stone and gravel access roads (some fairly steep and possibly muddy in poor weather). Electricity (6A) is available to approximately 140 pitches. Torches are advised. There are very many secluded corners mostly for smaller units and tents and plenty of space for children to explore (parents must supervise - some areas, although fenced, could be dangerous). A footpath leads from the site to the town where there are shops, restaurants and an outdoor pool (in season). This site is best suited to those not needing sophisticated on-site facilities, or for visiting local places of interest and the friendly, English speaking owner will advise. These include Chantilly, the Asterix Park and the Mer de Sable, a Western theme amusements park, both 20 km. Disneyland is 70 km. It is also possible to visit Paris by train (information at reception).

**Facilities:** At the entrance to the site a large building houses reception and two clean, heated sanitary units - one for tourers, the other usually reserved for groups. Two suites for disabled people double as baby rooms. Laundry facilities with washing machine and dryer. At quieter times only one unit is opened but facilities may be congested at peak times. Motorcaravan service facilities. Bread and milk delivered daily. Basic snack bar operates from mobile unit (July/Aug). **Off site:** Fishing 1 or 5 km, riding or golf 5 km.

**Charges 2003**

| | |
|---|---|
| Per unit | € 3.00 - € 5.00 |
| person | € 3.00 - € 5.00 |
| child (under 9 yrs) | € 2.00 - € 3.00 |
| small tent | € 2.50 - € 4.00 |
| dog | € 1.00 - € 2.00 |
| electricity | € 2.50 - € 3.50 |

**Tel:** 03 44 56 08 48. Fax: 03 44 56 28 75. E-mail: campixfr@aol.com. **Reservations:** Advisable for July/Aug. **Open** 7 March - 30 November.

**Directions:** St Leu-d'Esserent is 11 km. west of Senlis, 5 km. northwest of Chantilly. From the north on the A1 autoroute take the Senlis exit, from Paris the Chantilly exit. Site is north of the town off the D12 towards Cramoisy, and is signed or in the village.

## Camping Château du Gandspette

6203

62910 Eperlecques

This friendly, comfortable, family run site is in the grounds of the Château du Gandspette. It is conveniently situated for the channel ports and tunnel, providing useful overnight accommodation and a range of facilities for a longer stay. The 17th century building adjacent to the château now houses an attractive bar/restaurant. A gravel road gives access to three different camping areas and a central open space. There are 170 pitches (100 or 150 sq.m), of which 55 are taken by semi-permanent French holiday caravans which intermix with some of the touring pitches giving a real French ambience. All pitches have electricity (6/10A) and are delineated by trees and some hedging. Mature trees form the perimeter of the site, through which there is access to woodland walks. Used by tour operators (8 pitches). A `Sites et Paysages' member.

**Facilities:** A partially renovated sanitary block provides satisfactory facilities with a mixture of open and cubicled washbasins. The site reports a second new block. Covered dishwashing sinks. Washing machines and dryers. Good motorcaravan service point. Bar, grill restaurant and takeaway (all 15/5-15/9). Two swimming pools, one large and one smaller (15/5-30/9). New adventure style children's playground, and playing field. Tennis, petanque and a children's room with table tennis and electronic games. Entertainment is organised in season. **Off site:** Riding 3 km, fishing 3 km, golf 10 km. Small supermarket in village 1 km. Market Watten (Friday) and St Omer (Saturday).

**Charges 2002**

| | |
|---|---|
| Per unit incl. 2 persons | € 15.00 - € 19.00 |
| extra person (over 4 yrs) | € 4.00 |
| dog | free |
| electricity (6A) | € 3.50 |
| local tax | € 0.15 - € 0.30 |

**Tel:** 03 21 93 43 93. Fax: 03 21 95 74 98. E-mail: contact@chateau-gandspette.com. **Reservations:** Necessary for July/Aug. **Open** 1 April - 30 September.

**Directions:** From Calais follow N43 towards St Omer for 25 km. Southeast of Nordausques take D221 (east) and follow camp signs for 5-6 km. From St Omer follow N43 to roundabout at junction with D600. Turn right on D600 towards Dunkirk and in 5 km. turn left on D221. Site is 1.5 km. on right.

# Camping-Caravaning La Bien-Assise

**6201** D231, 62340 Guines

the **travel service**
TO BOOK
Ferry ✓
Pitch ✓
Accommodation ✗
01892 55 98 98

A mature, well developed site, the history of La Bien-Assise goes back to the 1500s. Today the château, farm and mill are all in the hands of the Boutoille family who can provide you with a fascinating brief history. The farm buildings house the facilities and pool complex. The entrance to a more formal and excellent restaurant, 'La Ferme Gourmande' is in the mellow farmyard opposite the dovecote, with the Auberge du Colombier next door. There are 220 grass pitches mainly set among mature trees, apart from on the newer field. Connected by gravel roads and of a good size (up to 300 sq.m) shrubs and bushes divide most of the pitches. The site's position, 15 minutes from Calais, the Channel Tunnel exit 6 km. and 20 minutes from Boulogne, make it a popular venue en-route north or south, but it is well worth a longer stay. Reception opens for long hours to meet the needs of those crossing the Channel and the site can have heavy usage at times (when maintenance can be variable). Used by tour operators (50 pitches).

**Facilities:** Three well equipped toilet blocks provide many washbasins in cabins, mostly British style WCs and provision for babies, clothes and dishwashing. The main block is in four sections, two unisex. Shop. Restaurant (open all year, closed Mon. and Sat. lunchtime). Bar/grill and takeaway (evenings from 1/5). TV room. Pool complex (10/5-10/9) with a sheltered and heated pool (16 x 6 m.), fun pool/toboggan and covered paddling pool with mushroom fountain. Play areas. Minigolf. Tennis court. Bicycle hire. **Off site:** Fishing 8 km. riding 10 km. Local market and walks from the site.

**Charges** 2003

| | |
|---|---|
| Per unit | € 11.30 |
| adult | € 4.50 |
| child (under 8 yrs) | € 3.50 |
| electricity (6A) | € 3.70 |
| dog | € 2.00 |

Less 10% in low seasons, **Tel:** 03 21 35 20 77. Fax: 03 21 36 79 20. E-mail: castel@bien-assise.com.
**Reservations:** Advised for July/Aug. or if arriving late in the evening. Made for any length with deposit (€ 39) and fee (€ 8) for stays 5 days or more. **Open** 25 April - 20 September.

**Directions:** From ferry terminal follow A16 south (Boulogne) for junction 15, turning towards St Pierre de Calais to immediately pick up Guînes signs before going under autoroute following the D127. Continue beside canal to Guînes. Site is just south west of village on D231 Marquise road. From Tunnel also follow A16 south (Boulogne) to immediately pick up Guînes signs at junction 11 and following D215 past St Tricat to Guînes. From south on autoroute A26, use exit 2 (Ardres, Guînes) onto N43 and D231 (15 km).

## Northern France
### Camping de La Vallée
**6207** 901 Rue Principale, 62179 Hervelinghen

De La Vallée is a recently created, modern campsite in a rural location, in the area known as the 'Terre des 2 Caps' (land of the two headlands). The ground is slightly sloping so levelling blocks may be necessary, but the 101 pitches are mostly individual and hedged, and all have electric hook-ups (6A). Most have lovely views of the valley and surrounding countryside. Reception shares space with the attractive bar/café that fronts the campsite and serves a good selection of meals and snacks. The surrounding area has several magnificent beaches, 400 hectares of conservation area, and is a cross-roads for more than 300 species of migrating birds. The site is also within walking distance of Hervelinghen village centre, and within a short drive of both Calais and Boulogne.

**Facilities:** A new building with up-to-date facilities includes washbasins in cubicles, pre-set hot showers (on payment - tokens from reception), laundry with washing machine and dryer (key from reception). Excellent unit with three separate rooms for disabled people, and dishwashing and laundry sinks set at low level also. A covered area adjacent to this building houses the normal dishwashing and laundry sinks. Bar/café. **Off site:** WW2 museum and 17th century Fort in Ambleteuse.

**Charges** 2002

| | |
|---|---|
| Per pitch | € 2.90 |
| adult | € 3.10 |
| child under 12 yrs | € 1.90 |
| car | € 1.60 |
| electricity | € 3.10 |
| animal | € 1.00 |

No credit cards. **Tel:** (0)3 21 36 73 96. **Reservations:** Contact site. **Open** 1 April - 31 October.

**Directions:** Hervelinghen is about 20 km. southwest of Calais. From Calais take D940 along the coast, passing through Sangatte, and 4 km. after leaving Escalles, turn left (east) on D244 for about 3 km. to site. Alternatively using the A16, take exit 9, and turn west on D244 for 3 km. to site.

## Northern France
### Camping-Caravaning St Louis
**6205** Rue Leulène, 62610 Autingues par Ardres

Convenient for the ferry port at Calais, this is a peaceful little site with 84 pitches. Many are taken by privately owned holiday homes, but there are around 25 pitches for tourists. In a garden-like setting, they are individual and grassy with some shade. Electricity hook-ups (4A) are available for all. In high season the site is usually full by 17.00 hrs, so arrive early.

**Facilities:** Clean and tidy unisex toilet facilities provide showers on payment and washbasins mostly in cubicles. Facilities for disabled people. Baby room. Dishwashing and laundry sinks, washing machine. Motorcaravan service point free to campers. Restaurant and takeaway every evening in July/Aug. Playground, Games room.

**Charges** 2002

| | |
|---|---|
| Per adult | € 2.50 |
| child (2-7 yrs) | € 1.00 |
| pitch | € 5.00 |
| electricity | € 2.50 |

**Tel:** 03 21 35 46 83. **Fax:** 03 21 00 19 78. **Reservations:** Advised for high season. **Open** 1 April - 31 October.

**Directions:** From Calais take N43 towards St Omer for 15 km, and just east of Ardres, turn south on D224, where site is signed.

## Northern France
### Caravaning du Château d'Hardelot
**6204** 21 rue Nouvelle, 62360 Condette

Within about 15 minutes drive of Boulogne and only 5 minutes by car from the long sandy beach at Hardelot, this modern site has 70 pitches with around 50 for touring units, the rest occupied by long stay or units to rent. Pitches are of varying size on level grass, all with access to electricity (6A). Hedging plants between the pitches are maturing well and there is shade from mature trees around the site. With friendly and accommodating owners, this site provides a useful overnight stop. an English-run pub/restaurant is within walking distance.

**Facilities:** Modern sanitary facilities in two small units (one heated) include large hot showers and baby bath. Dishwashing sinks, laundry facilities (washing machine and dryer). Motorcaravan services. Excellent playground and entertainment for children in season. Fitness room. **Off site:** Fishing 800 m, riding 1 km, bicycle hire or golf 3 km.

**Charges** 2002

| | |
|---|---|
| Per unit incl. 2 persons | € 12.50 - € 14.50 |
| extra person | € 3.70 - € 4.50 |
| child (under 7 yrs) | € 2.40 - € 3.00 |
| electricity (6A) | € 3.70 |

**Tel:** 03 21 87 59 59. **Fax:** 03 21 87 59 59. **E-mail:** campingduchateau@libertysurf.fr. **Reservations:** Advised - contact site **Open** 1 April - 31 October.

**Directions:** South of Boulogne, take N1 Amiens (Paris) road, the right fork for Touquet-Paris Plage (D940). Continue for 5 km. passing a garage and signs for Condette, then turn right at roundabout (site signed). At next roundabout right again. Site entrance (narrow) is on right after a short distance.

## Northern France
# Caravaning L'Orée du Bois

**6206** Chemin Blanc, 62180 Rang-du-Fliers

This fairly peaceful but extensive campsite is in a natural woodland setting, and only 3 km. from a large sandy beach. From reception you pass through a corner of the mobile home section, then through an area of natural, preserved woodland which separates the touring area. This has 120 individual, shady pitches, all with electric hook-ups (5A). On grass which can be slightly undulating, most are separated by hedges and bushes, but the emphasis is on 'nature'. A separate clearing in the woodland is reserved for tents, and useful for cyclists or backpackers is 'Camp Sherpa' comprising eight 2-berth wooden tents. A modern sanitary unit is central in the touring area, with a second smaller unit in the mobile homes area, Berck Plage is only 3 km. and has a magnificent sandy beach and promenade, with extensive free parking areas.

**Facilities:** Modern facilities have open and cubicle washbasins, a laundry and good facilities for disabled persons and babies. Water for the toilets is obtained from a borehole, and has a slight brownish colour. Basic motorcaravan service point by reception, with a full service area close to the nearby Intermarché. Bar/ brasserie. Animation in July/Aug. Fishing lake. Tennis. Several playgrounds. **Off site:** Small supermarket adjacent.

**Charges** 2002

| | |
|---|---|
| Per pitch incl. 2 persons and electricity | € 15.00 - € 20.00 |
| extra person | € 2.00 - € 4.00 |
| animal | € 2.00 |

Discounts for stays of 14 days. **Tel:** (0)3 21 84 28 51. Fax: (0)3 21 84 28 56. E-mail: oree.du.bois@ wanadoo.fr. **Reservations:** Essential for July/Aug, and advisable at other times. Made with deposit of 25% of total fees. **Open** 30 March - 20 October.

**Directions:** Rang du Fliers is just east of Berck Plage and about 15 km. south of Le Touquet. From Berck Plage take D917 east to roundabout by supermarket, turn left (north) at next traffic lights (site signed), site is 500 m. on left. From A16 exit 25, follow D917 towards Berck Plage. After several roundabouts, turn right at traffic lights (site signed), entrance is 500 m. on left.

## Northern France
# Camping Le Royon

**8004** 1271 route de Quend, 80790 Fort-Mahon-Plage

This busy family run site, some two kilometres from the sea, has 280 pitches of which 110 are used for touring units. Of either 95 or 120 sq.m, the marked and numbered pitches are divided by hedges and arranged either side of access roads. Electricity (6A) and water points are available to all. The site is well lit, fenced and guarded at night (€ 30 deposit for barrier card). A friendly clubroom and bar serves drinks and ices, sells bread and newspapers and has the usual games machines. Entertainment is organised for adults and children in July/Aug. The site is close to a the Baie de L'Authie which is an area noted for migrating birds.

**Facilities:** Four toilet blocks provide mostly unisex facilities with British or Turkish style WCs and some washbasins in cubicles. Units for disabled people. Baby baths. Dishwashing and laundry sinks under cover. Small shop (July/Aug). Mobile takeaway calls each evening in July/Aug. Clubroom. Attractive, heated, covered swimming pool (16 x 8 m; 29/4-15/9) with open air children's pool and terrace. Playground. Table tennis, multi-court, tennis court and boules. Bicycle hire. **Off site:** Fishing, riding or golf within 1 km. Windsurfing, sailing, sand yachting, canoeing nearby. Cinema, disco and casino near.

**Charges** 2002

| | |
|---|---|
| Per pitch incl. water tap, electricity (6A) and 3 persons | € 13.00 - € 25.00 |
| extra person over 1 yr | € 6.00 |
| local tax (over 10 yrs) | € 0.30 |
| dog | € 2.00 |

**Tel:** 03 22 23 40 30. Fax: 03 22 23 65 15. E-mail: barbara.dutot@wanadoo.fr. **Reservations:** Essential for July/Aug; made with deposit (€ 40 p/week) and fee (€ 10). **Open** 1 March - 31 October.

**Directions:** Site is on outskirts of Fort Mahon Plage, on D32 towards Quend.

# Northern France
## Castel Camping Le Château de Drancourt
BP 22, 80230 St-Valéry-sur-Somme

8001

travel
service
'O BOOK
rry ✓
tch ✓
ccommodation ✗
1892 55 98 98

A popular, busy and lively holiday site within easy distance of Channel ports, between Boulogne and Dieppe, Domaine de Drancourt is in four sections. The original section has 100 marked and numbered, grassy pitches of good size, with good shade. An extension taking some 90 units is in light woodland and two newer touring sections are on flat or gently sloping meadow, with little shade as yet. There are 356 pitches in total, of which 220 are occupied by several tour operators. The site also has 30 units for rent which leaves 80 pitches for touring units. Electricity (6A) is available in all areas. It can be dusty around the reception buildings and château in dry weather. The pools and toilet blocks can become stretched at times in peak season and maintenance and cleaning can be variable. English is spoken and the site is run personally by the energetic owner and his staff.

**Facilities:** Three modern, well equipped toilet blocks include washbasins in cubicles, family bathrooms and facilities for disabled visitors. Laundry and dishwashing sinks, washing machines and dryers. Drainage difficulties can still cause occasional problems. Shop (from 15/4). Pizzeria (from 20/4) open until late. Restaurant and takeaway (from 20/4, closed Tuesday in low season). Bar in château, new large first floor bar and pool-side bar with karaoke in season. Three TV rooms, one for children. Disco (free entry). Games room with table tennis. Three heated swimming pools (from 1/5), one indoor and two open air, one with water slide. Tennis court, golf practise range and minigolf. Bicycle hire. Pony riding in season (stables 15 km). Fishing (free). **Off site:** Stony beach at Cayeux 8 km, or sandy beach 25 km.

**Charges** 2002

| | |
|---|---|
| Per person | € 5.60 |
| child (under 5 yrs) | € 4.20 |
| pitch for caravan or tent | € 8.50 |
| car | € 2.80 |
| pitch for motorcaravan | € 11.50 |
| dog | free |
| electricity (6A) | € 2.90 |
| local tax (over 10 yrs) | € 0.30 |

**Tel:** 03 22 26 93 45. **Fax:** 03 22 26 85 87. E-mail: chateau.drancourt@wanadoo.fr. **Reservations:** Advised for the main season and made for any length, with deposit for longer stays. **Open** Easter - 15 September.

**Directions:** Site is 2.5 km. south of St Valéry, near Estreboeuf, and is signed from the St Valéry road N40.

# Northern France
## Camping-Caravaning Le Val d'Authie
20 route de Vercourt, 80120 Villers-sur-Authie

8009

In a village location, this well organised site is fairly close to several beaches, but also has its own excellent pool complex, small restaurant and bar. The owner has carefully controlled the size of the site, leaving space for a leisure area. There are 158 pitches in total, but with 100 holiday homes and 13 chalets, there are only 45 for touring units. These are on grass, some are divided by small hedges, with 3 or 6A electric hook-ups, and 15 have full services. Ideas for excursions include the 15/16th century chapel and hospice and the Aviation Museum at Rue, a pottery at nearby Roussent, a flour mill at Maintenay, and the steam railway which runs from Le Crotoy to Cayeux-sur-Mer around the Baie de Somme.

**Facilities:** Excellent modern toilet facilities include some shower and washbasin units, washbasins in cubicles, and limited facilities for disabled people and babies. Ice pack service. Well stocked shop by reception. Bar/restaurant serving good value meals, with choice of 17 ice-cream flavours (hours vary according to season). Heated swimming pool with small jacuzzi and paddling pool (April - mid-Sept, with lifeguards in July/Aug). Good playground for small children, club room with TV, and weekend entertainment in season. Multi-court, beach volleyball, football, boules and tennis court. Fitness trail and running track, mountain bike circuit, and plenty of good paths for evening strolls. Barbecues are not permitted.

**Charges** 2002

| | | |
|---|---|---|
| Per adult | | € 6.00 |
| child (under 7 yrs) | | € 3.00 |
| pitch | | € 4.50 |
| extra tent | | € 3.00 |
| electricity (4-10A) | € 3.00 - | € 7.00 |
| animal | | € 1.50 |

**Tel:** 03 22 29 92 47. **Fax:** 03 22 29 94 05. E-mail: camping@valdauthie.fr. **Reservations:** Advisable for high season, peak weekends and B.Hs. **Open** 30 March - 3 November.

**Directions:** Villers-sur-Authie is about 25 km. NNW of Abbeville. From A16 junction 24 take N1 to Vron, then left on D175 to Villers-sur-Authie. Alternatively use D85 from Rue, or D485 from Nampont St Martin. Site is at southern end of village at junction of minor road.

## Northern France
# Camping Le Val de Trie

Bouillancourt-sous-Miannay, 80870 Moyenneville

the travel service
TO BOOK
Ferry ✓
Pitch ✓
Accommodation ✓
01892 55 98 98

Le Val de Trie is a natural countryside site in a woodland location, near a small village. It is maturing into a well managed site with modern facilities. The 100 numbered, grassy pitches are of a good size, divided by hedges and shrubs with mature trees providing good shade in most areas, and all have electricity (6A) and water. Access roads are gravel (the site is possibly not suitable for the largest motor-caravans). There are good walks around the area and a notice board keeps campers up to date with local market, shopping and activity news. The site has a friendly, relaxed atmosphere and English is spoken. Very much off the beaten track, it can be very quiet in April, June, September and October. If you visit at these times and there is no-one on site, just choose a pitch or call at the farm to book in. There are a few Dutch tour operator tents (5).

**Facilities:** The original sanitary building has been extended and a second unit opened. They include washbasins in cubicles, units for disabled people, babies and children, plus laundry and dishwashing facilities. Washing machine and dryer. Basic motor-caravan services. Small shop (from 1/5) provides basic necessities, farm produce and wine, bread can be ordered each evening and butcher visits twice weekly in season. Bar, takeaway and terrace (15/5-15/9). Pleasant small swimming pool (6 x 12 m. open 1/6-31/8). Table tennis, boules and volleyball. Fishing lake (free). Bicycle hire. Play areas and small animal enclosure. **Off site:** Riding 2 km, golf 5 km.

**Charges 2002**

| | |
|---|---|
| Per unit incl. 2 persons | € 10.00 - € 13.00 |
| with electricity | € 13.00 - € 16.50 |
| extra person | € 2.90 - € 3.70 |
| child (under 7 yrs) | € 1.90 - € 2.20 |
| dog | € 0.80 |

No credit cards. **Tel:** 03 22 31 48 88. Fax: 03 22 31 35 33. E-mail: raphael@camping-levaldetrie.fr.
**Reservations:** Made with dates, plus deposit (€ 31; no fee for AR readers). **Open** 1 April - 1 November.

**Directions:** From A28 exit 3 turn northwest on D173 to Moyenneville. In town take road towards Miannay. After 2 km. turn left to Bouillancourt sous Miannay and site is signed in village.

Camping le Val de Trie ***
Quiet and relaxing
Swimming pools
Fishing pond

Situated at only 1 hour from Calais (A16)
Ideal spot for first or last night or longer stay
12 km from the coast

Cottages to rent

Moyenneville
tel. 00 33 (0)3 22 31 48 88
raphael@camping-levaldetrie.fr
www.camping-levaldetrie.fr

Seven days stay, six days to pay (outside July/August).

## Northern France
# Camping La Ferme des Aulnes

1 rue du Marais, Fresne-sur-Authie, 80120 Nampont-Saint-Martin

the travel service
TO BOOK
Ferry ✓
Pitch ✓
Accommodation ✗
01892 55 98 98

This peaceful site has been developed on the grassy meadows of a small, 17th century farm on the edge of the village of Fresne. Restored outbuildings house reception and the site's facilities, arranged around a central, landscaped courtyard that now boasts a fine heated swimming pool. Of the 85 pitches, 30 are available for touring units, with most of the remainder occupied by or for sale to private owners for holiday mobile homes. All tourist pitches have electricity (6A) and are fairly level. Many are individual and divided by shrubs and young trees, others are on an open, slightly sloping, grassy area.

**Facilities:** Smart, modern and well maintained toilet facilities include washbasins in cubicles with a large cubicle for disabled people. Dishwashing and laundry sinks. Shop (all season). Piano bar and restaurant. TV room. Swimming pool (16 x 9 m; heated and open mid June - end Aug). Fitness room. Aquagym and Balneo therapy. Beach volleyball, football. Golf practice range. Playground for small children. Table tennis, boules and archery. **Off site:** Fishing 800 m. Golf 3 km. Riding 8 km.

**Charges 2002**

| | |
|---|---|
| Per unit incl. 2 adults and 1 child (0-7 yrs) | € 23.00 |
| extra adult | € 6.00 |
| child (under 7 yrs) | € 3.00 |
| electricity (6A) | € 4.00 |
| dog | € 2.00 |

No credit cards. **Tel:** 03 22 29 22 69. Fax: 03 22 29 39 43. E-mail: camping.caravaning@free.fr.
**Reservations:** Contact site for details. **Open** 29 March - 5 November.

**Directions:** At Nampont St Martin turn off the N1 on to the D85E (site is signed), towards Fresne, site is on right after about 3 km.

## Northern France
## Camping Municipal Le Bois des Pêcheurs

**8008M** route de Forges Les Eaux, 80290 Poix-de-Picardie

In an area where good municipal sites are hard to find, the municipal site at Poix-de-Picardie is excellent for a one night stop, or even a few days to explore the region. The 135 pitches are on level, neatly mown grass, either individual or in hedged bays of four. Half the pitches at one end are often occupied by long stay or holiday groups, leaving the other half for tourists, with electricity (10A) available to most. The city of Amiens (28 km.) is worth visiting for its famous cathedral and quayside market (Thursday and Saturday) in the old, restored St Leu quarter.

**Facilities:** The well maintained, central toilet unit includes some washbasins in cubicles Two separate rooms provide ample dishwashing and laundry sinks. Washing machine and dryer. Camping gaz stocked. Small children's playground. Volleyball, boules and table tennis. TV room. Caravan storage. **Off site:** Fishing 1 km. Supermarket 200 m, other shops, services and swimming pool in Poix de Picardie approx. 1.5 km.

**Charges** 2002

| | |
|---|---|
| Per unit incl. 1 or 2 adults | € 10.00 |
| extra adult | € 2.00 |
| child under 12 yrs | € 1.50 |
| electricity | € 4.00 |
| dog | € 1.30 |

No credit cards. **Tel:** 03 22 90 11 71. E-mail: mairie@ville-poix-de-picardie.tr. **Reservations:** Write for details. **Open** 1 April - 30 September.

**Directions:** Site is southwest of the town on the D919 road, and is signed from the D901 Grandvilliers road.

## Northern France
## Camping du Port de Plaisance

**8003** route de Paris, 80200 Péronne

Run by a non-profit making association under the auspices of the Chamber of Commerce, this is a good quality site. Formerly a municipal site, it is informally laid out beside the Canal du Nord on the outskirts of the small town of Peronne, on the river Somme. The associations with the Great War (including a museum) are strong and the WW1 battlefields and cemeteries are numerous in this area. Only some two or three hours drive from the Channel ports and Tunnel, Peronne is convenient for overnight stops en-route to or from destinations further south or east. The site itself is attractive, being surrounded by trees, with 90 marked pitches (87 have 6/10A electricity hook-up) of varying shapes and sizes on mainly level grass, some being seasonal. An attractive heated swimming pool is open when the weather is suitable.

**Facilities:** The modernised toilet block is kept spotlessly clean, well maintained and heated in winter. Excellent provision for people with disabilities. Laundry area with washing machine and dryer. Motorcaravan service point. New reception building includes a small shop, bar and TV room (bread orders are taken). Children's play area. Fishing. **Off site:** Bicycle hire 2 km. Riding 10 km.

**Charges** 2003

| | |
|---|---|
| Per unit incl. 1-3 persons | € 12.20 - € 15.50 |
| extra person | € 3.00 - € 3.80 |
| child under 7 yrs | free |
| electricity 6A | € 3.00 - € 3.70 |
| electricity 10A | € 5.50 - € 6.50 |
| dog | € 0.70 - € 0.90 |

**Tel:** 03 22 84 19 31. **Fax:** 03 22 73 36 37.
**Reservations:** May be necessary in main season; contact site. **Open** all year.

**Directions:** From north and the ferries, on the A1 autoroute, take exit 14 and follow N17 south to Peronne. Take signs for town centre and continue through watching out for camp signs. Pass over river Somme and Canal du Nord and site is on right just past garage at Porte du Plaisance (2 km. from town centre). From south use exit 13 and follow RN29 to Villers Carbonnel to pick up the N17 going north. Look for signs on left.

**Camping du Port de Plaisance**

★ ★ ★

Route de Paris
80200 Péronne
Tel: 0033 322 84 19 31
Fax: 0033 322 73 36 37
Website: camping-plaisance.com
E-mail: contact@camping-plaisance.com

Picardie

# Paris/Ile de France

Map 3

Major cities: Paris, Versailles, Ivry, Melun, Nanterre, Bobigny, Creteil, Pontoise

Départements: 75 Paris, 77 Seine-et-Marne, 78 Yvelines, 91 Essone, 92 Hauts-de-Seine, 93 Seine-St-Denis, 94 Val de Marne, 95 Val d'Oise

How many millions of words have been written about Paris? Quite simply, it is a marvellous place of infinite variety - the list of things to do is virtually endless and could easily fill many holidays - window shopping, the Eiffel Tower, Montmartre, the Louvre, trips on the Seine, pavement cafés, the Moulin Rouge, etc, etc! Both the bus and Metro systems are excellent, efficient and reasonably priced, so there is no need to take your car into the centre. The history, customs and language of the Ile-de-France region have merged with those of Paris, and spread throughout the whole country. The destiny of France was played out in the Ile-de-France, in the magnificent castles of Fontainebleau, Compiègne, Provins, Saint-Germain and Versailles. This `garden of kings' is in fact made up of many smaller regions whose names - Valois, Beauvaisis, Vexin, Brie, Gatinais, Hurepoix - irresistibly evoke royal banners and the pageantry of past years. Square bell towers in gentle valleys, white silos on endless plains of wheat: subtle and harmonious landscapes painted and praised by Racine, La Fontaine, Corot and all the landscape painters. Paris is surrounded by forests: Fontainebleau, Compiègne, Saint-Germain-en-Laye, which attract Parisians in their thousands every weekend.
Note: site reports are laid out by département in numerical order.

## Cuisine of the region

Although without a specific cuisine of its own, Paris and Ile de France offer a wide selection of dishes from all the regions of France. Paris also has a wide choice of foreign restaurants, such as Vietnamese and North African.

## Places of interest

*Paris* – the list of places to visit is too extensive to include here – the city is the subject of innumerable guide books!

*Auvers-sur-Oise* – Van Gogh museum

*Fontainebleau* – château and national museum, history of Napoléon from 1804-1815

*Malmaison* – château and museum devoted to the story of Napoléon and Joséphine

*Meaux* – agricultural centre, Gothic cathedral, chapter house and palace

*Rambouillet* – château and park with national sheep farm and Queen's Dairy

*St Denis* – basilica, Funeral Art museum, tombs of the Kings of France

*St Germain-en-Laye* – château, Gallo-roman and Merovingian archeological museum.

*Sèvres* – ceramics museum, history of fine china and pottery

*Versailles* – the most famous Royal Castle in the world, Royal Apartments, Hall of Mirrors, Chapel, Royal Opera and French History Museum. Park with statues, fountains, the Grand Trianon, the Petit Trianon, the Temple of Love

*Vincennes* – château (fortified castle) and museum

## Leisure Parks

*Parc Astérix* (April-October) – Discover the world of the Gauls with Astérix and Obélix.

*Disneyland Paris* – the 'magic kingdom'. Discover the Mysteries of the Nautilus, experience Space Mountain, and much more

*France Miniature* (April-October) 150 historic monuments, 20 typical villages, countryside, scenes from everyday life.

*Mer de Sable* (April-September) – a page out of the history of the American West.

*Saint-Vrain* (April-October) – A prehistoric world with wild animals. Boat-safari.

*Thoiry* – château and Parc Zoologique, 450-hectare park with gardens and African reserve containing 800 animals

## Camping du Bois de Boulogne

**7502** 2 allée du Bord de l'eau, 75016 Paris

A busy site and the nearest to the city, this site is set in a wooded area between the Seine and the Bois de Boulogne. One can reach the Champs Elysees in 10-15 minutes by car or, from April to Oct, a shuttle bus runs from the site to the Metro station. The site is quite extensive but nevertheless becomes very full with many international visitors of all ages. There are 510 pitches (including mobile homes and a few chalets) of which 280 are marked, with electricity (10A), water, drainage and TV aerial connections. At the entrance is a functional, modern reception building (open 24 hrs) with a card operated barrier system. The site has undergone a huge improvement and re-development programme including the replacement of all toilet blocks. Reservations are made for the pitches - if not booked, arrive early in season (morning). Note: you are in a major city environment - take care of valuables.

**Facilities:** All toilet blocks have British and Turkish style WCs, washbasins in cubicles and showers with divider and seat with hot water throughout. All these facilities suffer from heavy use in season. Washing machines and dryers. Motorcaravan service point. Mini-market. Bar and snack bar (1/4-15/10). Bar open 7 am. - midnight at most times and until 2 am. in peak season. Children's playground. **Off site:** Organised excursions (July/Aug). Fishing 1 km, bicycle hire 2 km. Ticket sales for Disneyland, Asterix Parc, etc.

**Charges** guide

| Per unit incl. 2 persons, | |
|---|---|
| electricity, water and drainage | € 21.00 - € 26.00 |
| without services | € 16.50 - € 22.25 |
| tent incl. 2 persons | € 10.50 - € 13.50 |
| extra adult | € 5.00 |
| child (under 7 yrs) | € 2.60 |
| dog | € 2.00 - € 2.30 |
| local tax | € 0.15 |

**Tel:** 01 45 24 30 00. Fax: 01 42 24 42 95. E-mail: resa@mobilhome-paris.com. **Reservations:** Contact site. **Open** all year.

**Directions:** Site is on east side of Seine between the river and the Bois de Boulogne, just north of the Pont de Suresnes. Easiest approach is from Port Maillot, watch for traffic lights at site entrance. Follow signs closely and use a good map.

## Davy Crockett Ranch

**7701** BP 117, 77777 Marne-la-Vallée

The Paris Disneyland has its own campsite with an excellent indoor pool attractively planned like a Western movie set. Most sectors of the site contain log cabins (558) which are well equipped and quite attractively priced, but one sector, the Moccasin Trail, provides 60 numbered touring pitches. Each consists of a long, narrow hardstanding with a roughly 25 sq.m. sand-topped tent area at the far end (awnings are not therefore possible). Each place has an individual electric point, water supply and drain, a large picnic table and a robust iron barbecue. and is separated from the next by an area of small trees and shrubs and the whole site is well endowed with tall trees for shade This sector is furthest away (400m walk) from the main complex with the leisure facilities, but a small 'train' provides a useful way to get round the site. Connection with the Magic Kingdom is via the autoroute taking ten minutes (with free car parking at Disneyland for campers). There may be cheaper sites within range of Disneyland, but this one may offer you the Disney magic throughout your stay, although it can be somewhat impersonal with a heavy turnover of staff. The site is also eminently suitable for visits to that other magic city, Paris, only 35 km. away by autoroute or train. The site may be noisy with vehicles returning from the late evening shows (possibly also some noise from aircraft or the autoroute).

**Facilities:** The modern, heated toilet block is of ample proportions and contains every facility, including washing machines and dryers (free). Maintenance can be variable. In the main season the facilities may be under pressure with queuing, for example, in the early mornings. Shop providing a rather wider choice of Disney souvenirs than food, but all the basic requirements can be obtained. Self-service restaurant offering both French and American style food. Large leisure pool, with flume and jacuzzis (closed 15/5-19/5) inside a huge log cabin that opens onto a terrace overlooking 'Indian Meadows' ,a large field with adventure play equipment, archery, beach volleyball and basketball. Small animal enclosures and pony rides. Bicycle hire on daily or hourly basis. Good covered tennis court and half court. Dogs are not accepted. **Off site:** Disneyland 10 mins, Paris 35 km. Supermarkets near.

**Charges** guide

| Per pitch, all inclusive | € 46.00 - € 68.50 |
|---|---|
| local tax | € 0.23 - € 0.46 |

**Tel:** 01 60 45 69 00. Fax: 03 60 45 69 33. **Reservations:** For information and reservations phone 0990 030303 (UK). In high season you must reserve well in advance and be prepared for queues in reception. **Open** 1 April - 30 September, plus 20 Dec - 5 Jan.

**Directions:** From Paris take A4 eastwards following signs for Metz/Nancy. For Disneyland itself take exit 14, but for the Davy Crockett Ranch, turn right at exit 13. From Calais, follow Paris signs until just before Charles de Gaulle airport, then follow signs to Marne la Vallée - eventually you join the A4.

## Paris / Ile de France
# Camping International de Jablines
Base de Loisirs, 77450 Jablines

Redesigned in 1997, Jablines replaces an older site in an upmarket, modern style which, with the accompanying leisure facilities of the adjacent 'Espace Loisirs', provides an interesting, if a little impersonal alternative to other sites in the region. The whole complex close to the Marne has been developed around old gravel workings. Man-made lakes provide marvellous water activities - dinghy sailing, windsurfing, canoeing, fishing and supervised bathing, plus a large equestrian centre. In season the activities at the leisure complex are supplemented by a bar/restaurant and a range of very French style group activities. The 'Great Lake' as it is called, is said to have the largest beach on the Ile-de-France! The site itself provides 150 pitches, all of a good size with gravel hardstanding and grass, accessed by tarmac roads and clearly marked by fencing panels and newly planted shrubs. All have 10A electricity, nearly half water and waste connections.

**Facilities:** Two identical toilet blocks, heated in cool weather, are solidly built and well equipped. They include some washbasins in cubicles, indoor dishwashing and laundry facilities with washing machine and dryer. Motorcaravan service (charged). Shop (high season). Play area. Bar/restaurant adjacent at leisure centre/lake complex along with a range of watersports including 'water cable ski', and riding activities. Whilst staying on the site, admission to the leisure complex is free. Internet point. Ticket sales for Disneyland, Asterix and Sea Life.

**Charges** 2003

| Per standard pitch incl. 2 persons | |
|---|---|
| and 10A electricity | € 17.50 - € 20.00 |
| pitch incl. water and waste | € 18.50 - € 21.00 |
| extra person | € 4.50 - € 5.00 |
| child (under 12 yrs) | € 3.00 - € 3.50 |
| dog | € 1.00 |

**Tel:** 01 60 26 09 37. **Fax:** 01 60 26 43 33. **E-mail:** Jablines@free.fr. **Reservations:** Essential for July/Aug. and made with booking form from site and 30% deposit. **Open** 28 March - 2 November.

**Directions:** From A4 Paris - Reims autoroute take A104 north before Disneyland. From the A1 going south, follow signs for Disneyland immediately after Charles de Gaulle airport using the A104. Take exit 8 off the A104 and follow D404 and signs to Base de Loisirs Jablines (8 km). At park entry péage go to campsite lane.

Base Régionale de Plein-Air et de Loisirs de Jablines-Annet

Covering more than 450 hectares, a leisure and relaxation area unique in the Île de France.

77450 Jablines
Tel: 0033 160 26 09 37
Fax: 0033 160 26 43 33

L'espace loisirs

Camping ★★★

## Paris / Ile de France
# Caravaning des 4 Vents
77610 Crévecoeur-en-Brie

This peaceful, pleasant site has been owned and run by the same family for over 35 years and is within easy reach of Disneyland. There are around 200 pitches, with many permanent or seasonal units, however, there are 130 spacious grassy pitches for tourists, well separated by good hedges, all with 6A electricity and most with a water tap. The site is well landscaped with flowers and trees. This is a great family site with undercover and outdoor facilities and a superb swimming pool - at the top end of the site so that campers are not disturbed. Disneyland is an easy run up the D231 and then one intersection on the A4 (less than 16 km). Central Paris is just a 40 minute train ride from the nearest railway station (8 km).

**Facilities:** Three modern sanitary units provide a good number of British style WCs but rather fewer washbasins. Facilities for disabled people. Washing machine and dryer. Good motorcaravan service point. In July/Aug. a mobile snack bar and pizzeria visit, and a baker calls in the mornings. Well fenced, circular swimming pool (16 m. diameter) open 09.00-21.00 hrs. June to Sept. Excellent playground, large games room, volleyball, billiard hall and boules court. **Off site:** La Houssaye 1 km. Fontenay 5 km.

**Charges** 2002

| Per unit incl. 2 adults and electricity | € 21.00 |
|---|---|
| extra person | € 4.00 |
| child (under 5 yrs) | free |

**Tel:** 01 64 07 41 11. **Fax:** 01 64 07 45 07. **E-mail:** f.george@free.fr. **Reservations:** Essential for July/Aug. **Open** 1 March - 1 December.

**Directions:** From A4 exit 13, take D231 towards Provins for about 12 km. After passing a large obelisk turn right at signs to Crevecoeur and follow signs to site. Site is on western side of village.

## Paris / Ile de France
# Camping Municipal Les Prés
**7708M** 77880 Grez sur Loing

A typical municipal site, Les Prés has 136 grassy pitches and a fair number of long stay units. However, there are usually around 35 pitches available for tourists, all with 5A electricity hook-ups. The town of Grez sur Loing dates back to medieval times and is well worth investigating. The site makes an ideal base for fishing, cycling (the warden can provide a booklet with five suggested routes - in French, of course), walking and rock climbing in Fontainebleau.

**Facilities:** A two storey building has separate male and female facilities on the upper level, and unisex facilities at ground level. British and Turkish style toilets, dishwashing and laundry facilities, Excellent suite for disabled people. Small shop and limited takeaway (pizza and chips, 15/3-11/11). **Off site:** Golf 10 km. Riding 5 km. Bicycle hire 200 m.

**Charges** 2002

| | |
|---|---|
| Per adult | € 2.35 |
| child (3-11 yrs) | € 1.75 |
| pitch | € 3.95 - 5.40 |

**Tel:** 01 64 45 72 75. Fax: 01 64 45 72 75.
**Reservations:** Advised for July/Aug; contact site.
**Open** 15 March - 11 November.

**Directions:** Grez sur Loing is northwest of Nemours and south of Fontainebleau. From N7 north of town, turn at roundabout on D40D towards Montcourt, cross river bridge and almost immediately turn right (signed). Note: site access road is one-way. From south, continue on N7 until roundabout and follow directions above. Do not follow site signs south of village as the roads are too narrow for most units.

## Paris / Ile de France
# Camping La Belle Etoile
**7707** Quai Joffre, La Rochette, 77000 Melun

Ideally situated for visiting Fontainebleau and Paris, and alongside the River Seine, this site has an overall mature and neat appearance, although the approach road along the banks of the river is somewhat off putting with several industrial plants. Continue past this point and you discover that La Belle Etoile enjoys a pleasant position with pitches to the fore of the site within view of the barges which continually pass up and down the Seine. This is a friendly, family run site with English speaking owners who are pleasant and helpful. The 186 touring pitches, with electricity connections (6A), are on grass and laid out between the many shrubs and trees. There are no mobile homes or seasonal units.

**Facilities:** What lets this site down are the less than modern sanitary facilities. However, despite their age they are kept clean. Laundry room. Baby bath. Facilities for people with disabilities (shower, washbasin and WC). Motorcaravan service point. Small bar, snacks and limited shop (all high season). Swimming pool. Play area. **Off site:** Fontainebleau is a short drive and Paris easily accessible by train.

**Charges** 2003

| | |
|---|---|
| Per unit | € 4.20 - € 4.70 |
| adult | € 4.15 - € 4.65 |
| child (1-11 yrs) | € 1.90 - € 2.90 |
| electricity (6A) | € 2.90 - € 3.00 |

**Tel:** (0)1 64 39 48 12. Fax: (0)1 64 37 25 55. E-mail: info@camp-la-belle-etoile.com. **Reservations:** Made for min. 3 nights. **Open** 1 April - 31 October.

**Directions:** Travelling north on N6 Fontainebleau - Melun road, on entering La Rochette, pass Total petrol station on left and turn immediately right into Ave de la Seine. Continue to end of road and turn left at river, site on left in approx. 500 m.

## Paris / Ile de France
# Camping Domaine d'Inchelin
**7803** St Illiers la Ville, 78980 Bréval

Domaine d'Inchelin is in a village location, set in rolling countryside within easy reach of Paris and Versailles. It is an attractive site which has been developed around charming old farm buildings. The 150 pitches (50 for tourers) are large (250 sq.m.) and arranged amongst ornamental trees and shrubs, with well kept hedges. All have electricity (4/6A). Peacocks (rather noisy in spring!) and other tame birds parade the site and roost in the trees. The facilities are neatly arranged in the timbered buildings surrounding three sides of the old farmyard, with an attractive, sheltered swimming pool lying in the centre. Used by tour operators (50 pitches). A 'Sites et Paysages' member.

**Facilities:** Main sanitary facilities are split into two areas on opposite sides of the courtyard - one room with toilets, the other with spacious showers, washbasins in cabins, dishwashing and laundry facilities. Separate unit for disabled visitors. An additional block at the rear of the site is open mid-June - Sept. Small shop, bar (both May - Sept). Swimming pool. Covered play area and two playgrounds.

**Charges** guide

| | |
|---|---|
| Per adult | € 13.00 |
| child (4-12 yrs) | € 6.00 |
| dog | € 1.50 |
| electricity 4A/6A | € 4.50 - € 7.00 |

**Tel:** 01 34 76 10 11. **Reservations:** Contact site for details. **Open** 1 April - 15 October.

**Directions:** From A13 autoroute take Chaufour exit (15) onto N13. Turn off within 1 km. and left at traffic lights into Chaufour. Take D52 to Lommoye, through village then fork left via D89 to St Illiers la Ville. Take Bréval road and site is on the left.

# Camping-Caravaning International

**7801** 1 rue Johnson, 78600 Maisons-Laffitte

the **travel service**
TO BOOK
Ferry ☑
Pitch ☑
Accommodation ☑
01892 55 98 98

This busy, all year site on the banks of the Seine is convenient for Paris. Maisons-Laffitte is a pleasant suburb with a château, a racecourse and some large training stables. There is also a good train service to the centre of Paris, including an express service, to the Gare St Lazare. The site has multilingual and friendly reception staff and occupies a grassy, tree covered area bordering the river. There are 350 pitches, 57 occupied by mobile homes and 90 used by tour operators, plus two areas dedicated to tents. Most pitches are separated by hedges, are of a good size with some overlooking the Seine (unfenced access), and 200 have electricity hook-ups (6/10A). The roads leading to the site are a little narrow so large vehicles need to take care. Being so close to Paris this site is consistently busy. Train noise can be expected.

**Facilities:** There are three sanitary blocks, two insulated for winter use. The third, more open in style is only opened for July/August. The facilities are clean but with the volume of visitors, constant supervision is necessary. Provision for people with disabilities. Laundry and dishwashing areas. Motorcaravan service point - jeton available at reception. Self-service shop for summer months. Restaurant/bar with takeaway food and pizzeria. TV room, table tennis, billiards and football area. Internet point. **Off site:** Sports complex adjoins the site. The station for central Paris is 10 minutes walk with trains running every 10 minutes (journey time 15-30 minutes), returning until 12.30 am. Direct rail access to Disneyland (55 minutes).

**Charges** 2002

| | |
|---|---|
| Per unit incl. 2 persons | € 18.00 - € 22.20 |
| with electricity | € 21.40 - € 24.00 |
| tent incl. 2 persons | € 11.00 - € 13.50 |
| extra adult | € 4.80 - € 5.45 |
| child (5-10 yrs) | € 2.30 - € 2.65 |
| animal | € 2.50 |
| local tax | € 0.46 |

**Tel:** 01 39 12 21 91. Fax: 01 39 12 70 50. E-mail: ci.mlaffitte@wanadoo.fr. **Reservations:** Advisable for July/Aug. and made with deposit (€ 10). **Open** all year.

**Directions:** Site is best approached from A13 or A15 autoroute. From A13 take Poissy exit and signs to Maisons-Laffitte, then site signs before town centre. From A15 take N184 exit to St Germain, for approx. 300 m. After crossing large concrete bridge turn left at traffic lights to Maisons-Laffitte and follow camp signs. From A1 take A86, then Bezons exit for Poissy, Houilles and Maisons-Laffitte.

# Camping Municipal de L'Etang d'Or

**7804M** route du Château d'Eau, 78120 Rambouillet

This is a pleasant site in a peaceful forest location, with good tarmac access roads, site lighting and 280 touring pitches. Some of the individual pitches are divided by hedges, others are more open and sunny. All have electricity (6/10A), 83 also have water and drainage, with a few hardstandings. Campers get a discount brochure for local sites or activities (e.g. the municipal swimming pool, animal park, bowling and billiards, bicycle hire), and a special permit for the fishing lake. There are many good cycle and footpaths in the area. It is possible to visit Paris by rail, the Mobilis 'transport package' ticket is available from the railway station.

**Facilities:** Two heated sanitary buildings include British and Turkish style WCs, washbasins (a few in cubicles), dishwashing and laundry sinks, plus facilities for baby changing and for disabled persons. Facilities could be a little stretched during the high season. Washing machine and dryer. One block is closed in the winter months. Motorcaravan service point (€ 1,29). Café/bar and small shop (1/4-30/9). Good children's playground. **Off site:** Large supermarket at southern end of the town.

**Charges** 2002

| | |
|---|---|
| Per adult | € 3.70 - € 4.30 |
| child (2-10 yrs) | € 2.50 - € 3.00 |
| pitch | € 4.10 - € 4.90 |
| dog | € 1.50 |
| electricity (6-10A) | € 3.00 - € 3.80 |

**Tel:** 01 30 41 07 34. Fax: 01 30 41 00 17. E-mail: rambouillet.tourisme@wanadoo.fr. **Reservations:** Contact site for details. **Open** all year.

**Directions:** Rambouillet is 52 km. southwest of Paris, midway between Versailles and Chartres. Site is southeast of town, from N10 southbound take Rambouillet / Les Eveuses exit, northbound take Rambouillet centre exit, loop round and rejoin N10 southbound, taking next exit, where site is signed.

## Camping-Caravaning Le Bois de la Justice

91930 Monnerville

La Bois du Justice is a conveniently located site close to Paris and Versailles. It is situated in a wood in the middle of farm-land with a narrow, but recently resurfaced, 1.2 km. approach road. The 150 pitches, of which 50 are for touring units, are laid out among the trees, well shaded but sloping, with 12 in a newer, open area. Electricity is available throughout. The site is accept-able as an overnight stop for touring the area southwest of Paris - Chartres; Fontainbleau and Versailles are within easy range, Paris itself is only an hours drive and Disneyland not much more.

**Facilities:** The single large toilet block can be heated. It is well appointed and clean, although it is some way from the furthest pitches. No shop, but a bread and provisions van calls morning and evening. Bar with snacks is open during the day and early evening in July/Aug. Medium sized pool (approx. 1/6-15/9). Children's playground. Open air table tennis and volleyball court. **Off site:** Shops and restaurants are in the village (3 km), or a little further in Etampes. Riding 1.5 km, fishing 7 km.

**Charges** guide

| | |
|---|---|
| Per caravan, or large tent | € 3.05 - € 4.57 |
| 2 person tent | € 1.52 - € 2.29 |
| adult | € 3.05 - € 4.57 |
| child (2-17 yrs) | € 1.52 - € 3.05 |
| car | € 1.52 - € 2.29 |
| electricity (6A) | € 2.29 |
| dog | free |

**Tel:** 01 64 95 05 34. **Fax:** 01 64 95 17 31. **Reservations:** Contact site. **Open** 1 March - 30 November.

**Directions:** Going south on the N20 (Paris-Orléans), take exit for Monnerville. Keep right over N20 into village, straight over crossroads and site is well signed.

## Parc de Séjours de L'Etang

10 chemin des Bellevues, 95690 Nesles-la-Vallée

Parc de Sejour de L'Etang is small, infor-mal site 33 km. northwest of Paris. It is situated on the southern outskirts of the village of Nesles-la-Vallée in a pretty, tree-lined river valley not far from L'Isle-Adam, which is a popular destination for Parisiens at weekends. Many of the 165 pitches are occupied by seasonal caravans but there are 65 pitches available for touring units. The site is informally arranged around a duck pond with many trees to provide shelter and shade and semi-tame rabbits competing with the ducks for food and attention. Pitches are large and flat with electricity (3/9A) available. Chantilly, Parc Asterix and Disneyland are easily reached by car. By far the best way to visit Paris is by train from Valmondois, 5 minutes away via the D15 road (trains every half hour, journey time about 50 minutes).

**Facilities:** The main, central toilet block (heated in cooler weather) is a plain substantial building includ-ing washbasins in rather small cubicles and, in sepa-rate rooms, rather older style British and Turkish WCs. Covered dishwashing and laundry sinks. Washing machine. Smaller, much older unit includes facilities for disabled people. No shop (or bread). Good playground, volleyball and basketball areas, and under cover play barn with table tennis. **Off site:** Village and restaurant within walking distance. Fishing permits for the river available in village. Riding 500 m, golf 7 km.

**Charges** 2002

| | |
|---|---|
| Per pitch | € 3.00 - € 4.00 |
| with electricity (3-9A) | € 6.50 - € 7.35 |
| person | € 3.00 - € 4.00 |
| child (1-6 yrs) | € 2.00 |
| animal | € 1.00 |

**Tel:** 01 34 70 62 89. **Fax:** 01 34 70 62 89. **E-mail:** brehinier1@hotmail.com. **Reservations:** Contact site. **Open** 1 March - 15 November.

**Directions:** From A15 exit 10 take D915 to Pontoise, then D27 to Beauais which joins the D927 and then D79 to Nesles-la-Vallée. From N1 or A16 (exit 11) take the D992 southwest towards L'isle Adam, and then D64 northwest to Neslés la Vallée. Site is on the right as you enter the village.

## ALAN ROGERS' Britain & Ireland

Camping or caravanning at home this year? Remember the Alan Rogers' Guide to Britain & Ireland

**Available from**

**all good bookshops or**

**online at www.alanrogers.com**

# Eastern France

Map 4

The area we define as Eastern France combines three of the official French Regions:

| Champagne-Ardenne | Lorraine Vosges | Alsace |
|---|---|---|
| Major City: Reims | Major Cities: Nancy, Metz | Major City: Strasbourg |
| Départements:<br>08 Ardennes, 51 Marne,<br>10 Aube, 52 Haute-Marne | Départements:<br>54 Meurth-et-Moselle,<br>55 Meuse, 57Moselle,<br>88 Vosges | Départements:<br>67 Bas-Rhin, 68 Haut-Rhin |

This north-eastern area of France has seen many European Battles. In 1871 Alsace and a large part of Lorraine were acquired by Germany under the Treaty of Frankfurt and were only restored to France in 1919; to again be back in German hands in 1940, then to be liberated for the second time five years later at the end of World War Two. Today there are many poignant reminders and a noticeable German influence in, for example, architecture, cuisine and language.

Champagne is home to the most northerly vineyards in France where special processing turns the light, dry wine into 'le Champagne' and names such as 'Moet et Chandon' and 'Veuve Clicquot' spring to mind. Nowhere else in France, or even the rest of the world, are you allowed to make champagne or, more correctly you can make bubbly wine but you cannot call it champagne.

The area is also known for the spa towns such as Vittel, Bains-les-Bains and Plombières and the birth place of St Joan of Arc at Domrémy. The Vosges crests formed part of the World War One battle front and military requirements dictated the building of the road now known as the Route des Cretes which links these natural ramparts, taking in the major peaks of Hohneck and Grand Ballon. Today you can descend from the mountains into the Alsace vineyards and fairy tale wine villages. The 'Route des Vins' follows the vineyards along the Rhine valley from Mulhouse to Colmar and north almost to Strasbourg.

Note: the site reports are laid out by département in numerical order not by region.

## Cuisine of the region

Quiche Lorraine – made only in the classical manner with cream, eggs and bacon.
Potage Lorraine – potato. leek and onion soup
Tart (aux mirabelles) – golden plum tart. Also made with other fruits
Tarte a l' oignon Alsacienne – onion and cream tart

## Places of Interest

Épernay – the real capital of champagne – the drink. Here 72 miles of underground galleries in the chalk beneath the city store the wine for the delicate operations required to make the champagne. It was near by in the Abbey of Hautvillers that the blind Dom Perignon discovered how to put in the bubbles and keep them there

Le Linge – a football pitch-sized hilltop where in 1915, 17,000 French and German soldiers lost their lives. The opposing trenches including rusty barbed wire have been left as they were – a poignant reminder of the pain and futility of war

Reims – in 496, Clovis, the first king of France, was baptised in the cathedral and the Kings of France from Louis VII to Charles X were crowned in the city. The 13th century Gothic cathedral is a masterpiece

Riquewihr – almost untouched since the 18th century, whilst virtually every other village was decimated by war; 13/14th century fortifications and many medieval houses and courtyards

Verdun – some of the most savage fighting of World War 1 took place north of Verdun and the town is a centre for touring the battlefields and hill forts such as Fort de Vaux and Fort de Douaumont. There is also a large military cemetery at Douaumont.

## Eastern France
# Camping Municipal du Mont Olympe

rue des Paquis, 08000 Charleville-Mezieres

Attractively situated alongside the Meuse River, within easy walking distance across a footbridge to the centre of the pleasant large town, this site has been completely rebuilt in 2001/2, just a short distance from the old one. It now offers excellent facilities, with 72 grass pitches (increasing to 126), all with electricity (10A), water and waste water connections, 66 will be from 108 to 219 sq. metres, 48 up to 106 sq. metres and 12 smaller pitches especially for camping-cars.

**Facilities:** Heated buildings provide first class showers, private cabins, baby rooms and facilities for the disabled, plus inside dishwashing (including one for the disabled) and a well-equipped laundry room. TV and games room. **Off site:** Municipal pool next door. River boat trips. Attractive town centre close by.

**Charges** 2002

| | |
|---|---|
| Per person | € 3.00 |
| child (2-7 yrs) | € 1.50 |
| pitch and vehicle | € 4.50 - € 5.50 |
| motorcaravan overnight | € 10.00 |
| dog | € 1.35 |
| electricity (6/10A) | € 2.50 - € 3.50 |

**Tel:** 03 24 33 23 60. **Reservations:** Contact site. **Open** 15 May - 15 October.

**Directions:** Site is north of Charleville on the island of Montcy St Pierre and is signed from the city centre `Mont Olympe`. From the north D988/D1 follow the river, over the bridge, then immediately left. From the southeast (A203/N51/N43) take `centre` exit, head for `Gare` then follow Avenue Forest north and sharp left after the bridge.

## Eastern France
# Camping Départmental du Lac des Vieilles-Forges

Base de Loisirs Départemental, 08500 Les Mazures

An attractive lakeside site, a short way from the N43 and with a large range of facilities and activities, du Lac provides 300 large pitches (260 for tourers). They are all on individual gravel hardstandings (not suitable for tents), arranged on several terraces, but easily accessible via tarmac approach roads. Attractively arranged, the pitches have ample shade from a variety of trees and shrubs and all have electricity (3-10A). The site is set only 100 m. or so back from the large lake which offers a large variety of watersports, and its somewhat remote location is approached by a road which forms part of the Route des Fortifications.

**Facilities:** Four purpose built toilet blocks provide modern facilities with washbasins in private cabins, children's toilet, washing machines, dryers, etc. Freezer. TV room. Tennis, table tennis. Lake swimming (supervised July/Aug). Fishing. Sailing, windsurfing, and canoeing. Bicycle hire.

**Charges** guide

| | |
|---|---|
| Per person | € 2.74 |
| child (under 7 yrs) | € 1.37 |
| pitch | € 1.50 - € 3.00 |
| electricity 3/5A | € 1.83 - € 2.32 |
| dog | € 0.85 |

**Tel:** 03 24 40 17 31. **Reservations:** Not normally made or necessary, but if in doubt phone. **Open** all year.

**Directions:** From N43, 11 km. northwest of Charleville-Mézières and just east of Lonny, take the D988 north in the direction of Revin for approx. 8 km. The lake is signed on the left - follow the lake side road to the site; a one way system operates in high season.

## Eastern France
# Camping Départmental du Lac de Bairon

08390 Le Chesne

This modern lakeside campsite is in the heart of the French Ardennes, an area with relatively few good quality sites. Terraced on three levels, it has 172 pitches (150 for touring) which are generally arranged in bays for about six units, with waste bins and water taps by each area. All pitches have electricity (6/10A), and around 83 have gravel hardstanding. The terracing gives a real feeling of spaciousness and a line of tall trees running the length of the site supplies some shade. The lake beach and supervised swimming area are 800 m. drive or rather less by footpath. The site can be very busy at weekends or public holidays. There is no restaurant or shop on site, but Le Chesne is only about 3 km.

**Facilities:** Four modern toilet units, one heated in winter, include washbasins in cubicles. Dishwashing and laundry facilities, with washing machines and dryers. Facilities for disabled people at two units. Bar/snack bar (July/Aug). Bread van drives around the site each morning. Small playground with two adventure style units for 3-6 yrs and 4-12 yrs. Tennis. Table tennis, volleyball and boules. Canoe, kayak and bicycle hire. Fishing. **Off site:** Restaurant/bar 800 m. Lake with picnic areas and beach.

**Charges** guide

| | |
|---|---|
| Per adult | € 2.44 |
| child (under 7 yrs) | € 1.22 |
| pitch | € 2.60 |
| electricity (3-10A) | € 1.83 - € 3.96 |

**Tel:** 03 24 30 11 66. **Reservations:** Advisable for high season. Open all year.

**Directions:** From Le Chesne take D991 northwards for approx. 500 m, then turn right on to D212. Follow signs to site. Note: a bridge on the access road has a weight limit of 3500 kg.

# Eastern France
## Camping La Samaritaine

08240 Buzancy

**0804**

the **travel service**
TO BOOK
| Ferry | ☑ |
| Pitch | ☑ |
| Accommodation | ✗ |

01892 55 98 98

What a surprise and a pleasure it was to arrive at such a delightful new site in the heart of the Ardennes. It is peacefully situated just outside the village beside a stream, although there may be some high season noise from the nearby lake where you can swim or fish. Flowers decorate the entrance and bushes and saplings have been planted to separate the pitches, although there is not much shade at present. The 110 numbered touring pitches all have electricity (10A) and are on level grass off hard access roads. They vary in size up to 130 sq.m. 55 have water and waste water, and there are attractive small wooden containers for waste.

**Facilities:** A new building houses first class sanitary facilities, with private cabins, facilities for disabled people, washing machine and dryer,and dishwashing sinks. Large recreation room with tables. Table tennis. Bread collected daily. A few essentials kept in reception. Snack bar/takeaway (mid May - end Sept). High season accompanied walks and entertainment programme. **Off site:** Lake swimming supervised at certain times (2 m. deep). Restaurant in village.

**Charges** 2002
| | |
|---|---|
| Per pitch | € 7.00 - € 9.00 |
| electricity (10A) | € 3.00 |
| adult | € 3.00 - € 4.00 |
| child (under 10 yrs) | € 2.00 - € 3.00 |

**Tel:** 03 24 30 08 88. Fax: 03 24 30 29 39. **Reservations:** Contact site. **Open** 21 March - 29 September.

**Directions:** The village of Buzancy is about 22 km. east of Vouziers on the RD947 towards Stenay and Montmédy. Site is just over 1 km. from the centre of the village down a small road, well signed.

---

# Eastern France
## Camping Municipal Châlons-sur-Marne

rue de Plaisance, 51000 Châlons-en-Champagne

**5102M**

the **travel service**
TO BOOK
| Ferry | ☑ |
| Pitch | ☑ |
| Accommodation | ✗ |

01892 55 98 98

The location of Châlons, south of Reims and near both the A4 and A26 autoroutes, about 200 miles from Calais and Boulogne, make this an ideal stopover. It is also ideally situated for exploring this famous region in the plain of the River Marne and its historical connections. This site on the southwest edge of town is an example of a good municipal site. The wide entrance with its well tended appearance of neatly mown grass and flower beds sets the tone for the rest of the site. About half of the 130 pitches, accessed from hard roads, are on a gravel base with the rest on grass. Most have electricity (10/15A). The generously sized gravel pitches are separated by hedges and each group of four shares a water tap and drain. Trees abound although there is no shade in some parts.

**Facilities:** The two toilet blocks, one behind reception, the other at the far end of the site, have been refurbished. Sections of these facilities are of varying standards due to an ongoing programme of refurbishment. Some washbasins in cabins, facilities for disabled visitors, plus a washing machine and dryer. Bread to order. Snack bar. Games and TV rooms. Playground. Tennis, table tennis, volleyball, boules and place for mini-football. **Off site:** Fishing (free for campers) near. Bus stop at entrance.

**Charges** 2002
| | |
|---|---|
| Per person | € 4.00 |
| child (under 7) | € 1.65 |
| pitch and vehicle | € 7.05 |
| electricity | € 2.95 |

**Tel:** 03 26 68 38 00. Fax: 03 26 68 38 00. E-mail: camping.mairie.chalons@wnadoo.fr. **Reservations:** Write to site. **Open** 30 March - 31 October.

**Directions:** From north on the A4, take La Veuve exit (27) onto N44 which by-passes the town. Leave at last exit signed St Memmie and follow camp signs. From south on A26, take exit 28 on N77 and, head towards town. Site is well signed 'Camping'.

---

# Eastern France
## Camping de la Presqu'ile de Champaubert

52290 Braucourt-Eclaron

**5201M**

This is a good municipal site of the type found all over France. It is situated beside what is said to be the largest man-made inland lake in Europe (4,800 ha.), the Lac du Der Chantecoq. This provides superb facilities for windsurfing, sailing, etc. and even for swimming from a 100 m. beach alongside the site (lifeguard in main season). The site itself is situated on the shores of the lake, with 195 fairly level grassy pitches of a good size, mostly with electrical connections (10A). They are separated by hedges and trees that also provide a fair amount of shade. The general appearance and the views across the lake are very attractive.

**Facilities:** Toilet facilities in two modern blocks are fully equipped and of a good standard with individual small buildings for WCs. Washbasins are in cabins. Dishwashing and laundry facilities. Motorcaravan service point. Small shop for essentials in the reception area. Bar and snack service in the main season.

**Charges** 2002
| | |
|---|---|
| Per unit incl. 2 persons | € 16.00 |
| extra person | € 4.30 |
| child (under 7 yrs) | € 2.15 |
| electricity | € 3.80 |
| dog | € 0.80 |
| local tax | € 0.15 |

**Tel:** 03 25 04 13 20. Fax: 03 25 94 33 51. E-mail: lac-du-der@wanadoo.fr. **Reservations:** Required for high season - write to site with deposit (€ 54). **Open** 15 April - 30 September.

**Directions:** From St Dizier, take D384 past Eclaron to Braucourt and follow camp signs to site (3 km).

## Eastern France
# Castel Camping La Forge de Sainte Marie
52230 Thonnance-les-Moulins

The département of Haute-Marne is situated between the better known areas of Champagne and the Vosges. It is a sleepy land of rolling hills, forests and farmland. In the heart of this lies Thonnance-les-Moulins, 12 km. east of Joinville and the north-south N67 main road between St Dizier and Chaumont. In 1994 the dilapidated old forge buildings and the surrounding 40,000 sq.m. were transformed into a most attractive campsite. As soon as one enters through the arched gateway, one is impressed by the setting. A picturesque bridge links the upper part of the site with a lower road going to the section near the river. Opposite reception, another old building has been skilfully converted into apartments for letting. Grass pitches, 115 for touring units, are of a generous size on terraces amongst the trees or in more open areas. Electricity (6A) and water are available and some pitches are fully serviced. There is much of interest in the area - Joan d'Arc and General de Gaulle lived near and it is not too far to the Champagne vineyards and cellars at Reims. Nigloland for the children is within range and Joinville is worth exploring. There is a high proportion of mobile homes and tour operators but the enthusiastic British and Dutch managers are determined to make a success of the site.

**Facilities:** There are two modern sanitary blocks. Maintenance may not be so good in early or late season. Shop and excellent restaurant (both 15/5-15/9). Splendid heated indoor pool with a smaller one for children. Four play areas imaginatively placed around the site. Level open grass area for football and volleyball. Bicycle hire. Free fishing. Games room. Organized games for children in high season. Varied programme for adults including a farm visit by tractor with a barbecue, music, dancing and excursions.

**Charges** 2002

| | |
|---|---|
| Per pitch incl. 2 persons | € 14.00 - € 25.00 |
| extra person | € 3.00 - € 6.00 |
| child 2-7 yrs | € 1.50 - € 3.00 |
| animal | free |
| local tax | € 0.22 |

**Tel:** 03 25 94 42 00. Fax: 03 25 94 41 43. E-mail: la.forge.de.sainte.marie@wanadoo.fr. **Reservations:** Contact site for details. **Open** 24 April - 29 September.

**Directions:** Site is about 12 km. southeast of Joinville between Poissons and Germay on road D427. The site entrance may be a little tight for large units.

## Eastern France
# Camping Le Brabois
avenue Paul Muller, 54600 Villers les Nancy

This former municipal site, within the Nancy city boundary and 5 km. from the centre, was taken over by the Campeole group in 1998. Situated within a forest area, there is shade in most parts and, although the site is on a slight slope, the 190 good-sized, numbered and separated pitches are level. Of these, 160 pitches have electrical connections (5/15A) and 30 also have water and drainage. Being on one of the main routes from Luxembourg to the south of France, Le Brabois makes a good night stop. However, Nancy is a delightful city in the heart of Lorraine and well worth a longer stay, not only for the interesting 18th century Place Stanislas and 11th century city centre, but for the many other attractions of the area. The British manager has a wide range of tourist literature, publishes a monthly English newsletter and is pleased to help plan visits and day trips. Horse racing takes place every two weeks at the Nancy race track next to the campsite, and good wine is produced nearby

**Facilities:** : Six sanitary blocks spread around the site are old and in need of refurbishment. They have a mix of British and Turkish style WCs and some washbasins in cubicles. One block can be heated in cool weather. Two units for disabled visitors. Small shop (all season). Restaurant incorporating bar and small shop (15/6-31/8). Small library for book exchange. Playground for young children. Area for ball games and table tennis under cover. **Off site:** Restaurants and shops about 1 km. Excellent walks and cycle rides. Buses to Nancy every 15 minutes.

**Charges** 2002

| | |
|---|---|
| Per unit incl. 2 persons | € 8.84 - € 9.60 |
| hiker | € 5.34 - € 6.10 |
| extra adult | € 3.05 |
| child (2-7 yrs) | € 1.52 |
| dog | € 1.52 |
| electricity | € 2.74 |

**Tel:** 03 83 27 18 28. Fax: 03 83 40 06 43. E-mail: campeoles.brabois@wanadoo.fr. **Reservations:** Advised for July but site say no-one is turned away. **Open** 1 April - 15 October.

**Directions:** Take exit 2b 'Brabois' from autoroute A33, continue for about 500 m. to 'Quick' restaurant on left. Turn left here, pass the racetrack to T-junction, turn right and after about 400 m. turn right on to site entrance road.

## Camping Lac de la Liez

**5203** Peigney, 52200 Langres

Managed by the enthusiastic Baude family, this newly renovated lakeside site is near the city of Langres. With its old ramparts and ancient city centre, Langres was elected one of the 50 most historic cities in France. Situated only 10 minutes from the A5, Camping Des Lacs provides an ideal spot for an overnight stay en-route to the south of France. There is also a lot on offer for a longer stay, including the lake and an indoor pool complex. The site provides 135 fully serviced, terraced pitches with panoramic views of the 500 acre lake. There is direct access to the lake for swimming with a sandy beach and a harbour where boats and pedaloes may be hired.

**Facilities:** Three brand new toilet blocks have all facilities in cabins. Shop, bar and restaurant. Indoor pool complex with spa and sauna, Extensive children's games area and tennis court. Lake with beach and boat hire.

**Charges** 2002

| | |
|---|---|
| Per pitch | € 5.00 - € 8.00 |
| person | € 4.00 - € 6.00 |
| child (under 7 yrs) | € 2.00 - € 3.00 |
| electricity | € 3.00 - € 4.00 |
| dog | € 1.50 |

**Tel:** 03 25 90 27 79. Fax: 03 25 90 66 79. E-mail: campingliez@free.fr. **Reservations:** Contact site. **Open** 14 June - 1 November.

**Directions:** From A5 use Langres north exit and follow signs.

## Camping Les Breuils

**5501** allée des Breuils, 55100 Verdun

Thousands of soldiers of many nations are buried in the cemeteries around this famous town and the city is justly proud of its determined First World War resistance. Les Breuils is a pretty site beside a small fishing lake and close to the famous town and Citadel (1 km). It provides 184 flat pitches on two levels (144 for touring units), many with shade. Separated by trees or hedges, they are beside the lake and most offer the possibility of electricity connection (5A). A small shop doubles as reception, selling essentials with various local guide books. The overall appearance of the site is attractive.

**Facilities:** Sanitary facilities, in two blocks, are a mixture of old and new, the newer parts being of a good standard, including washbasins in cabins for ladies, washing machines and dryers. Motorcaravan services. Small shop (1/5-31/8). Breakfast and evening snacks (July/Aug). Swimming pool (200 sq.m; 1/6-31/8). Large fenced play area on gravel. **Off site:** Bicycle hire 1 km, riding 5 km.

**Charges** 2002

| | |
|---|---|
| Per person | € 3.66 |
| child (under 10 yrs) | € 1.83 |
| pitch | € 2.29 - € 3.05 |
| double axle caravan | € 12.20 |
| animal | € 1.07 |
| electricity (5A) | € 3.20 |

**Tel:** 03 29 86 15 31. Fax: 03 29 86 75 76. E-mail: camping.les.breuils@wanadoo.fr. **Reservations:** Advised for high season. **Open** 1 April - 30 September.

**Directions:** The RN3 forms a sort of ring road round the north of the town. Site is signed from this on the west side of the town (500 m. to site).

## Camping Municipal de Metz-Plage

**5705M** allée de Metz-Plage, 57000 Metz

As this site is just a short way from the autoroute exit and within easy walking distance for the city centre, it could make a useful night stop if travelling from Luxembourg to Nancy or for a longer stay if exploring the area. By the Moselle river, the 145 pitches are on level grass, most are under shade from tall trees and 80 have electricity (10A) and water connections. Tent pitches have a separate place on the river banks.

**Facilities:** The two sanitary blocks, one newer than the other, are acceptable if not luxurious. Baby room. Laundry and dishwashing sinks

**Charges** 2002

| | |
|---|---|
| Per pitch incl. electricity | € 4.27 |
| with water and drainage | € 6.40 |
| tent and vehicle | € 2.44 |
| person | € 2.44 |
| child (2-7 yrs) | € 1.20 |
| pet | € 0.76 |

**Tel:** 03 87 68 26 48. Fax: 03 87 38 03 89. **Reservations:** Not possible. **Open** 5 May - 26 September.

**Directions:** Take Metz-Nord exit from the autoroute, follow 'autres directions' sign back over the motor way and follow camp signs.

# Camping du Lac de la Liez

## Open 14<sup>th</sup> June - 1<sup>st</sup> November ★★★★

Close to the Champagne and Ardennes regions of France, Lac de Liez is a top quality 4 star site, ideal for the whole family

 **Comfort:**
spacious toilet blocks and modern facilities

 **Sport:**
covered pool complex, tennis courts, lake

 **Fun:**
organised activities for both adults and children

 **Relaxation:**
sauna, spa

 **Conviviality:**
bar, restaurant, warm welcome

✔ **Beautiful lakeside setting**
✔ **Beach for swimming**
✔ **Pedalos, water-bikes, boats...**

**Peigney, F-52200 Langres, tel 0033 (0)325 90 27 79, fax 0033 (0)325 90 66 79**
**campingliez@free.fr, http://www.camping-liez.com**

## Eastern France
# Camping Municipal Eichelgarten

**6701M**

route de Zinswiller, 67110 Oberbronn

This is an attractively situated, inexpensive site, set amidst the mountains and forests of northern Alsace, not far from the German border. There are good views over the valley to one side and the pretty village with trees sheltering the other. The circular internal road has pitches around the outside (100 for touring units, 50 for seasonals), as well as space in the centre where there is also a children's playground. The solar-heated swimming pool and children's pool are of excellent quality.

**Facilities:** The first well appointed toilet block, heated in cool weather, has some washbasins in cabins for ladies, washing machines and dryers, a baby room and facilities for disabled people. The second block is unisex and small. Small shop. General room with table football and air hockey. Swimming pool and children's pool (July/Aug). Playground. Tennis court. **Off site:** Supermarket in the village 1 km. Fitness circuit in the nearby forest. Riding 700 m. Fishing 3 km. Indoor pool adjacent to site.

**Charges** 2003

| | |
|---|---|
| Per person | € 3.10 |
| child (under 7) | € 1.90 |
| pitch and vehicle | € 3.60 |
| electricity per amp | € 0.80 |
| local tax | € 0.20 |

No credit cards. **Tel:** 03 88 09 71 96. Fax: 03 88 09 65 12. **Reservations:** Advised for high season. Write with precise dates; no deposit required. **Open** 18 March - 19 November.

**Directions:** Travel northwest from Haguenau on N62 for about 20 km. South of Niederbronn turn left on D28 for Oberbronn-Zinswiller - site is signed from here. From A4 exit 42 to Sarreguemines, then N62 and D620 towards Haguenau and as above.

---

## Eastern France
# Camping-Caravaning du Ried

**6703**

route de Rhinau, 67860 Boofzheim

The area between the main road from Strasbourg to Colmar and the river Rhine is usually bypassed by those who are exploring Alsace or passing through to Switzerland and Italy. However, if looking for a night stop or a different base in the region, Camping du Ried could well fit the bill. Situated on the edge of a small, picturesque village, it has 150 tourist pitches amongst the 120 static caravans. Most of these are under tall trees, on grass and separated by hedges. One might think that this is just another reasonable campsite until one sees the excellent pool complex just inside the site entrance which has an attractive outdoor pool for use in July and August and a heated indoor one open from May to September. We found this a pleasant site with very friendly management who would like to welcome more British visitors even though no English is spoken.

**Facilities:** The single toilet block is quite a large building and, although old, is well tiled and has all the usual facilities including for disabled people. Washing machines and dryer. Bar/restaurant. Splendid indoor and outdoor pools. Children's playground. Boules. Minigolf. Canoeing. High season animation for children and daily programme including a variety of excursions, guided canoe trips and competitions. Library. **Off site:** Supermarket outside gates.

**Charges** 2002

| | |
|---|---|
| Per unit incl. 2 persons | € 13.00 |
| extra person | € 4.00 |
| child (under 7 yrs) | € 2.00 |
| animal | € 2.00 |
| electricity (3/6A) | € 3.50 - € 5.00 |
| caravan over 5.5 m. plus | € 4.00 |

**Tel:** (0)3 88 74 68 27. Fax: (0)3 88 74 62 89. E-mail: info@camping-ried.com. **Reservations:** Made with deposit and fee; contact site. **Open** 1 April - 30 October.

**Directions:** Leave N83 Strasbourg - Colmar road at Benfeld and go east on D5 to Boofzheim. Site is 500 m. beyond village towards Rhinau.

BETWEEN STRASBOURG ANd COLMAR
AT 2 km FROM THE RHINE
2 HEATEd swimming pool (which one is covered)
MobilE Homes wiTH TERRACE FOR HIRE

CAMPING CARAVANING du RIEd
I RUE du CAMPING 67860 BOOFZHEIM
Tel : 0033 388 74 68 27 Fax : 0033 388 74 62 89
www.CAMPING-RIEd.COM
FREE brochURES ON REQUEST

# Camping Municipal Masevaux

**6803M**

3 rue du Stade, 68290 Masevaux

Masevaux is a pleasant little town in the Haut-Rhin département of Alsace, just to the north of the A36 Belfort - Mulhouse motorway in the Des Ballons region. The municipal camping site is situated in a quiet edge of town next to the sporting complex which has a good indoor pool and other sporting opportunities. The pretty flower decked entrance promises a neat, excellent site and one is not disappointed. The neatly mown 120 pitches for tourists are on level grass, of reasonable size, marked by trees and hedges, and all have electricity (3/6A). Most are well shaded by a variety of trees and have good views of the surrounding hills. The pleasant Gardien, who takes pride in the site, would like to welcome more British visitors. The attractive town is a short walk.

**Facilities:** A modern, well designed and well equipped sanitary block has most washbasins in private cabins. Baby room. Laundry and covered dishwashing area. Baker calls in high season. Ice-creams and soft drinks available at reception. Play area. Tennis courts and minigolf (extra charge). **Off site:** Supermarket, restaurants and indoor pool near. Fishing.

**Charges** 2002

| | |
|---|---|
| Per pitch | € 2.50 |
| person | € 2.50 |
| child under 7 yrs | € 1.25 |
| electricity (3/6A) | € 2.50 - € 4.70 |
| local tax | € 0.16 |
| dog | € 0.70 |

**Tel:** 03 89 82 42 29. **Fax:** 03 89 82 42 29.
**Reservations:** Made with € 31 deposit; contact site.
**Open** Easter - 30 September.

**Directions:** Site is well signed all around the town as 'Camping Complexe Sportif'.

---

# Camping de L'Ile du Rhin

**6801**

Zone Touristique, Ile du Rhin, 68600 Biesheim

In a pleasant island situation between the Rhine and the Canal d'Alsace, this site has views across the river to Breisach in Germany. It is well situated to explore the Vosges or the Black Forest. There are 251 hedged pitches, many occupied by seasonal static caravans, but including 65 touring pitches. Some vary in size but all have electrical connections and are on flat grass with good shade.

**Facilities:** Three well kept, sanitary blocks (one heated) include washbasins in cabins. Washing machine and dryer. Shop. Bar, small restaurant with covered terrace, and takeaway (all 15/6-15/9, weekends only until 30/9). Playground. Table tennis and boules. Caravan storage. **Off site:** Restaurant, heated pool (free entry for campers), sports ground and marina 200 m. Fishing 100 m, riding 1.5 km.

**Charges** 2002

| | |
|---|---|
| Per unit incl. 2 persons | € 12.30 |
| extra person | € 3.75 |
| child (under 7 yrs) | € 1.90 |
| electricity (4-10A) | € 3.00 - € 5.75 |
| local tax (over 14 yrs, 1/4-30/9) | € 0.30 |

**Tel:** 03 89 72 57 95. **Fax:** 03 89 72 14 21.
**Reservations:** Only made for longer stays. **Open** all year excl. Christmas and New Year.

**Directions:** Site is reached from the bridge into Germany using the N415 Colmar - Freiburg road, signed beside the frontier post. Proceed under bridge northwards and site is to left past restaurant.

---

# Camping Municipal Les Trois Châteaux

**6804M**

10 rue du Bassin, 68420 Eguisheim

The village of Eguisheim is on the Alsace 'Rue du Vin' to the west of Colmar. The three châteaux from which the site gets its name are clearly visible on the distant hills. About 400 m. from the village, Les Trois Châteaux is busy and popular. Flowers, shrubs and a variety of trees, along with the well tended grass areas make this a very pleasant place. The 125 pitches, 115 with electricity (6A), are either on a slight slope or a terrace, and are marked and numbered, most with good shade. The fascinating village of Eguisheim is close and the site is well located for exploring this delightful part of Alsace.

**Facilities:** The single sanitary block in the centre of the site has hot showers but cold water elsewhere. Playground. Caravans over 7 m. and/or 1 ton in weight are not accepted. **Off site:** Fishing 3 km.

**Charges** 2002

| | |
|---|---|
| Per person | € 3.10 |
| child (under 7) | € 1.40 |
| pitch | € 3.10 |
| dog | € 0.80 |
| local tax | € 0.30 |
| electricity (6A) | € 3.10 |
| unit over 5.5m long plus | € 1.30 |

**Tel:** 03 89 23 19 39. **Fax:** 03 89 24 10 19.
**Reservations:** Only made for July/Aug, write to site.
**Open** Easter - 30 September.

**Directions:** Eguisheim is just off the N83 and the site is well signed in the village.

## Camping Intercommunal Riquewihr

**6806M** route des Vins, 68340 Riquewihr

Surrounded by vineyards and minutes from the delightful village of Riquewihr, this well run site has earned its reputation not only from the quality of its facilities, but also from the welcome reception accorded to campers by the couple who manage the site. Situated in the heart of the Alsace wine region the site covers three hectares with views across the open countryside. Immediately to the right of the security barrier stands a modern, part-timbered building housing reception and information area. Close by is a small summer house and both are heavily garlanded with flowers. The 150 spacious grass pitches, many with shade and divided by hedging, have electrical connections (6A). The tent area is separate and also offers individual pitches. A novelty is two visiting storks who arrive at 7 pm. each evening to be fed by the Madame.

**Facilities:** There are three clean sanitary blocks, one of a more modern design. Facilities include private cabins with basins, baby room and excellent facilities for disabled people. Dishwashing and laundry areas. Motorcaravan service point. Campers' room with tables and chairs. Shop for basic necessities, drinks and papers (from 1/5). **Off site:** Children's play area and sports field adjacent. Fishing 3 km, bicycle hire 5 km.

**Charges** 2002

| | |
|---|---|
| Per person | € 3.51 |
| child (under 7 yrs) | € 1.52 |
| pitch | € 3.96 |
| electricity | € 3.81 |
| dog | € 1.07 |
| local tax | € 0.30 |
| use of motorcaravan services | € 4.57 |

**Tel:** 03 89 47 90 08. Fax: 03 89 49 05 63. **Reservations:** Not accepted. **Open** Easter - 31 October.

**Directions:** Travelling south on N83 Sélestat - Colmar road turn west onto D106 to Ribeauvillé. At roundabout turn left onto D1B Riquewihr (do not enter village). Site is on left approx. 800 m. past junction with D3 to Riquewihr. Travelling north on N83, go northwest on N415 at Ingersheim (west of Colmar) and then north on D10 to Riquewihr; site is signed at roundabout.

## Camping Les Sources

**6807** route des Crêtes, 68700 Wattwiller

Wattwiller is just off the N83 Alsace 'Rue du Vin', tucked away in the forest hills beyond the vineyards, but not far from them, in the popular region of the Vosges. Camping Les Sources occupies a fairly steep slope above the village under a covering of tall trees. The 300 tourist pitches, all with electricity (5A) are mainly single ones in clearings on scant grass. The trees mean that the site is very shady, so it can be rather gloomy in overcast or wet weather. A narrow hard road meanders between pitches and is steep in places making it difficult for large units, although staff will assist with a tractor if required. Les Sources would suit those who wish to enjoy the quiet, secluded location although there would appear to be plenty on offer during high season. The site issues a map for walking in the area and a sheet in English with places to visit, and staff will be pleased to give further information.

**Facilities:** Three old, but clean toilet blocks are spread around the site and are fully equipped. No provision for disabled visitors who would find the steep roads difficult. Washing machines and dryers. Motorcaravan service point. Shop. Good restaurant. Two swimming pools, one outdoor (15/4-30/9) and another heated and covered (all season). Arena for horse riding activities. Tennis court, table tennis, minigolf and volleyball. Bicycle hire. Entertainment area. Play area. Games room. Organised programme with walking, games and creative activities.

**Charges** 2002

| | |
|---|---|
| Per person | € 5.50 |
| child (1-7 yrs) | € 3.50 |
| pitch | € 7.30 |
| electricity (5A) | € 3.10 |
| animal | € 1.10 |
| local tax | € 0.15 |

**Tel:** 03 89 75 44 94. Fax: 03 89 75 71 98. E-mail: camping.les.sources@wanadoo.fr. **Reservations:** Made with deposit (€ 77) and fee (€ 7,62). **Open** 1 April - 15 October.

**Directions:** From N66 Thann - Mulhouse road, go north to Cernay and continue through Uffholtz to Wattwiller. Turn left after village sign and follow camp signs. From the north leave N83 for Berrwiller and go south on D5 to Wattwiller.

## Camping Clair Vacances

**6808** Route de Herrlisheim, 68127 Sainte Croix-en-Plaine

Alsace is a popular and picturesque area of lovely villages, large vineyards, mountains and forests, and it is also on the route taken by many heading for Switzerland or Italy. Clair Vacances, opened in '97, is a very neat, tidy and pretty site with 60 level pitches of generous size which are numbered and separated by trees and shrubs. All have electricity connections (4-13A) and 10 are fully serviced with water and drainage. The site has been imaginatively laid out with the pitches reached from hard access roads. This is a quiet family site. The friendly couple who own and run it will be pleased to advise on the attractions of the area. The site is 1 km. from the A35 exit, not far from Colmar.

**Facilities:** The excellent, central toilet block includes washbasins in cabins, a well equipped baby room and good facilities for disabled visitors. Shop with limited supplies. Swimming pool and children's pool with large sunbathing area. Children's playground. Community room. Archery in high season. Dogs are not accepted in July/Aug. **Off site:** Colmar with restaurants and shops is not far away.

**Charges** 2002

| | |
|---|---|
| Per unit incl. 2 adults | € 11.00 - € 15.00 |
| extra adult | € 3.20 - € 5.03 |
| child (under 7 yrs) | € 1.52 - € 3.04 |
| electricity (4/13A) | € 1.98 - € 4.42 |

**Tel:** 03 89 49 27 28. Fax: 03 89 49 31 37. E-mail: clairvacances@wanadoo.fr. **Reservations:** Made with deposit (€ 15,24). **Open** week before Easter - 25 October.

**Directions:** Site is signed from exit 27 of the A35 south of Colmar on the Herrlisheim road (D1).

## Camping-Caravaning Domaine des Messires

**8807** 88600 Herpelmont

Domaine des Messires nestles under a cover of tall trees by a landscaped lake on the edge of the small village of Herpelmont. It is well situated for exploring the rural countryside of the Vosges, the lakes and mountains of the region and the interesting towns of St Dié, Colmar and Épinal. The 125 good sized pitches are on grass over stones, with some by the lakeside. Each has a water tap, drain and electricity hook-up (4A) and most have good shade cover, except for those at the end of the site which are in the open. The lake is available for non-powered boats and there are sections for both swimming and fishing. If you write to reserve a pitch, ask for their very comprehensive route from Calais to the site.

**Facilities:** The fully equipped modern toilet block includes all washbasins in cabins, provision for disabled visitors (key from reception) and a baby room. Small shop and restaurant overlooking the lake (both 1/7-1/9). Two small children's play areas. Games and TV room. Programme of activities for children and adults in high season. **Off site:** Weekly markets in nearby Bruyères, Corcieux and St Dié.

**Charges** 2002

| | |
|---|---|
| Per person | € 4.00 - € 5.00 |
| child (0-6 yrs) | € 2.00 - € 2.50 |
| pitch incl. 3 services | € 10.00 - € 12.00 |
| local tax | € 0.33 |

**Tel:** 03 29 58 56 29. Fax: 03 29 58 56 29. **Reservations:** Made with 25% deposit and € 11,43 fee. **Open** 1 May - 15 September.

**Directions:** From Épinal, exit N57 on N420 for St Dié and follow signs until you pick up signs for Bruyères. Lac du Messires is signed as you leave Bruyères on D423, at Laveline go south to Herpelmont and site.

## Eastern France
# Camping Club du Lac de Bouzey

19 rue du Lac, 88390 Sanchey

travel service
TO BOOK

Ferry ✔
Pitch ✔
Accommodation ✔

01892 55 98 98

Camping-Club Lac de Bouzey is 8 km. west of Épinal, overlooking the lake, at the beginning of the Vosges Massif. It is well placed for exploring the hills, valleys, lakes and waterfalls of the south of Alsace Lorraine The word 'Club' has been added to the name to indicate the number of activities organised in high season. The 160 fairly small, level, back-to-back grass pitches are arranged on either side of tarmac roads with electricity (4-12A). They are on a gentle slope, divided by beech hedging, under a cover of tall, silver birch trees and overlooking the 130 ha. lake. The lake has a number of sandy beaches. Many water sports may be enjoyed, from pedaloes to canoes, windsurfing and sailing. The large, imposing building at the entrance to the site houses a restaurant and bar with terraces overlooking the lake. Two bars by the lake would indicate that the lake-side is popular with the public in summer but the camping area is quiet, separated by a road and well back and above the main entrance. An 'all year' site, there is lots going on for teenagers. English is spoken. A 'Sites et Paysages' member.

**Facilities:** The central sanitary block, partly below ground level, includes a baby room and one for disabled people (although there is up and down hill walking on the site). In winter a small, heated section in the main building with toilet, washbasin and shower is used. Well stocked shop. Bar, restaurant. Heated swimming pool of an original shape and backed by two sunbathing terraces (1/4-30/9). Fishing, riding and bicycle hire on site. Below ground, under the restaurant, is a sound-proof room for cinema shows and discos for those staying on site only. Staff escort young people back to their pitch at the end of the evening. High season programme of activities for all ages, including excursions, entertainment, sports and a mini-club. **Off site:** Golf 8 km

**Charges** 2002

| | |
|---|---|
| Per unit incl. 2 adults | € 15.00 - € 22.00 |
| extra person | € 3.50 - € 6.50 |
| child (4-7 yrs) | free - € 4.50 |
| electricity (6A) | € 4.00 |
| dog | free - € 2.00 |

**Tel:** 03 29 82 49 41. Fax: 03 29 64 28 03. E-mail: camping.lac.de.bouzey@wanadoo.fr. **Reservations:** Made with deposit (€ 10 per day booked) and fee (€ 25). **Open** all year.

**Directions:** Site is 8 km. west of Épinal on D460 and is signed from some parts of Épinal. Follow signs for Lac de Bouzey and Sanchey.

## Eastern France
# Camping de Belle Hutte

1 bis Vouille de Belle Hutte, Belle Hutte, 88250 La Bresse

Bell-Hutte is a pleasant site in the heart of the Vosges mountains that makes a good base for either winter ski-ing or summer walking. It is a little off the beaten track, on one of the southern routes to the Col de la Schlucht. Attractively situated surrounded by mountains and trees, it occupies an open hill slope (900 m. above sea level) with 100 numbered grass pitches on six terraces. Places of about 90 sq.m. are divided by hedges and all have electrical connections. To reach the site you would have to depart from the usual main through routes but it is a good site in pleasant surroundings.

**Facilities:** The well built, brick sanitary block is centrally placed and of excellent quality. Heated in cool weather, it also has facilities for disabled people and babies. Laundry room with washing machines and dryers, and a drying room. Motorcaravan service point. Reception office carries basic food supplies. Rest room with open fire and TV. Small swimming pool (10 x 4 m; no Bermuda shorts) for children open for July/Aug. Children's playground. Play room with table tennis. Fishing on site. Ski storage room. **Off site:** Fishing 4 km, riding 10 km. Village 400m with shops and restaurants.

**Charges** 2002

| | |
|---|---|
| Per person | € 2.20 - € 4.20 |
| child (under 7 yrs) | € 1.60 - € 2.50 |
| car | € 1.30 - € 1.70 |
| caravan or tent | € 1.30 - € 2.20 |
| motorcaravan (less for over 1 night) | € 3.90 - € 5.60 |
| dog | € 1.30 - € 1.60 |
| electricity (2/10A) | € 1.30 - € 7.70 |
| local tax | € 0.30 |

**Tel:** 03 29 25 49 75. Fax: 03 29 25 52 63. E-mail: camping-belle-hutte@wanadoo.fr. **Reservations:** Necessary in winter (not summer). Write for booking form and return with € 23 deposit. **Open** all year except 1-14 April.

**Directions:** Site is about 9 km. from La Bresse on the D34 road towards the Col de la Schlucht.

## Eastern France
# Camping Les Deux Ballons
**8801** 17 rue du Stade, 88560 Saint Maurice sur Moselle

St Maurice-sur-Moselle is in a narrow valley 7 km. from the source of the River Moselle in the massif of Haute-Vosges, on the main N66 which leads to the Col de Bussang. This is a pleasant leafy area for winter skiing and summer outdoor activities. Les Deux Ballons lies in a small valley surrounded by mountains with a stream running through the site and a cover of trees giving shade in most parts. The 180 pitches are on stony ground under the firs or on two terraces, and all have electrical connections (4A). English is spoken (ask for Véronique).

**Facilities:** Four good sanitary blocks, one new, the others recently renovated, include baby rooms Washing machines and dryers. Motorcaravan service point. Gas supplies. Bar with terrace (30/6-25/8). Snack bar and takeaway incl. pizzas. Large swimming pool (30 x 20 m.) with water slide and smaller pool for children (15/6-31/8). Organised walks, fishing, bowls, riding, paragliding and summer sledging in high season. TV room. Tennis court, table tennis, volleyball and basketball. Fishing. **Off site:** Bicycle hire 5 km, riding 3 km.

**Charges** 2002

| | |
|---|---|
| Per caravan or tent incl. 1 or 2 persons | € 16.31 |
| Low season (per person, per pitch) | € 3.81 - € 4.27 |
| extra person | € 3.96 |
| child (2-7 yrs) | € 2.90 |
| electricity (4/15A) | € 3.66 - € 4.88 |
| dog | € 1.75 - € 1.83 |
| local tax | € 0.30 |

**Tel:** 03 29 25 17 14. **Fax:** 03 29 25 27 51. **E-mail:** verocamp@aol.com. **Reservations:** Write with deposit (25%) and booking fee (€ 12,19). **Open** 30 March - 30 September.

**Directions:** Site is on main N66 Le Thillot - Bussang road on northern edge of St Maurice near filling station (entrance partly obscured - keep a look out).

## Eastern France
# Castel Camping Domaine des Bans
**8808** rue James Wiese, 88430 Corcieux

the **travel service** TO BOOK

| Ferry | ✓ |
| Pitch | ✓ |
| Accommodation | ✓ |

01892 55 98 98

Corcieux is in the heart of the Vosges mountains, near the lakeside resort of Gerardmer, the Alsace 'Route de Vin' and on the edge of the Ballons des Vosges National Park. Domaine des Bans is a large, very well organised campsite in a country setting. where there are plenty of opportunities to be active. Although there is a high percentage of static and tour operator units, there are said to be 250 tourist places. Pitches (all with electricity, water and drainage), numbered and separated by hedges, vary in size with some on low terraces with access from tarmac roads. There is little shade. Some pitches are tucked away in quiet areas with others nearer to where activities take place. The centre-piece of the site is the large, heated swimming pool, part of which is covered and surrounded by a sun terrace with snack bar. Domaine des Bans really is a campsite for all ages, for those who want sport and entertainment and those who enjoy a quiet peaceful holiday. Not really a site for short stays but excellent for enjoying what is on offer, as well as being a base for exploring the varied and interesting countryside, Haut Koenigsbourg Castle with Colmar, Épinal and Strasbourg within range for day trips.

**Facilities:** Six well built, modern sanitary blocks of excellent quality are spread around the site. Some washbasins are in cabins. Well stocked shop (15/6-31/8). Bar, takeaway and splendid restaurant (all 1/6-10/9). Swimming pool (1/6-10/9). Children's playground and open area for ball games. Tennis, table tennis, badminton, minigolf, volleyball and archery. Bicycle hire. Riding. Lakes for fishing and boating. Golf driving range under construction. High season entertainment programme including discos (soundproof underground room), performances in the splendid theatre and other live music. 'Goats Castle' with about two dozen goats provides extra interest for children. **Off site:** Smaller restaurant just outside the site boundary with others a short distance away in the village.

**Charges** guide

| | |
|---|---|
| Per person | € 6.10 |
| child (under 6 yrs) | € 3.05 |
| pitch incl. electricity | € 12.20 |
| local tax | € 0.36 |

**Tel:** 03 29 51 64 67. **Fax:** 03 29 51 64 72. **E-mail:** les-bans@domaine-des-bans.com. **Reservations:** Advised in high season and made with 25% deposit and € 11,43 booking fee. **Open** 1 April - 31 October.

**Directions:** From D8 St Dié - Gerardmer road, turn west on D60 just north of Gerbepal to Corcieux.

# Vendée Charente

Map 5

We have exercised a little license with this area taking one département from the official WESTERN LOIRE region, namely number **85 Vendée**, and one from the Poitou-Charentes region, number **17 Charente-Maritime**.

The Vendée along with the coastal area stretching down from La Rochelle past Rochefort to Royan, ie. Charente-Maritime, has become well known as a tourist destination. It is popular with British visitors because of its micro climate and marvellous sandy beaches yet within a fairly easy drive from the Normandy or Brittany ferry ports.

The Vendée was the centre of the counter-revolutionary movement between 1793 and 1799 and a two hour 'son et lumiere' extravaganza held at the Chateau Puy-du-Fou from mid June to end of August (Fri and Sat) tells the whole story with the aid of ultra-modern technology. On the Ile de Noirmoutier, mimosa blooms in February, so mild is its climate. Les Sables d'Olonne is its main resort renowned for its excellent sandy beach and it also has a thriving sardine fishing industry.

The area between the Vendée and Charentes, the Marais Poitevin, is one of the most unusual in France - a vast tract of marshland with a thousand or more tree-lined canals and streams where everything is moved by punt, including the animals. Further south the port of La Rochelle, once a Protestant stronghold, with massive medieval towers, buzzes with life. The islands of Ré (toll bridge), a haven for cyclists, and Oléron (free toll bridge 2 miles long) are popular with those seeking beaches and small, quiet ports. Royan is the leading seaside resort at the confluence of the Gironde estuary and the Atlantic ocean and is said to have launched the fashion for sea bathing in the 19th century. La Palmyre, where pine forests planted to stabilise the dunes flank the beaches, is popular with the British.

Note: the site reports are laid out by département in numerical order.

## Cuisine of the region

Fish predominates, both fresh water (eel, trout, pike), and sea water (shrimps, mussels etc), and '*huitres*' – oysters!

*Cagouilles* – snails from Charentes

*Chaudrée* – ragout of fish cooked in white wine, shallots and butter

*Chevrettes* – local name for crevettes (shrimps)

*Mouclade* – mussels cooked in wine, egg yolks and cream, served with Pineau des Charentes

*Soupe de moules à la Rochelaise* – soup of various fish, mussels, saffron, garlic, tomatoes, onions and red wine

*Sourdons* – cockles from the Charentes

## Wine

Light fruity wines from Haut-Poitou, Deux-Sèvres and Charente

Very popular – Cognac and Pineau des Charentes (an aperitif of grape juice and Cognac)

## Places of interest

*Marais Poitevin* – marshes known as the 'Green Venice'

*Angoulême* – Hill-top town surrounded by ramparts; cathedral, Renaissance château

*La Rochelle* – port, Porte de la Grosse Horloge (clock gate), Museum of the New World

*Le Puy-du-Fou* – 15th-16th century castle, sound and light show involving over 700 participants

*Les Sables d'Olonne* – fishing port and seaside resort

*Noirmoutier* – linked to the mainland by a 3 mile bridge

*Saint Savin* – 17th century abbey, mural painting

# Airotel Le Puits de L'Auture

**1702** 151 avenue de La Grande-Côte, 17420 St-Palais-sur-Mer

This popular region has a very sunny climate and Le Puits de l'Auture is well situated with the sea outside the gates, just across the road, and a long sandy beach starting 400 m. away. As soon as you enter the site there is a feeling that it is well cared for, with an abundance of flower beds at the entrance. The 400 numbered pitches are level and have electricity connections (6A), a fair number are separated by bushes and some trees give shade (many were lost in recent storms). Water and drainage is provided on 120 pitches. There is a good number of mobile homes on site. Used by a tour operator (10%). Considering its close proximity to the beach and its popularity, there is a remarkably calm and relaxed atmosphere and it is well worth considering.

**Facilities:** Well maintained toilet blocks are more than adequate for the number of visitors. Most WCs are British type and all washbasins are in cabins, showers are adjustable and hot water is plentiful. Baby baths and showers, and full facilities for disabled people. Washing machines and ample sinks for dishwashing and laundry. Well stocked shop, takeaway food and bar (all 10/6-25/9). Three swimming pools with sunbathing areas which are most attractive with banana plants making a backdrop with a difference. Volleyball, table tennis and games room. Play area. Bicycle hire. Barbecues are only allowed in a special area. Dogs are not accepted. **Off site:** Riding and golf 800 m. Several restaurants nearby specialise in sea food.

**Charges** 2002

| | |
|---|---|
| Per unit incl. up to 3 persons | € 17.60 - € 29.00 |
| with 6A electricity | € 23.00 - € 33.00 |
| with 10A electricity | € 26.00 - € 36.00 |
| with water and drainage | € 33.00 - € 41.00 |
| extra person (over 3 yrs) | € 4.60 - € 6.50 |

**Tel:** 05 46 23 20 31. Fax: 05 46 23 26 38. E-mail: camping-lauture@wanadoo.fr. **Reservations:** Made for min. 5 days with deposit and fee. **Open** 1 May - 30 September.

**Directions:** Site is on the coast, 2 km. from St Palais and 8 km. from Royan. From Royan take D25 past St Palais following signs for La Palmyre. At two lane junction system turn back left signed Grande Côte and St Palais and site is 800 m.

# Le Logis du Breuil

**1719** 17570 St-Augustin-sur-Mer

Space - no, not the final frontier, but the first impression on arrival at the reception area of this impressive campsite. Between the site buildings, pool and shop, bar/restaurant and the camping area is a 200 metre expanse of farm pasture where, on different areas, cattle graze and children play. The camping areas themselves are set among rows of mature and shady trees which give a very restful, dappled effect to the tents, caravans and grassy pitches. The 320 pitches are very large and have direct access to wide, unpaved alleys, which lead on to the few tarmac roads around the site (3/6A electricity available). The campsite facilities are centralised around the reception area and the pool complex. The area around the site is very pleasant agricultural land and the beaches of the Atlantic coast are nearby, as are the oyster and the mussel beds of Marennes and La Tremblade. The Gagnard family started the campsite about 25 years ago and obviously take great pride in what it has now become a peaceful, friendly and very pleasant site from which to explore a delightful holiday area. A 'Sites et Paysages' member.

**Facilities:** Four very well maintained toilet blocks are well spaced around the camping area. Each block caters for all toilet, washing up and laundry needs. Swimming pools. Shop, bar and snacks and takeaway (run on a franchise basis) are well cared for, clean, friendly and popular. No evening entertainment. Children's play area. Indoor area providing archery, pool and table tennis. Bicycle hire. Tennis and basketball.

**Charges** 2002

| | |
|---|---|
| Per unit incl. 2 adults | € 13.00 - € 15.00 |
| with 3A electricity | € 16.20 - € 18.30 |
| extra adult | € 3.50 - € 4.35 |
| child (under 7 yrs) | € 3.00 - € 3.70 |
| dog | € 1.60 |
| local tax | € 1.80 |

**Tel:** 05 46 23 23 45. Fax: 05 46 23 43 33. E-mail: camping.Logis-du-Breuil@wanadoo.fr. **Reservations:** Advised for high season and made with deposit (€ 32,01) and booking fee (€ 6,86). **Open** 15 May - 15 September.

**Directions:** On approaching Royan follow signs to St Palais sur Mer, bypassing Royan centre. Continue straight on past first set of traffic lights and roundabout. At second set of lights turn right towards St Augustin. Site is approx. 2 km on left after passing village.

## Vendée Charente
# Camping Bois Soleil

**1701** | 2 avenue de Suzac, 17110 St Georges-de-Didonne

Close to the sea and the resort of St Georges, Bois Soleil is a fairly large site in three separate parts, with 208 serviced pitches for touring caravans and several for tents. The main part, 'Les Pins', is mature and attractive with ornamental trees and shrubs providing shade. Opposite is 'La Mer' which has direct access to the beach and is used only in the main season. It has some areas with rather less shade and a raised central area for tents. The sandy beach here is a wide public one, sheltered from the Atlantic breakers although the sea goes out some way at low tide. The third and largest part of the site, 'La Forêt', is mainly for static holiday homes (many privately owned), although there are some touring pitches here for both tents and caravans. The areas are well tended with the named pitches (not numbered) cleared and raked between clients and with an all-in charge including electricity and water. This lively site offers something for everyone, whether they like a beach-side spot or a traditional pitch, plenty of activities or the quiet life - it is best to book for the area you prefer. It can be full mid-June - late August.

**Facilities:** Each area is served by one large sanitary block, supplemented by smaller blocks providing toilets only. Another heated block is near reception. Well designed and appointed buildings, cleaned twice daily, they include washbasins in cubicles, facilities for disabled people (WC, basin and shower) and for babies. Launderette. Nursery for babies. Supermarket, bakery (July/Aug) and beach shop. Upstairs restaurant and bar with terrace, excellent takeaway (from April). Little pool for small children. 'Parc des Jeux' with tennis, table tennis, bicycle hire, boules and children's playground. TV room and library. Comprehensive tourist information and entertainment office. Internet terminal. Charcoal barbecues are not permitted but gas ones can be hired by the evening. Dogs or other animals are not accepted. **Off site:** Fishing and riding within 500 m, golf 2 km.

**Charges** 2002

| | |
|---|---|
| Per unit incl. 2 persons, electricity | € 16.00 - € 27.50 |
| 3 persons | € 19.00 - € 27.50 |
| tent incl. 2 persons | € 13.00 - € 24.50 |
| extra person | € 3.50 - € 5.00 |
| child (3-7 yrs) | € 1.50 - € 3.50 |
| electricity 10A | € 3.40 - € 5.00 |
| local tax (1/7-31/8) | € 0.25 |

**Tel:** 05 46 05 05 94. Fax: 05 46 06 27 43. E-mail: camping.bois.soleil@wanadoo.fr. **Reservations:** Made with 25% deposit and € 26 fee. **Open** 1 April - 15 September.

**Directions:** From Royan centre take coast road (D25) along the sea-front of St Georges-de-Didonne towards Meschers. Site is signed at roundabout at end of the main beach.

## Vendée Charente
# Camping International Bonne Anse Plage

**1704** | La Palmyre, 17570 Les Mathes

the **travel service**
TO BOOK

| | |
|---|---|
| Ferry | ✓ |
| Pitch | ✗ |
| Accommodation | ✓ |

**01892 55 98 98**

On the edge of the Forêt de la Coubre, just beyond the popular resort of La Palmyre, Bonne Anse has a lovely setting amongst pine trees, just a short stroll from an extensive tidal inlet. It is a spacious, gently undulating site, carefully designed to provide 865 level, marked pitches, of which 600 are for touring units (500 have electricity). Most are shaded by the pines, the ones nearer the sea less so (these are rather more sandy). The site's amenities are centred around the entrance and reception building and include a restaurant and bar with a spacious outdoor terrace and an impressive pool complex. This forms the social focus of the site and overlooks the boules area with the pool complex opposite. English is spoken and rallies welcomed with visit programmes organised. Used by tour operators (35 pitches). With plenty to do for the active, the site is perhaps a little impersonal.

**Facilities:** Seven sanitary blocks include some washbasins in cabins, British style toilets with a few Turkish, hot and cold showers. Facilities for disabled visitors and babies. Washing up and laundry sinks under cover. Launderette. Motorcaravan service point. Shopping centre (all season) includes a supermarket, excellent delicatessen and takeaway, crêperie, shops for bread and pastries, holiday goods and papers, plus visiting traders' stalls (wines, seafood, etc) in high season. Restaurant and bar (20/6-30/8). Splendid, lively swimming pool complex with heated pool (35 x 25 m), three water toboggans and a water slide. Children's playground, large video games room, TV (satellite), minigolf and table tennis. Enclosed area with an all-weather surface for football, volleyball or basketball. Direct access to cycle tracks (bicycle hire available) that avoid the main road. Entertainment in season. Only gas barbecues are permitted. Dogs are not accepted. **Off site:** Fishing or riding 1 km, golf 5 km, plus facilities for watersports and tennis nearby. Supervised, safe beaches close by, also fitness track.

**Charges** 2002

| | |
|---|---|
| Per unit incl. 3 persons | € 29.00 |
| Per unit incl. 1 or 2 persons | € 25.00 |
| extra person (over 1 yr) | € 7.00 |
| electricity (6A) | € 5.00 |
| local tax | € 0.20 - € 0.40 |

**Tel:** 05 46 22 40 90. Fax: 05 46 22 42 30. E-mail: Bonne.Anse@wanadoo.fr. **Reservations:** Min. 5 days - phone, fax or write for details. **Open** 18 May - 8 September.

**Directions:** Leave A10 autoroute at Saintes and head for Royan (N150). In Royan take signs for La Palmyre (D25). At La Palmyre roundabout follow Ronce-les-Bains and site is 1 km. on the left.

# Bois Soleil

## Camping ★★★★
## Charente-Maritime

Surrounded by pine trees and a sandy beach on the Atlantic Coast, with one direct access to the beach, Bois Soleil proposes to you many attractions like tennis, tabletennis, children playgrounds and entertainment.
Shops, take-away and snack-bar with big TV screen.

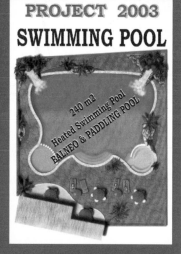

PROJECT 2003
SWIMMING POOL
240 m2
Heated Swimming Pool
BALNEO & PADDLING POOL

## Spring and Summer 2003

2, avenue de Suzac - 17110 ST GEORGES DE DIDONNE
Tel: 0033 546 05 05 94 - Fax: 0033 546 06 27 43
www.bois-soleil.com / e-mail: camping.bois.soleil@wanadoo.fr

## Vendée Charente
# Camping-Caravaning Monplaisir
**1711** route de la Palmyre, 17570 Les Mathes-La Palmyre

the **travel service**
TO BOOK
| | |
|---|---|
| Ferry | ✓ |
| Pitch | ✓ |
| Accommodation | ✗ |

01892 55 98 98

Monplaisir provides a small, quiet haven in an area with some very hectic campsites. It is ideal for couples or families with young children. The site is quite close to the town set back from the road, and the entrance leads through an avenue of trees, past the owners home to a well kept, garden-like site with many varieties of trees and shrubs. There are only 114 level, marked pitches and all but 9 have electrical connections (6A). There is no shop, bar or restaurant but it is a happy, friendly site with visitors who return year after year.

**Facilities:** The toilet block has good facilities including some washbasins in cabins and excellent facilities for disabled people. Laundry and dishwashing sinks outside, but under cover. Washing machine and dryer. Ice pack service and gas supplies in reception. Bread delivered daily. Takeaway available from reception five days a week. TV, games room and library. Swimming pool and paddling pool (15/5-15/9). Small play area. Bicycle hire. Minigolf adjacent (owned by the site). Winter caravan storage. **Off site:** Fishing 500 m, riding 1 km, golf 5 km. Supermarket short walk.

**Charges** 2002
| | |
|---|---|
| Per pitch incl. 2 persons | € 15.00 |
| incl. 3 persons | € 17.00 |
| extra person | € 4.00 |
| baby under 2 yrs | € 2.00 |
| electricity | € 3.00 |
| dog | € 1.50 |
| local tax (over 13 yrs) | € 0.40 |

**Tel:** 05 46 22 50 31. Fax: 05 46 22 50 31.
**Reservations:** Made with deposit and fee, min. stay 4 nights. **Open** 1 April - 1 October.

**Directions:** Follow the D25 to La Palmyre and, in the town, turn north to Les Mathes. At roundabout turn right to town centre and site is on left. From north on D14 La Tremblade road turn to Les Mathes at Arvert. Site is in western outskirts of the town on the D141 La Palmyre road.

## Vendée Charente
# Camping L'Orée du Bois
**1705** 225 route de la Bouverie, La Fouasse, 17570 Les Mathes

L'Orée du Bois has 388 pitches of about 100 sq.m. in a very spacious, pinewood setting. There are 150 for touring units, including 40 large pitches with hardstanding and individual sanitary facilities (built in small, neat blocks of four and containing your own shower, toilet, washbasin and washing up sink). The pitches are on flat, fairly sandy ground, separated by trees, shrubs and growing hedges and all have electrical connections (6A). The forest pines offer some shade. Sandy beaches (with lifeguards in season) are fairly near, plus opportunities for walking, riding or cycling in the 10,000 hectare Forêt de la Coubre. A very lively site in high season, suitable for all age groups, it can be noisy but is tranquil in low season with large, spacious pitches. Used by several tour operators.

**Facilities:** Four attractively designed, main toilet blocks have good fittings, including some washbasins in cabins. Three blocks have laundry rooms, dishwashing under cover and fully equipped units for disabled people. Well stocked shop. Excellent bar, restaurant, crêperie and takeaway service. Large swimming pools, including water toboggan, and paddling pool (proper swimming trunks, not shorts). Two children's play areas. Tennis court, boules, volleyball, table tennis, football and basketball areas. Games room and TV lounge (with satellite). Bicycle hire. Twice weekly discos and free, all day children's entertainment organised in July/Aug. Barbecues allowed in special areas. **Off site:** Fishing 4 km, riding 300 m, golf 20 km.

**Charges** 2002
| | |
|---|---|
| Per unit incl. 2 persons | € 15.00 - € 28.00 |
| with private sanitary facility | € 22.00 - € 36.00 |
| extra person (over 3 yrs) | € 5.00 |
| local tax | € 0.15 - € 0.30 |
| animal | € 2.00 |

**Tel:** 05 46 22 42 43. Fax: 05 46 22 54 76. E-mail: info@camping-oree-du-bois.fr. **Reservations:** Made with 30% deposit plus fee (€ 21); min. 7 days in high season. **Open** 12 April - 28 September.

**Directions:** From north follow D14 La Tremblade road. At Arvert turn on D141 to Les Mathes and turn east, signed La Palmyre, to second roundabout where site signed. From the south, at Royan take D25 towards La Palmyre, then towards Les Mathes to roundabout where site is signed. Note: there is now a new roundabout with a boat on it - follow sign for La Tremblade. Site is signed from this road, and this way is said to be quicker.

## Camping Les Charmilles

St Laurent de la Prée, 17450 Fouras

Fouras is a relatively little known resort situated between La Rochelle and Rochefort which retains much of the charm missing from some of the larger, more commercialised resorts in the area. Les Charmilles is a member of the Chadotel group and is about a mile from the town centre. There are 270 large pitches, the majority taken up with the site's own mobile homes or chalets. The touring pitches all have electricity (6A) and many also have water and drainage. Roughly a third are well shaded, with the remainder having a sunnier, more open setting. The latter area also has the advantage of being well away from the busy road which runs past the front of the site. A variety of entertainment is provided which can mean that the site is noisy until at least midnight.

**Facilities:** Five modern toilet blocks provide most washbasins in cubicles and facilities for babies and disabled people. A reader reports cleaning and the hot water supply can be variable. Washing machines and dryers. Small shop (1/6-15/9). Bar and snack bar (15/5-15/9). Heated pool and slide (15/5-15/9). Good playground. Minigolf, table tennis and basketball. Bicycle hire. Entertainment. Minibus service to beach in July/Aug. Charcoal barbecues not permitted.

**Charges** 2002

| | |
|---|---|
| Per pitch incl. 2 adults | € 11.50 - € 20.50 |
| with electricity | € 15.00 - € 24.00 |
| extra person | € 3.30 - € 5.20 |
| animal | € 2.50 |

**Tel:** 05 46 84 00 05. Fax: 02 51 33 94 04.
**Reservations:** Necessary for high season with deposit and fee. Central reservations: Siege Social - Centrale de Reservation, BP 12, 85520 Jard sur Mer. **Tel:** (0)2.51.33.05.05. Fax: (0)2.51.33.94.04. E-mail: chadotel@wanadoo.fr. **Open** 1 April - 25 September.

**Directions:** Leave N137 at exit for Fouras and St Laurent de la Prée, joining D937 towards Fouras. Site is on left in about 800 m.

## Camping Le Clos Fleuri

8 impasse du Clos Fleuri, 17600 Médis

Camping Le Clos Fleuri really does live up to its name. A profusion of different trees and, in the more open area, well-tended grass and flower beds give this small site a very garden like atmosphere. Created by the Devais in 1974, the care and attention given to the plantings is matched by their care for the campers who visit. The 140 pitches are generously sized (a little uneven in places), varying in the amount of shade they receive and 100 have electricity. The bar/restaurant is a converted barn with chalk and stone walls and a high timbered ceiling - a cool haven on hot days and a convivial venue for evening entertainment. The surrounding countryside is very pleasant with crops of sunflowers, wheat and maize, while beaches of all sorts are within easy reach. All in all the Clos Fleuri combines a great deal of charm, beauty and friendliness with a location from which the attractions of the Charente Maritime may be discovered.

**Facilities:** Toilet facilities are in two blocks which are kept scrupulously clean. One block is segregated male and female, the other is unisex with each unit in its own cubicle. Baby baths, washing machines and dryers. Attractive small pool with separate paddling pool and sunbathing terrace. Sauna. Good shop with fresh meat and vegetables, restaurant (both 1/7-31/8) and bar (1/7-15/9) are housed in the old farm buildings, which form the nucleus of the site. In high season two 'soirees' weekly, boules and archery competitions are organised. Minigolf and small football pitch. Security barrier closed at night. **Off site:** Shops close by in Médis (500 m).

**Charges** 2003

| | |
|---|---|
| Per pitch incl. 2 adults | € 22.00 |
| incl. 3 adults | € 26.00 |
| extra person (over 7 yrs) | € 7.00 |
| child (2-7 yrs) | € 4.50 |
| dog | € 3.00 |
| electricity (5/10A) | € 4.00 - € 5.00 |

**Tel:** 05 46 05 62 17. Fax: 05 46 06 75 61. E-mail: clos-fleuri@wanadoo.fr. **Reservations:** Essential for high season and made with deposit (€ 100) and fee (€ 20). **Open** 1 June - 15 September.

**Directions:** From Saintes on the A10 take N150 towards Royan, for about 30 km. At Médis, at the traffic lights take left lane and then left following signs Clos Fleuri for just over 2 km. to site on left.

## Haven Camping La Pignade

**1718**

45 avenue de Monard, 17390 Ronce les Bains

the travel service
TO BOOK

| | |
|---|---|
| Ferry | ✓ |
| Pitch | ✓ |
| Accommodation | ✗ |

01892 55 98 98

If you are looking for a busy, active well appointed site offering a wide range of facilities and daily entertainment all season, then La Pignade, a Haven Europe park, may be just what you want. The 500 or so pitches, of which 150 are reserved for tourers, are located around well spaced pine trees which, while giving some shade, also give an open aspect. The ground is sandy but site roads are tarmac so dust is not a problem. The pitches are generous in size, most separated by low, evergreen hedges. Much accommodation is in mobile homes. Entertainment and catering facilities are central, well contructed and maintained to a high standard with an impressive range of pools and water slides. Good sandy beaches are nearby, while the fascinating oyster producing area of Marennes is only a few kilometres away. Also close by is the island of Oleron. All in all La Pignade offers a great holiday base in an area full of attractive, interesting places.

**Facilities:** Four refurbished, fully equipped toilet blocks are centrally placed in four separate areas. Open style dishwashing and laundry sinks. Baby packs for hire. Washing machines and dryers. Separate provision for disabled people. Large minimarket and gift shop. Choice of food outlets, waiter service restaurant or takeaway. Spacious well stocked and attractively staffed bar. Barbecue areas. Swimming pools - large pool heated (supervised). Practice golf, crazy golf, archery and bicycle hire (charged). Clubs for children (free) and a daily programme of games, competitions, activities and entertainment. Not all breeds of dog are accepted. **Off site:** Nearby riding, tennis and watersports.

**Charges** guide

| | |
|---|---|
| Per unit incl. 2 persons, electricity | € 12.96 - € 28.81 |
| extra person | € 3.05 - € 5.34 |
| extra vehicle | € 1.52 - € 3.05 |

**Tel:** (0)5 46 85 18 16. **Fax:** (0)5 46 85 52 92.
**Reservations:** Accepted at any time for min. 4 days; no booking fee. Contact site or Haven Europe in the UK on 0870 242 7777 for information or reservation.
**Open** 11 May - 21 September.

**Directions:** Site is signed 250 m. south of the town of Ronce-les-Bains off the D25 La Tremblade road.

La Pignade is a typically French parc, ideal for families, with swimming pool, restaurant and entertainment facilities at the heart of the parc.

- Shaded clusters of touring pitches with easy access to the central area
- Heated outdoor pools with waterslide & children's pool
- Wide range of sports & leisure activities
- Superb low season prices
- Restaurant, takeaway & bar set around an attractive piazza
- 3 children's clubs for all ages
- Bilingual staff on parc
- Site open from: 10 May - 19 September

**La Pignade** ★★★★
Ronce-les-Bains

La Pignade, La Tremblade, 17390 Ronce-les-Bains, France
**Tel:**00 33 546 36 15 35  **Fax:**00 33 546 85 52 92
To book please call the number above, quoting code FAR03

ABTA
V2819

**1722**

## Camping La Brande

route des Huitres, 17480 Le Château-d'Oléron

A quality site, run and maintained to the highest standard, La Brande offers an ideal holiday environment on the delightful Ile d'Oleron, close to a sandy beach. The Barcat family ensure that their visitors not only enjoy quality facilities, but Gerard Barcat offers guided bicycle tours and canoe trips. This way you discover the nature, oyster farming, vineyards and history of Oléron. Pitches here are generous and mostly separated by hedges and trees, the greater number for touring outfits. All are on level grassy terrain and have electricity hook-ups, some are fully serviced. A feature of this site is the heated pool which can be covered under a sliding roof in cool weather. The many activities in the high season, plus the natural surroundings, make it an ideal choice for families.

**Facilities:** Three heated, bright and clean sanitary blocks have spacious, well equipped showers and some open washbasins, but most in cabins. Baby bath/changing area. Excellent facilities for people with disabilities. Laundry room with hot water and sinks, plus washing machine and dryers. Drive over motorcaravan service point. Restaurant/takeaway in July/Aug. Bar (late June - early Sept). Shop with basics in low season, but well stocked in main season. Play area on grass. Football field, tennis, minigolf, fishing and archery. Bicycle hire.

**Charges** 2002

| | |
|---|---|
| Per unit incl. 1 or 2 persons | € 12.00 - € 26.00 |
| extra person | € 3.50 - € 6.00 |
| electricity 6-10A | € 3.20 - € 3.80 |
| dog | € 2.40 |

**Tel:** (0)5 46 47 62 37. **Fax:** (0)5 46 47 71 70. **E-mail:** camping.labrande@wanadoo.fr. **Reservations:** Made with 25% deposit and € 16 fee.

**Directions:** After crossing bridge to L'Ile d'Oléron turn right towards Le Château d'Oléron. Continue through village and follow sign for Route des Huitres. Site is on left after 3 km.

## Vendée Charente
# Sunêlia Interlude

Plage de Gros Jonc, 17580 Le Bois-Plage-en-Ré

**1721**

The Island of Ré, which is no more than 30 km. long and 5 km. wide, lies off the coast at La Rochelle and is reached by a toll bridge. It is a paradise for cyclists, walkers and those who wish to commune with nature. Here you will find the well managed Camping Interlude which offers first class facilities and enjoys a pleasant location with access to an excellent beach. A popular site even in low season, it is has 387 pitches, 136 of which are for touring outfits. Pitches are sand based, vary in size from 80 - 120 sq.m. and are mostly divided by hedged on part undulating terrain. Many are placed to the left of the site in a pine forest setting, others mingle with the tour operators and mobile homes. Choosing a shady pitch is not a problem for there are many tree varieties. Interlude makes an ideal base for exploring the island of Ré and for those planning an early holiday, the facilities on site are all operational from the end of March. It is a suitable site for all ages, with plenty of recreational pursuits to keep the entire family happy, both on and off site.

**Facilities:** Two modern, clean and well equipped sanitary blocks provide washbasins in cabins and some showers units, suitable for families, with twin washbasins. Baby room, child size toilets, en suite facilities for visitors with disabilities, laundry sinks, washing machines and dryers, plus dishwashing areas. Motorcaravan service point. Restaurant/bar and shop (all season). Two swimming pools, one outdoor and one inside. Children's play area. Volleyball, boules. Organised events and entertainment for young and old. Games/TV room. Tennis courts. Bicycle hire.

**Charges** 2002

| | |
|---|---|
| Per unit incl. 2 persons | |
| 100 sq.m. pitch | € 12.00 - € 23.00 |
| 120 sq.m. incl. water and electricity | € 16.00 - € 29.00 |
| 140 sq.m. pitch incl. drainage also | € 16.00 - € 32.50 |
| extra person | € 4.60 - € 8.90 |
| pet | € 2.25 - € 6.65 |

**Tel:** (0)5 46 09 18 22. Fax: (0)5 46 09 23 38. E-mail: interlude@iledere.com. **Reservations:** Advisable all season; contact site. **Open** 29 March - 21 September.

**Directions:** After crossing toll bridge to Ile de Ré follow sign for Le Bois Plage. Turn left at first round about and continue straight on at second and third roundabout, then left at fourth roundabout where site is signed (charges toll bridge: low season 1/1-19/6 car and caravan € 15 return; high season € 27; motorcaravan € 9-16).

N
O    E
S

SPECIALIST OF LOW SEASON

Interlude

50 METERS FROM THE BEACH

Plage du Gros Jonc - 17580 Le Bois-Plage en Ré - Tel. 0546091822 - Fax. 0546092328
Site internet : www.interlude.fr - E-mail : interlude@iledere.com

# Castel Camping Sequoia Parc

La Josephtrie, 17320 Saint Just-Luzac

the travel service
TO BOOK
Ferry ☑
Pitch ☑
Accommodation ☑
01892 55 98 98

Approached by an impressive avenue of flowers, shrubs and trees, Séquoia Parc is a Castel site set in the grounds of La Josephtrie, a striking château with beautifully restored outbuildings and a spacious courtyard. The site itself is designed to a high specification with reception in a large, light and airy room retaining its original beams and leading to the courtyard area where you find the shop, bar and restaurant. The pitches are 140 sq.m. in size with 6A electricity connections and separated by young shrubs. The pool complex with water slides, large children's pool and sunbathing area is impressive. The site has a good number of mobile homes and chalets. Used by tour operators (125 pitches). This is a popular site with entertainment and reservation is necessary in high season. A Yelloh Village member.

**Facilities:** Three luxurious toilet blocks, maintained to a high standard, include units with washbasin and shower, a laundry, dishwashing sinks, facilities for disabled visitors and baby baths. Motorcaravan service point. Gas supplies. Shop. Restaurant/bar and takeaway. Impressive swimming pool complex with paddling pool. Tennis, volleyball, football field. Games and TV rooms. Bicycle hire. Pony trekking. Organised entertainment in July/Aug.

**Charges** 2002

| | |
|---|---|
| Per unit incl. 2 persons and electricity | € 15.00 - € 31.00 |
| extra person | € 5.00 - € 7.00 |
| child (3-7 yrs) | € 3.00 - € 5.00 |
| dog | € 3.00 |
| local tax | € 0.30 |

**Tel:** 05 46 85 55 55. Fax: 05 46 85 55 56. E-mail: sequoia.parc@wanadoo.fr. **Reservations:** Made with 30% deposit and € 30 booking fee. **Open** 18 May - 9 September.

**Directions:** Site is 2.5 km. southeast of Marennes. From Rochefort take D733 south for 12 km. Turn west on D123 to Ile d'Oléron. Continue for 12 km. and turn southeast on D728 towards Saintes. Site clearly signed, in 1 km. on the left.

Magnificent castle campsite near the Atlantic Ocean

**Dutch/French** owned campsite situated on an estate of 45 ha wih a Château. **Wide** sandy beaches at 5 km away. **High** quality facilities, bar/restaurant, pizzeria, take away, children's club during the whole season and sport facilities. **Impressive** swimmingpool complex of 1600 m². **Pony** ranch and horse riding, tennis courts and bicycle hire. **Luxurious** Châltes and Cottage mobilehomes for hire. **Large** pitches of 140 M². **Low** season discounts.

**In France:** 17320 Saint Just-Luzac, tel.: 0033 546 85 55 55, fax: 0033 546 85 55 56, E-mail: sequoia.parc@wanadoo.fr, Internet: www.sequoiaparc.com

SÉQUOIA PARC
Castel Camping Club Vacances

## Camping Le Soleil

**1709M** avenue Michel Crépeau, 17000 La Rochelle

Neatly and attractively landscaped, Le Soleil has 158 level pitches amongst trees and shrubs. Numbered and marked with low wooden fences, many have electricity (10A). Those in a circular, central area are designed for motorcaravans with part gravel hardstanding. There may be some noise from the road and an industrial area nearby, but accessibility to the amenities of the town balance this to a degree (5 minutes to grassy picnic areas by the harbour and 20 minutes to the town centre shops, restaurants and bars or to the beach). A half hourly bus service to town runs from outside the site and a ferry service across the harbour to town. Very busy in high season, reservation is advised. Maintenance can be variable.

**Facilities:** Two toilet blocks provide British and Turkish style toilets, pre-set hot water, some wash-basins in cabins and 12 hot and 2 cold showers, all opening from the outside. Facilities for disabled visitors. Laundry and dishwashing sinks. Launderette near. Delivery vans call with bread, milk, etc. Table tennis tables, boules and barbecue areas, plus an area for dogs.

**Charges** 2002

| | |
|---|---|
| Per unit incl. 1 person | € 6.80 |
| extra person | € 3.10 |
| child (under 10 yrs) | € 2.10 |
| electricity | € 3.10 |
| double axle caravan plus | € 3.60 |
| local tax | € 0.15 |

**Tel:** 05 46 44 42 53. **Reservations:** Made with fee (€ 15,30) for min. 5 days. Contact site when open, or from 15 Jan - 15 May write to Camping de Port Neuf, Bvd. Aristide Rondeau, 17000 La Rochelle (stating that you wish to book at Le Soleil). **Open** 15 May - 15 September.

**Directions:** From ring road (peripherique), follow signs for 'Gare' or 'Centre-Ville' and from either follow signs to 'Vieux Port Sud', Aquarium or 'Port les Minimes'. From there follow small signs to site.

## Camping Municipal du Château Benon

**1715M** 17170 Benon

Benon was once the capital of this area and had strong English connections, its castle being built in 1096, although now all that remains is a single round tower. However the mayor and villagers are still anxious to welcome English visitors. The municipal campsite is beautifully kept, with open and shady areas and is ideal for those wanting a peaceful stay, and to stroll or cycle through the fields and woods which surround Benon. There are 70 pitches on neat grass, 60 with 10A electricity. High season entertainment includes dances and organised dinners. This is a pretty, quiet site where visitors are made welcome.

**Facilities:** The reasonably modern toilet block is fully equipped, with hot water always available and facilities for disabled visitors. Motorcaravan service point. Tennis court. **Off site:** Auberge, general shop and post office near and La Rochelle is within easy reach (25 minutes) for shopping, beaches, etc. Fishing or bicycle hire 7 km, riding 5 km, golf 13 km.

**Charges** 2002

| | |
|---|---|
| Per pitch | € 1.12 |
| adult | € 2.24 |
| child (under 11 yrs) | € 1.28 |
| electricity | € 2.08 |

**Tel:** 05 46 01 61 48. Fax: 05 46 68 22 01. E-mail: mairie-benon@smic17.fr. **Reservations:** Advised for 14 July - 15 Aug; contact the Mairie. **Open** 1 May - 30 September.

**Directions:** Benon is 28 km. east of La Rochelle on the N11. Turn south at 'Relais de Benon', Benon 2 km. and site in centre of village.

## Camping-Caravaning Au Fil de l'Eau

**1720** 6 Rue de Courbiac, 17100 Saintes

Saintes is a 2,000 year old Gallo-Roman city, well worth a couple of days to visit the Cathedral, the Abbey, the Arch of Germanicus, the Amphitheatre and several museums, all of which are within walking distance of the campsite (reception can provide a city map). Do take a stroll through the well tended, very pretty public gardens by the riverside. There is a fresh produce market in the town centre every morning except Monday. This pleasant, well run site has 214 mostly shady and generally grassy level pitches, with 132 electric hook-ups (5A), and a few mobile homes and caravans for rent.

**Facilities:** The main sanitary facilities are housed in a large, modern building, with two smaller older units opened at peak times, and include washbasins in cubicles. Facilities for disabled people. Motorcaravan service point. Bar, restaurant and takeaway (Jul/Aug). TV room. Boules, table tennis, badminton, volleyball and minigolf. Small playground. **Off site:** Adjacent open air pool complex free for campers (23/6-10/9).

**Charges** 2002

| | |
|---|---|
| Per adult | € 4.00 |
| child (under 7 yrs) | € 2.00 |
| pitch | € 4.10 |
| electricity | € 3.00 |

**Tel:** (0)5 46 93 08 00. Fax: (0)5 46 93 61 88. **Reservations:** Advisable for high season. **Open** 16 May - 15 September.

**Directions:** Site is north of the city centre, on west bank of River Charente, well signed. Follow the road on western bank north and site entrance is on right.

## Camping du Jard

123 Route de la Faute, 85360 La Tranche-sur-Mer

**8502**

the **travel service**
TO BOOK
Ferry ✔
Pitch ✔
Accommodation ✗
01892 55 98 98

Camping du Jard is a well maintained site between La Rochelle and Les Sables d'Olonne. First impressions on booking in are good, with a friendly welcome from M. Marton or his staff and each new arrival being personally shown to their pitch. The 350 pitches are level and grassy, hedged on two sides by bushes. The smallest are 100 sq.m. (the majority larger) and most are equipped with electricity, half with water and drainage. It is a comparatively new site, but the large variety of trees is beginning to provide a little shade. An impressive pool complex has a toboggan, paddling pool and an indoor pool with jacuzzi. The site is 700 m. from a sandy beach with many shops and restaurants near. The security barrier is closed at night. Used by tour operators (100 pitches).

**Facilities:** Three well designed and maintained toilet blocks are light and airy with excellent facilities for babies and disabled people. Most washbasins are in cabins. Washing machines and dryer. Dishwashing and laundry sinks. Small shop, restaurant (both 1/6-10/9), and bar (24/5-10/9). Heated pool with toboggan and paddling pool, plus good heated indoor pool with jacuzzi (no bermuda-style shorts). Sauna, solarium and fitness room. Tennis court, minigolf, table tennis. Play area, games room and TV room. Card operated barrier. Dogs not accepted.

**Charges** guide

| | |
|---|---|
| Per standard pitch incl. 2 persons | € 20.58 |
| with electricity (6 or 10A) | € 24.93 |
| extra person | € 3.20 - € 4.65 |

**Tel:** 02 51 27 43 79. **Fax:** 02 51 27 42 92. **E-mail:** info@camping-du-jard.fr. **Reservations:** Advisable for July/Aug. (min. 1 week, Sat.- Sat.) with deposit (€ 100). **Open** 25 May - 15 September.

**Directions:** Site is east of La Tranche-sur-Mer on the D46. From D747 (La Roche-sur-Yon to La Tranche) follow signs for La Faute-sur-mer along the new bypass. Take exit for La Grière and then turn east to site.

---

## Camping' Bel

rue du Bottereau, 85360 La Tranche-sur-Mer

**8542**

Camping Bel's owner, M. Guicau, who has a very dry sense of humour, takes an individual approach. The first priority is the contentment of the children, who receive various small gifts during their stay. The site was almost full when we visited in July with a large proportion of returning French clients, despite the large presence of British tour operators (130 pitches). At this time other nearby sites were not so full. The 70 touring pitches are on level, sandy grass which was well worn in July. They are separated by hedges with some mature trees giving shade. It is only 150 m. from a good sandy beach and 500 m. from La Tranche sur Mer. This is a good site for a family beach holiday.

**Facilities:** Two modern toilet blocks have washbasins in cabins, very good baby units and facilities for disabled visitors. Shop (25/5-8/9) with basic provisions. Bar (25/5-8/9). Heated outdoor pool with jacuzzi (25/5 8/9). Plenty of entertainment for children aged 6-14 yrs (July/Aug). Table tennis. Fitness area. Tennis. **Off site:** Bicycle hire 100 m. Supermarket with fuel 200 m. Fishing 1 km. Watersports 150 m.

**Charges** 2002

| | |
|---|---|
| Per unit incl. 2 persons | € 18.30 |
| with electricity (6A) | € 21.40 |
| extra person | € 3.90 |
| child (under 5 yrs) | € 3.10 |
| local tax | € 0.10 |

**Tel:** (0)2 51 30 47 39. **Fax:** (0)2 51 27 72 81. **Reservations:** Contact site. **Open** 25 May - 8 September.

**Directions:** Follow signs from the roundabout on the La Tranche bypass, near 'Super U' supermarket.

---

## Camping Club La Bolée d'Air

Route de Longeville, 85520 St Vincent sur Jard

**8543**

the **travel service**
TO BOOK
Ferry ✔
Pitch ✔
Accommodation ✔
01892 55 98 98

This well managed Chadotel site has good facilities and a varied programme of high season entertainment. The 120 touring pitches are all level and well grassed on sandy soil. Many are situated around the perimeter of the site and are separated by trimmed hedges giving good privacy but little shade. Long electricity cables may be required on some pitches. The main road runs along one side of the site and may cause traffic noise at some times. A refurbished complex at the entrance houses all the amenities. A good, sandy, supervised beach is just 900 m .away, the village of St Vincent sur Jard 1.5 km.

**Facilities:** Three modernised, unisex sanitary blocks provide washbasins in cabins, plenty of sinks for dishwashing and laundry, washing machines and dryers. Shop and takeaway (1/6 31/8). Bar (1/5 30/9). Heated indoor pool (1/4 30/9), outdoor pool (1/6 30/9) with slide, jacuzzi and paddling pool. Tennis. Minigolf. Bicycle hire. Table tennis.

**Charges** 2002

| | |
|---|---|
| Per unit incl. 2 persons | € 11.50 - € 20.50 |
| with electricity | € 15.00 - € 24.00 |
| extra person | € 5.20 |
| child (under 7 yrs) | € 3.30 |

**Tel:** 02 51 90 36 05. **Fax:** 02 51 33 94 04. **Reservations:** Made with deposit, fee and cancellation insurance. **Open** 1 April - 30 September.

**Directions:** Site is just off the D21 Les Sables La Franche road, just east of St Vincent-sur-Jard and is well signed from the main road.

---

## Vendée Charente
# Camping Les Brunelles
Le Bouil, 85560 Longeville sur Mer

8544

This is a well managed site with good facilities and a varied programme of high season entertainment for all the family. The owner, M. Guinard is justifiably proud of his campsite. In mid July the site was very busy but there was an atmosphere of well ordered calm. M. Guinard believes that if children are happy and occupied then parents are also happy. The 60 touring pitches are all level on sandy grass and separated by hedges, away from most of the mobile homes on site. There is a mixture of sunny and shaded pitches and all have easy access to electricity (6A). Water points are not so frequent. A good sandy beach is just 900 m. away, the village of St Vincent sur Jard 2 km.

**Facilities:** Four old but well maintained and modernised toilet blocks have British and Turkish style toilets, washbasins both open style and in cabins, plenty of sinks for dishwashing and laundry. Washing machines and dryers. Shop (1/6-15/9). Takeaway (15/6-7/9). Large airy bar (8/6-15/9) with games area. New covered pool with jacuzzi (5/4-15/9). Outdoor pool with slides and paddling pools (15/5-15/9), both heated but unsupervised. Fenced area for football, volleyball and basketball. Table tennis. Tennis. Bicycle hire.

**Charges** 2002
| | |
|---|---|
| Per unit incl. 2 persons | € 14.00 - € 18.00 |
| with electricity | € 17.00 - € 22.00 |
| extra person | € 3.00 - € 5.00 |

**Tel:** 02 51 33 50 75. **Fax:** 02 51 33 98 21. **E-mail:** camping@les-brunelles.com. **Reservations:** Made with 25% deposit and € 20 fee. **Open** 30 March - 29 September.

**Directions:** From D21 Talmont - Longeville road, site is well signed south towards the coast. Turn left in village of Le Bouil and site is 800 m. on left.

## Vendée Charente
# Camping-Caravaning Jarny-Ocean
Le Bouil, 85560 Longeville sur Mer

8524M

the travel service TO BOOK
| | |
|---|---|
| Ferry | ✓ |
| Pitch | ✓ |
| Accommodation | ✗ |

01892 55 98 98

Jarny Ocean is the sort of the site the French love - wooded (though less so than before the storms of Dec. 99) and with many pitches separated by thick hedges giving plenty of privacy. There are other areas, however, which are more open and with plenty of sun. There are 303 grassy pitches of average size on level ground, of which 250 are for touring units, around 25% well shaded. All have electricity (6/10A), about 15 also with water and drainaway. In high season a range of children's activities and lots of French style evening entertainment are organised (could be noisy). A beach is within easy walking distance (800 m) or a beach with lifeguards (and parking) is 4 km. English is spoken.

**Facilities:** Five toilet blocks (mixed use) of differing ages have British and Turkish style WCs. Small shop for basics in July/Aug (bread to order all season). Takeaway in the Centre de Vacances that shares the site (from 1/5). Bar (weekends in low season, 11.00 - 01.00 hrs in July/Aug). Heated pool (1/5 -15/9, trunks only). Large central play area. Table tennis. Tennis (free in low season). Bicycle hire. Volleyball. Basketball. **Off site:** Minigolf near. Riding or fishing 4 km.

**Charges** guide
| | |
|---|---|
| Per unit incl. 2 adults | € 9.00 - € 18.00 |
| with 6A electricity | € 10.00 - € 21.00 |
| extra person | € 2.00 - € 3.00 |
| local tax (July/Aug; over 10 yrs) | € 0.34 |

**Tel:** 02 51 33 42 21. **Fax:** 02 51 33 95 37. **E-mail:** jarny-ocean@wanadoo.fr. **Reservations:** Made with deposit and fee. **Open** 1 May - 30 September.

**Directions:** From D21 Talmont - Longeville road, soon after Jard, pass through St Vincent and very shortly the site is signed towards the coast (before Longeville). Turn left in village of Le Bouil (site signed) and site is on left in 800 m.

## Vendée Charente
# Camping Les Mancellières
route de Longeville-sur-Mer, 85440 Avrillé

8537

the travel service TO BOOK
| | |
|---|---|
| Ferry | ✓ |
| Pitch | ✓ |
| Accommodation | ✗ |

01892 55 98 98

This is a family run site on the edge of the small town of Avrillé, on the road between La Rochelle and Noirmoutiers, yet only a short drive from some of the delightful beaches of the southern Vendée. It is a simple, traditional and well-established site with 130 pitches (82 touring pitches), most with a mixture of sun and shade, but some very shaded. The fact that the snack bar is not licensed might appeal to those who prefer a simple life! Weekly outdoor disco, accompanied by moules-frites and other activities including pétanque, volleyball, water polo and table-tennis competitions, and France v. The Rest football match at the nearby stade (all these July/Aug).

**Facilities:** The two sanitary blocks are kept clean, with mainly British style WCs, washbasins (some in cubicles), baby bath in the ladies' wash rooms, an en-suite unit for disabled visitors. Sinks for dishwashing and laundry. Washing machine. Small shop and snack bar (July/Aug). Swimming pool and slide (until 15 Sept). Play area and good sized sports area. Two games rooms. **Off site:** Tennis 800 m. Riding 7 km. Golf 10 km. Sea 5 km.

**Charges** 2002
| | |
|---|---|
| Per unit incl. 2 persons | € 13.57 |
| extra person | € 2.74 |
| electricity (6A) | € 2.74 |

**Tel:** 02 51 90 35 97. **Fax:** 02 51 90 39 31. **Reservations:** Advised for high season. **Open** 1 May - 30 September.

**Directions:** Avrillé is on the D949 Les Sables d'Olonne - Luçon road, 23 km. from Les Sables. Site is about 1 km. south of the town, on D105 to Longeville-sur-Mer.

## Camping Municipal du Bois du Bouquet

**8534M** 85540 Moutiers les Mauxfaits

This is a fairly traditional municipal site with none of the bells and whistles of its coastal counterparts. It offers excellent value with its attractive, well maintained camping area, high quality toilet block and friendly ambience - you are quite likely to meet the Mayor who takes a personal interest in the site. Just a short walk from the centre of the pleasant little market town of Moutiers les Mauxfaits, Le Bois de Bouquet has 70 large, marked, grassy pitches, most with electricity (6A), in a mixture of sunny and shady locations. There is also an open area without electricity. A barrier controls the arrival and departure of over-height vehicles (caravans, motorcaravans, etc.) which is operated by the warden. After his departure at 8 pm, any such vehicles would be unable to drive on to or off the site except by prior arrangement (if you are delayed you should ring the site).

**Facilities:** The new toilet block is first-class, including excellent facilities for disabled visitors. Plenty of sinks for dishwashing and laundry. Washing machine. **Off site:** Shops, bars and restaurants in the town and nearest beaches 20 minutes drive away.

**Charges** 2002

| | |
|---|---|
| Per pitch incl. 2 adults | € 6.86 |
| extra person | € 1.83 |
| electricity | € 1.52 |

**Tel:** 02 51 98 96 41. **Reservations:** Unlikely to be necessary. **Open** 15 June - 1 September.

**Directions:** Site is on the D747 (La Roche sur Yonne - La Tranche sur Mer), just south of Moutiers, and is well signed.

## Camping La Grand' Métairie

**8530** 8 rue de la Vineuse en Plaine, 85440 St Hilaire la Forêt

Just 5 kilometres from the super sandy beach at Jard sur Mer, La Grand' Métairie offers many of the amenities of its seaside counterparts, but with the important advantage of being on the edge of a delightful, sleepy village, otherwise untouched by tourism. It is a busy well run site with a lively entertainment programme in high season and a new covered pool planned. The site has 172 pitches (72 touring pitches), all with electricity (6A), water and drainage. The pitches as yet have little shade but are all separated by small trees and bushes and are generous in size.

**Facilities:** Two modern toilet blocks are kept very clean and include washbasins mainly in cabins. Units for disabled people. Washing machines and dryers. Fridge hire. Basic provisions kept on site (village store 100 m). Smart bar/restaurant (15/5-15/9). Attractive, kidney-shaped heated pool with jacuzzi and paddling pool. Tennis, minigolf (both free in low season). Visiting hairdresser. **Off site:** High season free minibus service runs to the beach and to a number of local markets. Riding, fishing within 5 km.

**Charges** 2002

| | |
|---|---|
| Per unit incl. 2 persons, electricity | € 12.96 - € 18.29 |
| extra person | € 3.35 - € 4.57 |
| child (under 5 yrs) | € 2.13 - € 3.05 |
| dog | € 2.29 |

**Tel:** 02 51 33 32 38. Fax: 02 51 33 25 69. E-mail: grand-metairie@wanadoo.fr. **Reservations:** Advised for high season with 25% deposit and fee (€ 18,29). **Open** 1 April - 30 September.

**Directions:** Site is in centre of St Hilaire la Forêt. From Les Sables d'Olonne take D949 (La Rochelle) towards Talmont St Hilaire and Luçon. 7 km. after Talmont turn right on D70 to St Hilaire la Forêt. Site is on the left before village centre.

# Camping Les Ecureuils

route des Goffineaux, 85520 Jard-sur-Mer

Les Ecureuils is a wooded site in a quieter part of the southern Vendée. It is undoubtedly one of the prettiest sites on this stretch of coast, with an elegant reception area, attractive vegetation and large pitches separated by low hedges with plenty of shade. Of the 261 pitches, some 120 are for touring units, each with water and drainage, as well as easy access to 10A electricity. Jard is rated among the most pleasant and least hectic of Vendée towns. The harbour is home to some fishing boats and rather more pleasure craft, and has a public slipway for those bringing their own boats. This site is very popular with tour operators (126 pitches). And in case you are curious, yes there are squirrels on site, including red ones! A new indoor pool and spa should now be complete.

**Facilities:** Two toilet blocks, well equipped and kept very clean, include baby baths, and laundry rooms. Small shop. Takeaway service (pre-order). Snacks and ice-creams available from the friendly bar. Good sized L-shaped swimming pool and separate paddling pool. Modern children's play area. Minigolf, table tennis and a pool table. Club for children (5-10 yrs) daily in July/Aug. Bicycle hire. Only gas barbecues are allowed. Dogs are not accepted. **Off site:** Nearest beach 400 m. Fishing 400 m. Range of places to eat at nearby marina or in town which has good supermarket and weekly market.

**Charges** 2002

| | |
|---|---|
| Per pitch | € 11.00 |
| Per pitch with electricity (10A) | € 14.50 |
| person over 10 yrs | € 5.50 |
| child 0-4 yrs | € 2.00 |
| child 5-9 yrs | € 4.00 |
| local tax (July/Aug, over 10 yrs) | € 0.50 |

**Tel:** 02 51 33 42 74. Fax: 02 51 33 91 14. E-mail: camping-ecureuils@wanadoo.fr. **Reservations:** Advised for July/Aug. **Open** 15 May - 15 September.

**Directions:** Jard-sur-Mer is on the D21 road between Talmont St Hilaire and Longeville sur Mer. Site is well signed from the main road - caravanners will need to follow these signs to avoid tight bends and narrow roads.

## Vendée Charente
# Camping L'Oceano d'Or

58 rue Georges Clémenceau, BP 12, 85520 Jard-sur-Mer

| the travel service |
|---|
| TO BOOK |
| Ferry ✔ |
| Pitch ✔ |
| Accommodation ✗ |
| 01892 55 98 98 |

This Chadotel site should appeal to families with children of all ages. It is very lively in high season but appears to be well managed, with a full programme of activities in high season (it can therefore be noisy, sometimes late at night). The site is only 999 metres from the excellent beach. There are 431 flat, grass and sand pitches of which 40% are occupied by tour operators and mobile homes. The 200 for touring units, all with 10A electricity, are quite large (about 100 sq.m.). Some are separated by high hedges, others are more open with low bushes between them. A modern complex at the entrance houses all the facilities. There are shops, bars and restaurants, and a weekly market in the pleasant little town of Jard-sur-Mer.

**Facilities:** Four modern, unisex toilet blocks include washbasins all in cabins, plenty of dishwashing and laundry sinks and washing machines and dryers. Small shop (1/6-15/9). Bar and snack bar (both 15/6-15/9, but limited hours outside high season). Swimming pool (15/5-15/9) with slide and children's pool. Walled (three sides) play area. Tennis, table tennis, volleyball, pétanque and minigolf. Charcoal barbecues are not allowed. **Off site:** Golf, riding, karting and numerous other activities within 15 km. Excellent beach within walking distance.

**Charges** 2002

| | |
|---|---|
| Per pitch incl. 2 adults | € 13.50 - € 21.00 |
| with electricity | € 17.00 - € 24.50 |
| extra adult | € 5.20 |
| child (under 5 yrs) | € 3.30 |
| animal | € 2.50 |

**Tel:** 02 51 33 05 05. Fax: 02 51 33 94 04. E-mail: chadotel@wanadoo.fr. **Reservations:** Necessary for high season with deposit and fee. Central reservations: Siege Social - Centrale de Reservation, BP 12, 85520. **Open** 1 April - 25 September.

**Directions:** Site is on the D21 Talmont St Hilaire - Longeville sur Mer, just east of the turning to the town centre.

---

## Vendée Charente
# Camping des Batardières

85440 St Hilaire-la-Foret

Camping des Batardières is a haven of tranquillity on the edge of an unspoilt village, yet just 5 km. from the sea. It is an attractive, unsophisticated little site, lovingly maintained by its owners for the past 23 years. Many clients (including British) return year after year, and it was one of these who described it as a 'haven of tranquillity'. There are 75 good-sized pitches (a few up to 130 sq.m.) and all are available for touring units (there are no mobile homes and no tour operators!) All have easy access to water and electricity (6A, or 2A for tents). Otherwise there are few facilities on site.

**Facilities:** The centrally positioned sanitary block is kept very clean and visitors are encouraged to keep it that way. Some washbasins in cubicles for ladies. Dishwashing and laundry facilities, including a washing machine and a dryer. TV room, table tennis and a tennis court. Play area and a huge field for games, kite-flying etc. **Off site:** Village shop and bar 200 m.

**Charges** 2002

| | |
|---|---|
| Per unit incl. 2 persons | € 13.57 |
| with electricity | € 16.62 |
| extra person | € 2.74 |
| child (under 7 yrs) | € 1.83 |

**Tel:** 02 51 33 33 85. **Reservations:** Contact site. **Open** 27 June - 5 September.

**Directions:** Site is on edge of St Hilaire-la-Forêt. From Les Sables d'Olonne take D949 (la Rochelle) road towards Talmont St Hilaire and Luçon. 7 km. after Talmont turn right on D70 to St Hilaire-la-Forêt and site is signed to right on approach to village.

---

## Vendée Charente
# Camping Les Pirons

rue des Marchais, La Pironnière, 85180 Château-d'Olonne

| the travel service |
|---|
| TO BOOK |
| Ferry ✔ |
| Pitch ✔ |
| Accommodation ✔ |
| 01892 55 98 98 |

This is a modern, well run site of which the new owner M. Chailloleau is very proud. The site is a short walk from the sandy beach and within easy reach of the attractive seaside town of Les Sables d'Olonne. The 114 touring pitches are well grassed and either level or on a slight slope. They are concentrated in one central area of the campsite away from the large number of mobile homes (over 300). The large new sanitary block is particularly impressive, as is the swimming pool complex overlooked by the bar's sun terrace. There are several small French tour operators (56 pitches). In early season the site is quiet and facilities are limited. In high season there is an excellent animation programme for all.

**Facilities:** Four toilet blocks, three new, have washbasins in cubicles and units for disabled people, babies and dogs. Washing machines and dryers. Bar (29/6-31/8). Shop (29/6-31/8). Takeaway (29/6-31/8). Covered, heated pool, outdoor pools with slide and children's pool. Good play area. Table tennis, volleyball, football. Tennis. Pétanque. Indoor games area. Bicycle, scooter and motorbike hire. Activities day and evening for all ages (29/6-31/8). **Off site:** Beach, sea fishing, riding and sailing all within 5 km.

**Charges** 2002

| | |
|---|---|
| Per unit incl. 3 persons | € 13.72 - € 18.29 |
| with electricity (6A) | € 16.46 - € 21.34 |
| extra person | € 1.83 - € 3.05 |

**Tel:** 02 51 95 26 75. Fax: 02 51 23 93 17. E-mail: camping.les.pirons@wanadoo.fr. **Reservations:** Contact site. **Open** 1 April - 31 October.

**Directions:** From D949 Les Sables - La Rochelle road, site is well signed at traffic lights on western outskirts of Les Sables d'Olonne.

## Camping La Loubine

1 route de la Mer, 85340 Olonne-sur-Mer

**8503**

La Loubine is an attractive, lively family site with friendly atmosphere and good facilities for teenagers. It has 368 level and grassy pitches of which some 180 are used for touring units. All have electricity (6A), and some with water and drainage are available at a small extra cost. The original part of the site has shady pitches, elsewhere they are more open. The buildings around a pleasant courtyard overlooking the impressive pool complex have been tastefully converted to provide the bar etc. and it is here that evening entertainment takes place (of the disco/karaoke variety). There is a night security barrier. Used by tour operators (70 pitches).This is a busy site, popular with families with children and teenagers. It can be quite noisy late in the evenings in high season.

**Facilities:** Four modern toilet blocks include mainly British style WCs and washbasins in cabins. Babies and disabled people are well catered for. Washing machines, dryers, washing lines and irons. Ample supply of dishwashing and laundry sinks. Motorcaravan services. Shop, bar, takeaway and restaurant (all 15/5-15/9). Indoor pool with jacuzzi, sauna and fitness room (free). Outdoor pools (from 1/5; no bermuda style shorts) consisting of two heated outdoor pools with five water slides and children's pool. Large play area. Tennis (free in low season). Table tennis, minigolf, badminton. Bicycle hire. Activities and sports organised. Daily club for children in July/Aug. No dogs are accepted. **Off site:** Riding 200 m, golf 3 km, fishing 3 km. Beach at Sauveterre 1.8 km, Les Sables d'Olonne 5 km.

**Charges** guide

| | |
|---|---|
| Per pitch incl. 2 persons | € 18.90 |
| with electricity (6A) | € 21.19 |
| with all services | € 22.71 |
| extra adult | € 3.81 |
| child (under 7) | € 2.29 |

**Tel:** 02 51 33 12 92. Fax: 02 51 33 12 71. E-mail: camping.la.loubine@wanadoo.fr. **Reservations:** Made with deposit and € 18,29 fee (min. 7 days in Jul/Aug.) **Open** 1 April - 30 September (full facilities from 15/5)

**Directions:** Site is west of Olonne beside the D80 road. Turn towards the coast at traffic lights, signed La Forêt d'Olonne and site (75 m).

## Camping La Trévillière

Rue de Bellevue, 85470 Bretignolles-sur-Mer

**8531**

the travel service
TO BOOK
Ferry ✓
Pitch ✓
Accommodation ✓
01892 55 98 98

A member of the Chadotel group, La Trévillière has a pleasant semi-rural setting on the edge of the little resort town of Bretignolles. Although just 2 km. from the nearest beach and less than 5 km. from the Plage des Dunes (one of southern Vendée's best beaches), La Trévillière has a more 'laid-back' feel than many other sites in the area, particularly in low season. The 180 pitches are grassy and either level or on a slight slope; all have easy access to electricity (6/10A) and water. They are separated by hedges or low bushes and there is a mix of shady or more open positions. The site has around 50 mobile homes and chalets on site and it is used by three small tour operators, but it remains very much a camping and caravanning site. Early in the season the site is very quiet; in July/Aug. it becomes much livelier with a good range of morning activities for children, afternoon events for families and evening entertainment for all.

**Facilities:** Three modern, clean toilet blocks include washbasins in cubicles, a unit for disabled people and baby room with bath, shower and toilet. Washing machines and dryers. Bar (limited opening in low season). Small independently operated shop and snack bar with takeaway (20/6-8/9). Children's play area. Mingolf, table tennis. Charcoal barbecues are not allowed. **Off site:** Golf, riding, karting, water sports and water parks are all within easy reach.

**Charges** 2003

| | |
|---|---|
| Per pitch incl. 2 adults | € 12.00 - € 21.00 |
| with electricity | € 15.50 - € 24.70 |
| extra adult | € 5.30 |
| child (under 5 yrs) | € 3.40 |
| animal | € 2.60 |

**Tel:** 02 51 33 05 05. Fax: 02 51 33 94 04. **Reservations:** Necessary for high season with deposit and fee. Central reservations: Siege Social - Centrale de Reservation, BP 12, 85520 Jard sur Mer. **Tel:** (0)2.51.33.05.05. Fax: (0)2.51.33.94.04. E-mail: chadotel@wanadoo.fr. **Open** 1 April - 25 September.

**Directions:** Bretignolles is on the D38 coast road (Noirmoutier - Les Sables d'Olonne). From north, after St Gilles go through Bretignolles-La Sauzaie (take left fork) and before reaching Bretignolles itself turn left (sign for site) on sharp right hand bend, heading for water tower. Site is on right in 800 m. From south, after centre of Bretignolles, turn right (sign 'Ecoles') and then left (signs for sports centre and site). Site is signed to left after stadium.

## Vendée Charente
# Camping Bois Soleil
chemin des Barres, 85340 Olonne-sur-Mer

This site has a very French feel, the majority of the population when we visited seeming to be French. It is a traditionally laid out site with 170 marked pitches, separated by hedges, on flat or gently sloping ground. There is just one (French) tour operator and a scattering of mobile homes and chalets, leaving some 100 pitches available for tourers and tents. All have electricity (6A, French style sockets) and water points adjacent and many also have waste water pipes. The main buildings house a small reception and tourist information room as well as the bar and attached shop. There is an excellent new swimming pool complex with sunbathing areas, paddling pool and a separate pool for the two water slides and impressive flume. In July and August a range of daily activities is organised for adults and children.

**Facilities:** The two well equipped and maintained toilet blocks have copious hot water, mainly British style toilets, with washbasins in cubicles in the new block. This block is locked overnight, but basic toilet facilities are provided. Covered dishwashing and laundry sinks. Two washing machines. Shop in July and August only with 'eat in' or takeaway food service; bread (and cooked chicken) must to be ordered the previous day. Swimming and paddling pools. Sandy children's play area (caged), trampoline and table tennis. **Off site:** Beaches are just 2 km. The thriving resort of Les Sables d'Olonne is 5 km along the coast.

**Charges** guide

| | |
|---|---|
| Per unit incl. 2 persons | € 7.30 - € 14.20 |
| with electricity | € 13.75 - € 17.25 |
| extra adult | € 2.45 - € 3.00 |
| child (under 7 yrs) | € 1.85 - € 2.15 |
| animal | € 1.85 |

**Tel:** (0)2 51 33 11 97. **Fax:** (0)2 51 33 14 85.
**Reservations:** Advised for July/Aug. and made with 25% deposit and booking fee in July/Aug of € 12,20. **Open** 1 May - 16 September.

**Directions:** Site is off the D80 coast road between Olonne-sur-Mer and is clearly signed on the inland side.

## Vendée Charente
# Camping-Caravaning Les Roses
Rue des Roses, 85100 Les Sables d'Olonne

A Chadotel site, Les Roses has an urban location with the town centre and the beach just a short walk away. There is an informal air with the 210 pitches arranged interestingly on a knoll. Mature trees give good shade to parts of the site. There are 107 touring pitches of varying size, many being more suitable for tents than caravans. All pitches have access to electricity (10A) and water but long cables may be needed. In high season caravanners might find access to the site tricky at times due to overloaded town centre traffic systems. The site has 103 mobile homes and chalets but no tour operators. There is an entertainment programme in high season for all ages. The town of Les Sables with its lively night life is readily accessible.

**Facilities:** Three well maintained toilet blocks have washbasins in cubicles. Unit for disabled visitors, baby room, washing machines and dryers. Bar (15/5-15/9). Very basic shop (10/6-15/9). Small attractively laid out heated outdoor pool with water slide and paddling pool (1/5-30/9). Children's play area, volleyball, basketball, petanque, table tennis. Bicycle hire. Electric barbecues are not allowed. **Off site:** Golf, riding, karting, water sports, zoo, sea and river fishing all within easy reach.

**Charges** 2002

| | |
|---|---|
| Per pitch incl. 2 persons | € 13.50 - € 21.00 |
| with electricity | € 17.00 - € 24.50 |
| extra person | € 3.30 |
| child (under 5 yrs) | € 2.50 |

**Tel:** 02 51 33 05 05. **Fax:** 02 51 33 94 04.
**Reservations:** Contact site. **Open** 1 April - 31 October.

**Directions:** Site is signed from the D949 Les Sables to La Rochelle road, north of the 'Géant Casino' roundabout. Turn south at minor junction.

## Vendée Charente
# Camping La Dune des Sables
La Paracou, 85100 Les Sables d'Olonne

**8546**

the **travel service**
TO BOOK

| | |
|---|---|
| Ferry | ✓ |
| Pitch | ✓ |
| Accommodation | ✓ |

01892 55 98 98

La Dune des Sables, a Chadotel site, has a splendid coastal setting with views towards the northwest Vendée coast. Its terrain is undulating with no shade and limited protection from wind off the sea. Access to the sandy/rocky beach is by a locked gate (opened by your barrier key) at the bottom of the site. The 120 touring pitches, all with electricity (although long cables may be needed) and water are situated throughout the site and vary in size. There is little grass on the sandy pitches some of which are separated by hedges or fences. There are 90 mobile homes and 160 tour operator pitches. In high season there is a lively animation programme for all ages, including teenagers.

**Facilities:** Three well maintained toilet blocks provide washbasins in cabins, a unit for disabled people, a baby room, washing machines and dryers. Bar (1/6-7/9) with wide terrace and outdoor stage. Shop (15/6-7/9). Restaurant (1/7-31/8). Takeaway (15/6-9/9). Circular, heated swimming pool with slide. Play area. Tennis, minigolf, table tennis. Bicycle hire. **Off site:** Golf, fishing, water sports, zoo nearby.

**Charges** 2002

| Per pitch incl. 2 persons | € 13.50 - € 21.00 |
|---|---|
| with electricity (10A) | € 17.00 - € 24.50 |
| extra person | € 3.30 |
| child (under 5 yrs) | € 2.50 |

**Tel:** 02 51 33 05 05. **Fax:** 02 51 33 94 04. **Reservations:** Contact site. **Open** 5 April - 5 September.

**Directions:** From Les Sables or Brem-sur-Mer follow D87a and at autoroute follow signs west on minor road at small roundabout. Site is on right after 500 m.

## Vendée Charente
# Camping Pong
rue du Stade, 85220 Landevieille

**8513**

the **travel service**
TO BOOK

| | |
|---|---|
| Ferry | ✓ |
| Pitch | ✓ |
| Accommodation | ✗ |

01892 55 98 98

A comfortable family run site, Camping Pong is in a rural situation on the edge of a neat village, 12 km. southeast of St Gilles-Croix-de-Vie, and 5 km. from the coast at Brétignolles. It has 185 pitches, all with electricity (4/6A) and of a good size with some larger ones (up to 180 sq.m.) costing a little more. The original part of the site around the small, lightly fenced fishing lake (parents need to watch children) has a mixture of mature trees, whereas, in the newer, terraced area, the trees and bushes are less developed. The new field provides large pitches, but may be poorly drained. An attractive pool area includes a delightful paddling pool with many fascinating features for children and a pretty patio area overlooked by the bar. There are no tour operator pitches.

**Facilities:** Three modern, unisex sanitary blocks provide toilets of mixed styles and some washbasins in cabins. Facilities for disabled people, separate baby room, dishwashing under cover and laundry room. Maintenance can be variable. Small shop with takeaway and bar (both 15/6-15/9). Swimming pools including heated pool with jacuzzi, toboggan and paddling pool (from 15/5). Small gym, TV lounge and games room. Bicycle hire. Exciting new fenced play area and regular children's club. **Off site:** Tennis 200 m. Golf or riding 5 km. Large Lac du Jaunay 2.5 km.(canoeing and pedaloes). Nearest beach 6 km.

**Charges** 2003

| Per unit incl. 2 persons | € 11.50 - € 23.00 |
|---|---|
| extra person | € 3.00 - € 4.00 |
| child (under 5 yrs) | € 2.25 - € 3.00 |
| electricity 4/6A | € 3.00 - € 4.00 |

**Tel:** 02 51 22 92 63. **Fax:** 02 51 22 99 25. **E-mail:** lepong@free.fr. **Reservations:** Made deposit and fee. **Open** Easter - 30 September.

**Directions:** Site is on edge of Landevieille, signed from both D32 (Challons - Les Sables d'Olonne) and D12 (La Mothe Achard - St Gilles) roads.

## Vendée Charente
# Camping-Caravaning Le Chaponnet
Rue du Chaponnet, 85470 Brem sur Mer

**8548**

This well established family run site is within five minutes walk of Brem village centre and 1.5 km. from a long sandy beach. The 100 touring pitches are level with varying amounts of grass, some with shade from mature trees. All pitches are separated by tall hedges and there are frequent water and electricity points. A warm welcome is given at the large reception area, often from Mme. Guebert herself, whose influence can be felt in the well ordered calm of the campsite. Tour operators take 70 pitches and there are 70 mobile homes and chalets. The pool complex has indoor (heated) and outdoor pools Entertainment for all ages provide family fun rather than teenage activities.

**Facilities:** The six sanitary blocks are modern light and airy, well maintained and cleaned. Washbasins are in cubicles. Good facilities for babies and disabled people. Washing machines, dryers and ironing boards. Bar, snack bar and takeaway (1/6-6/9). No shop but bread and croissants available at the bar. Good play area. Table tennis, tennis and bicylce hire. Indoor games room. **Off site:** Fishing 5 km. Golf 12 km. Riding 10 km.

**Charges** 2003

| Per unit incl. 2 persons | € 16.00 - € 24.80 |
|---|---|
| with electricity | € 19.50 - € 28.20 |
| extra person | € 3.50 - € 4.50 |
| local tax | 0.35 |

**Tel:** 02 51 90 55 56. **Fax:** 02 51 90 91 67. **E-mail:** chaponnet@free.fr. **Reservations:** Contact site. **Open** 1 May - 15 September.

**Directions:** Brem is on the D38 St Gilles - Les Sables d'Olonne road. Site is clearly signed, just off the one-way system in the centre of the village.

## Camping Le Pas Opton

**8506** route de Nantes, 85800 Le Fenouiller

A well established site, Le Pas Opton is under new management. Spring Harvest Holidays are investmenting much money in developing the site and its facilities and will be operating it as a Christian holiday centre. It is 6 km. back from the sea at St Gilles Croix de Vie and quietly situated. With a well ordered atmosphere, it offers a range of amenities including a pool and water slide. There are 200 pitches, most with electricity and some with hardstanding, water and drainage - the new owners are adding more mobile homes. The pitches in the original part are well shaded by mature trees and tall hedges. The newer areas have less shade but are developing well with a more spacious feel. The river Vie runs past the rear of the site - it is fenced and gated (no bolt).

**Facilities:** Three toilet blocks include washbasins mainly in cabins for women, partly for men, and a unit for disabled people. Laundry facilities. Motorcaravan service point. Shop (30/6-1/9). Bar, café and takeaway (all 1/7-31/8). Heated swimming pool (20/5-10/9) with water slide and children's pools. Playground. Volleyball, basketball, and table tennis. Entertainment and some dancing organised in season. Fishing (licences available in the village). **Off site:** Riding, golf, bicycle hire within 7 km, sailing centre and windsurfing 2 km. and markets at St Gilles-Croix two or three times weekly.

**Charges** 2002

| | | |
|---|---|---|
| Per unit incl. 2 persons, electricity | € 15.85 - | € 21.95 |
| with water and drainage | € 18.29 - | € 24.39 |
| extra adult | | € 4.27 |
| child (under 7) | | € 2.44 |

**Tel:** 02 51 55 11 98. **Fax:** 02 51 55 44 94. **E-mail:** enquiries@springharvestholidays.com. **Reservations:** Made from Jan. (min. 1 week) with deposit and fee. **Open** 20 May - 10 September.

**Directions:** Site is northeast of St Gilles, on D754 past Le Fenouiller towards the junction with D32.

---

## Camping-Caravaning Val de Vie

**8532** rue du Stade, 85190 Maché

Opened in 1999, Val de Vie is a small, good quality site run with enthusiasm and dedication by its English owners on the outskirts of a rural village back from the coast. There are currently 52 pitches for touring units (42 with electricity; 4, 6 or 10A) that vary in size from 80-137 sq.m. on mostly level grass with new hedging. The ground can become hard so steel pegs are advised. The pitches are arranged in circular fashion around the toilet block which, with reception, is built in local style with attractive, red tiled roofs. The owners, the McClearns, want you to experience real French village life and culture and encourage you to enjoy the local amenities. The Vendée coast is 25 km.

**Facilities:** The toilet block provides excellent, modern facilities including some washbasins in cabins, baby bath, facilities for disabled people, dishwashing and laundry sinks, and washing machines. Reception also offers wine, beer, soft drinks and ice cream. Small play area. Swimming pool (from mid May). **Off site:** Opposite site are a heated outdoor municipal pool and tennis courts. Shops, bar, etc. all within walking distance.

**Charges** 2002

| | | |
|---|---|---|
| Per unit incl. 2 persons | | € 12.50 |
| extra person | | € 3.10 |
| child (under 10 yrs) | | € 2.50 |
| electricity 4-10A | € 2.50 - | € 3.10 |
| dog | | € 1.50 |

**Tel:** 02 51 60 21 02. **Fax:** 02 51 60 21 02. **E-mail:** campingvaldevie@aol.com. **Reservations:** Contact site. **Open** 1 May - 30 September.

**Directions:** From D948 at Aizenay take D107 north west to Maché (6 km). Site signed in the village.

---

## Camping Les Prairies du Lac

**8541** route de Maché, 85220 Apremont

The owners of this traditional campsite are constantly updating and improving the facilities and are very keen to welcome British holidaymakers. It is in the countryside, on a plateau above the attractive little town of Apremont whose excellent restaurant picturesquely nestles between the castle on one hill and the church on the other. At the bottom of the street is a shady river (the Vie) with flat-bottomed boats, canoes and pedaloes and further along the road, a lake with swimming and a range of water-craft. The main touring area is flat with plenty of established trees to provide shade. Electricity (6/10A) is available, although at present lengthy cables are provided for some pitches.

**Facilities:** The toilet building is smart, with everything inside fresh and clean when we visited. Mixed British and Turkish style toilets, some washbasins in cubicles. Dishwashing and laundry sinks. Washing machine and tumble dryer. Pleasant little bar, snack bar and takeaway (all 1/7-31/8). Basic supplies including bread (not gas). Two swimming pools.

**Charges** 2003

| | | |
|---|---|---|
| Per unit incl. 2 persons | € 17.00 - | € 19.00 |
| extra adult | | € 4.00 |
| child (2-7 yrs) | | € 3.00 |
| electricity (6/10A) | € 3.00 - | € 5.00 |
| animal | | € 2.00 |

**Tel:** (0)2 51 55 70 58. **Fax:** (0)2 51 55 76 04. **E-mail:** infos@les-prairies-du-lac.com. **Reservations:** Made with deposit and fee. **Open** 1 June - 30 September.

**Directions:** Site is on the D40 main road from Maché to Apremont, just before you reach the town. The D40 is off the D948 Challans to La Roche-sur-Yon road, 6 km northwest of Aizenay.

# Castel Camping La Garangeoire

St Julien-des-Landes, 85150 La Mothe-Achard

8504

La Garangeoire is one of a relatively small number of seriously good sites in the Vendée, situated some 15 km. inland near the village of St Julien des Landes. One of its more memorable qualities is the view of the château through the gates as you drive in. Imaginative use has been made of the old Noirmoutiers 'main road' which passes through the centre of the site and now forms a delightful, quaint thoroughfare, nicknamed the Champs Elysée. Providing a village like atmosphere, it is busy at most times with the facilities opening directly off it. The site is set in the 200 ha. of parkland which surrounds the small château of La Garangeoire. The peaceful fields and woods, where campers may walk, include three lakes, one of which is used for fishing and boating (life jackets supplied from reception). The site has a spacious, relaxed atmosphere and many use it as a quiet base. The main camping areas are arranged on either side of the old road, edged with mature trees. The 300 pitches, each with a name not a number and individually hedged, are especially large (most 150-200 sq.m.) and are well spaced. Most have electricity (12A), some water and drainage also. The site is popular with British tour operators (144 pitches).

**Facilities:** Ample sanitary facilities are of good standard, well situated for all areas. One excellent block has facilities for babies and disabled people. All have washbasins in cabins. Good laundry facilities. Motorcaravan service point. Good shop. Full restaurant, takeaway and a separate crêperie with bars and attractive courtyard terrace overlooking the swimming pool complex (from 1/5) with water slides, fountains and a children's pool. Large playing field with play equipment for children's activities, whether organised or not. Games room. Two tennis courts. Bicycle hire. Table tennis, crazy golf, archery and volleyball. Riding in July/Aug. Fishing and boating. **Off site:** Beaches 15 km.

**Charges** 2003

| | |
|---|---|
| Per unit incl. 2 persons | € 14.00 - € 24.00 |
| with electricity | € 17.00 - € 28.00 |
| with services | € 18.50 - € 30.00 |
| extra person | € 3.50 - € 5.50 |
| child (under 10 yrs) | € 2.00 - € 2.50 |
| dog | € 2.00 - € 3.00 |
| local tax | free - € 0.50 |

**Tel:** 02 51 46 65 39. Fax: 02 51 46 69 85. E-mail: garangeoire@wanadoo.fr. **Reservations:** Made for min. 7 days with deposit (€ 61) and fee (€ 22,87). **Open** 5 April - 24 September.

**Directions:** Site is signed from St Julien; the entrance is to the north off the D21 road.

CASTEL CAMPING - CARAVANNING

★★★★

# La Garangeoire

The peace and tranquility of a large private estate, 15 km from the Atlantic coast beaches.
A lot of activities provided for children and adults.

**St-Julien-des-Landes - 85150 La Mothe-Achard
Tel: 0033 251 46 65 39 - Fax: 0033 251 46 69 85
www.camping-la-garangeoire.com - E-mail: garangeoire@wanadoo.fr**

## Vendée Charente
# Village de la Guyonnière
La Guyonnière, 85150 St. Julien des Landes

**8526**

La Guyonnière is a spacious, rural site, away from the hertic coast. It is popular for many reasons, the main ones being the free and easy atmosphere and its reasonable pricing. It is Dutch owned and the majority of its customers are Dutch, but English is spoken and British visitors are made very welcome. It is a farm type site with four different fields, each being reasonably level and each having a toilet block. The 181 pitches are sunny and very large (the few smaller ones are cheaper) and are separated by a tree and a few bushes. All have access to electricity connections (6A) although long leads may be required. Bar/restaurant facilities are housed in the original farm buildings attractively converted. Entertainment is provided in the bar on high season evenings. A perfect place for families, with large play areas on sand and grass,and paddling pond with shower. Being in the country it is a haven for cyclists and walkers, with many signed routes from the site. A pleasant 500 m. walk takes you to the Jaunay lake where fishing is possible (permits from the village), canoeing (lifejackets from reception) and pedaloes to hire. There are no tour operators and, needless to say, no road noise.

**Facilities:** Toilet blocks are modern, functional and central for each area. Most cubicles are quite small but they serve their purpose and were very clean when we visited; however, perhaps not adequate in high season. Washbasins are in cubicles. Provision for babies and disabled visitors. Dishwashing and laundry sinks at each block. Small shop (1/5-30/9; order bread from reception outside these dates). Bar with TV and pool table and pleasant restaurant (1/5-30/9). Pizzeria with takeaway. Small swimming pool, new heated pool with jacuzzi and slide, very attractive and can be covered in cool weather. Paddling pool. Children's play areas, sand pit. Table tennis, volleyball and football fields. Bicycle hire. **Off site:** Riding 3 km, golf 8 km, beaches 10 km.

**Charges** guide

| | |
|---|---|
| Per unit incl. 2 persons | € 20.12 |
| extra person | € 4.42 |
| child (under 10 yrs) | € 2.90 |
| electricity | € 2.74 |
| animal | € 2.29 |
| local tax (10 yrs and over) | € 0.34 |

**Tel:** 02 51 46 62 59. Fax: 02 51 46 62 89. E-mail: camping-guyonniere@wanadoo.fr. **Reservations:** Made with 25% deposit. **Open** 1 May- 30 October.

**Directions:** Site is off the D12 road (La Mothe Achard - St Gilles Croix de Vie), approx. 4 km. west of St Julien-des-Landes. It is signed about 1 km. from the main road.

**CAMPING ★ ★ ★**        **VENDÉE**

# VILLAGE DE LA GUYONNIÈRE

10 km from the Atlantic coast. The campsite is on an estate of 30 hectares. Each pitch is approximately 200/225 metres square. Our campsite is particularly suitable for young families. On site we have a restaurant, small shops, bar, swimming pool, children's play area, table tennis, library, mini-zoo, football pitch and «parcours de santé». Children's play leader every day in July and August. Hot showers free of charge, washbasins in individual cubicles. Baby corner with baby bath. Washing machines.
***New: Heated indoor pool, Slide, Jacuzzi and Fishing Lake.***
To rent: pitches all year - Mobile homes/chalets
Do not hesitate to call us if you require more information.
Open 01/05 - 30/09
PIERRE JASPERS AND ANNIE VAN DER LOOP
85150 St Julien des Landes
Tel. 0033 251 46 62 59 - Fax 0033 251 46 62 89
Internet: www.laguyonniere.com - E-mail: info@laguyonniere.com

# Hotellerie de Plein Air La Puerta del Sol

**8508**

Les Borderies, chemin de Hommeaux, 85270 St-Hilaire-de-Riez

La Puerta del Sol is a good quality campsite a short distance away from the busy coast. It is suitable not only for families with teenage children to entertain, but also for those seeking a more peaceful and relaxing holiday. There are 216 pitches, of which 158 are used for touring units. Pitches are level with dividing hedges and many receive shade from the mature trees on the site. Each pitch is fully serviced with water, waste water point and electricity. In July/Aug. a range of activities is provided for adults and children, including a children's club, aqua aerobics, swimming lessons, tournaments and games, with evening entertainment in the bar. There is one small French tour operator on site (20 pitches).

**Facilities:** Three well maintained toilet blocks of identical design have a mix of Turkish and British style WCs, washbasins in cabins and baby baths. Dishwashing and laundry sinks. Laundry with washing machines and irons. Fully equipped rooms for disabled visitors. Small shop (1/7-31/8). Bar (15/5-15/9). Self-service restaurant and takeaway (1/7-31/8) overlooking the swimming and paddling pools (15/5-15/9; no bermuda style shorts). Play area. Tennis. Bicycle hire. Volleyball, table tennis and video games. **Off site:** Riding, fishing and golf within 5 km. Nearest sandy beach 5 km. St Jean de Monts 7 km.

**Charges** guide

| | |
|---|---|
| Per unit incl. up to 2 persons | € 14.48 - € 27.40 |
| extra person | € 4.26 - € 5.79 |
| child (under 7) | € 2.13 - € 2.89 |
| animal | € 1.52 |

**Tel:** 02 51 49 10 10. Fax: 02 51 49 84 84. E-mail: puerta-del-sol@wanadoo.fr. **Reservations:** Advised for high season; made with deposit (€ 138) and fee (€ 30,49). **Open** 1 May - 15 September.

**Directions:** From Le Pissot (which is 7 km. north of St Gilles Croix-de-Vie on D38) take the D59 towards Le Perrier. The site is 2 km. along this road on the right side down a short side road. There is a large sign for the site 200 m. before the turning and another sign on the left directly opposite the turn.

---

# Camping Le Marais Braud

**8519**

298 route du Perrier, 85270 St-Hilaire-de-Riez

Le Marais Braud is a small, unsophisticated site occuping a peaceful wooded setting, slightly inland from the busy coastal areas of the Vendée, but only 7 km. from sandy beaches. There are 150 spacious pitches, of which 109 are available for touring units. The level, shaded pitches are sandy with some grass, and some are divided by low hedges. Electricity is available within 30 m. of every pitch (although this may sometimes require that cables cross the road). At the far end of the site is a small lake for fishing, which is also home to white and black swans, and geese. There are no tour operators. Although the site is only open for a short season, the owners, M. & Mme Besseau, ensure that it provides a welcoming, family atmosphere, suitable for families or couples looking for a budget holiday.

**Facilities:** Two toilet blocks (one smaller and newer than the other), both provide mostly British style toilets, some washbasins in cabins, dishwashing and laundry sinks and a washing machine. Facilities for disabled visitors. Little shop for basics. Friendly bar incorporating a games area with a skittle alley and crêperie with takeaway (all 1/7-31/8). Small heated swimming pool with water slide and children's pool (from 1/6; no bermuda style shorts). Tennis court, boules area and play areas. Caravan storage. **Off site:** Bicycle hire 6 km, riding 7 km.

**Charges** 2002

| | |
|---|---|
| Per unit incl. 2 persons | € 14.00 |
| with electricity (6A) | € 17.00 |
| extra person | € 3.40 |
| child (under 7 yrs) | € 2.20 |
| dog | € 1.50 |
| local tax July/Aug. (over 10 yrs) | € 0.30 |

**Tel:** 02 51 68 33 71. Fax: 02 51 35 25 32. **Reservations:** Advised in high season and made with deposit (€ 69) and fee (€ 15,24). **Open** 1 June - 15 September.

**Directions:** From Le Pissot roundabout (north of St Hilaire de Riez), take D59 signed Le Perrier. Site is well signed about 3 km. along this road on the right.

## Vendée Charente
# Camping La Parée Préneau
23 Avenue de la Parée Préneau, 85270 St Hilire de Riez

**8553**

This site was founded in 1968 by the grandfather of the present owner. It has been gradually and thoughtfully expanded to its present size (206 pitches). Of these, 150 are touring pitches of varying shapes and sizes, interestingly arranged. Mature trees proliferate to give varying amounts of shade to the undulating site, although the pitches are level. Of sandy grass or pine needles, all have electricity (6A) and many also have water and drainage. The calm atmosphere is enhanced by the absence of tour operators. The cosy welcoming bar overlooks the swimming pool area. The friendly welcome in campsite reception is indicative of the caring attitude of those running the site.

**Facilities:** Two modern toilet blocks include washbasins (some in cubicles), facilities for babies and disabled visitors. WCs are a mixture of British and Turkish. Laundry and dishwashing sinks, washing machine and dryer. No restaurant or shop but bread and other essentials sold. Mobile takeaway calls in high season. Heated indoor and outdoor pools with jacuzzi and paddling pool. Large play area. Table tennis (indoor). Bicycle hire. **Off site:** Fishing 7 km. Golf 7 km. Riding 3 km. Sailing 7 km. Beach 1 km. Shops, bars, restaurants 5 km.

**Charges** 2002

| | |
|---|---|
| Per unit incl. 2 persons | € 12.00 - € 18.50 |
| extra person | € 3.00 - € 3.90 |

**Tel:** 02 51 54 33 84. **Fax:** 02 51 55 29 57. **E-mail:** camplapareepreneau@free.fr. **Reservations:** Contact site. **Open** 1 May - 15 September.

**Directions:** From large roundabout on D38 just north of St Hilaire-de-Riez, turn south signed St Hilaire for 400 m. Take first exit at next roundabout signed Les Plages and in another 400 m. continue straight on at junction. Site is on left after 3 km.

## Vendée Charente
# Camping-Caravaning Sol a Gogo
61 avenue de la Pége, 85270 St-Hilaire-de-Riez

**8516**

A popular site right beside the sea, Sol a Gogo has 196 level, sandy pitches, of which 30 are used for touring units. Each pitch has electricity, water and drainage, and the pitches are clearly marked by bushes. These are growing slowly and do not provide a great deal of shade or privacy so the site is rather open, although reed type fencing has been used effectively in some areas. Although there is a private path from the campsite to the sandy beach (guarded in high season), the well designed pool complex is also very popular with areas around the pool for sunbathing (free loungers provided). Very popular with tour operators (around 50% of the pitches).

**Facilities:** Two clean and well designed toilet blocks include washbasins in cabins. Laundry and dishwashing facilities under cover outside each block. Washing machines and dryers. Bar and restaurant (15/5-5/9). Takeaway. Heated pool with central water fountain, children's pool, water slide. Covered pool, slide and jacuzzi. Tennis. Table tennis, pétanque. Play area. **Off site:** Small supermarket 200 m. Bicycle hire 200 m, riding 3 km, golf 6 km.

**Charges** guide

| | |
|---|---|
| Per pitch with all facilities, 3 persons and car | € 29.50 |
| extra person | € 3.20 - € 4.73 |
| local tax (over 10 yrs) | € 0.37 |

**Tel:** 02 51 54 29 00. **Fax:** 02 51 54 88 74. **E-mail:** solagogo@wanadoo.fr. **Reservations:** Possible except in high season. **Open** 15 May - 15 September.

**Directions:** Driving south on D38 St Jean de Monts - St Gilles road, turn right at L'Oasis restaurant in Orouet (6 km. outside St Jean de Monts), signed Les Mouettes. After 1.5 km. at roundabout turn left signed St Hilaire de Riez and site is 1.5 km.

## Vendée Charente ✓
# Camping Le Bois Tordu
84 avenue de la Pège, 85270 St-Hilaire-de-Riez

**8517**

Set in a popular holiday area, with a full range of amenities close to hand, Le Bois Tordu is a small but busy site, well suited for a quiter holiday. The site itself has 110 pitches, of which 14 are available for touring caravans and tents. Pitches are grassy and sandy, and most have some shade. All pitches have electricity (6A), water and drainage, and are divided by low hedging. Although it is close to a large and inviting beach, 300 m. across the road, the site also has its own new swimming pool, paddling pool and splash pool for the water slide with feature sliding roof. There are two tour operators on site. The site is under the same ownership as Sol a Gogo (no. 8516).

**Facilities:** The sanitary block is near the front of the site, providing unisex facilities including some washbasins in cubicles. Facilities for disabled visitors and a baby bath. Dishwashing and laundry sinks. Washing machine and dryer, New pool, water slides and jacuzzi. Play area. Table tennis. **Off site:** Beside the front entrance are a supermarket, bar, snack bar, bakery, newsagent and bicycle hire.

**Charges** guide

| | |
|---|---|
| Per pitch incl. 3 persons | € 26.53 |
| extra person (over 5 yrs) | € 3.05 - € 4.57 |
| local tax (over 10 yrs) July/August only | 0.37 |

**Tel:** 02 51 54 33 78. **Fax:** 02 51 54 08 29. **E-mail:** arondeau@wanadoo.fr. **Reservations:** Not accepted in high season. **Open** 1 April - 15 October.

**Directions:** Driving south on D38 St Jean de Monts - St Gilles road, turn right at L'Oasis hotel/restaurant in Orouet (6 km. outside St Jean de Monts), signed to Les Mouettes. After 1.5 km. you come to a roundabout. Turn left here signed to St Hilaire de Riez and site is 1.5 km. on the left

### Vendée Charente

## Camping Le Domaine de Beaulieu

**8549** Givrand, 85800 St-Gilles-Croix-de-Vie

Domaine de Beaulieu has an open airy feel in a pleasant semi-rural setting on the edge of the village of Givrand, just one kilometer from a good sandy beach. The 180 touring pitches all have easy access to electricity and water; those in the older part have shade from mature trees and are divided by hedges whilst those in the newer part are more open. Some pitches may be subject to traffic noise in high season. This Chadotel site has 130 mobile homes and tour operators (one French, one Dutch) occupy 100 pitches. Early and late in the season the site is quiet, whereas in July/August there is a lively and wide-ranging entertainment programme for all ages including teenagers.

**Facilities:** Three well maintained toilet blocks have washbasins in cubicles, baby room, unit for disabled people, washing machines and dryers. Shop (15/6-10/9). Bar (1/5-10/9). Takeaway and restaurant (1/7-31/8). Heated outdoor pool with toboggan and paddling pool. Multi-sport terrain. Minigolf, tennis. Bicycle hire. Table tennis. **Off site:** Shops and restaurants of St Gilles 3 km. Golf, riding, karting, quads and water parks all within easy reach.

**Charges** 2002

| | |
|---|---|
| Per pitch incl. 2 persons | € 11.50 - € 20.50 |
| with electricity (10A) | € 15.00 - € 24.00 |
| extra person | € 3.30 |
| child (under 5 yrs) | € 2.50 |

**Tel:** 02 51 33 05 05. **Fax:** 02 51 33 94 04. **Reservations:** Contact site. **Open** 1 April - 25 September.

**Directions:** Site is signed from roundabout on D38 at Givrand, 3 km. south of St Gilles-Croix-de-vie, 7 km. north of Brétignolles.

### Vendée Charente

## Camping Le Bahamas Beach

**8550** 168 Routes des Sable, 85800 St Gilles-Croix-de-Vie

A member of the Chadotel group, Le Bahamas Beach is separated from the sandy beach by 600 m. of sand dunes and the River Jaunay. The site attracts a greater proportion of French holidaymakers than many others in the area. The 80 touring pitches are scattered amongst the total of 225, of which 90 are mobile homes. There are two tour operators, one French, one British (84 pitches). Pitches are grassy and level on sandy soil, separated by hedges or low bushes and all have easy access to electricity and water. There are few trees and little shelter from the wind off the sea. A good range of high season entertainment is designed for all ages.

**Facilities:** Three well maintained toilet blocks include washbasins in cubicles, a unit for disabled people and baby rooms. Washing machines and dryers. Bar, restaurant and takeaway (15/5-15/9) with limited opening in low season. Shop (16/5-15/9). Heated outdoor pool with slide and paddling pool. Play area. Minigolf. Table tennis. Bicycle hire. **Off site:** Golf, riding, karting, watersports within easy reach.

**Charges** 2002

| | |
|---|---|
| Per pitch incl. 2 persons | € 13.50 - € 21.00 |
| with electricity | € 17.00 - € 24.50 |
| extra person | € 3.30 |
| child (under 5 yrs) | € 2.50 |

**Tel:** 02 51 33 05 05. **Fax:** 02 51 33 94 04. **E-mail:** chadotel@wanadoo.fr. **Reservations:** Contact site. **Open** 1 April - 30 September.

**Directions:** From roundabout at southern end of D38 St Gilles bypass, take exit signed St Gilles Grande Plage. Campsite is 500 m. on left.

### Vendée Charente

## Camping Domaine des Renardières

**8552** 13 Chemin du Chêne Vert, 85270 Notre Dame de Riez

Just seven kilometres from the busy coastal strip with its many large, multi-activity campsites, Des Renardières is an oasis of calm in the traditional French manner. Converted from the family farm in 1970 by the present owner's father, the site consists of three fields with varying amounts of shade. The visitors are 65% French, many of whom, together with British visitors, return year after year. The 100 touring pitches are well grassed and level; torches and long cables are advisable. Mme Raffin's benevolent authority is to be seen everywhere. There is an abundance of flowers and plants, the facilities are scrupulously maintained and all visitors are provided with a set of campsite rules which are also explained at the regular Sunday welcome meeting. The site is very well organised with a soft touch.

**Facilities:** The sanitary block is old but well maintained and meticulously cleaned. A mixture of toilet types, some open washbasins, some in cubicles. Showers are closed at night except for one cold shower. Dishwashing is under cover. Washing machine and dryer. Small shop and takeaway (1/7-30/8). Bar with TV, video games and pool (1/7-30/8). Small outdoor pool attractively laid out (15/4-15/9). Play area. **Off site:** St Hilaire de Riez (7 km) has shops, bars, restaurants and all entertainments as well as a good sandy beach. Fishing 700 m.

**Charges** 2002

| | |
|---|---|
| Per unit incl. 2 persons | € 12.00 |
| with electricity (6A) | € 14.50 |
| extra person | € 3.10 |
| child (under 5 yrs) | € 2.00 |
| dog | € 3.10 |
| local tax | € 0.17 |

**Tel:** (0)2 51 55 14 17. **Fax:** (0)2 51 54 96 13. **Reservations:** Made with deposit and € 10 fee. **Open** Easter - 15 September.

**Directions:** Site is well signed from the centre of the village of Notre Dame de Riez.

## Camping Acapulco

avenue des Epines, 85160 St-Jean-de-Monts

85522

Ideal for family holidays, this friendly site is situated mid-way between St Jean de Monts and St Hilaire de Riez, and 600 m. from the beach. The young, friendly site owner provides lively entertainment and sporting activities for all ages in high season. The site has 410 pitches (60 for touring units). All pitches have water and electricity, but few have any shade as yet. The site is popular with tour operators (120 pitches).

**Facilities:** Three main sanitary blocks boast clean, modern facilities including washbasins in cabins, baby baths and facilities for disabled visitors. Sinks for laundry and dishwashing. Washing machines in each block. Motorcaravan service point. Well stocked shop (all season). Large bar and snack bar. Games room. Interestingly shaped, heated swimming pool with water slide and paddling pool. Further slides are planned. **Off site:** Shops, bars and restaurants all within 1 km. Golf 10 km, bicycle hire 200 m, riding 2 km.

**Charges** 2002

| | |
|---|---|
| Per unit incl. 3 persons, electricity | € 21.00 - € 26.00 |
| local tax (July/Aug) | € 0.34 |

**Tel:** 02 51 59 20 64. Fax: 02 51 59 53 12. E-mail: info@sunmarina.com. **Reservations:** Necessary in July/Aug. **Open** 8 May - 15 September.

**Directions:** Driving south on the D38 St Jean de Monts - St Gilles road, turn right at L'Oasis bar/restaurant in Orouet, signed Les Mouettes. Site is on left after 1 km.

## Camping Les Biches

route de Notre-Dame-de-Riez, 85270 St-Hilaire-de-Riez

85507

Les Biches is a popular, quality site 4 km. from the sea. It is set in a pinewood so nearly everywhere has shade. There are almost 400 pitches with around 90 available for touring units. The large, spacious pitches are mostly hedged and on fairly sandy ground, all with electricity, water and drainage. The majority for tents and caravans are in the far part of the campsite behind the tennis courts, although a few others are scattered through the rest of the site. A very attractive pool complex is near the site entrance, overlooked by the bar and terraces. Various activities such as boules tournaments and sporting events are organised during high season. It is a useful site for families with children and, as it is popular with British tour operators (65%), it tends to be busy and active all season.

**Facilities:** The four sanitary blocks are clean and well maintained, with extremely spacious cubicles for pre-set showers. Some washbasins are in cabins with a bidet alongside. All blocks have laundry and dishwashing facilities. Washing machines and dryers. Facilities for disabled visitors. Shop (all season) with ice service. Large bar (all season). Restaurant and crèperie (1/6-9/9). Takeaway (20/5-16/9). Two heated swimming pools (unsupervised), children's pool, water slide with splash pool, jacuzzi and indoor pool. Tennis courts. Volleyball, table tennis and minigolf. Games room with amusement machines. Large adventure type children's playground. Bicycle hire. Disco. TV room with satellite TV. Internet terminal. **Off site:** Private fishing lake 2.5 km, riding 4.5 km. and golf 6 km. Beach 4 km.

**Charges** 2002

| | |
|---|---|
| Per pitch incl. 3 persons and car | € 33.00 |
| with electricity | € 37.00 |
| extra person | € 7.00 |
| child (under 7 yrs) | € 3.50 |
| dog | € 2.00 |
| local tax (over 10 yrs) July/August | € 0.37 |

**Tel:** 02 51 54 38 82. Fax: 02 51 54 30 74. E-mail: campingdesbiches@wanadoo.fr. **Reservations:** Required for high season and made with deposit (€ 61) and fee (€ 15,24). **Open** 15 May - 15 September.

**Directions:** Site is about 2 km. north of St Hilaire, close to and well signed from the main D38 road.

## Camping Les Biches, 85270 St. Hilaire-de-Riez

**Tel: 0033 251 54 38 82  Fax: 0033 251 54 30 74**

LARGE SHADY PITCHES - NEW INDOOR POOL - SWIMMING POOL with SPA and 'TOBOGGAN AQUATIQUE'
TENNIS - COMFORTABLE TOILET BLOCKS WITH PLENTIFUL HOT WATER
RESERVATIONS ARE RECOMMENDED FOR MAIN SEASON

# Camping Les Ecureuils

100 avenue de la Pège, 85270 St-Hilaire-de-Riez

**8523**

Of the numerous sea-side sites on the Vendée, Les Ecureuils has to be one of the best, run by a friendly and most helpful family whose aim is for everyone to be 'très content'. Just 300 m. from a superb beach, the site is ideally situated for exploring from Les Sables d'Olonne to Noirmoutier. Developed on what was originally the family farm, there are 230 pitches (79 for touring units) of sandy grass, all with electricity (6A), water and drainage. The well kept hedges and mature trees give shade and privacy, although some more open pitches are also available for sun lovers. Everything on Les Ecureuils is clean and well maintained with an abundance of flowers and shrubs planted throughout the site giving a very attractive appearance. Popular with British tour operators (60%).

**Facilities:** The two main sanitary blocks are spacious, and include some washbasins in cubicles, and facilities for babies and disabled people. Laundry and dishwashing sinks. Laundry room. Small shop (25/5-6/9). Restaurant (all season). Large, airy bar with screened terrace. Swimming pool complex including pool for small children with its own 'mini aqua park', large heated swimming pool, and an adult-sized water slide with separate splash pool. New indoor pool, paddling pool and jacuzzi. **Off site:** Supermarkets, bars and restaurants all within 500 m. Bicycle hire 200 m, fishing 4 km, riding 5 km, golf 6 km.

**Charges** 2002

| | |
|---|---|
| Per unit incl. 2 persons | € 20.60 - € 27.30 |
| extra person | € 3.81 - € 4.73 |
| child (under 5 yrs) | € 2.13 - € 2.90 |
| dog | € 1.98 - € 2.74 |
| local tax (July/Aug, over 10 yrs) | € 0.36 |

**Tel:** 02 51 54 33 71. Fax: 02 51 55 69 08. E-mail: info@camping-aux-ecureuils.com. **Reservations:** Advised for July/Aug. **Open** 15 May - 15 September.

**Directions:** Driving south on D38 St Jean-de-Monts - St Gilles road, turn right at L'Oasis restaurant in Orouet (6 km. outside St Jean de Monts), signed Les Mouettes. After 1.5 km. at roundabout turn left signed St Hilaire de Riez and site is 500 m. on left.

0033 251 540711

# Camping-Caravaning La Ningle

Chemin des Roselières, 85270 St Hilaire de Riez

**8535**

the travel service
TO BOOK

| Ferry | ✓ |
| Pitch | ✓ |
| Accommodation | ✗ |

01892 55 98 98

Camping La Ningle is well situated to explore the beautiful port of St Gilles Croix de Vie, with its abundance of restaurants (where seafood is served direct from the morning's catch) and pedestrianised shopping area with a variety of individual boutiques. You are guaranteed to receive a warm welcome at this site from M. & Mme. Guibert, who have established a very pleasant campsite with a friendly, family atmosphere. There are 155 pitches, 90 available for touring units. All have electricity (6A) and a limited number are fully serviced (electricity, water and drainage). Pitches are spacious with dividing hedges and all have some shade. The nearest beach is a 500 m. walk through a pine forest, but there are also three small swimming pools on site.

**Facilities:** Two regularly cleaned toilet blocks include some washbasins in cubicles. Well equipped toilet/shower room for disabled people and large family shower room in the main block. Laundry and dishwashing facilities. Washing machines and dryer. Bread available July/Aug. Takeaway three evenings per week. Bar (July/Aug) with entertainment twice a week in high season. Main swimming pool, larger children's pool and paddling pool. Small fitness suite with range of equipment (no instructor, but free). Tennis court. Games field with volleyball and table tennis. Games room with pinball and arcade machines. Small lake for fishing (free). Children's activities (July/Aug), and regular petanque and tennis competitions. **Off site:** Small supermarket and takeaway 200 m.

**Charges** guide

| | |
|---|---|
| Per pitch incl. 3 persons | € 13.72 - € 18.45 |
| with electricity (6A) | € 16.01 - € 20.88 |
| supplement for 10A electricity | € 1.07 |
| extra person | € 2.90 - € 3.51 |
| child (under 7 yrs) | € 1.52 - € 1.98 |
| dog | € 1.83 |
| local tax (over 10 yrs. July/Aug.) | € 0.34 |

**Tel:** 02 51 54 07 11. Fax: 02 51 54 99 39. E-mail: campinglaningle@wanadoo.fr. **Reservations:** Made with deposit (€ 77.50) and fee (€ 15,25). **Open** 15 May - 15 September.

**Directions:** Driving south on D38 St Jean de Monts - St Gilles road, turn right at L'Oasis restaurant in Orouet (6 km. outside St Jean de Monts), signed Les Mouettes. After 1.5 km. you come to a round about. Turn left here signed St Hilaire de Riez. After passing two campsites (Les Ecureuils and Bois Tordu) take next left turn, signed La Ningle. Site is approx. 150 m. on the left.

# Camping La Yole

8515

chemin des Bosses, Orouet, 85160 St-Jean-de-Monts

La Yole is an attractive, popular and well run site, 1 km. from a sandy beach. It offers 278 pitches, the majority under trees with ample shade and separated by bushes and the trees. All have electricity, water and drainage and are of 100 sq.m. or more. The pool complex is surrounded by a paved sunbathing area and over-looked by a new bar and restaurant which have a large terrace. A pleasant walk through pine woods then by road leads to two sandy beaches. The security barrier is closed at night. Used by tour operators (50%). A Sites et Paysages member. This a friendly, popular site with welcoming owners.

**Facilities:** Two toilet blocks of older design, one refurbished, include washbasins in cabins, units for disabled people and new baby baths, all kept very clean. The third block in the newer part of site is very modern with baby room. Laundry with washing machine, dryer and iron. Well stocked shop. Takeaway. Bar (all season) and restaurant (18/5-31/8). Swimming pool with water slide, paddling pool and an indoor heated pool with jacuzzi. Children have exceptional space with a play area on sand, large field for ball games, picnics and a club room. Tennis. Table tennis, pool and video games. Organised entertainment in high season. No dogs are accepted. Only gas barbecues are permitted. **Off site:** Fishing, golf and watersports 6 km. at St Jean

**Charges** 2002

| Per tent incl. 2 persons, | | |
|---|---|---|
| electricity and water | € 14.48 - € 22.25 |
| or for caravan incl. drainage also | € 16.65 - € 26.45 |
| extra person | € 3.51 - € 5.60 |
| extra child (2-9 yrs) | € 1.98 - € 4.00 |
| baby (0-2 yrs) | free - € 3.05 |
| local tax (July/Aug. over 10 yrs) | € 0.34 |

**Tel:** 02 51 58 67 17. Fax: 02 51 59 05 35. E-mail: contact@la-yole.com. **Reservations:** Advised, particularly for July/Aug. **Open** 8 May - 15 September.

**Directions:** Signed off the D38, 6 km. south of St Jean de Monts in the village of Orouet.

Camping La Yole ★★★★

Wake up to the sound of birdsong in a wooded park of 17 acres with four star comfort. Space, security, informal atmosphere: LA YOLE, tucked away between fields and pine trees, only 1 km from the beach.

– Chemin des Bosses - Orouet - F 85160 Saint Jean de Monts –
– Tel: 0033 251 58 67 17 - Fax: 0033 251 59 05 35 –
– contact@la-yole.com / www.la-yole.com –

## Vendée Charente
# Camping L'Abri des Pins

**8509** route de Notre Dame de Monts, 85160 St-Jean-de-Monts

L'Abri des Pins is situated on the outskirts of the pleasant, modern resort of St Jean-de-Monts and is separated from the sea and long sandy beach by a strip of pinewood. From the back entrance of the site it is a pleasant 15 minute walk to the beach. Bathing is said to be safer here than on most of the beaches on this coast, but is nevertheless supervised in July/August. The site has 218 pitches, 78 of which are for touring units with 30 larger than average, with electricity, water and drainage. Electricity is also available to the other pitches which are around 100 sq.m, fully marked out with dividing hedges and quite shady. Many pitches are occupied by privately owned mobile homes, but there are no tour operators on the site. Throughout the season visitors may use the facilities at Les Places Dorées (under the same family ownership) across the road.

**Facilities:** The two sanitary blocks have been modernised and include washbasins in cabins, laundry and dishwashing sinks. Good small shop and bar/restaurant on the far side of the site provides good quality, value for money meals, both to eat in and take away (all 1/7-31/8). New outdoor, heated swimming pool and water slide, plus small pool for children, with decked sunbathing area (1/6-15/9; no bermuda style shorts). Daily children's club, football, petanque, aqua aerobics. **Off site:** Supermarket 10 minutes walk. Many restaurants close. Walking, cycling, fishing and riding within 1 km.

**Charges** 2002

| | |
|---|---|
| Per unit incl. 3 persons, electricity | € 17.68 - € 25.46 |
| incl. water and drainage | € 18.45 - € 26.22 |
| extra adult | € 2.74 - € 3.96 |
| child (under 5 yrs) | € 1.68 - € 2.44 |
| pet | free - € 2.44 |
| local tax (over 10 yrs) July/August | € 0.34 |

**Tel:** 02 51 58 83 86. **Fax:** 02 51 59 30 47. **E-mail:** abridespins@aol.com. **Reservations:** Advised for high season; min. stay 12 nights between 14/7-15/8. Made with deposit (€ 92) and fee (€ 23). **Open** 1 June - 15 September.

**Directions:** Site is 4 km. from the town centre on St Jean-de-Monts - Notre Dame-de Monts/ Noirmoutiers road (D38), on left heading north, just after Camping les Amiaux.

## Vendée Charente
# Camping Les Places Dorées

**8528** route de Notre Dame de Monts, 85160 St-Jean-de-Monts

Les Places Dorées is owned by the same family as L'Abri des Pins (8509) which is just across the road. It is a much newer site, but maturing trees are gradually beginning to offer some shade. The site has a range of facilities, including a pool complex, but one of the main reasons for visiting the Vendée is for its beaches and the closest beach to Les Places Dorées is a pleasant 15 minute walk away (through L'Abri des Pins and then alongside the pine forest and sand dunes). The site has 245 grassy pitches, the quietest being towards the back of the site. Each one is separated, all have electrical connections (6A) and some are also equipped with water and drainage. One small British tour operator is on site (18 pitches). In low season the site is quiet but it can be noisy in high season with the bar and disco closing late.

**Facilities:** Three modern toilet blocks include washbasins in cubicles. Facilities for disabled visitors. Laundry and dishwashing sinks. Washing machines and dryers. Swimming pool complex with water slides, jacuzzi area and waterfall (no bermuda style shorts). In high season the site becomes quite lively with plenty of organised entertainment, most based around the bar/restaurant area. High season children's club at L'Abri des Pins, also organised activities for adults (petanque tournaments, aqua aerobics, etc). The facilities at L'Abri des Pins may be used - well stocked shop (July/Aug), tennis court, fitness room, swimming pools and a games room.

**Charges** 2002

| | |
|---|---|
| Per pitch incl. 3 persons, electricity | € 18.20 - € 26.70 |
| extra person | € 2.80 - € 4.40 |
| child | € 1.70 - € 2.80 |
| dog | free - € 2.50 |
| local tax (over 10 yrs) | 0.34 |

**Tel:** 02 51 59 02 93. **Fax:** 02 51 59 30 47. **Reservations:** Advised for high season; min. stay 12 nights between 14/7-15/8. **Open** 16 June - 1 September.

**Directions:** Site is 4 km. north of St Jean de Monts on the D38 St Jean de Monts - Notre Dames de Monts road on the right hand side, almost opposite L'Abri des Pins.

## Vendée Charente
# Haven Camping Le Bois Dormant

**8510**

168 rue des Sables, 85160 St-Jean-de-Monts

Owned by Haven Europe and with a good range of facilities, Le Bois Dormant is on the outskirts of the pleasant, modern resort of St Jean de Monts, 3 km. from the beach. The site has 565 pitches, most occupied by tour operators or privately owned mobile homes, with 30-odd pitches available throughout the site for touring units. Pitches are sandy, separated by hedges and all with electricity and water. This site can be expected to be very busy for most of the season, with many organised activities for children of all ages.

**Facilities:** Four well deigned sanitary blocks offer good facilities including washbasins in cabins, baby baths and toilets, facilities for disabled people. Sinks for laundry and dishwashing, washing machines and dryers. Small shop. Bar/restaurant, also serves takeaway snacks. Large (200 sq.m.) swimming pool, paddling pool and water slides (no bermuda style shorts). Games room, minigolf, table tennis, multi-sport sports pitch with track and tennis courts. Only gas barbecues are permitted. **Off site:** All the facilities of the site's larger, busier sister site Le Bois Masson are available to campers here.

**Charges** 2002

| Per pitch incl. up to 2 persons | |
| --- | --- |
| and electricity | € 10.67 - € 31.86 |
| extra person | € 2.29 - € 4.57 |

**Tel:** 02 51 58 01 30. Fax: 02 51 59 35 30.
**Reservations:** Accepted at any time for min. 4 days; no booking fee. Contact site or Haven Europe in the UK on 0870 242 7777 for information or reservation. **Open** 23 March - 5 October.

**Directions:** Site is well signed from roundabout at southeast end of the St Jean de Monts bypass (CD38). Follow signs off the roundabout to 'centre ville' and site is about 500 m. on the left.

One of two great parcs with swimming pools, sports & family activities. Enjoy the quiet life at Le Bois Dormant, with the option of using facilities at the more lively sister Le Bois Masson.

- Superb touring pitches set amongst a pine forest
- Heated outdoor pools with 4-lane waterslide & waterchute (open 26 Apr - 13 Sept)
- spa bath (open July - August)
- Multi-sports pitch, 2 play areas, tennis court & games room
- Poolside bar, serving meals & takeaway
- 3 children's clubs for all ages
- Superb low season prices
- Bilingual staff on parc
- Site open from: 12 April - 4 October

**Le Bois Dormant** ★★★★
St. Jean de Monts

Le Bois Dormant, 168 Rue des Sables, 85167 St Jean de Monts, France
**Tel:**00 33 251 58 62 62 **Fax:**00 33 251 58 29 97
To book please call the number above, quoting code FAR03

A B T A
V2819

---

**8551**

## Vendée Charente
# Camping Le Bois Joli

2 rue de Châteauneuf, 85710 Bois de Céné

This site is a hidden gem in a small village away from the hustle and bustle of the seaside resorts. Suitable for people looking for a quiet holiday, it is still within driving distance of the Vendée coast (20 km). A warm welcome is given by the English speaking Urvoy family, who make every effort to make your stay enjoyable. On site is a small lake with free fishing (carp and eels), and a very large sports field (with a new portacabin style toilet block). The site also has a small swimming pool and paddling pool. A local farmer visits the site three times a week offering local produce. There are 130 pitches of which 90 are for touring units. All pitches have 6A electricity, although not every pitch is serviced with water.

**Facilities:** Three toilet blocks - old, but with modern, bright tiles and very clean. All are unisex with some washbasins in cubicles, some controllable showers, two baby baths, two washing machines, dishwashing and laundry sinks. Bar with evening entertainment. Children's activities. Good play area with swings. Table tennis. Tennis court. Volleyball. Petanque. Bicycle hire. **Off site:** Supermarket in the village (two minutes walk). Walking, cycling and canoeing near. Riding 5 km.

**Charges** 2002

| Per pitch incl. 2 persons | € 8.40 - € 12.50 |
| --- | --- |
| extra person | € 2.40 - € 3.40 |
| child (under 7 yrs) | € 1.25 - € 1.80 |
| electricity (6A) | € 1.75 - € 2.50 |
| animal | € 1.35 - € 1,90 |

**Tel:** 02 51 68 20 05. Fax: 02 51 68 46 40. E-mail: campingboisjoli@free.fr. **Reservations:** Advised and made with deposit (€ 80 per week) and fee (€ 15). **Open** Easter - 15 September.

**Directions:** From Challans take D58 direct to Bois de Céné (10 km). Turn left at road junction in centre of village and site is immediately on right.

## Camping La Forêt

**8536** 190 chemin de la Rive, 85160 St-Jean-de-Monts

Camping La Forêt has been owned by M. and Mme. Jolivet for the past few years and they work hard to provide a small, quality site. Well run and attractive, with a friendly, family atmosphere, it provides just 60 pitches with 51 for touring units. Of 100 sq.m. in size, the pitches are surrounded by mature hedges and have water and electricity. Over 50 species of trees are planted on the site, providing shade to every pitch, and the Jolivets provide an information panel by reception to help you identify the various types. There is one tour operator on the site (15 pitches), but their presence is in no way intrusive and the site has a quiet and relaxed atmosphere, ideal for couples or families with young children.

**Facilities:** The central toilet block is kept very clean and includes washbasins in cubicles. Laundry and dishwashing sinks. Baby bath. Facilities for disabled people. Washing machine and although clothes lines are prohibited, free-standing clothes airers are loaned for drying. Motorcaravan waste tanks can be emptied on request. Range of basic provisions sold in reception, including fresh bread. Takeaway at excellent prices all season. Small, but inviting swimming pool (end May - Sept). Children's play area. Table tennis. Bicycle hire. Only gas and electric barbecues allowed, communal barbecue in centre of site. **Off site:** Local beach 400 m. along forest path. Network of cycle paths runs through the forest and local marshland.

**Charges** 2002

| | |
|---|---|
| Per pitch incl. 2 persons | € 15.25 - € 20.58 |
| extra person | € 3.05 - € 3.81 |
| child (under 7 yrs) | € 2.29 |
| dog | € 1.52 |
| electricity (6A) | € 3.05 |

**Tel:** 02 51 58 84 63. Fax: 02 51 58 84 63.
**Reservations:** Advised, particularly for high season and made with € 34 deposit; min. 15 nights 2/7-19/8. **Open** 15 April - 30 September.

**Directions:** Site is 5.5 km. from town centre, just off the D38. Follow D38 out of St Jean de Monts, towards Notre Dame de Monts. After 4.5 km. you come to a roundabout with a pizzeria called Les Tonnelles. Go straight over the roundabout, and in 1 km. turn left at sign for site and 'Plage de Pont d'Yeu'. Follow road as it almost doubles back on itself and site is on left in about 100 m.

## Camping La Petite Boulogne

**8520M** 12 rue du Stade, 85670 St-Etienne-du-Bois

Set in countryside 24 kilometres. northwest of La Roche sur Yon, St Etienne-du-Bois is a quiet village, well away from the hustle and bustle of the big Vendée resorts. This campsite, owned by the local council, has 35 grassy pitches (most slightly sloping), all with electricity (6A), water and drainage. Pitches are marked by low hedges giving the site an open and sunny aspect. Although the site is inland, it is only 20 km. to the coast with its large sandy beaches, but there are also many attractions and places to visit inland in the Vendée, and this good value municipal provides a great base from which to explore the whole region.

**Facilities:** The modern, heated toilet block includes some washbasins in cabins. Laundry and dishwashing sinks. Room for disabled people with toilet and shower. Washing machine and dryer. Reception sells bread and a few other essentials. Small unheated pool (June - Aug). TV room. Table tennis. Small children's play area. Two free tennis courts. Bicycle hire. Daily events in area listed in reception and occasional animation organised in high season, introducing the region and its produce. **Off site:** Open-air, heated pool nearby. Bar and restaurant both few minutes walk away in village. Fishing possible in the nearby Petite Boulogne river. Volleyball and petanque at local sports centre (300 m.). Supermarket 8 km at Legé.

**Charges** guide

| | |
|---|---|
| Per unit incl. 2 persons | € 9.15 |
| extra person | € 1.52 |
| child (under 7 yrs) | € 0.76 |
| dog | € 0.76 |
| electricity (6A) | € 1.52 |

**Tel:** 02 51 34 54 51. Fax: 02 51 34 54 10. E-mail: la.petite.boulonge@wanadoo.fr. **Reservations:** Made with deposit (€ 31). **Open** 1 May - 31 October.

**Directions:** From Legé take D978 south towards Palluau for 7 km. then turn left on D94 towards St Etienne-du-Bois. Go straight through village and, as you come out the other side, cross a small bridge over the river. Site is 50 m. further on, on the right.

# Camping à la Carte

A choice of three great holiday options from the company you can trust

| | |
|---|---|
| ✓ A Unique Site and Ferry Reservations service | ✓ The Low Cost Pitch and Ferry Reservations service |
| ✓ Over 100 top European Sites | ✓ 90 sites in 9 countries to suit all tastes |
| ✓ Maps, guides and free children's gift included | ✓ Quality guaranteed, no frills, no hassle |
| ✓ English speaking Couriers on site | ✓ Tailor-made insurance policies |
| ✓ Children's Club | |

**Eurocamp Independent**

✓ A Unique Site and Ferry Reservations service

✓ Over 100 top European Sites

✓ Maps, guides and free children's gift included

✓ English speaking Couriers on site

✓ Children's Club

**Phone our friendly reservations team on:**

## 01606 787 954

**sites abroad**

✓ The Low Cost Pitch and Ferry Reservations service

✓ 90 sites in 9 countries to suit all tastes

✓ Quality guaranteed, no frills, no hassle

✓ Tailor-made insurance policies

**For advice from the experts phone:**

## 01606 787 899

**Touring Cheque**

✓ Low Season Go as You Please vouchers

✓ Save up to 50% on normal site fees

✓ No need to pre-book sites

✓ Great ferry inclusive deals

**Phone today on:**

## 01606 787 969

Visit our website at www.eurocampindependent.co.uk

# Loire Valley

We have taken the liberty of enlarging the official Loire Valley region to make a more easily identifiable tourist region which the British understand. The area includes all the Loire Valley.

| Loire Valley | Western Loire | Poitou-Charentes |
|---|---|---|
| Major cities: Orleans, Tours<br><br>Departements: 18 Cher, 28 Eure-et-Loir, 36 Indre, 37 Indre-et-Loire, 41 Loir-et-Cher, 45 Loiret | From this offical region we include the following départements:<br><br>49 Maine-et-Loire, 53 Mayenne, 72 Sarthe | From this offical region we include the following départements:<br><br>79 Deux Sevres, 86 Vienne |

For centuries the Loire Valley was frequented by French royalty and the great River Loire winds its way past some of France's most magnificent châteaux. Known as the Garden of France, it is a most productive and lush area with large farms and a mild climate making it a favourite with visitors. Well known for its wines, over 100 different ones are produced from vineyards stretching along the 1,000 km (620 mile) course of the River Loire. Imposing abbeys, troglodyte caves, tiny Romanesque churches, woodlands such as the Sologne and sleepy, picturesque villages reward exploration. Cities like Blois and Tours are elegant with fine architecture and museums and Paris is only one hour by the TGV. Today Poitiers is home to Futuroscope, the 'museum of the moving image'.

Note: Reports are laid out by département in numerical order not by region.

## Cuisine of the region

Wild duck, pheasant, hare, deer, and quail are classics and fresh water fish such as salmon, perch and trout are favourite. A tasty 'beurre blanc' is the usual sauce with fish.

This is the home of *Tarte Tatin* – upside down tart of caramelised apples and pastry

*Tarte a la citrouille* – pumpkin tart

*Bourdaines* – apples stuffed with jam and baked

Such specialties as rillettes, andouillettes, tripes, mushrooms and the regional cheeses of Trappiste d'Entrammes and Cremet d' Angers, Petit Sable and Ardoises d'Angers cookies.

## Places of interest

*Amboise* – château by the river, Clos Lucé and Leonardo da Vinci museum with scale models of his inventions

*Azay-le-Rideau* – Renaissance château

*Beauregard* – château near Chambord, famous for its Delft tiled floors and timbered ceilings

*Blois* – château with architecture from Middle Ages to Neo-Classical periods

*Chambord* – Renaissance château, park and terraces, grandiose creation of François I

*Chartres* – cathedral with famous stained glass windows

*Chaumont-sur-Loire* – annual International Garden Festival with about 30 themed landscape gardens

*Chenonçeau* – château with great gallery and bridge

*Cheverny* – delightful privately owned château

*Chinon* – old town, Pavillon de l'Horloge, Joan of Arc museum

*Langeais* – château and tapestry collection

*Loches* – old town, château and its fortifications

*Orléans* – Holy Cross cathedral, house of Joan of Arc

*Tours* – Renaissance and Neo-Classical mansions, cathedral of St Gatien, museums of archeology and modern art

*Vendôme* – Tour St Martin, La Trinité

*Villandry* – famous renaissance gardens

## Loire Valley
### Camping Municipal de Mont Jouvin

route de Brou, 28120 Illiers-Combray

This well kept site is very green and offers 85 grass pitches on a slope in most areas, with 48 electricity connections (5A). Tall trees surround the camping areas and there is plenty of shade and tranquillity. All restaurant, shop and bar amenities are to be found in the town itself (2 km). There are boules pitches, bicycle hire, a children's playground and table tennis on site, and the municipal swimming pool is adjacent. This is a site really for those who want peace and quiet or a convenient overnight stop. The campsite is not open on Sundays.

**Facilities:** The two large, bright and airy sanitary blocks are fully tiled, with some washbasins in cabins and the usual under cover laundry and dishwashing sinks. Good facilities for disabled people including telephone booths and, although the site is on a slope, it could possibly be acceptable for wheelchair users.

**Charges** 2002

| | |
|---|---|
| Per pitch | € 2.80 |
| adult | € 2.10 |
| child (under 7 yrs) | € 1.10 |
| electricity | € 2.50 |

**Tel:** 02 37 24 03 04. **Fax:** 02 37 24 16 21.
**Reservations:** Contact site. **Open** 1 April - 31 October (not Sundays).

**Directions:** Site is on D921 Illiers-Combray to Le Mans road.

## Loire Valley
### Camping Municipal de Bonneval

Bois de Chievre, 28800 Bonneval

On the outskirts of Bonneval and within walking distance of the centre, this municipal site offers good facilities in peaceful surroundings. The site has thick cover from trees in most parts with some pitches entirely hidden for those who like lots of privacy. Nearly all the pitches are marked out on grass in clearings, some on a slope, but the majority fairly flat. Of the 130 pitches, 120 have 6A electricity, some hardstanding. The site has no bar, restaurant or shop, but all are available in Bonneval itself or, when open, in the municipal swimming pool and tennis complex adjacent (reduced rates for campers). Caravans with double axles or more than 5.6 m. are not accepted.

**Facilities:** Sanitary facilities consist of one large block, plus three smaller units without showers. The large block has chain operated hot showers, some washbasins in cubicles and facilities for disabled people. Laundry room with washing machine and ironing facilities. Laundry and dishwashing sinks. Motorcaravan services. Large TV/games room, children's playground, bicycle hire and fishing. **Off site:** Swimming pool and tennis adjacent.

**Charges** 2002

| | |
|---|---|
| Per pitch incl. 1 person | € 5.03 |
| with electricity | € 7.01 |
| incl. 2 persons | € 7.47 - € 9.45 |

**Tel:** 02 37 47 54 01. **Fax:** 02 37 96 26 79. **E-mail:** camping.bonneval@wanadoo.fr. **Reservations:** Contact site. **Open** March - 30 November.

**Directions:** Site signed from Bonneval town centre on N10 from Châteaudun to Chartres (on Rte de Vouvray).

## Loire Valley
### Camping Municipal Le Val Vert

36400 La Chatre

In a peaceful rural location, 3 km. from the town, this neatly presented, terraced site has 77 level grassy pitches with only a little shade. Some pitches are individual, others are in small bays for two or three units, with low dividing hedges. All have electricity connections. La Châtre is chiefly known for its connections to George Sand (pseudonym of the writer Armandine Lucie Dupin). Nearby, and also worth a visit, is the distinctive Château de Sarzay.

**Facilities:** The modern toilet block provides British and Turkish WCs, some washbasins in cubicles, covered dishwashing and laundry sinks, baby bathroom and a WC for disabled people. Motorcaravan service point. Table tennis. Two children's playgrounds. Covered terrace with picnic tables. Reception opens 09.00-12.30 and 15.00-19.30. Barrier closed 22.00-07.00.

Charges guide

| | |
|---|---|
| Per unit incl. 2 persons | € 7.62 |
| extra adult | € 2.29 |
| child (3-7 yrs) | € 1.07 |
| serviced pitch | € 2.29 |
| electricity | € 2.29 |
| local tax | € 0.15 |

**Tel:** 02 54 48 32 42. **Fax:** 02 54 48 32 87.
**Reservations:** May be necessary for July/Aug. only. Open 5 June - 15 September.

**Directions:** From La Châtre take D943 towards Montluçon, then, just outside the town fork right on D83A towards Briantes. Site is 3 km from town.

## Loire Valley
# Camping Municipal Les Vieux Chênes
36310 Chaillac

**3605M**

A delightful site on the outskirts of an attractive village, this is another little gem - a small site within walking distance of the centre, where there are shops, bars, cafés, restaurants, etc. The 34 grass pitches, all with electricity (15A), are very generous in size, slightly sloping, with hedging and some mature trees. The well manicured appearance and relaxed atmosphere add to the attraction of this peaceful environment. The adjacent lake is for fishing only, although there is access to a larger lake just 1 km. away where varied watersports - swimming, windsurfing, canoeing and pedaloes - can be enjoyed. In high season it is possible some noise may carry from this area to the site.

**Facilities:** Heated sanitary facilities are insulated for winter use and include washbasins in private cabins. Bicycle hire. Winter caravan storage. **Off site:** Shops 200 m. Fishing 25m. Watersports 1 km.

**Charges** 2002

| | |
|---|---|
| Per person (over 14 yrs) | € 1.52 |
| child | free |
| pitch | € 1.52 - € 2.29 |
| electricity | € 1.52 |

**Tel:** 02 54 25 61 39. **Fax:** 02 54 25 65 41.
**Reservations:** Not made. **Open** all year.

**Directions:** From the north leave A20, south of Argenton sur Creuse, take D1 to St Benoit (16 km.) and then west to Chaillac on D36 (8.5 km). From the south leave A20 at exit 21, take D10 to St Benoit, then D36 as before. Go through the village and turn left by the Mairie.

## Loire Valley
# Camping Municipal Les Chênes
40 route de Loches, 36600 Valençay

**3607M**

Les Chênes is directly off the D960, within walking distance of the town of Valençay, which lies in a green belt and is noted for its fine château. This is an excellent municipal site with flags flying to herald an easily negotiable entrance, a modern reception area and broad parking space. Behind reception is the town swimming pool (July/Aug) and a small fishing lake which is overlooked by several pitches. Large oaks dominate the entrance, beyond which are 50 spacious, level, grass pitches, divided by hedges. A forest borders the site to the left and many trees give shade. An excellent base for exploring the countryside around the Indre.

**Facilities:** The centrally positioned toilet block is of modern design. With high standard facilities and kept very clean, there are washbasins in cubicles, children's sinks, facilities for disabled people and dishwashing and laundry sinks with very hot water. Washing machine. Covered wet weather area for campers. Shop (July/Aug). Table tennis. Children's play field and three adjacent tennis courts. Bicycle hire.

**Charges** 2002

| | |
|---|---|
| Per pitch (acc to facilities) | € 3.05 - € 5.03 |
| adult | € 2.90 |
| child (2-10 yrs) | € 1.52 |
| electricity (4/6/10A) | € 1.52 - € 3.05 |

**Tel:** 02 54 00 03 92. **Fax:** 02 54 00 03 92.
**Reservations:** Contact site. **Open** 1 May - 30 September.

**Directions:** Site is 800 m. west of Valençay on the D960 road.

## Loire Valley
# Camping Municipal Au Bord du Cher
RN 76, 37270 Veretz

**3711M**

This is an inexpensive, well laid out site on the banks of the River Cher with views through tall elm trees to the Château of Veretz. Monsieur Menard and his wife live in a caravan on site during the season and are always pleased to welcome British tourists. With 64 pitches, most divided by small hedges and all with at least 6A electricity, the site is just outside the town of Veretz where shops, restaurants, bars, etc. can be found. A wooden chalet houses reception and plenty of tourist information. The manager is always willing to offer information and advice about where to go and what to see in the area. Of particular interest for railway enthusiasts are restored steam trains and track in the area. River trips are possible. English is spoken.

**Facilities:** Large, modern sanitary block includes British and Turkish style WCs, dishwashing under cover, laundry and washing machine. Motorcaravan service point. Takeaway with covered area to sit and eat (from mid-June). Communal barbecue. Children's playground and table tennis. **Off site:** Fishing nearby. Outdoor swimming pool (July/Aug) 4 km. Bicycle hire 12 km. Riding 3 km. Tennis 1 km. Baker 700 m. Bus service from Tours station to Bleré passes site entrance.

**Charges** 2002

| | |
|---|---|
| Per pitch | € 1.83 |
| adult | € 1.83 |
| child (under 7 yrs) | € 0.76 |
| vehicle | € 1.83 |
| electricity (6A) | € 2.29 |

**Tel:** 02 47 50 50 48. **Fax:** 02 47 50 33 22.
**Reservations:** Contact site. **Open** 22 May - 26 September.

**Directions:** Site is at Veretz, via the N76 road, 10 km. southeast of Tours (much better than the municipal at St Avertin en-route).

## Loire Valley
# Camping de la Mignardière
22 avenue des Aubépines, 37510 Ballan-Miré

arry ✓
tch ✓
ccommodation ✗
1892 55 98 98

The situation of this site may appeal, it being just southwest of the city of Tours, yet within easy reach of several of the Loire châteaux, notably Azay-le-Rideau, and with various sports amenities on or very close to it. There are 177 numbered pitches of which 157 are for touring units, all with electricity (6A) and 37 also with drainage and water. The pitches are on rather uneven grass but are of good size. Onsite facilities are limited because just across the road is a small 'parc de loisirs' with refreshments and bar, pony rides, minigolf, small cars, playground and other amusements. The barrier gates with card (with deposit) are closed 22.30 - 07.30 hrs. Reservation is essential for most of July/August.

**Facilities:** Four rather ordinary sanitary blocks include washbasins in private cabins, a unit for disabled people, baby bath in heated block near reception, and laundry facilities. Motorcaravan service point. Shop(15/5-15/9). Takeaway (1/7-31/8) Two heated, large swimming pools (15/5-15/9). Good tennis court. Table tennis. Bicycle hire. **Off site:** Fishing 500 m, riding 1 km, golf 2 km. Attractive lake catering particularly for windsurfing 300 m. (boards can be hired or use your own) and family fitness run. Tours centre 8 km.

**Charges** 2002

| | |
|---|---|
| Per unit incl. 2 persons | € 13.50 - € 17.50 |
| with electricity, water & drainage | € 19.00 - € 23.60 |
| extra person | € 3.80 - € 4.80 |
| child (2-10 yrs) | € 2.44 - € 2.85 |
| electricity (6A) | € 2.85 |

**Tel:** 02 47 73 31 00. Fax: 02 47 73 31 01. E-mail: info@mignardiere.com. **Reservations:** Made for any length with 30% deposit (minimum amount € 40). **Open** 10 April - 30 September.

**Directions:** From A10 autoroute take exit 24 and D751 towards Chinon. Turn right after 5 km. at Campanile Hotel following signs to site. From Tours take D751 towards Chinon.

## Loire Valley
# Camping Caravanning La Citadelle
avenue Aristide Briand, 37600 Loches en Touraine

A pleasant, well maintained site, La Citadelle is within walking distance of Loches, noted for its perfect architecture and its glorious history, at the same time offering a rural atmosphere in the site itself. Most of the 103 level, good-sized pitches (all with 10A hook-up) offer some shade from trees, although sun lovers can opt for a more open spot. Campers are given free entry to the adjacent municipal swimming pool and tennis courts and there are many organised activities during July and August. Loches, its château and dungeons, is 500 m. A free bus/little train runs from the campsite to the centre of Loches during the summer. A 'Sites et Paysage' member.

**Facilities:** Three sanitary blocks provide British and Turkish style WCs, washbasins (mostly in cabins) and showers. Dishwashing and laundry sinks. Laundry facilities and a motorcaravan service area at the block nearest reception. Two excellent baby units and provision for disabled people. Play equipment for children. Boules, volleyball and games room. Small snack bar offering a variety of food and drink in a lively environment (1/7-31/8). **Off site:** Supermarket 3 km; market on Wednesday and Saturday mornings. Riding or golf 10 km.

**Charges** 2002

| | |
|---|---|
| Per pitch incl. 2 adults | € 10.50 - € 13.80 |
| extra person | € 2.50 - € 3.10 |
| child (2-10 yrs) | € 1.30 - € 1.70 |
| electricity (10A) | € 2.80 |

**Tel:** 02 47 59 05 91. Fax: 02 47 59 00 35. E-mail: camping@lacitadelle.com. **Reservations:** Advised in July/Aug. **Open** 19 March - 19 October.

**Directions:** Site is south of Loches. From RN143 Châteauroux - Tours, follow signs to Loches centre at roundabout (look for Leclerc supermarket). Campsite is about 3 km. on right.

Loire Valley

# Camping Le Moulin Fort

37150 Chenonceaux

**3703**

the **travel service** TO BOOK

| | |
|---|---|
| Ferry | ✓ |
| Pitch | ✓ |
| Accommodation | ✗ |

01892 55 98 98

The 137 pitches on this tranquil, riverside site are enhanced by an interesting variety of shrubs and trees. With water points nearby, there are 80 pitches with access to electricity (6A). The new British owners, John and Sarah Scarratt are working hard to reopen the site after a period of closure. It has unusual features, not least the River Cher flowing near the restored old mill building. There is access to the swimming pool over the mill race by a wooden walkway from the terraced snack bar. Although not visually intrusive, there is some noise from the nearby railway line - a few trains run at night. The campsite is just under 2 km. from the renowned château at Chenon-ceaux, where a `Soirée Nocturne' is held every evening in high season.

**Facilities:** Two toilet blocks with all the usual amenities of a good standard and include washbasins in cubicles and baby baths. Bar. Swimming pool. Minigolf. TV and play room. Animation for children, plus wine tasting and quiz evenings for the whole family.

**Charges** 2002
| | |
|---|---|
| Per unit incl. 2 persons | € 8.60 |
| extra adult | € 3.00 |
| child 4-15 yrs | € 2.00 |
| electricity (6A) | € 3.40 |
| dog | € 3.00 |

**Tel:** (0)2 47 23 86 22. **Fax:** (0)2 47 23 80 93. E-mail: lemoulinfort@wanadoo.fr. **Reservations:** Contact site. **Open** Easter - 30 October.

**Directions:** Take D40 Tours - Chenonceaux road. Go through the village and after 2 km. turn right on D80 to cross the river at Chisseaux. Site is on left just after the bridge. Site is also signed from the N76 Tours - Vierzon road.

Loire Valley

# Camping L'Arada Parc

rue de la Baratière, 37360 Sonzay

**3706**

Although Camping L'Arada Parc is a relatively new site (only in its second full year) it has already become popular as an overnight stop, or as a quiet location from which to visit the numerous châteaux in this beautiful part of France. The 87 grass pitches all have a 10A hook-up, and 28 of them have fresh water and waste disposal points. Pitches are clearly marked and separated by maturing trees, shrubs and flowers that will, in time, provide some shade. Snacks and meals in the restaurant are cooked to order with barbecue chicken available at weekends. Campers can enjoy a snack or drink on the terrace overlooking the attractive (unheated) swimming pool.

**Facilities:** Two modern toilet blocks provide unisex toilets, showers and washbasins in cubicles. Excellent baby/toddler room and en suite facilities for disabled visitors). Dishwashing and laundry sinks under cover at each block. Laundry with washing machine, dryer and ironing board. Shop (1/4-3/11). Bar, restaurant and takeaway (1/4-3/11). Swimming pools. Play area, covered games area. Boules, volleyball, badminton and table tennis. TV room. Bicycle hire. Entertainment, themed evenings and activities for children organised in July/Aug. **Off site:** Tennis 200 m. Fishing 9 km. Golf 12 km. Riding 7 km.

**Charges** 2002
| | |
|---|---|
| Per unit incl. 2 persons | € 14.00 |
| extra person | € 4.00 |
| child 2-7 yrs | € 3.00 |
| electricity (10A) | 43.00 |
| animal | € 1.00 |

**Tel:** (0)2 47 24 72 69. **Fax:** (0)2 47 24 72 69. E-mail: laradaparc@free.fr. **Reservations:** Made with deposit (€ 45); contact site. **Open** 1 April - 3 November.

**Directions:** Sonzay is northwest of Tours. Take D959 Tours - Château-la-Vallière road, then D6 to Sonzay and follow camping signs. Site is signed from the D959.

Loire Valley

# Camping de L'Ile Auger

Quai Danton, 37500 Chinon

**3707M**

This is a well-placed site for exploring the old medieval town of Chinon and its impressive castle that was a home of England's Henry II and includes a museum to Joan of Arc. Alongside the River Vienne, it is a five minute walk over the main bridge to the town centre. The 300 pitches are numbered but not separated, with electricity connections for most of them. A few are shaded by tall shrubs.

**Facilities:** Six toilet blocks around the site have British style WCs. A very good new block is next to the office building. Washing up sinks did not have hot water. Barrier locked 22.00 - 07.00 hrs. **Off site:** Tennis. Indoor and outdoor pools nearby.

**Charges** 2003
Not available

**Tel:** (0)2 47 93 08 35. **Fax:** when closed (0)2 47 93 53 00. **Reservations:** Contact site or the Mairie, tel: (0)2 47 93 53 00. **Open** 15 March - 15 October.

**Directions:** From Chinon town cross the river and turn right at the end of the bridge, the campsite entrance is about 100 m. on the right.

## Castel Camping Château de la Grenouillière

41500 Suévres

**4102**

Château de la Grenouillère is a comfortable site with good amenities on the N152 midway between Orléans and Tours. It is well situated for visiting many of the Loire châteaux and there are enough attractions on site and locally to make it suitable for a longer stay holiday. It is set in a 28-acre park and the 250 pitches (including 88 for tour operators and mobile homes) are in three distinct areas. The majority are in a well wooded area, with about 60 in the old orchard and the remainder in open meadow, although all pitches are separated by hedges. There is one water point for every four pitches and only 10 lack an electric hook-up (5A). Additionally, there are 14 'grand confort' pitches with a separate luxury sanitary block in the outbuildings of the château. Weekly trips to Paris, a canoe-kayak trip and wine and cheese tasting visits are organised in high season.

**Facilities:** Three sanitary blocks, one for each area, are modern and well appointed, including some washbasins in cabins. Washing machines and dryers in a small laundry. Shop. Bar. Pizza takeaway. Restaurant. New bar for dairy product and wine tasting. Swimming complex of four pools (one covered) and a water slide. Tennis, squash, table tennis, pool, baby foot and video games. Internet point. Bicycle and canoe hire (July/Aug). Guided tours organised once a week, musical evenings and children's entertainment in high season. **Off site:** Fishing 5 km, golf 10 km, riding 5 km, aqua sports 5 km.

**Charges** 2002

| | |
|---|---|
| Per unit incl. 2 persons | € 27.50 |
| with 5A electricity | € 31.00 |
| with full services | € 40.00 |
| extra person | € 6.00 |
| child up to 7 yrs | € 4.00 |

**Tel:** 02 54 87 80 37. **Fax:** 02 54 87 84 21. **E-mail:** la.grenouillere@wanadoo.fr. **Reservations:** Made for min. 5 days with € 77 deposit. **Open** 15 May - 10 September.

**Directions:** Site is between Suevres and Mer on north side of the N152 and is well signed.

---

## Camping Château des Marais

27 rue de Chambord, 41500 Muides-sur-Loire

**4104**

the travel service TO BOOK

| | |
|---|---|
| erry | ✓ |
| tch | ✓ |
| ccommodation | ✗ |

1892 55 98 98

The Château des Marais campsite is well situated to visit the chateau at Chambord (its park is impressive) and the other châteaux in the `Vallée des Rois`. The site, providing 133 large touring pitches, all with electricity (6/10A), water and drainage and with ample shade, is situated in the oak and hornbeam woods of its own small château (in which there are rooms to let). An excellent swimming complex offers pools and two flumes. English is spoken and the reception from the enthusiastic owners and the staff is very welcoming. In high season, canoe trips on the Loire are popular: campers are taken by coach to Muides-sur-Loire and are collected three hours later at Boire. Used by tour operators (90 pitches). A `Sites et Paysages` member.

**Facilities:** Four modern, purpose built sanitary blocks have good facilities including some large showers and washbasins en-suite. Washing machine. Motorcaravan service point. Shop and takeaway. Bar/restaurant with large terrace. Swimming complex with heated and unheated swimming pools and water slide. TV room. Bicycle hire. Fishing lake. Excursions by coach to Paris, an entertainment programme and canoe trips organised in high season. **Off site:** Riding 5 km, golf 12 km. Village of Muides sur Loire is five minutes walk.

**Charges** 2003

| | | |
|---|---|---|
| Per pitch incl. vehicle and 2 persons | | € 27.00 |
| extra person | | € 6.00 |
| child (under 5 yrs) | | € 4.00 |
| dog | | € 4.00 |
| electricity 6/10A | € 4.00 - | € 6.70 |
| local tax (over 16 yrs) | | € 0.31 |

**Tel:** 02 54 87 05 42. **Fax:** 02 54 87 05 43. **E-mail:** chateau.des.marais@wanadoo.fr. **Reservations:** Advised July/Aug. **Open** 15 May - 15 September.

**Directions:** From A10 autoroute take exit 16 to Mer, then cross the Loire to join the D951 and follow signs. Site is signed off D103 to southwest of village. 600 m. from junction with the D112.

## Camping-Caravaning La Grande Tortue

3, route de Pontlevoy, 41120 Candé-sur-Beuvron

This is a pleasant, rustic site that has been tastefully developed in an old forest. It provides 106 touring pitches are set amongst trees which provide shade as well as some sunshine. The grass is kept a little longer than normal, especially during the early season, to maintain the forest environment. The majority of the pitches are more than 100 sq.m. and all have 6/10A electricity. During July and August, the family owners organise a programme of trips including wine/cheese tastings, canoeing, and an all-day visit to the Loire Valley. There are markets at Amboise (Sunday), Montrichard (Monday) and Blois (Monday). Used by tour operators.

**Facilities:** Three sanitary blocks offer British and Turkish style WCs, washbasins in cabins, showers (chain operated in two blocks and press button in the third), plus a very basic chemical emptying point. Laundry with deep sinks, washing machine, dryer and ironing board. Shop selling provisions, cards and small gifts. Terraced bar and restaurant with reasonably priced food and drink (15/5-15/9). Trampolines, a ball crawl with slide and climbing wall, bouncy castle, table tennis, an adult swimming pool, and two shallower pools for children (all 15/5-15/9). **Off site:** Walking and cycling. Fishing 500 m. Golf 7 km. Riding 8 km.

**Charges** 2002

| | |
|---|---|
| Per pitch and 2 people | € 12.00 - € 18.50 |
| with electricity | € 15.00 - € 21.50 |
| extra adult | € 4.00 - € 5.50 |
| child (under 7 yrs) | € 3.00 - € 4.00 |
| local tax | € 0.08 - € 0.15 |

**Tel:** 02 54 44 15 20. Fax: 02 54 44 19 45. E-mail: grandtortue@libertysurf.fr. **Reservations:** Necessary in July/Aug. **Open** 5 April - 30 September.

**Directions:** Site is just outside Candé-sur-Beuvron on the D751, midway between Amboise and Blois. From Amboise, turn right just before entering Candé, then immediately left into the campsite - well signed from the road.

Camping Caravaning International ★★★★

# La Grande Tortue

3, route de Pontlevoy
41120 CANDÉ-sur-BEUVRON
Tel: 0033 254 44 15 20 - Fax: 0033 254 44 19 45
Website: www.la-grande-tortue.com

## Le Parc du Val de Loire

**4101**

route de Fleuray, 41150 Mesland

Between Blois and Tours, quietly situated among vineyards away from the main roads and towns, this family owned site is nevertheless centrally placed for visits to the châteaux; Chaumont, Amboise and Blois (21 km.) are the nearest in that order. There are 174 touring pitches of reasonable size, either in light woodland marked by trees or on open meadow with separators. All of the pitches have electricity (6A), and 77 of them also have water and drainage. Sports and competitions are organised in July/Aug. with weekly disco and dance for adults. Wine tasting opportunities each Friday and a coach to Paris one day each week. There are local walks on marked footpaths (maps € 0,30). Used by tour operators (100 pitches).

**Facilities:** Two original toilet blocks of varying standards include washbasins in cabins. A third block is more modern. Units for disabled visitors, baby bathrooms and laundry facilities. Motorcaravan service point. Large shop with bakery. Bar adjacent to the pools, with restaurant, snack service, pizzeria and takeaway, TV room and large recreation room. Three swimming pools, smaller pool with popular water slide, and small children's pool. Tennis court, good playgrounds with skate board facilities, bicycle hire, table tennis, minigolf, BMX track, football pitch, volleyball, badminton and basketball. Pony rides. **Off site:** Fishing or golf 2 km, riding 10 km.

**Charges** 2002

| | |
|---|---|
| Per unit incl. 2 persons | € 14.10 - € 21.70 |
| large pitch (150 sq.m.) | € 18.80 - € 27.00 |
| extra person | € 3.60 - € 5.50 |
| child (2-7 yrs) | € 2.00 - € 3.10 |
| electricity 6-10A | € 2.00 - € 3.50 |
| animal | € 1.90 |

**Tel:** 02 54 70 27 18. Fax: 02 54 70 21 71.
**Reservations:** Made for min. 4 days with deposit (€ 77) and fee (€ 20). **Open** 30 March - 11 November.

**Directions:** Mesland village is 5 km. northwest of Onzain, accessible from Château-Renault/Amboise exit of A10 autoroute via D31 to Autrèche, Continue for 5 km, left at La Hargardière and 8 km. to site.

Open from 29 March to 30 September 2003

*Le Parc du Val de Loire* ★★★★

**41150 MESLAND**
Tel. 0033 254 70 27 18 - Fax: 0033 254 70 21 71
Email : parc.du.val.de.loire@wanadoo.fr
www.parcduvaldeloire.com
*"In the heart of Loire Chateaux country and the vineyards of Touraine"*
**CHALETS AND MOBILE HOMES TO LET**
• Swimming pool complex with 3 pools, 2 of which are heated and a water slide.
• Tennis, mini-golf, football pitch, volleyball, basketball and boules (pétanque).
• Childrens' play area and BMX track, bicycle hire.
• Electronic games, children entertainment and sports tournament during July and August.
• Self-service, bar, restaurant, take-away and TV room.

## Camping de Dugny

**4106**

CD 45 (la Cabinette), 41150 Onzain

This well organised campsite started life as an 'à la ferme' back in 1976. Since then it has grown into a eight hectare camping site surrounded by many acres of wonderfully quiet farmland. Still under the same ownership, it now opens all year round. There are 226 pitches, with mobile homes (privately owned and to rent) leaving 160 tourist pitches. Generously sized, they are partially separated, some with shade and others open. All have electricity (10A), water and drainage. This is a campsite for active people, both young and older. There are play areas and sports fields, a marquee provides entertainment for children and a large barn offers table tennis. Quad bikes can be hired or you can take a flight in a microlight from the site landing strip. Most activities take place away from the camping area to guard a quiet atmosphere.

the **travel service**
TO BOOK
Ferry ✓
Pitch ✓
Accommodation ✗
01892 55 98 98

**Facilities:** Three sanitary units include some washbasins in cubicles and provision for disabled people. Dishwashing and laundry sinks. Bread, soft drinks and gas are stocked. Small restaurant and takeaway. Outdoor pool (15 x 7 m) and children's pool. Large play areas for 4-12 year olds. Minigolf, table tennis, volleyball, basketball. Horse riding. Quad bikes and microlight flights. Varied activity programme including children's disco, boules and table tennis tournaments and camp-fire evenings. Coach trips to chateaux, wine cellars, etc. arranged in July/Aug.

**Charges** 2002

| | |
|---|---|
| Per adult | € 5.00 - € 7.00 |
| child (5-14 yrs) | € 4.00 - € 5.00 |
| pitch | € 3.00 |
| electricity | € 3.05 - € 3.96 |

**Tel:** 02 54 20 70 66. Fax: 02 54 33 71 69. E-mail: info@camping-de-dugny.fr. **Reservations:** Not normally required, but made with 25% deposit. **Open** all year.

**Directions:** Onzain is southwest of Blois (15 km). Take N152 Blois - Tours road, turn right on D1 signed Onsain. Site signed after railway bridge. Turn right on D58, then left on D45 following signs.

# Camping Sologne Parc des Alicourts

**4103** Domaine des Alicourts, 41300 Pierrefitte-sur-Sauldre

A secluded holiday village set in the heart of the forest and with many sporting facilities, Parc des Alicourts is midway between Orléans and Bourges, to the east of the A71. There are 300 pitches (just under half used by tour operators and with a number of mobile homes). All pitches have electricity connections (4/6A) and good provision for water, and most are 150 sq.m. (min. 100 sq.m). Locations vary from wooded to more open areas, thus giving a choice of amount of shade. All facilities are open all season and the leisure amenities are exceptional. Competitions are organised for adults as well as children and, in high season organised activities include a club for children with an entertainer twice a day, a disco once a week and a dance for adults. An inviting water complex (all season) includes two swimming pools, a pool with wave machine and beach area, and a spa, not forgetting three water slides (good for children).

**Facilities:** Three modern sanitary blocks include some washbasins in cabins and baby bathrooms. Washing machines and dryers. Excellent facilities for disabled visitors in one block (but with shallow step to reach them). Motorcaravan services. Shop with good range of produce in addition to the basics (the nearest good-sized town is some way). Restaurant with traditional cuisine, plus a takeaway service in a pleasant bar with terrace. Water complex. 7 hectare lake with fishing, bathing, canoes, pedaloes and play area. Five hole golf course (very popular). Football pitch, volleyball, tennis, minigolf, table tennis, boules. Roller skating/ skateboard area (bring your own equipment). Bicycle hire with cyclo-cross and mountain bikes and a way-marked path for walking and cycling.

**Charges** 2003

| | |
|---|---|
| Per unit incl. 2 persons | € 15.00 - € 36.00 |
| with water and drainage | € 25.00 - € 41.00 |
| extra person | € 6.00 - € 8.50 |
| child 7-17 yrs | € 4.00 - € 6.50 |
| child 1-6 yrs | free - € 5.50 |
| dog | € 7.00 |
| local tax (1/6-13/9) | € 0.11 - € 0.23 |

**Tel:** 02 54 88 63 34. **Fax:** 02 54 88 58 40. **E-mail:** Parcdesalicourts@wanadoo.fr. **Reservations:** Made for min. 7 days for July/Aug. only, with 25% deposit and fee (€ 15,24). **Open** 17 May - 7 September.

**Directions:** From A71, take the Lamotte Beuvron exit (no 3) or from N20 Orléans to Vierzon (which runs parallel with the A71) turn left on to D923 towards Aubigny. After 14 km, turn right at camping sign on to D24E. Site is clearly marked from there in about 4 km.

---

# Camping des Grands Prés

**4105M** rue Geoffrey Martell, 41100 Vendôme

Vendôme is a fascinating and beautiful old town situated on, and criss-crossed by tributaries of, the River Loir (not to be confused with the Loire) and it is well worth a visit. Camping des Grands Prés is conveniently situated beside the river, only a 250 m. level walk from the town centre and next door to the swimming pool (July/Aug), children's play area, boules pitches and canoeing centre. The 180 touring pitches, 140 with electricity (4/6A), are on mainly flat grass, clearly marked, but not actually separated. There is variable shade from a variety of trees. The site is busy over an extended season and the pitches beside the river are quickly taken up. Some traffic noise from the N10 which passes the rear of the site.

**Facilities:** The modern, purpose built toilet block is well equipped. Washbasins in cabins, dishwashing sinks. Laundry facilities in separate building. Small shop for basics. Snack bar (mid-June - mid-Sept). **Off site:** Town 250 m. Swimming pool (free to campers) and canoe centre next door.

**Charges** guide

| | |
|---|---|
| Per unit incl. 2 persons | € 6.86 |
| extra adult | € 1.98 |
| child (5-15 yrs) | € 1.37 |
| electricity 4-6A | € 2.59 - € 3.81 |
| local tax | € 0.30 |

**Tel:** 02 54 77 00 27. **Fax:** 02 54 89 43 58. **E-mail:** camping.vendome@free.fr. **Reservations:** Advisable in main season. **Open** 1 April - mid September.

**Directions:** Site is signed from the N10 through the town.

## Sunêlia Les Bois du Bardelet

**4501** route de Bourges, Poilly, 45500 Gien

This attractive family site in a rural setting, is well situated for exploring the less well known eastern part of the Loire Valley. A lake and pool complex have been attractively landscaped in 12 hectares of former farmland, blending old and new with natural wooded areas and more open field areas with rural views. Bois du Bardelet provides 260 pitches with around 140 for touring units. All are larger than 100 sq.m. and all have electrical connections (10A), with some fully serviced (electricity, water and waste water). The communal areas are based on converted former farm buildings with a wide range of leisure facilities. A family club card can be purchased to make use of the activities (some high season only). Various activities and excursions are organised, the most popular being to Paris on Wednesdays, which can be pre-booked.

**Facilities:** Three sanitary blocks (only one open outside 15/6-31/8) include washbasins in cabins and facilities for people with disabilities and babies. Washing machines. Shop (1/4-15/9). Pleasant terraced bar. Snack bar, takeaway and restaurant (1/4-15/9) and pizzeria. Three pools including a children's pool and an indoor pool (heated and charged for). Aqua gym, fitness and jacuzzi room. Archery. Lake for canoeing and fishing. Tennis, minigolf, boules and table tennis. Bicycle hire. Play area for under-8s. **Off site:** Supermarket 5 km. Walking and cycling routes.

**Charges** 2002

| | |
|---|---|
| Per unit incl. 2 persons | € 20.60 |
| with electricity and water | € 25.00 |
| extra person (over 2 yrs) | € 5.00 |
| animal | € 1.80 |
| family leisure card (per week) | € 35.00 - € 45.00 |

**Tel:** 02 38 67 47 39. **Fax:** 02 38 38 27 16. **E-mail:** contact@bardelet.com. **Reservations:** Made with deposit (€ 54) and fee (€ 16). **Open** 1 April - 30 September.

**Directions:** From Gien take D940 towards Bourges. After 5 km. turn right (signed) and right again to cross the road and follow signs to site. From Argens sur Sauldre take D940 towards Gien and site is signed to right after approx. 15 km. (narrow road).

Les Bois du Bardelet ★★★★
LOIRE VALLEY

With the family card:
Canoeing, Archery Tennis, Heated Indoor Swimming Pool, Mini-golf, Fishing. Visit Paris Wednesday in high season. Evenings with entertainment.
**www.bardelet.com**

Club Vacances

## Camping-Caravaning La Vallée des Vignes

**4907** 49700 Concourson-sur-Layon

The two young couples of English/French owners at La Vallée des Vignes are truly proud of their quality campsite and this is reflected in their care and attention to detail. Flowers, vines and an old wine press at the entrance welcome visitors. Many young trees and shrubs have been planted to add to the existing mature trees that surround the site. Bordering the river Layon, the 54 good sized touring pitches are reasonably level and fully serviced (10A electricity, water tap and waste). Five pitches have a hardstanding for cars. Attractions include a generously sized sun terrace surrounding the pool and in high season activities are organised. These include a hog roast (or similar) followed by boules and palet competitions (palet is a game unique to the region).

**Facilities:** The comfortable and well appointed toilet block includes washbasins in cabins, with dishwashing and laundry facilities at either end, under cover. Bar from 15/5, serving meals snacks and takeaway 1/6-15/9. Swimming and paddling pools (from 15/5). Children's playground, games area and small football pitch. Minigolf, fitness trail, volleyball, basketball, table tennis. Bicycle hire. Fishing on site's own stretch of river. Caravan storage.

**Charges** 2002

| | |
|---|---|
| Per unit incl. 2 persons | € 13.00 - € 18.00 |
| extra adult | € 3.00 - € 4.00 |
| child (2-12 yrs) | € 2.00 - € 2.50 |
| electricity (10A) | € 2.50 |
| local tax | 40.30 |

**Tel:** 02 41 59 86 35. **Fax:** 02 41 59 09 83. **E-mail:** campingvdv@aol.com. **Reservations:** Contact site. **Open** 1 May - 30 September.

**Directions:** Site signed off D960 Doué - Vihiers road, just west of Concourson-sur-Layon.

## Camping L'Etang de la Brèche

**4901** route Nationale 152, 5 Impasse de la Breche, 49730 Varennes-sur-Loire

The Saint Cast family have developed L'Etang de la Brèche with loving care and attention on a 25 ha. estate 4 km. south-east of Saumur on the edge of the Loire behind the dykes. It is a peaceful base from which to explore the famous châteaux, abbeys and wine cellars in this region. The site provides 201 large, level pitches with shade from mixed tall trees and bushes, facing central, less shaded grass areas used for recreation. There are electrical connections to most pitches (in some cases a long cable may be required), with water and drainaway on some of them. The restaurant, also open to the public, blends well with the existing architecture and, together with the bar area and terrace, provides a social base and is probably one of the reasons why the site is popular with British visitors. The swimming complex includes three pools: one with a removable cover, one outdoor, and a lovely pool for toddlers. The site includes a small lake (used for fishing) and wooded area ensuring a quiet, relaxed and rural atmosphere. and making L'Étang de la Brèche a comfortable holiday base for couples and families. A Les Castels site used by tour operators (85 pitches).

**Facilities:** Three toilet blocks, modernised to good standards, include facilities for babies with two units for people with disabilities. Washing up sinks and laundry. Shop and epicerie. Good, reasonably priced restaurant, pizzeria and takeaway. Three heated pools. Tennis, basketball, minigolf and a field for football. Bicycle hire. General room, games and TV rooms. Well organised, varied sporting and entertainment programme (10/7-25/8). Child minding is arranged in afternoons. Low season excursions 'Getting to know the Area' and wine tastings are organised. Torch useful. **Off site:** Riding 2 km, golf 8 km.

**Charges** 2002

| | |
|---|---|
| Per unit incl. 2 persons | € 15.00 - € 22.00 |
| incl. 3 persons | € 18.50 - € 25.00 |
| extra adult | € 3.50 - € 5.00 |
| hild (under 10 yrs) | € 2.00 - € 3.00 |
| electricity (10A) | free - € 3.00 |
| water and drainage | € 2.00 |

**Tel:** 02 41 51 22 92. **Fax:** 02 41 51 27 24. **E-mail:** mail@etang.breche.com. **Reservations:** Made for min. 7 nights in high season (3 days in low season) with deposit and fee. **Open** 17 May - 9 September.

**Directions:** Site is 100 m. north off the main N152, about 4 km. southeast of Saumur on the north bank of the Loire.

## Camping Municipal du Pont des Fées

**4910M** Chemin du Pont des Fées, 49150 Baugé

Good for an overnight stop, this site is peacefully situated alongside a small river and next to the town tennis courts and swimming pool. There are 50 pitches on level grass each with electricity and separated by small, neat box hedges. There is no shop on the site but it is only a ten minute walk to the town centre. Animals are welcomed.

**Facilities:** Two toilet blocks are in good condition with British style WCs. Some washbasins are in cabins and roomy hot showers are free. Resident site warden, gates locked overnight.

**Charges** guide

| | |
|---|---|
| Per pitch | € 1.40 - € 3.00 |
| person | € 2.00 - € 300 |

**Tel:** (0)2 41 89 14 79. **Fax:** when closed (0)2 41 84 12 12. **Reservations:** Contact site or out of season, the Mairie (0)2 41 89 14 79. **Open** 15 May - 15 September.

**Directions:** Leaving Baugé to the south turn left on D766 for Tours. Site is signed to the left within the built-up area.

# Camping de Chantepie

St Hilaire-St Florent, 49400 Saumur

**4902**

the **travel service** 'O BOOK
| | |
| --- | --- |
| rry | ✓ |
| tch | ✓ |
| commodation | ✓ |

1892 55 98 98

The drive along the winding road bordered by apple orchards and vineyards is well rewarded on arriving at the floral entrance to Camping de Chantepie. Reception at this friendly site is housed in a tastefully restored ancient farmhouse. Linked by gravel roadways (can be dusty), the 150 grass pitches are all level and spacious. They are separated by low hedges of flowers and trees which offer some shade and most have electrical connections (5A). The panoramic views over the Loire from the pitches on the terraced perimeter of the meadow are stunning. There is, from here, a footpath leading to the river valley. Leisure activities for all ages are catered for in July/Aug. by the Chantepie Club, including wine tastings, excursions and canoeing. This is a good site for families.

**Facilities:** The toilet block is very clean and facilities are adequate with washbasins in cubicles and facilities for disabled visitors. Well stocked shop. Bar and terraced restaurant and separate takeaway (from 5/5). Paddling pool and two heated swimming pools are protected from the wind by a stone wall. Play area. Minigolf. Volleyball. TV, video games and table tennis. Pony rides. Bicycle and mountain bike hire. **Off site:** Fishing 200 m, riding 6 km, golf 2 km.

**Charges 2002**

| | |
| --- | --- |
| Per unit incl. 2 persons | € 15.85 - € 19.82 |
| extra adult | € 3.78 - € 4.25 |
| child (2-10 yrs) | € 2.20 - € 2.74 |
| electricity | € 2.32 - € 2.90 |
| local tax | € 0.15 - € 0.30 |

**Tel:** 02 41 67 95 34. Fax: 02 41 67 95 85. E-mail: camping.chantepie@wanadoo.fr. **Reservations:** Made with € 11 fee; contact site for details. **Open** 29 April - 14 September.

**Directions:** From Saumur take D751 signed Gennes. Turn right at roundabout in St Hilaire-St Florent and continue until Le Poitrinea and campsite sign, then turn left. Continue for about 3 km. and then turn right into road leading to site.

*On the route of the castles of the Loire*
*2 campsites welcome you*

Camping de Chantepie
★★★★

St-Hilaire-St-Florent
49400 SAUMUR
Tél. +33 (0)2 41 67 95 34
Fax +33 (0)2 41 67 95 85
info@campingchantepie.com
www.campingchantepie.com

*The same spirit of hospitality*

CAMPING DE L'ÉTANG ★★★★

49320 BRISSAC
Tél. +33 (0)2 41 91 70 61
Fax +33 (0)2 41 91 72 65
info@campingetang.com
www.campingetang.com

Association de Chantepie et de l'Etang N° 2002/DRTEFP/280

# Camping de L'Etang

St Saturnin sur Loire, 49320 Brissac

**4904**

the **travel service** TO BOOK
| | |
| --- | --- |
| Ferry | ✓ |
| Pitch | ✓ |
| Accommodation | ✗ |

01892 55 98 98

Originally the farm of the ancient Château de Brissac, the tasteful conversion has retained the tranquillity and ambience of bye-gone days and added the necessary comforts expected by today's campers. A rural campsite with pleasant views across the countryside, there are over 150 good sized, level touring pitches. Separated and numbered, some have shade and all have 10A electricity with water and drainage nearby. A small bridge crosses the river Aubance which runs through the site and there are two lakes where fisherman can enjoy free fishing. The site has its own vineyard and the wine produced is highly recommended and can be purchased on the campsite. The production of the wine and the maintenance of the campsite, vineyards and the adjacent pleasure park offer, under guidance, employment to handicapped personnel.

**Facilities:** Three well maintained sanitary blocks are of a high standard. Laundry room with washing machines, dryer, together with baby and toddler facilities. Disabled visitors are well catered for. Motorcaravan service point. The adapted farmhouse houses reception, small shop, bar and takeaway (from 15/6). Restaurant planned. Two swimming pools, one heated, and paddling pool. Wide variety of evening entertainment in high season. **Off site:** The adjacent Parc de Loisirs is a paradise for children with activities including boating, pony rides, miniature train, water slide, bouncy castle and swings (free entry for campers). Golf 10 km.

**Charges 2003**

| | |
| --- | --- |
| Per unit incl. 2 persons | € 16.25 - € 20.30 |
| extra adult | € 3.85 - € 4.85 |
| child (2-10 yrs) | € 2.25 - € 2.80 |
| electricity | € 2.40 - € 3.00 |
| local tax | € 0.15 - € 0.30 |

**Tel:** 02 41 91 70 61. Fax: 02 41 91 72 65. E-mail: info@campingetang.com. **Reservations:** Contact site. **Open** 25 May - 13 September.

**Directions:** Take D748 south from Angers. Follow signs to Brissac-Quincé but do not enter the town, proceed to site along D55 (well signed) in direction of St Mathurin.

# Camping Ile d'Offard

4908  rue de Verden, Ile d'Offard, 49400 Saumur

**the travel service TO BOOK**

Ferry ✓
Pitch ✓
Accommodation ✓

01892 55 98 98

Situated on an island between the banks of the Loire and within walking distance of the centre of Saumur, this site is useful as an overnight stop en-route south or as a short-term base from which to visit the numerous châteaux in the region. The 190 touring pitches are on grass at the far end or hardstanding nearer the entrance. Some 67 pitches are occupied by tour operators and caravan holiday homes and these can be intrusive in some areas. As the site only closes from mid December until mid January, it is ideal for winter travellers. Some pitches have access to an electric hook-up (5-16A). The adjacent municipal swimming pools and minigolf (open in July/Aug) are free for campers.

**Facilities:** Three sanitary blocks, one heated in winter, include provision for disabled visitors. Toilet facilities in all blocks are unisex. Block 1 has a well equipped laundry. The other blocks are only open in high season. Basic restaurant and bar (end April - early Sept) with takeaway. Table tennis, volleyball. Play area. Some activities (a children's club, wine tastings, etc. in high season). Torches useful. **Off site:** Riding 5 km. Fishing in the Loire (permits from Saumur). Thursday market 500 m, Saturday morning market 2 km.

**Charges** 2002

| Per unit incl. 2 adults | € 13.50 - € 18.50 |
| extra adult | € 4.00 |
| child (2-10 yrs) | € 2.00 |
| electricity | € 3.00 |
| local tax | € 0.15 - € 0.30 |

**Tel:** 02 41 40 30 00. Fax: 02 41 67 37 81. E-mail: iledoffard@wanadoo.fr. **Reservations:** Advised for July/Aug. with 25% deposit plus charge for registration. **Open** all year excl. 15 Dec - 15 Jan.

**Directions:** From N147 take exit for 'Saumur Centre'. At roundabout follow signs for Châtellerault and Chinon (keeping McDonalds on left) and continue alongside river towards town centre. At next roundabout (Office du Tourisme in front) turn left over bridge (Pont Cessart) onto island. Drive through shops and just before next bridge turn right past Hotel Adagio. Site is ahead beside municipal pool and sports stadium.

# Camping L'Isle Verte

avenue de la Loire, 49730 Montsoreau

4909

the travel service TO BOOK
erry ✓
tch ✓
ccommodation ✗
1892 55 98 98

This friendly, natural site, with pitches overlooking the Loire, is just 100 m. from the centre of Montsoreau, an ideal starting point to visit the western Loire area. Most of the 83 shaded, level and good-sized pitches are separated by low hedges. Fishermen are particularly well catered for here, there being an area to store their equipment and live bait (permits are available in Saumur). Attractions within walking distance of the campsite include the château (500 m), Troglodyte (mushroom caves and restaurant) 500 m, wine tasting in the cellars opposite the site, and a Sunday market in the town. Good English is spoken in the reception and bar.

**Facilities:** A single building provides separate male and female toilets. Washbasins, some in cabins, and showers are unisex. Separate facilities for disabled campers. Baby room. Laundry room with deep sinks, washing machine and dryer. Dishwashing area under cover at the front of the building. Bar and snack bar. Swimming and paddling pools. Small play area. Table tennis, volleyball. Bicycle hire (June - August or by special request). Fishing. Torches useful.

**Charges** 2002

| Per unit incl. 2 adults | € 10.00 - € 14.00 |
| --- | --- |
| extra adult | € 3.00 |
| child (2-10 yrs) | € 1.50 |
| electricity (16A) | € 2.50 |
| local tax | € 0.30 |

**Tel:** 02 41 51 76 60. **Fax:** 02 41 51 08 83. **E-mail:** isleverte@wanadoo.fr. **Reservations:** Advised for July/Aug. with 25% fee and booking fee. **Open** 1 April - 30 September.

**Directions:** Take D947 from Saumur to Montsoreau and site is clearly signed on left along the road into town.

# Camping L'Européen de Montsabert

Montsabert, 49320 Coutures

4906

the travel service TO BOOK
erry ✓
Pitch ✓
Accommodation ✗
01892 55 98 98

This extensive campsite, now under new ownership, has a rural atmosphere in the shadow of Montsabert château, from where visiting peacocks happily roam in the spacious surroundings. Mature trees provide shade to the mostly large (some are enormous) pitches that are divided by hedges and are well marked. A few of the 107 pitches for touring units have a hard-standing, all have water tap, waste water point and electricity (5A) close by. Fringed by impressive redwood trees, this partially wooded site offers the peace of the countryside and yet easy access to Saumur and Angers. It is an ideal base for exploring, whether by foot, bicycle or car. Used by tour operators (19 pitches).

**Facilities:** The main central toilet block can be heated and has washbasins and bidets in cabins. Outside dishwashing and laundry facilities. Washing machine and dryer. A second block serves the pool and another unit provides more WCs. Restaurant and takeaway (both 15/6-15/9). Bar (1/6-15/9). Shop (1/6-30/8). Large 25 m. heated swimming pool (1/6-15/9; no bermuda style shorts). Sports hall, minigolf, volley and basketball, table tennis and tennis. Bicycle hire. Picnic tables are provided in the shade near the entrance with a communal barbecue area. Torch useful. **Off site:** Windsurfing, canoeing and sailing near. Fishing 5 km, golf 5km, riding 8 km.

**Charges** 2002

| Per pitch incl. 2 persons | € 13.00 - € 18.30 |
| --- | --- |
| extra person | € 3.30 - € 4.25 |
| electricity (5A) | € 2.75 |
| cyclists (1 or 2 persons) | € 10.70 |

**Tel:** 02 41 57 91 63. **Fax:** 02 41 57 90 02. **E-mail:** anjoucamp@wanadoo.fr. **Reservations:** Made with 30% deposit and fee (€ 7,62). **Open** 15 May - 15 September.

**Directions:** From Le Mans, direction Angers, take exit 12 direction Seiches s Loire. Turn left to the D74 signed Bauné, Château Montgeoffroy, Mazé. In Mazé take the D55 towards St Maturin s Loire, pass the bridge and follow the signs L'Européen and Coutures.

L'EUROPÉEN de MONTSABERT

Spacious Pitches
Heated Swimmingpool
Sportshall, Tennis, Tabletennis,
Volley, Soccer, Midget Golf, etc.
Bicycle rent, Walking- and
Cyclingroutes
Restaurant, Entertainement
English spoken
Holiday homes to let

www.camping-europeen.com   Tel: (0033) 241 57 91 63

## Camping du Lac de Maine

4900

avenue du Lac de Maine, 49000 Angers

The Parc de Loisirs du Lac de Maine is a leisure area with all sorts of activities, located to the southwest of the city. The campsite is at the southern end of the Parc towards Bouchmaine. Most of the level 141 individual pitches for tourists are part grass and part gravel hardstanding, with the remainder being all gravel. All have water, drain and electricity hook-up (6A). The park entrance has a height restriction of 3.2 m, however there is an alternative gate for higher vehicles. The adjacent 100 acre lake has a sandy beach for swimmers, windsurfing, sailing and pedaloes available, while the parkland provides tennis courts and a nature reserve. This is a useful site, open for a long season and only five minutes from the city centre.

**Facilities:** Two sanitary blocks, one which can be heated and includes some washbasins in cubicles. Facilities for babies and visitors with disabilities. Dishwashing and laundry sinks. Washing machines. Excellent motorcaravan service point. Restaurant/bar (both early June - mid Sept). Heated L-shaped swimming pool. Volleyball. Pétanque. Bicycle hire. Playground. Internet point.

**Charges** 2003

| | |
|---|---|
| Per unit incl. 2 persons | € 9.90 - € 13.40 |
| extra adult | € 2.00 |
| child (under 7 yrs) | € 1.25 |
| electricity (10A) | € 3.00 |
| local tax | € 0.46 |

**Tel:** 02 41 73 05 03. **Fax:** 02 41 73 02 20. **E-mail:** camping@lacdemaine.fr. **Reservations:** Advised for July/Aug. and made with € 6 fee and deposit of € 8 per night of stay. **Open** 25 March - 10 October.

**Directions:** Leave N23 (Angers ringroad) at signs for Quartier de Maine and Lac de Maine. Follow signs for Pruniers and Bouchemaine. Site is on the D111 and is well signed. Site also signed from centre of Angers (5 km).

---

## Camping Parc des Loisirs de Vaux

5301M

BP 27, 53300 Ambrières les Vallées

This very pleasant municipal site is adjacent to a sports complex that provides an outdoor heated swimming pool, canoe and kayak rental, tennis and badminton courts, archery, horse riding, minigolf, pétanque, bicycle hire and a playground for youngsters. The site has 55 tourist pitches, all on grass and with 10A electricity (long leads may be necessary on some pitches). Mobile homes are intermingled with the touring pitches and there are also 12 modern chalets suitable for all year use. The low season price includes access to the minigolf, while the high season charge also includes entrance to the pool.

**Facilities:** Sanitary facilities are in two units, one close to the entrance and a smaller one at the far end of the site. Both are fairly modern and well cared for, with some washbasins in cubicles and a laundry building. Bar (July/Aug). Site is not suitable for American RVs. **Off site:** Shop, bars and restaurants within 1 km. Play area outside the campsite. Swimming pool (24/6-31/8).

**Charges** 2002

| | |
|---|---|
| Per unit incl. 2 persons - 1 night | € 7.50 - € 9.20 |
| extra person | € 1.80 - € 2.30 |
| child up to 10 yrs | € 0.90 - € 1.10 |
| electricity | € 2.20 |

Less for longer stays. **Tel:** 02 43 04 00 67. **Fax:** 02 43 08 93 28. **Reservations:** Contact site for details. **Open** 1 April - 22 September.

**Directions:** Ambrières-les-Vallées is 12 km. north of Mayenne. Site is well signed from D23, 1.5 km. south of town centre.

---

## Camping Municipal du Gué St-Léonard

5309M

Rue de St-Léonard, 53100 Mayenne

This is an attractive site on the northern outskirts of Mayenne, an old port town which boasts a castle and cathedral, built on the steep banks of the river of the same name. It is 200 kilometres. from Cherbourg and could make a useful night stop or possible base for visiting the Le Mans 24 hour race (70 km). Well cared for and with a tranquil, peaceful atmosphere, tall poplars and weeping willows over the river lend it charm (and shade). The 100 pitches are on fairly level grass and include a number right beside the river. Most have electricity (5/10A). There are 8 winter pitches with electricity on the hardstanding area above the site. At the northern end the adjacent Moulinex factory has 24-hour generators with a constant hum.

**Facilities:** New sanitary blocks have British style WCs. Children's play area. Football, volleyball, and games room. **Off site:** Town 800 m. Adjacent swimming pool, fishing and canoeing on the river (possibly dangerous for young children).

**Charges** 2002

| | |
|---|---|
| Per unit incl. up to 3 persons | € 9.50 |
| extra person | € 1.80 |
| electricity (10A) | € 1.80 |

**Tel:** 02 43 04 57 14. **Fax:** 02 43 30 21 10. **Reservations:** Contact site. **Open** 15 March - 30 September.

**Directions:** Site is well signed from the town, 1 km. north of Mayenne centre, just off N12 to Caen.

## Loire Valley
# Castel Camping Le Château de Chanteloup
72460 Sillé-le-Philippe

**7203**

A peaceful, pleasant and friendly site with a certain rural charm, 15 km. from Le Mans, Chanteloup is situated in the park of a 19th century château in the heart of the Sarthe countryside. There are 100 pitches, some along the edge of the woods, many on the lawn and completely open, and a few overlooking the lake, so the degree of shade varies. The pitches are open and all have electricity (6A) although long leads will be required in some instances. This lack of regimentation enhances the atmosphere and feeling of spaciousness in the grounds surrounding the old château. Tours of the grounds and the village by pony and cart can be arranged.

**Facilities:** Sanitary facilities in the château outbuildings are quite a walk from some pitches. Washbasins in cabins. Dishwashing and laundry sinks, and washing machine under cover. Small shop. Pleasant bar (31/5-6/9)with terrace in the château with breakfast, lunch and dinner served (all 10/6-22/8). Swimming pool. Play area (supervision essential), games room, tennis, volleyball, table tennis. Mountain bike hire. Organised activities in high season. Torches useful. **Off site:** Golf 14 km, riding 7 km. Free use of tennis club in Le Mans (tennis, squash and badminton).

**Charges** 2003

| | |
|---|---|
| Per pitch | € 8.00 - € 10.00 |
| adult | € 4.50 - € 6.00 |
| child (under 7 yrs) | € 3.00 |
| electricity | € 3.00 |

**Tel:** 02 43 27 51 07. Fax: 02 43 89 05 05. E-mail: chanteloup.souffront@wanadoo.fr. **Reservations:** No minimum length. **Open** 1 June - 8 September.

**Directions:** Site is 15 km. northeast of Le Mans. From autoroute take exit for Le Mans Est, then follow D301 for Yvré l'Evèque, Savigne l'Evèque and Bonnétable. Site is halfway between these last two villages (road is narrow).

## Loire Valley
# Camping La Route d'Or
allée de la Providence, 72200 La Flèche

**7201M**

This is a very busy site as La Flèche lies at the junction of the Le Mans-Angers and Laval-Saumur roads, along which Britons frequently travel. Set in quiet, park-like surroundings on the south bank of the River Loir (not the River Loire which is a few miles to the south), the site is only a pleasant stroll from the town centre. There are 200 pitches marked out on flat grass, many in excess of 100 sq.m. and some with dividing hedges. Some pitches are in the open park, others are shaded by tall trees. Electrical connections (6/10A) in available in all areas (long leads may be needed) and there are 35 shady pitches with water and drainawayand one overnight hardstanding suitable for larger units or American RVs - please phone in advance.

**Facilities:** Two original sanitary blocks are of the older style with rather cramped showers and British and Turkish style toilets. The central block is more modern including a unit for disabled visitors. An additional separate block with facilities for disabled visitors and housing a laundry can be heated in cool weather (used by other campers in winter). Good motorcaravan service point. Tennis, boules, playground. Swimming and paddling pools. River fishing (permit available locally). Pedaloe and canoe hire. Bicycle hire. **Off site:** Shops.

**Charges** 2002

| | |
|---|---|
| Per person | € 2.80 |
| child (under 7 yrs) | € 1.40 |
| pitch and vehicle | € 1.55 - € 2.80 |
| electricity (6A) | € 1.30 - € 2.65 |
| local tax | € 0.15 |

**Tel:** 02 43 94 55 90. Fax: 02 43 94 33 78. E-mail: camping@ville-laffeche.fr. **Reservations:** Made without deposit for min. 7 days, but space is usually available. **Open** 1 March - 31 October.

**Directions:** Site is in southwest outskirts of town just off D938 road to Saumur and is signed from a junction on the bypass.

## Loire Valley
# Camping Municipal du Lac
rue du Lac, 72120 Saint-Calais

**7202M**

St Calais is a small town 37 km. east of Le Mans. Camping du Lac has 59 marked pitches, most separated by hedges and all with electricity (3/6A), water and drain. A separate area is for tents. Pizzas are sold on Saturday evenings and in high season there are theme evenings (crêpes or pizzas with guitar music), walks, competitions, children's activities, and communal meals (campers take own food and dance to music). Reception is welcoming, the value is excellent and this would make a good night stop or base for visiting the Le Mans 24 hour race. Some road noise.

**Facilities:** Two sanitary blocks provide some washbasins in private cabins. Washing machine in larger block. Bread and croissants (to order). Two small play areas. **Off site:** Swimming pool adjacent. Local supermarket just a short walk.

**Charges** 2002

| | |
|---|---|
| Per pitch | € 1.98 |
| adult | € 2.21 |
| child (under 10 yrs) | € 1.07 |
| electricity (3/6A) | € 1.45 - € 2.36 |
| local tax | € 0.84 |

**Tel:** 02 43 35 04 81. **Reservations:** Made with deposit (€ 15,24). **Open** 1 April - 15 October.

**Directions:** Well signed from N157, site is beside lake north of the town, near the station.

## Loire Valley
# Camping Municipal du Val de Sarthe

7206M 72170 Beaumont sur Sarthe

This delightful, inexpensive riverside site is conveniently located just a short walk from the pretty little town, and its shops and services. The 73 level, grassy individual pitches are large, divided by growing hedges and all have electricity (5A). Some of the pitches along the river's edge may require a longer cable. An excellent activity area provides swings and other children's play equipment, boules pitches, tennis, netball, and a trim trail. Those intending to stay longer than one night require a barrier card (refundable deposit). No double axle caravans are accepted. Reception opens 08.00-22.00 daily.

**Facilities:** The central sanitary unit is accessed by a flight of steps although there is a long and fairly steep ramp for disabled people. Modern and well looked after facilities include some washbasins in cubicles and spacious showers. Dishwashing and laundry sinks, washing machine. Motorcaravan service point. Bread to order and a few basic products available from reception. Activity area. River fishing. Room for campers' use (July/Aug).

**Charges** 2002

| | |
|---|---|
| Per caravan incl. 2 adults | € 4.93 |
| extra adult | € 1.44 |
| child (under 7 yrs) | € 0.72 |
| pitch | € 1.13 - € 2.06 |
| electricity | € 1.89 |
| dog | € 0.30 |

**Tel:** 02 43 97 01 93. **Fax:** 02 43 97 02 21. **E-mail:** beaumont.sur.sarthe@wanadoo.fr. **Reservations:** Not normally necessary. **Open** 1 May - 30 September.

**Directions:** Site is well signed from approach roads and from the town centre.

## Loire Valley
# Camping Municipal de Noron

7901M 21 boulevard Salvador Allendé, 79000 Niort

A good example of the better type of municipal, this well kept and agreeable site should be highly satisfactory for overnight or a bit longer. On flat ground, in a quiet setting beside the River Sèvre (fenced with gate) with mature trees and next to exhibition grounds, it has 168 individual pitches with good shade over most of the site and a general meadow with a play area. Electricity hook-ups are available (3, 8 or 13A). The barrier is closed 22.00-07.00 hrs. There is road noise on many pitches.

**Facilities:** The toilet block is quite old but is kept very clean and includes some washbasins in cabins and facilites for disabled visitors. Washing machine and ironing board. Playground. Bicycle hire. Fishing. Winter caravan storage. **Off site:** Riding or golf 5 km. Shopping centre 800 m.

**Charges** 2002

| | |
|---|---|
| Per person | € 2.59 |
| child (under 7 yrs) | € 1.52 |
| pitch and vehicle | € 2.74 |
| electricity (5A) | € 2.29 |

**Tel:** 05 49 79 05 06. **Fax:** 05 49 79 05 06. **Reservations:** Contact site or Tourist office (tel: (0)5.49.24.18.79) **Open** 1 April - 30 September.

**Directions:** Site is west of the town, well signed and adjacent to the ring road running between the N148 and N11 roads.

## Loire Valley
# Camping de Courte Vallée

7902 79600 Airvault

A very warm welcome is given to all campers that arrive on site a glass of wine and a friendly chat with the new owners Irene and Bruce Gibson. This very attractive site has 41 pitches on level grass amongst trees and shrubs electricity hook-ups (8A). The owners are spending lots of time and work in improving what is already a well laid out site. They are planning another facilities block and hardstanding for motorcaravans for 2003. This is an ideal location for short stay or as a base for touring the Poitou-Charentes region and the Loire valley. Nearby is Futurescope at Poitiers and the Puy-Du-Fou medieval theme park (where you can watch chariot racing and battle re-enactments). After all that excitement you can return to the peace and quiet of your pitch or venture into Airvault for a meal at one of the many restaurants and bars.

**Facilities:** A modern unisex block hash spacious cubicles for showers and washbasins, and shower and WC cubicles for disabled visitors, all kept to a very high standard of cleanliness. Dishwashing area under cover. Laundry. Swimming pool. Boules. Table tennis. Play area. Reception sells snacks, drinks and gas. Internet access. Caravan storage. Weekly wine tasting events and barbecues. **Off site:** Airvault is 15 minutes walk. Fishing 300 m. Riding 8 km.

**Charges** 2002

| | |
|---|---|
| Per person | € 3.50 |
| child (under 7) | € 1.70 |
| pitch and vehicle | € 6.50 |
| animal | € 1.52 |
| electricity (8A) | € 2.50 |

**Tel:** 05 49 64 70 65. **Fax:** 05 49 64 70 65. **E-mail:** camping@caravanningfrance.com. **Reservations:** Contact site for details. **Open** 15 April - 30 September.

**Directions:** From D938 (Parthenay-Thours) take D725 Airvault then left over bridge. At T-junction at top of hill turn sharp left, take second exit at roundabout and left at junction to site on left. Site is well signed from Airvault. Note: caravans are not allowed in the village.

## Loire Valley
# Camping Le Relais du Miel
route d'Antran, 86100 Châtellerault

With very easy access from the A10 and N10 roads, in the northern outskirts of Châtellerault, this site is being developed in the 10 acre grounds of a rather grand house dating from Napoleonic times. Beside the River Vienne, it is surrounded by majestic old trees. Twin barns form two sides of a courtyard behind the house, one of which has already been converted very stylishly into reception, a high ceilinged function and games room. Beyond are an orchard and stone gateposts leading onto ground, previously the home farm, that now forms 80 large, flat pitches. The grass is gradually growing and over 1,000 trees and bushes have been planted, some now providing a little shade. All the 100-200 sq.m. pitches have electricity and water, 20 with drainage connections. You are welcome to stroll in the gardens and there is a gate in the walled grounds to the river bank where you may fish. The outer gates are closed at 10 pm. and you need a code to get in after this time.

**Facilities:** First class toilet facilities have been created from three sets of outbuildings including washbasins in cabins, facilities for disabled people, dishwashing sinks, and a washing machine and dryer. Basic essentials and gas are kept. Bar and restaurant serving good value meals. Takeaway. Small snack bar with outdoor tables, sheltered by canopy, open in evenings in season. Swimming pool (15 x 7 m; not open all season). Children's playground. Tennis. Volleyball, basketball. Bicycle hire. Boules and games room with electronic games, pool and table tennis. Telescope. Torch useful. **Off site:** Riding 5 km, golf 11 km. Supermarket 400 m. Futuroscope 16 km.

**Charges** 2002

| | |
|---|---|
| Per pitch incl. 2 persons, electricity and water | € 19.00 - € 24.00 |
| extra person over 5 yrs | € 3.00 - € 5.00 |
| extra tent | € 3.00 - € 5.00 |
| dog | € 3.00 |
| motorcaravan longer than 5 m, plus | € 3.00 - € 5.00 |

**Tel:** 05 49 02 06 27. **Fax:** 05 49 93 25 76. **E-mail:** camping@lerelaisdumiel.com. **Reservations:** Made with 10% deposit. **Open** 15 May - 2 September.

**Directions:** Take exit no. 26 from the A10 autoroute (Châtellerault-Nord) and site is signed just off the roundabout. From the N10 follow signs for Antran north of the town.

Enjoy rest and comfort

CAMPING
★★★★
Le Relais du Miel

www.lerelaisdumiel.com
Tel: 0033 (0)549 02 06 27

Easy access : A10 Exit 26
Longitude: 0°32'5"
Latitude: 46°50'17"

## Loire Valley
# Camping Municipal Le Riveau
86270 La Roche-Posay

This 200 pitch site is in two parts, one new (flatter and more open), the other more mature on something of a slope but with the benefit of shade from tall trees. Each section has some electrical connections (16A). The two sections are divided by a small stream with access to the river Creuse, on which boating and fishing are allowed. There are few other facilities, but the town is only about 1.5 km. A pleasant, well run site, satisfactory enough and useful for a night-stop or as a base to tour the area.

**Facilities:** Two good fully equipped toilet blocks, one in each section, include facilities for washing, dishwashing, etc. in clean, modern surroundings. Excellent facilities for disabled visitors. Children's play area

**Charges** 2002

| | |
|---|---|
| Per pitch incl. 1 person | € 4.90 |
| extra adult | € 3.35 |
| child (4-10 yrs) | € 1.50 |
| electricity (16A) | € 2.30 |
| local tax | € 0.08 - € 0.15 |

**Tel:** 05 49 86 21 23. **Reservations:** Not made and said not to be necessary. **Open** 1 March - 31 October.

**Directions:** Site is signed from the D725 town bypass, turning north at roundabout onto D5 towards Lesigny. Site is 50 m. on right.

# Camping Le Petit Trianon

**8601** Saint Ustre, 86220 Ingrandes-sur-Vienne

A family run site situated between Tours, Poitiers and Futuroscope, Le Petit Trianon has been a popular overnight stop reasonably close to the N10, one of the main routes to the southwest, for a good number of years. An original, albeit narrow, gateway leads into the campsite which consists of a slightly sloping meadow surrounded by trees in front of the château and a newer, large, more open field to one side, with a woodland area between. The 99 spacious, open but marked pitches are arranged to leave plenty of free space and there is shade in parts. More than 70 pitches have electricity (6/10A) and 12 are fully serviced. Reception is housed in the château and this and the traditional, old outbuildings contain many of the main facilities, where several rooms can be heated, including the original toilet block. The pool area is located on the sunny side of a rather picturesque castled facade in which is a large, very cool reading room. Futuroscope at Poitiers is well worth at least a day's visit (if you stay for the after dusk laser, firework and fountain show, remember your late night entry code for the site gate).

**Facilities:** The original toilet unit (looking a little dated and in need of some refurbishment) includes washbasins in cabins, some washbasin and shower combination units, baby baths, laundry with washing machines and dryer, and sinks for dishwashing. Smaller blocks have been added to serve the newer parts of the site and one contains facilities for disabled people. Motorcaravan service point. Shop with essentials and drinks (open certain hours). Takeaway cooked dishes. Heated swimming pool and paddling pools. Children's playground. Table tennis, minigolf, badminton, croquet, volleyball and boules. TV room with satellite, books and games. Bicycle hire. Local wine and cognac tastings on site and organised excursions. Caravan storage. **Off site:** Fishing 3 km. Restaurant 50 m. away with menu displayed on site.

**Charges** 2002

| | |
|---|---|
| Per person | € 6.30 |
| child (0-6 yrs) | € 1.00 - € 3.15 |
| pitch and vehicle | € 7.40 |
| dog | € 2.00 |
| electricity (5/10A) | € 3.80 - € 4.20 |
| serviced pitch | € 2.40 |
| local tax (over 3 yrs) | € 0.15 |

**Tel:** 05 49 02 61 47. Fax: 05 49 02 68 81. E-mail: chateau@petit-trianon.fr. **Reservations:** Made with 25% deposit and fee (€ 12,50); min. 5 days in July/Aug. **Open** 15 May - 20 September.

**Directions:** Ingrandes is signed from the N10 north of the town, which is between Dangé and Châtellerault. From autoroute A10 take exit 26 for Châtellerault-Nord and at roundabout follow signs for Tours to Ingrandes where site is signed.

# Camping-Caravaning Les Peupliers

**8608** 86700 Couhé

Family owned and run since 1968, Les Peupliers is located in a valley south of Poitiers. The site is arranged on the banks of a river (unfenced), the 130 pitches on both sides or around a fishing lake. On level grass, most are separated and all have electricity hook-ups (16A), 55 fully serviced with electric, water and waste water drain. There is a good swimming pool complex that includes an impressive 80 metre waterslide with a drop of 10 metres, a heated main pool and a paddling pool. For 2003 this will also include a 350 sq.m. lagoon with two slides for younger children (under 10 yrs) and water games. There is a local market for every day of the week (Chaunay, Lezay, Civray, Gencay, Rouillé or Vivonnet). Nearby Vaux has an ostrich farm, and at Romagne there is 'La Vallée des Singes' with 25 species of monkey, ape and gorilla.

**Facilities:** The three toilet blocks are in Mediterranean style, with washbasins in cubicles, dishwashing and laundry sinks, washing machines and facilities for babies and disabled people. The newest block is in regular use, with the other two coming into service as the season progresses. Fridge rental. Small, well stocked shop by reception. Snack bar, restaurant and bar with covered terrace and entertainment in peak season. Swimming pool cmplex (1/6-30/9). Children's playground. Fishing lake. Minigolf, table tennis and some pedaloes. **Off site:** Tennis court 800 m.

**Charges** 2003

| | |
|---|---|
| Per adult | € 5.50 |
| child (2-10 yrs) | € 3.50 |
| pitch | € 7.00 |
| electricity | € 3.00 |
| electricity, water and drainage | € 4.50 |

**Tel:** (0)5 49 59 21 16. Fax: (0)5 49 37 92 09. E-mail: info@lespeupliers.fr. **Reservations:** Contact site. **Open** 1 May - 30 September.

**Directions:** Couhé is about 30 km. south of Poitiers. Site is 1 km. north of Couhé, just off N10 (signed).

## Camping du Parc de Saint Cyr

86130 Saint Cyr

**8609**

This well organised, five hectare campsite is part of a 300 hectare leisure park, based around a large lake with sailing and associated sports, and an area for swimming (supervised July/Aug). Land based activities include tennis, two half-courts, table tennis, fishing, badminton, pétanque, TV room, and a well equipped fitness suite, all of which are free of charge. In high season there are extra free activities including a kids club, beach club, archery and an entertainment programme. Also in high season but charged for are fly-fishing, sailing school, aquatic toboggan, windsurfing, canoe, kayak, water bikes and stunt bikes. Campers also get 20% discount on green fees at both the 9 and 18 hole golf courses. If all this sounds a bit too exhausting, you could escape to the small, peaceful formal garden in the centre of the site. The campsite has around 185 tourist pitches and 13 mobile homes for rent. The marked and generally separated pitches are all fully serviced with electricity (10A), water and drain.

**Facilities:** The main toilet block is modern and is supplemented for peak season by a second, recently refitted unit, which should prove adequate for demand, although they do attract some use by day-trippers to the leisure facilities. They include wash-basins in cubicles, dishwashing and laundry sinks, washing machines and dryers, and facilities for babies and disabled persons. Shop, restaurant and takeaway (April - Sept). Children's playground on the beach. Many activities as detailed above. Bicycle hire. Barrier locked 22.00-07.00 hrs (€ 7,62 deposit for card).

**Charges** 2002

| Per pitch incl. electricity, | |
|---|---|
| water and drainage | € 4.60 - € 10.00 |
| adult | € 2.40 - € 4.00 |
| child (under 7 yrs) | € 1.50 - € 2.00 |
| animal | free - € 1.50 |
| local tax | € 0.30 |

**Tel:** (0)5 49 62 57 22. Fax: (0)5 49 52 28 58. E-mail: contact@parcdesaintcyr.com. **Reservations:** Advisable for high season, made with fee (€ 7,62). **Open** 1 April - 30 September.

**Directions:** Saint Cyr is approx. midway between Châtellerault and Poitiers. Site is signed to the east of the N10 and St Cyr village, off the D82 towards Bonneuil-Matours, and is part of the Parc de Loisirs de Saint Cyr.

# Camping Le Futuriste

86130 St-Georges-les-Baillargeaux

**8604**

On raised ground with panoramic views over the strikingly modern buildings and night-time bright lights that comprise the popular attraction of Futuroscope, Le Futuriste is a neat, modern site, open all year. It is ideal for a short stay to visit the park which is only 1.5 km. away (tickets can be bought at the site) but it is equally good for longer stays to see the region. With a busy atmosphere, there are early departures and late arrivals. Reception is open 08.00-22.00 hrs. There are 112 individual, flat, grass pitches divided by young trees and shrubs which are beginning to provide some shelter for this elevated and otherwise rather open site (possibly windy). There are 28 pitches without electricity for tents, 22 with electricity (16A) and a further 62 with electricity, water, waste water and sewage connections. All are accessed via neat, level and firmly rolled gravel roads. Of course, the area has other attractions and details are available from the enthusiastic young couple who run the site. Note: it is best to see the first evening show at Futuroscope otherwise you will find youself locked out of the site - the gates are closed at 23.30 hrs.

**Facilities:** Excellent, very clean sanitary facilities are housed in two modern blocks which are insulated and can be heated in cool weather. The facilities in the newest block are unisex. and include some washbasins in cabins and facilities for disabled people. Dishwashing and laundry sinks. Washing machine and dryer. Small shop (1/5-30/9) provides essentials (order bread the night before). New bar/restaurant. Snack bar and takeaway. Two outdoor pools, one with a slide (1/5-30/9). Free fishing in lake on site. Youth groups are not accepted. **Off site:** Bicycle hire 500 m, golf 5 km. Supermarkets near.

**Charges** 2002

| | |
|---|---|
| Per pitch incl. 1-3 persons | € 12.00 - € 16.50 |
| extra person | € 1.50 - € 2.20 |
| local tax | € 0.15 |
| dog | € 1.60 |
| electricity | € 2.20 - € 3.00 |

**Tel:** 05 49 52 47 52. Fax: 05 49 52 47 52. E-mail: d.Radet@libertysurf.fr. **Reservations:** Phone bookings accepted for min. 2 nights. **Open** all year.

**Directions:** From either A10 autoroute or the N10, take Futuroscope exit. Site is located east of both roads, off the D20 to St Georges-Les-Baillargeaux. From all directions follow signs to St Georges. The site si on the hill; turn by the water tower and site is on the left.

# Parc du
# FUTUROSCOPE

## New Thrills!!

**To discover urgently**

Come now and discover the unforgettable thrills of the Parc du Futuroscope.

Take part in the **Race for Atlantis** and plunge to the depths of the ocean to save King Poseidon. Take a trip to **CyberWorld**, a fascinating journey through a virtual universe the likes of which you have never seen before. Become a hero in the 3D interactive game of **Metropole Challenge**...

Located just 8km north of Poitiers in Western France, the Parc du Futuroscope has over 2000 hotel rooms on site, it's very own TGV high speed train station and is now only one and a half hours away from London Stansted with regular direct flights to Poitiers.

# Burgundy

Map 8

Major city: Dijon

Départements: 21 Côte d'Or, 58 Nièvre, 71 Saône-et-Loire, 89 Yonne

Burgundy (Bourgogne), in the rich heartland of France, is an historic region, once a powerful independent state and important religious centre. Its golden age is reflected in the area's magnificent art and architecture – the grand palaces and art collections of Dijon, the great pilgrimage church of Vézelay, the Cistercian Abbaye de Fontenay and the evocative abbey remains at Cluny, once the most powerful monastery in Europe.

However Burgundy is best known for its wine including some of the world's finest, produced from the great vineyards of the Côte d'Or and Chablis, and perhaps for its rich cuisine including such dishes as 'Boeuf Bourguignon'. No-one can visit Burgundy without going to the 15th century Hotel Dieu at Beaune. It is both an attractive home for the elderly and where the annual Burgundy wine auctions are held. Once inside, take the conducted tour and you will see the wonderful patterned tile roofs and even the old hospital wards where patients were laid two to a bed.

The area is criss-crossed by navigable waterways and also includes the 'Parc Régional du Morvan' good walking country. It is interesting to note that Dijon itself is only an hour and a half from Paris on the TGV.

Note: the site reports are laid out by département in numerical order.

## Cuisine of the region

Many dishes are wine based, eg. 'Coq au Chambertin' and 'Poulet au Meursault'

Dijon is known for its spiced honey-cake (pain d'épice) and spicy mustard

Boeuf Bourguignon – braised beef simmered in a red wine-based sauce

Charolais (Pièce de) – steak from the excellent Charolais cattle

Garbure – heavy soup, a mixture of pork, cabbage, beans and sausages

Gougère – cheese pastry based on Gruyère

Jambon persillé – parsley-flavoured ham, served cold in jelly

Matelote – fresh-water fish soup, usually based on a red wine sauce

Meurette – red wine-based sauce with small onions, used with fish or poached egg dishes

## Wine

Burgundy is produced mainly from vineyards in the sheltered valleys that stretch south from Dijon to Lyon. The region is further subdivided into five main areas (north to south): Chablis, Côte d'Or, Côte Chalonnaise, Mâconais and Beaujolais. It is the Côte d'Or region centred around Beaune that produces the great wines on which Burgundy's reputation depends

## Places of interest

Autun – 12th century St Lazare cathedral.

Beaune – medieval town; its Hospices are a masterpiece of Flemish-Burgundian architecture; Museum of Burgundy Wine

Cluny – Europe's largest Benedictine abbey

Dijon – Palace of the Dukes, Fine Arts Museum, Burgundian Folklore Museum. Unfortunately development has ruined much of the original medieval city centre

Fontenay – Fontenay Abbey and Cloister

Joigny – medieval town

Mâcon – Maison des Vins (wine centre)

Paray-le-Monial – Romanesque basilica, pilgrimage centre

Sens – historic buildings, museum with fine Gallo-Roman collections

Vézelay – fortified medieval hillside, Magdalene Basilica

# Camping Lac de Panthier

21320 Vandenesse-en-Auxois

An attractively situated lakeside site in Bungundy countryside, Camping Lac de Panthier is in fact two distinct campsites - one where the site activities take place and the other where the reception and other facilities can be found, the latter offering a quieter and more attractive setting. The 207 pitches (167 for touring units) all have electricity connections (6A) and are mostly on level grass, although in parts there are shallow terraces. The site has a swimming pool complex but the most obvious attraction is its proximity to the lake with its many watersports facilities. This site is in beautiful countryside within 2 km. of the lovely Canal de Bourgogne, which links the Seine and the Saône rivers. Used by tour operators (50 pitches). A 'Sites et Paysages' member.

**Facilities:** Four good quality toilet blocks (two for each site) also provide for babies and disabled people. Shop, bar and restaurant (all 15/5-22/9). Swimming pool complex with adults' pool, children's pool and water-slide (15/5-15/9). Watersports. **Off site:** Boat excursions from Pouilly en Auxois (8 km). Dijon, Autun and Beaune are also within easy reach.

**Charges** 2003

| | |
|---|---|
| Per pitch | € 4.10 - € 6.80 |
| adult | € 3.70 - € 6.10 |
| child (under 7 yrs) | € 1.80 - € 3.00 |
| electricity | € 4.00 |
| dog | € 1.50 |
| local tax (over 17 yrs) | € 0.30 |

**Tel:** 03 80 49 21 94. Fax: 03 80 49 25 80. E-mail: info@lac-de-panthier.com. **Reservations:** Contact site. **Open** 20 April - 29 September.

**Directions:** From the A6 use exit 24 (where the A6 joins the A38). Take the N81 towards Arnay Le Duc (back over the A6), then almost immediately turn left on D977 for 5 km. Fork left again for Vandenesse en Auxois. Continue through village on D977 for 2.5 km, turn left again and site is on left.

## The Alan Rogers' Travel Service

This unique service enables our readers to reserve their holidays as well as ferry crossings and comprehensive insurance cover at extremely competitive rates. The majority of participating sites are in France and we are able to offer a selection of some of the very best sites in this country.

the travel service TO BOOK

| Ferry | ✔ |
|---|---|
| Pitch | ✔ |
| Accommodation | ✔ |

01892 55 98 98

Share our experience and let us help
to ensure that your holiday will be a complete success.

Alan Rogers Travel Service 01892 55 98 98 or www.alanrogers.com

## Camping Municipal Louis Rigoly

esplanade Saint Vorles, 21400 Châtillon-sur-Seine

**2101M**

This well kept, small, hillside municipal site has 54 pitches. Mainly individual and separated, they are on fairly flat grass, 48 with electricity (4A) with mature trees providing shelter. Adjoining the site is the municipal swimming pool complex with both indoor and outdoor pools (on payment), and minigolf. There is no shop, but the town is close. The site, which has much transit trade, can become full by evening in season.

**Facilities:** The main toilet block at the lower end of the site is satisfactory. A smaller heated unit behind reception contains facilities for babies, a washing machine and dryer. Facilities for disabled visitors provided in a separate block. Snack bar July/Aug. Children's play area. **Off site:** Fishing or bicycle hire 1 km, riding 4 km.

**Charges** 2002

| | |
|---|---|
| Per person | € 2.75 |
| child (under 7) | € 1.25 |
| vehicle | € 1.00 |
| motorcycle | € 1.00 |
| pitch | € 2.25 |
| electricity (4A) | € 2.15 - € 4.30 |

**Tel:** 03 80 91 03 05. Fax: 03 80 91 21 46. E-mail: tourism-chatillon-sur-seine@wanadoo.fr. **Reservations:** Not officially made, but if you write shortly before your visit, they will reserve until 7 p.m. **Open** 1 April - 30 September.

**Directions:** On northeast outskirts of town; site is signed from centre (steep hills approaching site, narrow roads).

## Camping Municipal de Fouché

rue du 8 Mai 1945, 21230 Arnay le Duc

**2104M**

Useful as an overnight stop en-route to or from the Mediterranean or indeed for longer stays, this quite large but peaceful, lakeside site has good facilities and the added advantage of being open all year. It can be very busy during the school holidays, and is probably better visited outside the main season. There are 190 good sized pitches, on fairly level grass and all with 10A electricity (some with water). This part of Burgundy is popular and Arnay le Duc itself is an attractive little town with an interesting history and renowned for its gastronomy, with many hotels and restaurants. The pitches, many hedged, offer a choice of shade or more open aspect.

**Facilities:** Two of the four sanitary blocks are reasonably modern and well maintained, including some British style WCs, washbasins in cabins, facilities for disabled visitors. Washing machines and dishwashing under cover. Shop in season (with bread) and snacks and drinks are served. TV/games room. Boules. Table tennis. Playground. **Off site:** Site is within walking distance of the town centre, which has an indoor swimming pool and tennis courts, etc.

**Charges** 2002

| | |
|---|---|
| Per unit incl. 2 persons | € 7.60 - € 9.20 |
| extra person | € 2.10 - € 2.60 |
| child (under 7 yrs) | € 1.10 - € 1.30 |
| electricity | € 2.70 |
| animal | € 0.80 - € 1.00 |
| local tax (1/4-30/9) over 16 yrs | € 0.30 |

**Tel:** 03 80 90 02 23. Fax: 03 80 90 11 91. E-mail: camparnay@wanadoo.fr. **Reservations:** Advised; contact site. **Open** all year.

**Directions:** Site is on east side of town (well signed), 15 km. from A6 autoroute (exit at péage de Puilly en Auxois).

## Camping Municipal Les Cents Vignes

10 rue Auguste Dubois, 21200 Beaune

The Côte de Beaune, situated southeast of the Côte d'Or, produces some of the very best French wines. Beaune is also a city of art and has a charm all of its own and there are several 'caves' in the town just waiting to be visited. Les Cents Vignes is a very well kept site offering 116 individual pitches of good size, separated from each other by neat beech hedges high enough to keep a fair amount of privacy. Rather over half of the pitches are on grass, ostensibly for tents, the remainder on hard-standings with electricity for caravans. A popular site, within walking distance of the town centre, Les Cent Vignes becomes full mid-June to early Sept. but with many short-stay campers there are departures each day and reservations can be made.

**Facilities:** Two modern, fully equipped and well constructed, sanitary blocks, one of which can be heated, should be large enough. Nearly all wash-basins are in cabins. Dishwashing and laundry sinks. Washing machines. Shop, restaurant with takeaway (all 1/4-15/10). Playground. Sports area with tennis, basketball, volleyball, boules and table tennis. TV room. Barbecue area. **Off site:** Fishing or golf 4 km, bicycle hire 1 km. windsurfing 4km.

**Charges** 2002

| | |
| --- | --- |
| Per person | € 3.00 |
| child (2-7 yrs) | € 1.50 |
| pitch | € 4.00 |
| electricity (6A) | € 3.00 |
| local tax | € 0.35 |

**Tel:** 03 80 22 03 91. **Reservations:** Made before 30 May without deposit. **Open** 15 March - 31 October.

**Directions:** From autoroute exit 24 follow signs for Beaune centre on D2 road, camping signs to site in approx. 1 km. Well signed from other routes.

## Camping Municipal Savigny-lès-Beaune

Les Premiers Pres, 21420 Savigny-les-Beaune

This popular site is ideally located for visiting the Burgundy vineyards, for use as a transit site or for spending time in the town of Beaune. During the high season it is full every evening, so it is best to arrive by 4 pm. The 90 level pitches are marked and numbered, with electric hook-ups and room for an awning. If reception is closed when you arrive, find a pitch and report later, otherwise 'Madame' will allocate a place. Whilst the famed wine region alone attracts many visitors, Beaune, its capital, is unrivalled in its richness of art from times gone by. Narrow streets and squares are garlanded with flowers, pavement cafés are crammed with tourists and over-looking the scene is the Hotel Dieu.

**Facilities:** Well kept sanitary facilities are housed in a modern building behind reception. Additional WCs and water points are conveniently placed towards the middle of the site. Table tennis. Motorcaravan service point. Torch useful. **Off site:** Sunday market in the village.

**Charges** 2002

| | |
| --- | --- |
| Per person | € 1.90 |
| child (under 7 yrs) | € 1.10 |
| pitch | € 2.80 |
| electricity | € 3.15 |
| local tax | € 0.10 - € 0.15 |

**Tel:** 03 80 26 15 06. Fax: 03 80 21 56 63. **Reservations:** Not accepted. **Open** 1 May - 30 September.

**Directions:** From A6 autoroute take exit 24 signed Beaune and Savigny-lès-Beaune onto D2. Turn right towards Savigny-lès-Beaune (3 km) and follow signs to site.

## Camping Les Bouleaux

21200 Vignoles

Camping les Bouleaux is an excellent little campsite located at Vignoles, northeast of Beaune. There are just 40 pitches, all with an electrical connection (3- 6A, long leads may be required on some pitches). The large flat pitches are attractively laid out and most are separated by hedges and trees giving some shade. Monsieur Rossignal takes great pride in his camp-site, keeping the grounds and facilities exceptionally clean and tidy, and by planting bright flowers near the reception. Les Bouleaux makes a perfect overnight stop, especially as it's open throughout the year (including Christmas Day). The nearest shops and restaurants are 3 km. from the site - there are none on-site.

**Facilities:** An older unisex building provides Turkish style WCs, while the adjacent modern block houses British style WCs (no paper). Washbasins in cabins or communal; excellent facilities for disabled visitors. Laundry and dishwashing sinks but no machines. The only water point is at the central block - you probably need a hose to fill fresh water containers. Gas exchange. **Off site:** Fishing 3 km. Golf 3 km. Riding 6 km. Bicycle hire 3 km.

**Charges** 2002

| | |
| --- | --- |
| Per unit incl. 2 persons, electricity | € 13.80 |
| adult | € 3.10 |
| child under 12 yrs | € 1.90 |

**Tel:** 03 80 22 26 88. **Reservations:** Not usually required, but phone during July/August to confirm availability. **Open** all year.

**Directions:** Vignoles is northeast of Beaune. Leave A6 at junction 24.1 south of Beaune. Turn right at roundabout, straight on at lights (centre lane), then right at next roundabout. Cross autoroute, turn left at sign for Vignoles and follow campsite signs.

## Camping La Grappe d'Or

2 route de Volnay, 21190 Meursault

2105

Meursault, the capital of the great white wines of Burgundy, is southwest of Beaune and Camping La Grappe d'Or offers terraced pitches overlooking acres of vineyards. Most of the 118 touring pitches are flat, of varying sizes, and some have shade from mature trees. They all have electrical connections (15A). There is an outdoor pool and flume and, in high season, aqua gym and other water activities are organised. A second part of the site is located 100 m. towards the village in the grounds of the owners' house. Here there are caravan holiday homes for rent as well as those used by tour operators. This is a reasonable campsite from which to enjoy some of the cycle/walking tours that take you around the local vineyards.

**Facilities:** Sanitary facilities are in three blocks with some washbasins in cabins. Child/baby room, facilities for visitors with disabilities, laundry and undercover dishwashing sinks. Shop, bar, restaurant, takeaway and swimming pool, all open from 15/5 - 15/9 although hours may vary. Play area, volleyball, tennis courts. Bicycle hire. **Off site:** Fishing 8 km, golf or riding 7 km. Indoor swimming pool 7 km.

**Charges** 2002

| | |
|---|---|
| Per unit incl. 2 persons | € 11.00 - € 14.50 |
| extra person | € 3.00 - € 3.70 |
| child up to 7 yrs | € 1.50 - € 1.90 |
| electricity | € 3.50 |
| large motorhome in high season plus | € 8.00 |
| animal | € 1.00 - € 1.30 |

**Tel:** (0)3 80 21 22 48. Fax: (0)3 80 21 65 74. **Reservations:** Made with € 25 deposit plus € 5 fee. **Open** 1 April - 15 October.

**Directions:** Site is north of Meursault. Take N74 from Beaune and follow the sign for Meursault; campsite is well signed from the town.

## Camping des Bains

15 avenue Jean Mermoz, 58360 Saint-Honoré-les-Bains

5801

the travel service
TO BOOK
Ferry ✔
Pitch ✔
Accommodation ✗
01892 55 98 98

This is an attractive site, owned and run by the Luneau family who are keen to welcome British visitors. As the site is low-lying, pitches can be rather soft in wet weather and it can also be quite cold at night in early or late season. That said, it is well situated for exploring the Morvan area. Most of the 120 large, separated pitches (100 sq.m) have a 6A electricity connection, although some may require a long cable. The actual thermal park is next door and there are opportunities locally for `taking the waters`, which, combined with the clean, pollution free environment, is said to be very good for asthma sufferers (`cures` run for three week periods). A `Sites et Paysages` member.

**Facilities:** The two main sanitary units have mostly British style WCs, washbasins in separate cabins and ample hot showers (one block may be closed in low season). Dishwashing sinks, baby bath, laundry. Facilities for disabled people. Traditional family bar (1/6-30/9) also provides food and a takeaway service (1/6-15/9). The site has its own small swimming pool (12 x 12 m) with a separate aqua slide (15/6-15/9). Excellent children`s play area and two small streams for children to fish. Table tennis, minigolf and entertainment weekly for children in July/Aug. **Off site:** Canal-side cycle route runs for 50 km. from Vandenesse (6 km). Bicycle hire or riding 500 m, fishing 5 km.

**Charges** 2003

| | |
|---|---|
| Per unit incl. 2 persons | € 14.50 |
| extra person | € 4.20 |
| child (2- 7 yrs) | € 2.80 |
| dog | € 1.50 |
| electricity (6A) | € 3.00 |
| local tax | € 0.30 |

**Tel:** 03 86 30 73 44. Fax: 03 86 30 61 88. E-mail: camping-les-bains@wanadoo.fr. **Reservations:** Write to site with deposit (€ 65) and fee (€ 12,20). **Open** 1 May - 10 October.

**Directions:** From Nevers, travel east on D978; turn right onto D985 towards St Honoré-les-Bains, from where site is signed `Village des Bains`.

# Castel Camping Manoir de Bezolle

58110 St-Pereuse-en-Morvan

**5803**

Manoir de Bezolle is well situated to explore the Morvan Natural Park and the Nivernais area. It has been attractively landscaped to provide a number of different areas, some giving pleasant views over the surrounding countryside. Pitches of varying sizes are on level grass with some terracing and most have access to electricity (6A or more). Features worthy of special mention include two small lakes, one used for fishing and a Red Indian village with ponies for children. This site is good for families with a range of activities provided for them.

**Facilities:** Two main toilet blocks (opened as needed) provide washbasins in cabins, mostly British style WCs, bath, provision for disabled visitors and a baby bath. A fibreglass unit contains two tiny family WC/basin/shower suites for rent. A smaller, older block is by the pools. Laundry. Motorcaravan services. Shop (15/5-15/9; bread to order at other times). Bar and restaurant (15/5-15/9). Pizza and takeaway (main season only). Internet point. Two swimming pools with sunbathing terrace (1/6-15/9). Riding (June-Sept). Table tennis, minigolf. Fishing. Animation is organised in season.

**Charges** 2002

| | |
|---|---|
| Per pitch incl. 2 persons | € 12.00 - € 20.00 |
| extra person | € 3.00 - € 5.00 |
| child under 7 yrs | € 2.00 - € 4.00 |
| electricity 10A | € 4.00 |
| animal | € 1.50 |
| local taxes | € 0.50 |

**Tel:** 03 86 84 42 55. Fax: 03 86 84 43 77. E-mail: info@bezolle.com. **Reservations:** Made with deposit (€ 45,70) and fee (€ 15,20). **Open** 15 April - 30 September.

**Directions:** Site is between Nevers and Autun (mid-way between Châtillon-en-Bazois and Château-Chinon), just north of the D978 by the small village of St Péreuse-en-Morvan.

# Camping de L'Etang Neuf

L'Etang Neuf, 71760 Issy-l'Évêque

**7108**

This is a jewel in the French countryside and is well worth visiting just for its wonderful tranquillity. You immediately feel at home as you enter the flag-decorated archway that forms the entrance to this quiet site flanked by a forest on one side, a château on another, and overlooking a lake. The managers, Marc and Rita Pille, insists that noise levels are kept to a minimum at all times, especially after 10.30 in the evening. All but one of the 71 large, level, grass pitches have a small hardstanding to park a car on (some are large enough for a motorcaravan) and a 5A electricity connection. Pitches are clearly marked and separated by low hedges, with a separate area for tent campers. A large, children's play area is gradually being developed in a hollow adjacent to the small swimming and paddling pools (fenced off for security). There are a number of walks and cycle routes (all-terrain) that begin at the site - maps are for sale and the proceeds at the end of the year are given to the villagers who look after the footpaths.

**Facilities:** Two very clean sanitary blocks include British and Turkish style WCs, and washbasins in cabins. Dishwashing and laundry sinks. Washing machine, dryer and ironing board in the upper block. Baby room planned. Separate shower and toilet rooms for disabled people are at the lower block. Motorcaravan service point. Bar/restaurant. Bread and croissants to order. Boules pitch, TV room, games room, table tennis and volleyball. **Off site:** Just outside the site entrance is crazy golf. Nearest shop 1 km. in Issy l'Éveque. Riding 500 m. Dried flower demonstrations and sales 2.5 km.

**Charges** 2002

| | |
|---|---|
| Per unit incl. 2 adults | € 13.00 |
| with 5A electricity | € 16.00 |
| extra adult | € 3.50 |
| child (3-8 yrs) | € 1.50 |

**Tel:** 03 85 24 96 05. Fax: 03 85 24 96 05. E-mail: marc.pille@compaqnet.be. **Reservations:** Advised for July and August. **Open** 1 May - 15 September.

**Directions:** From D973 (Luzy - Bourbon-Lancy) turn left onto D25 (just west of Luzy) and continue for about 12 km. Turn right on D42 in centre of Issy l'Évêque, signed to campsite. Take care as the road narrows considerably as you approach the site entrance on the right.

## Burgundy
# Camping Municipal Le Val d'Arroux
71320 Toulon sur Arroux

This budget priced, well managed and neatly laid out site, is located on a quieter more minor cross-country route, where good sites are not that easy to find. About 30 of its 68 pitches are available to tourists and these are reasonably level, grassy and divided into small sections by hedges and flowers, with some mature trees for shade. All have electricity (6A). Reception is open from 07.30-12.00 and 14.00-22.00 hrs in the main season. A map of walks around the area is available for a small charge.

**Facilities:** A central unisex sanitary unit includes washbasins in cubicles, facilities for disabled people, dishwashing and laundry sinks. Small children's playground. Floodlit minigolf (free to campers). Fishing in adjacent river. Covered area, games machines and table tennis. **Off site:** The town with its shops and other services within walking distance.

**Charges** 2002

| | |
|---|---|
| Per pitch - tent or caravan | € 1.15 |
| pitch - motorcaravan | € 2.30 |
| vehicle | € 1.15 |
| person | € 1.40 |
| child up to 7 yrs | € 0.75 |
| electricity | € 2.45 |

**Tel:** 03 85 79 51 22. Fax: 03 85 79 52 76.
**Reservations:** Not normally necessary. **Open** mid-April - mid-october.

**Directions:** Site is just off the D985 and is well signed from the town. It is on the western edge of town, on the west bank of the river.

## Burgundy
# Camping Moulin de Collonge
71940 Saint-Boil

This well run, family site offers an 'away from it all' situation surrounded by sloping vineyards and golden wheat fields. It has an instant appeal for those seeking a quiet, relaxing environment. There are 57 level pitches, most with electrical hook-ups although long cables may be required. Hanging flower arrangements are in abundance and, like the shrubs and grounds, are constantly being attended by the proprietor and his family (M. Gillot's other interest is the restoration of classic cars). Beyond the stream that borders the site are a swimming pool, patio and a pizzeria (also open to the public all year). A new lake, 1.8 m. deep, has been created for leisure activities. The 'Voie Vert', a 40 km. track for cycling or walking starts nearby.

**Facilities:** Toilet facilities housed in a converted barn are tastefully decorated and well kept. Some washbasins are in cubicles, there are outside sinks for dishes and laundry. Washing machine and dryer under cover. Freezer for campers' use. Bread is delivered at 8.30 each morning. Ices and cool drinks can be purchased. Pizzeria. Swimming pool covered by plastic dome - some of the walls can be opened in good weather. Bicycle hire. Table tennis. Fishing. Pony trekking. **Off site:** Riding 4 km. Chateaux, wine route, churches.

**Charges** 2002

| | |
|---|---|
| Per adult | € 4.75 |
| child (under 7 yrs) | € 2.29 |
| electricity | € 3.05 |

**Tel:** 03 85 44 00 40. Fax: 03 85 44 00 40.
**Reservations:** Accepted - contact site. **Open** 1 March - 30 September.

**Directions:** From Chalon-sur-Saône travel 9 km. west on the N80. Turn south on D981 through Buxy (6 km). Continue south for 7 km. to Saint-Boil and site is signed at south end of the village.

## Burgundy
# Camping Municipal St Vital
rue des Griottons, 71250 Cluny

Close to this attractive small town (300 metres walk) and adjacent to the municipal swimming pool (free for campers), this site has 174 pitches. On gently sloping grass, with some small hedges and shade in parts, 6A electricity is available (long leads may be needed). Some rail noise is noticeable during the day but we are assured that trains do not run 23.30-07.00 hrs. The town has the largest number of Roman houses in France, the National Stud farm, and don't miss the Cheese Tower for the best views of Cluny. Ask for a free copy of 'Cluny, town of Art and History', at reception or the tourist office. The really excellent traffic free cycle path from Cluny to Givry is highly recommended.

**Facilities:** Two sanitary buildings provide British and Turkish style WCs, some washbasins in cubicles and controllable showers (no dividers). Dishwashing and laundry sinks. Washing machine and dryer. A rubbish recycling system operates. In high season, on Friday evenings, there is a presentation of local produce in the 'salle de reunion'. **Off site:** Fishing 100m, bicycle hire 100m. Wine routes, chateaux, churches.

**Charges** 2002

| | |
|---|---|
| Per pitch and vehicle | € 3.80 |
| adult | € 3.20 |
| child (under 7 yrs) | € 1.80 |
| electricity | € 2.50 |
| local tax | € 0.07 - € 0.15 |

**Tel:** 03 85 59 08 34. Fax: 03 85 59 08 34. E-mail: Cluny_camping@Wanadoo.fr. **Reservations:** Advised for high season. **Open** 15 May - 30 September.

**Directions:** Site is east of town, by the D15 road towards Azé and Blanot.

# Castel Camping Château de L'Epervière

71240 Gigny-sur-Saône

Peacefully situated on the edge of the little village of Gigny-sur-Saône, yet within easy distance of the A6 autoroute, this site sits in a natural woodland area near the Saône river (subject to flooding in winter months). With 135 pitches, nearly all with 6A electricity, the site is in two fairly distinct areas. The original part has semi-hedged pitches on part-level ground with plenty of shade from mature trees, close to the château and fishing lake - you may need earplugs in the mornings because of the ducks! The centre of the second area has a more open aspect, with large hedged pitches and mature trees offering shade around the periphery and central open grass area. An unfenced road across the lake connects the two areas of the site (care is needed with children). The managers, Gert-Jan and Francois, and their team enthusiastically organise a range of activities for visitors that includes wine tastings in the cellars of the château and a Kids' Club in July/Aug. The site is actually owned by Christophe Gay the founder and driving force behind 'Camping Cheques', the low season 'Go as you please' package that gives flexibility to visit Camping Cheque sites in Europe. Used by tour operators (60 pitches). A member of 'Les Castels' group.

**Facilities:** Two well equipped toilet blocks, one beside the château and a newer one on the lower section include washbasins in cabins, dishwashing and laundry areas under cover. Washing machine and dryer. Shop providing bread and basic provisions (1/5-30/9). Tastefully refurbished restaurant in the château with a distinctly French menu (1/4-30/9). Second restaurant with more basic menu and takeaway service. A converted barn houses an attractive bar, large screen TV and games room. Unheated swimming pool (1/5-30/9), partly enclosed by old stone walls protecting it from the wind, plus a smaller indoor heated pool with jacuzzi, sauna and paddling pool. Children's play area. Bicycle hire. **Off site:** Riding 15 km, golf 20 km.

**Charges** 2003

| | |
|---|---|
| Per adult | € 5.10 - € 6.10 |
| child (under 7 yrs) | € 3.10 - € 4.10 |
| pitch | € 6.60 - € 9.20 |
| dog | € 2.10 - € 2.60 |
| electricity | € 3.10 - € 4.10 |

**Tel:** 03 85 94 16 90. Fax: 03 85 94 16 97. E-mail: domaine-de-lepervière@wanadoo.fr. **Reservations:** Contact site. **Open** 1 April - 15 October.

**Directions:** From N6 between Châlon-sur-Saône and Tournus, turn east on D18 (just north of Sennecey-le-Grand) and follow site signs for 6.5 km. From A6, exit Châlon-Sud from the north, or Tournus from the south.

Welcome to the heart of Burgundy

Camping Cheque

Camping Caravaning
★★★★

## Château de l'Epervière

71240 Gigny sur Saône
Tel: 0033 385 94 16 90
Fax: 0033 385 94 16 97
domaine-de-leperviere@wanadoo.fr

LES CASTELS
★★★★★

## Burgundy
# Le Village des Meuniers
71520 Dompierre-les-Ormes

**71102M**

the **travel service**
TO BOOK
Ferry ✓
Pitch ✓
Accommodation ✗
01892 55 98 98

In a tranquil setting with panoramic views, the neat appearance of the reception building sets the tone for the rest of this attractive site. It is an excellent example of current trends in French tourism development. The 116 terraced, grassy pitches, some with hardstanding, are all fairly level, each with electricity (15A) and ample water points. They all enjoy stunning views of the surrounding countryside - the Beaujolais, the Maconnais, the Charollais and the Clunysois. An extensive sunbathing area surrounds the attractively designed swimming pool complex. This is a superb site, tastefully landscaped, with a high standard of cleanliness in all areas. As the hedges and trees mature they will offer more shade. This is an area well worth visiting, with attractive scenery, interesting history, excellent wines and good food. Used by tour operators (22 pitches).

**Facilities:** Sanitary facilities mainly in an unusual, purpose designed hexagonal block, with modern fittings, of high standard. Smaller unit in the lower area of the site, plus further toilets in the main reception building. Motorcaravan service point in car park. Café, bar, shop and takeaway. Swimming pool complex with three heated pools and toboggan run (from 1/6). Children's activities organised in high season. Minigolf. **Off site:** Fishing 1.5 km, riding 10 km. Village 500 m. for all services (banks and some shops, closed Sun/Mon).

**Charges 2002**

| | |
|---|---|
| Per person | € 4.00 - € 5.50 |
| child (under 7 yrs) | € 2.00 - € 3.00 |
| pitch | € 4.50 - € 6.00 |
| electricity | € 2.50 |
| family rate (2+ children) | € 17.00 - € 23.00 |

**Tel:** 03 85 50 36 60. Fax: 03 85 50 36 61. E-mail: levillagedesmeuniers@wanadoo.fr. **Reservations:** Advised for July/Aug. **Open** 15 May - 15 September.

**Directions:** Town is 35 km. west of Macon. Follow N79/E62 (Charolles, Paray, Digoin) road and turn south onto D41 to Dompierre-les-Ormes (3 km). Site is clearly signed through village.

Campsite opened from the 15th of May until the 15th of September

CHALETS AND GITES OPENED ALL YEAR LONG
SWIMMING - POOL, MINIGOLF, WALKING PATHS

71 520 DOMPIERRE LES ORMES
Tél. (+33) 385 50 36 60
Fax : (+33) 385 50 36 61
@ : levillagedesmeuniers@wanadoo.fr
Website: villagedesmeuniers.com

## Burgundy
# Camping Municipal Mâcon
route Nationale 6, 71000 Mâcon

**71101M**

Always useful and well cared for, this site is worth considering as a stopover or for longer stays as it is close to the main route south. The 275 good sized pitches, all with 5A electricity and some with fresh and waste water points, are on mown, flat grass, accessed by tarmac roads. There is a generally bright and cheerful ambience. A central play area is divided, part with a rubber base for toddlers and part with adventure equipment for 7-15 year-olds. The bar/restaurant is open all year and seems to be a favourite haunt for the locals at lunchtime. Gates closed 10.00-06.30 hrs. but large units note - the security barrier has a 3.8 m. height restriction.

**Facilities:** Sanitary facilities in three modernised, well maintained units are fully equipped with British and Turkish style WCs, and washbasins in cubicles. A fourth modern block is by the swimming and paddling pools (for campers only). Facilities for disabled visitors. Dishwashing and laundry sinks. Washing machine and dryer. Some sanitary facilities closed out of peak season. Excellent motorcaravan service point (with Fiamma sewage couplings). Shop/tabac. Bar. Takeaway and restaurant. TV lounge. Playground. **Off site:** Swimming pool, sports stadium and supermarket nearby.

**Charges 2002**

| | |
|---|---|
| Per unit incl. 2 adults | € 11.00 |
| with electricity (5A) | € 13.30 |
| extra adult | € 2.95 |
| child (under 7 yrs) | € 1.55 |
| dog | € 0.70 |

**Tel:** 03 85 38 16 22. Fax: 03 85 39 71 24. **Reservations:** Not normally required. **Open** 15 March - 31 October.

**Directions:** Site is on northern outskirts of Mâcon on main N6, 3 km. from the town centre (just south of A40 autoroute junction).

## Camping-Caravaning Château de Montrouant

71800 Gibles

**7106**

This is a small, pretty site beside a lake in the grounds of an imposing chateau, located in a steep valley in the rolling Charolais hills. There is ample shade from the many mature trees and the 45 pitches (12 used by tour operators) are on reasonably flat grassy terraces, mainly separated by small hedges. All have electrical connections (min. 6A). The overall appearance is attractive with some pitches overlooking the lake and some next to a field where ponies graze. This site is probably best for smaller units as the access roads are very steep and not in very good condition; caravans (and motorcaravans) are towed off site if required. The enthusiastic owner organises several unusual and interesting activities during the main season, including stone masonry, model boat building, walks, wine tours, etc. Good fishing is possible in the site's lakes and is a feature of the site. Regrettably the season here is short and the site becomes quickly full mid-July - mid-Aug. and is very popular with the Dutch. The best times could be from late June - mid July or the second half of August. Motorcaravan owners should always check in advance as there may not be a suitable pitch. Used by a Dutch tour operator.

**Facilities:** The sanitary facilities, not too well designed and with maintenance that can be variable, are housed in a part of the château. They include washbasins in cabins. Dishwashing sinks. Washing machine and dryer. Essentials are available from reception. Very small open-air bar/restaurant for evening barbecues (only open certain evenings). Swimming pool with secluded sunbathing area, has been sympathetically landscaped. Half-court tennis. Fishing. Pony riding. Torches useful. **Off site:** The village of Gibles, with shops, restaurant, etc. is 2 km. Riding 10 km.

**Charges** 2002

| | |
|---|---|
| Per person | € 4.50 |
| child (under 7) | € 3.00 |
| pitch | € 4.00 |
| vehicle | € 4.00 |
| electricity (6A) | € 4.00 |
| dog | € 2.00 |
| local tax | € 0.23 |

**Tel:** 03 85 84 54 30. Fax: 03 85 84 54 30.
**Reservations:** Essential for 8/7-25/8 and made with 25% deposit. **Open** 1 June - 10 September.

**Directions:** Site is to the west of Mâcon and can be reached from the A6 via the N79 to Charolles (approx. 55 km). Take the D985 road south from Charolles for 19 km. to La Clayette, then follow signs for Gibles and site (approx. 7 km). Alternatively the site can be reached from the D982 Roanne - Digoin road. Exit for Pouilly, pass through Charlieu and Châteauneuf to La Clayette.

## Camping Municipal du Port d'Arciat

71680 Crêches-sur-Saône

**7110M**

This campsite is ideally located by a lake on one side and by the River Arlois (which joins the much wider Saône) on another. Herve Clair, the manager, works enthusiastically to keep it clean and tidy. There are 160 large, flat, grass pitches with 6A European electric hook-ups, those overlooking the lake and river being in most demand. Security is assured with a barrier at the entrance monitored by a receptionist during the day and a guardian during the night. During July and August there are pony and carriage rides, with a fireworks display and dance taking place around 14 August. Just outside the site perimeter is a licensed bar/restaurant offering well priced meals, drinks and ice creams, as well as bread, croissants and other basic provisions. Swimming is permitted in the lake and there's a beach area with ample space for sunbathing. A small lakeside bar sells snacks, ice creams and non-alcoholic drinks. Campers can use the slipway to launch their boats, and there's a pontoon to moor and service boats. Maps are available at reception for walking and cycling. Many vineyards are within 10 km.

**Facilities:** The larger of the two toilet blocks is on two levels: dishwashing and laundry sinks on ground level, with separate ladies` and men`s toilets, washbasins (open and in cabins) up a flight of stairs. The second block, on one level, provides similar facilities plus a separate shower and toilet room for disabled visitors. In addition, an ancient typically French facility with Turkish toilets and urinals remains in use. Washing machine and several clothes lines. Children`s play area. Boules pitch. **Off site:** Bar/restaurant and basic provisions adjacent. Nearest shops 1 km; large commercial centre 2 km. Lake fishing.

**Charges** 2002

| | |
|---|---|
| Per unit incl. 1 person | € 6.10 |
| extra adult | € 3.10 |
| child (under 7 yrs) | € 1.70 |
| electricity (6A) | € 2.90 |
| dog | € 1.00 |

**Tel:** 03 85 37 11 83. Fax: 03 85 36 57 91. E-mail: si-creches@netcourrier.com. **Reservations:** Not normally required. **Open** 15 May - 15 September.

**Directions:** From A6 junction 29, take N6 (direction Lyon) to Crêches-sur-Saône from where campsite is well signed.

## Camping Intercommunal du Lac de St-Point

**7109** 71520 St Point

Managed by a young husband and wife team, this site would make a convenient overnight stop. The area is renowned for its wine and cheese as well as Roman churches, abbeys and chateaux. There are 34 reasonably level touring pitches, mostly separated by low hedges, and 46 tent pitches on a sloping and partly terraced field behind. On-site activities include swimming in the lake (lifeguard on duty during July and August), with pedaloes for hire and fishing. Routes for walking or cycling are on sale in reception.

**Facilities:** Two sanitary blocks, one adjoining the reception and the other towards the back of the site up a slope, provide all the usual facilities and a washing machine. Shower and toilet/washbasin in separate cabins for campers with disabilities. Snacks, bread, croissants and milk available in high season. Play area. Volleyball, basketball, badminton, table tennis, games room and boules pitch. Mountain bike hire. **Off site:** Nearest shop 300 m. Tennis 4 km. Pony club 5 km. Organised walks on Wednesdays 4 km. Bicycle hire 4 km.

**Charges** 2002

| | | |
|---|---|---|
| Per unit incl. 2 adults, 2 children | | € 11.00 |
| with electricity | € 14.00 - | € 16.50 |
| extra adult | | € 1.40 |
| child (up to 7 yrs) | | € 0.75 |
| dog | | € 1.50 |

**Tel:** 03 85 50 52 31. Fax: 03 85 50 51 92. E-mail: camping.stpoint@wanadoo.fr. **Reservations:** Advised in July/August. **Open** 1 April - 31 October.

**Directions:** Leave A6 at junction 29 and take the N79 as far as the Cluny exit. Bear left and follow the signs to Saint-Point; campsite is on the outskirts of the village on the right.

**Camping du Lac de Saint-Point Lamartine** ★ ★ ★

Very comfortable campsite
Near Beaujolais and Mâconnais vineyards, Cluny (romanesque abbey)
An excellent location by a lake
Quiet, shady, family atmosphere
Bathing, fishing, hiking, playground, sportsground, games room, snack-bar...
Open 1st April - 31st October

Le Lac - 71520 Saint-Point
Tel: 0033 385 50 52 31 - Fax: 0033 385 50 51 92
E-mail: camping.stpoint@wanadoo.fr
http://perso.wanadoo.fr/camping.stpoint

Southern Burgundy

## Camping du Lac

**7111** Le Fourneau, 71430 Palinges

Camping du Lac is a very special campsite and it is all due to Monsieur Labille, its guardian. Firstly, he thinks of the campsite as his home and every visitor as his guest; secondly, the central amenity block is spotlessly clean; and thirdly, the campsite is adjacent to a lake with a beach and safe bathing. Monsieur Labille provides tables and chairs for tent campers and he freezes bottles of water for cyclists to take away (free of charge). Guests can also use the washing machine and fridge free of charge. If you want visit a specific place, then Monsieur knows exactly where you should go - he never recommends anything that he hasn't personally tried out. All the more extraordinary, because the campsite is owned by the municipality. The campsite comprises 30 good sized grass pitches, each with a small hardstanding. All the pitches have two 10A electricity connections, and six have water and waste points.

**Facilities:** The central sanitary block provides showers, washbasins in cubicles, and facilities for campers with disabilities. Washing machine and fridge for campers' use. Bread and croissants to order at reception. Boules. Play area and TV room. Sports field, lake beach and swimming adjacent. Bicycle hire and pedaloe hire in July/Aug. **Off site:** Just outside the gates is a bar/snack bar serving very reasonably priced drinks, food and ice creams. Palinges is within walking distance, cycle and walk routes, museums, cruises on canals, chateaux, museographical complex.

**Charges** 2002

| | |
|---|---|
| Per pitch incl. 2 persons | € 10.55 |
| with electricity | € 13.29 |
| extra adult | € 1.24 |
| child under 10 yrs | € 0.71 |
| animal | € 1.24 |
| double axle caravan | € 25.15 |

**Tel:** (0)3 85 88 14 49. **Reservations:** Advised in July and August. **Open** early June - early September.

**Directions:** Palinges is midway between Montceau les Mines and Paray le Monial. From Montceau take N70, then turn left onto D92 to Palinges. Follow campsite signs. Site is also well signed from D985 Toulon-sur-Arroux to Charolles road.

## Camping Les Coullemières

89270 Vermenton

**8903M**

On the banks of the River Cure, 500 m. from the N6, this small site achieves note-worthy quality at reasonable cost. A warm welcome at the flower bedecked bureau and the immediately inviting environment sets the tone for a restful stay. The 50 level pitches are of good size and separated by hedging and interspersed with mature trees. Water points are strategically placed and almost every pitch has electricity (6A). There is infrequent intrusive train noise but the close proximity to the station offers the added attraction of a day excursion to Paris (2 hours). Balloon flights can be booked.

**Facilities:** Facilities: Impeccable, heated, central sanitary block includes washbasins in private cubicles, and mixture of British and Turkish style toilets. Washing machine, dryer and iron. Provision for visitors with disabilities (paths are convenient for manoeuvring wheelchairs). Motorcaravan services. Milk and very basic provisions kept at reception. Covered community room. Emergency night bell. Bicycles, pedaloes and canoes for hire. Adjacent to site landscaped leisure area, tennis courts, football pitch, table tennis, cycle track and boule court. Fishing. Twin axle caravans not accepted. **Off site:** riding 8 km.

**Charges** 2002

| | |
|---|---|
| Per adult | € 2.90 |
| child (under 10 yrs) | € 1.50 |
| car or motorcycle | € 1.50 |
| caravan or tent | € 1.90 |
| motorcaravan | € 3.05 |
| animal | € 1.00 |
| electricity (6A) | € 2.50 |

**Tel:** 03 86 81 53 02. Fax: 03 86 81 63 95.
**Reservations:** Contact site in season or the Mairie when site closed. **Open** 10 April - 10 October.

**Directions:** Site is well signed from the N6 in Vermenton. Proceed through town towards station and site is a little way beyond. From A6 use Nitry exit (15 km).

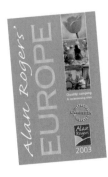

# Franche Comté

Map 9

Major city: Besançon

Départements: 25 Doubs, 39 Jura, 70 Haute-Saône, 90 Tre. de Belfort

Geographically Franche-Comté is really two regions. The high valley of the Saône is wide, gently rolling country with a certain rustic simplicity, while the Jura mountains are more rugged with dense forests, sheer cliffs, deep gorges and torrents of water. In winter this means cross-country skiing over 2,000 km of marked trails and, in the summer, rafting along the gentle Lison and Loue rivers or the more challenging Saône or Doubs. Nature lovers can climb, bike and hike in the mountains or explore the hills honeycombed with over 4,000 caves. The streams and lakes provide world-class fishing. The spa towns of Salins les Bains and Besançon offer relaxation and a chance to 'take the waters'. The Region's position, bordering Switzerland and close to Germany, is reflected in its culture and the great diversity of architectural style in the many fine buildings.

## Cuisine of the region

Freshwater fish such as trout, grayling, pike and perch are local specialities

*Brési* – wafer-thin slices of dried beef; many local hams

*Jésus de Morteau* – fat pork sausage smoked over pine and juniper

*Poulet au vin jaune* – chicken, cream and 'morilles' (chestnuts) cooked in 'vin jaune'

*Gougère* – hot cheese pastry based on the local 'Comté' cheese

## Wine

The region has a rare wine known as 'vin de paille' as well as vin jaune (deep yellow and very dry) and vin du jura, Jura wine

*Pontarlier* – aniseed liqueur

*Kirsh* – cherry flavoured liqueur

## Places of interest

*Arbois* – Pasteur Family Home and Museum, Museum of Wine and Wine Growing

*Belfort* – sandstone lion sculpted by Bartholdi; castle and Vauban fortifications; Memorial and Museum of the French Resistance

*Besançon* – citadel with good views over the city; cathedral is a mixture of influences ranging from a Roman altar to a 19th century astronomic clock

*Champlitte* – Museum of Folk Art and Franche Comté Traditions

*Dole* – lovely old town, Louis Pasteur's birthplace

*Gray* – Baron Martin Museum

*Luxeuil-les-Bains* – Tour des Echevins Museum and Abbey

*Morez* – Eyeglass Museum

*Morteau* – Watch Museum

*Morains-en-Montagne* – the House of Toys

*Ornans* – Gustave Courbet birthplace and museum

*Ronchamp* – Chapel of Notre-Dame du Haut de Ronchamp designed by Le Corbusier

*Saline* – Royale d'Arc et Senans Royal Salt Works

*Salins-les-Bains* – Salt mines and tunnels

*Sochaux* – Peugeot Museum

# Camping du Bois de Reveuge

**2503** 25680 Huanne

the travel
service
TO BOOK

| ferry | ✓ |
| pitch | ✓ |
| Accommodation | ✗ |

01892 55 98 98

As Bois de Reveuge was only opened in 1992, it still has a new look about it, in as much as there is little shade yet from the young trees. Being on a hillside, the pitches are on terraces with good views across the surrounding countryside and leading down to two lakes which may be used for fishing and canoeing. The site also has private use of a 10 hectare lake set in a park 10 km. away where there is a watersports school and boating opportunities. Tall trees have been left standing at the top of the hill where there are a few pitches, although most of these have been used for the site's mobile homes. The 200 pitches available for tourists each have a water supply as well as electricity (6A) and some are extra large (150 - 180 sq.m). There is a good solar heated swimming pool (15/5-15/9) which can be covered in cool weather and another pool with four water slides. Several supervisors are in attendance during the summer who, as well as acting as a lifeguards, sometimes offer swimming lessons.

**Facilities:** Three modern sanitary blocks are nicely spaced around the site and have British and Turkish style WCs and washbasins mainly in cabins. Kiosk for basic food supplies and restaurant with terrace (both 1/6-3/9). Swimming pools (20/4-15/9). Three children's play areas. High season 'baby club' with a large tent for wet weather, large video screen and some music and other entertainment for adults. Groups may request activities such as orienteering. A package deal includes use of canoes as well as archery, fishing, bicycle hire and pedaloes.

**Charges** 2003

| Per unit incl. 2 persons | € 17.00 - € 29.00 |
| extra person (over 6 yrs) | € 3.00 - € 5.00 |
| child (2-6 yrs) | € 2.00 - € 4.00 |
| animal | € 2.00 |
| supplement for large pitch | free - € 6.00 |

**Tel:** 03 81 84 38 60. Fax: 03 81 84 44 04.
**Reservations:** Made with 30% deposit and fee (€ 20). **Open** 19 April - 20 September.

**Directions:** Site is well signed from the D50. From A36 autoroute south of the site, take exit for Baume-les-Dames and head north on D50 towards Villersexel for about 7 km. to camp signs.

# Camping Le Val de Bonnal

**2500** Bonnal, 25680 Rougemont

This is an impressive, well managed site in a large country estate, harmoniously designed in keeping with the surrounding countryside, well away from main roads and other intrusions. Having said that, the site itself is very busy, with a wide range of activities and amenities. The 320 pitches, all of a good size and with electricity (5A), are separated by a mixture of trees and bushes, carefully landscaped. Some of the newer pitches are less secluded, but the ambience generally is peaceful despite the size of the site (300 pitches in a large area) and its deserved popularity. The main attraction must be the variety of watersports on the three large lakes and nearby river which include swimming, pedaloes, and fishing as well as water skiing, windsurfing and canoeing. In fact, the range of activities available in high season is almost inexhaustible, not to say exhausting! Used by tour operators (140 pitches).

**Facilities:** Four clean toilet blocks include washbasins in cabins. Separate washing up blocks. Washing machines, ironing boards and sinks for laundry. Riverside restaurant, snack bar/takeaway, bar and terrace, shop (all 20/5-8/9), sympathetically converted from former farm buildings. New swimming pool complex features water slides. Well equipped children's play areas. Range of sport facilities including table tennis, boules, bicycle hire, and water sports, etc. **Off site:** Golf 6 km. Day trips to Switzerland.

**Charges** 2002

| Per pitch with electricity, incl. 2 persons | € 30.00 |
| extra person | € 7.00 |
| local tax | € 0.30 |

**Tel:** 03 81 86 90 87. Fax: 03 81 86 03 92. E-mail: val-de-bonnal@wanadoo.fr. **Reservations:** Only made for pitches with electricity. **Open** 8 May - 15 September.

**Directions:** From Vesoul take D9 towards Villersexel. After approx. 20 km. turn right in the village of Esprels at sign for Val de Bonnal. Follow for 3.5 km. and site is on the left. From autoroute A36 take exit for Baume-les-Dames; go north on A50, then A18 to Rougemont and follow signs to site.

## Franche Comté
# Camping Municipal de Saint Point-Lac

 **2505M**

8 rue du Port, 25160 Saint Point-Lac

A good example of a municipal campsite in which the village takes a pride, this site is on the banks of a small lake with views to the distant hills. The 84 level, numbered pitches are on grass and 60 have electricity (16A). It is worth making a detour from the Pontarlier - Vallorbe road or for a longer stay. The village shop and restaurant are an easy 200 m. walk from the site entrance.

**Facilities:** Good central sanitary block has British style WCs and free hot water. Hot snacks and take-away in high season (July/Aug). Fishing. **Off site:** Bicycle hire 5 km.

**Charges** 2003

| | |
|---|---|
| Per pitch incl. 2 persons | € 7.50 - € 9.00 |
| with electricity | € 11.50 - € 13.00 |
| extra person | € 1.00 - € 2.50 |
| local tax (over 10 yrs) | € 0.25 |

**Tel:** 03 81 69 61 64. Fax: 03 81 69 65 74. E-mail: camping-stpointlac@wanadoo.fr. **Reservations:** Made with deposit (€ 45) and fee (7,60). Contact site from 1 May, or the Mairie in writing only (fax and postal address as above). **Open** 1 May - 30 September.

**Directions:** From north, take D437 south of Pontarlier and keep on west side of the lake to the second village (Saint Point-Lac); from south exit N57 at Les Hopitaux-Neufs and turn west to lake.

## Franche Comté
# Camping La Plage Blanche

**3901**

3 rue de la Plage, 39380 Ounans

the **travel service**
TO BOOK
Ferry ✔
Pitch ✔
Accommodation ✘
01892 55 98 98

Situated in open countryside, along the banks of the River Loue, this site has 220 good sized, marked pitches on level ground, all with electricity (6A). Trees provide both fully shaded and semi-shaded pitches. Approximately a kilometre of riverside and beach provide the ideal setting for children to swim and play safely in the gently flowing, shallow water - inflatables are popular and there is a canoe/kayak base. The site also has a swimming pool.

**Facilities:** Modern, well kept sanitary facilities in three unusual blocks include separate washing cabins. Dishwashing facilities are in blocks of 8 sinks. Launderette. Motorcaravan service area. Bar/restaurant with terrace (1/4-30/9). Pizzeria and takeaway (all season). TV room. Swimming pool and children's pool. Play area. River fishing, table tennis, and bicycle hire. **Off site:** Golf 10 km.

**Charges** 2002

| | |
|---|---|
| Per adult | € 4.27 |
| child (1-7 yrs) | € 2.59 |
| pitch | € 5.34 |
| electricity | € 2.90 |
| local tax | € 0.30 |

**Tel:** 03 84 37 69 63. Fax: 03 84 37 60 21. E-mail: reservation@la-plage-blanche.com. **Reservations:** Made with deposit (€ 31) and fee (€ 7,62). **Open** 1 April - 30 September.

**Directions:** Ounans is 20 km southeast of Dole. From A39 from Dijon or A36 from Besançon, take Dole exit and then D405 to Parcey. After Parcey take N5 to Mont Sous Vaudrey (8 km) then D472 towards Pontarlier to Ounans where site is signed.

## Franche Comté
# Camping Domaine de Chalain

**3903**

BP. 96, Doucier, 39003 Lons le Saunier

the **travel service**
TO BOOK
Ferry ✔
Pitch ✔
Accommodation ✘
01892 55 98 98

Doucier lies east of Lons-le-Saunier among the wooded hills of the Jura and rather away from the main routes. This large, park-like site (804 pitches) is on the edge of the Lac de Chalain surrounded on three sides by woods and some cliffs. Large areas are left for recreation. The lake shelves gently at the edge but then becomes deep quite suddenly. Day visitors can be very numerous at fine weekends. The site has an attractive pool complex. The site is divided into two parts, one nearer the lake with larger pitches (costing more). You should find room in the other part, but for July and August, it is better to reserve to make sure. There are over 200 electrical connections; little shade. Used by tour operators (100 pitches).

**Facilities:** Nine sanitary blocks include washbasins with warm water (all in cabins). Showers are in separate blocks. One block can be heated with facilities for babies and disabled people. Washing machines. Shops (15/5-15/9). Bar, takeaway and snacks (1/5-20/9). Heated indoor pool, outdoor pools with slide, sauna and spa. Tennis, table tennis, minigolf and pedaloes for hire. Fishing. Bicycle hire. Animals and birds in enclosures. Cinema and organised activities, plus a disco for the young. Dogs not permiitted on the lake beach. **Off site:** Riding 2 km. Golf 25 km.

Charges 2002

| | |
|---|---|
| Per unit incl. 3 persons | € 17.53 - € 30.03 |
| electricity | € 2.44 |
| extra person | € 3.81 - € 7.62 |

Tel: 03 84 24 29 00. Fax: 03 84 24 94 07. E-mail: chalain@chalain.com. Reservations: Contact site. Open 1 May - 20 September.

Directions: Site can only be approached via Doucier: from Switzerland via N5 (from Geneva), then the N78 and D39; from other directions via Lons-le-Saunier or Champagnole.

# Sunêlia La Pergola

**3904** 39130 Marigny

Close to the Swiss border and overlooking the sparkling waters of Lac de Chalain, La Pergola is a neat, tidy and terraced site set amongst the rolling hills of the Jura. Awaiting discovery as it is not on the main tourist routes, La Pergola is very well appointed, with 350 pitches, mainly on gravel and separated by small bushes, and all with electricity, water and drainage. Arranged on numerous terraces, connected by steep steps, some have shade and the higher ones have good views over the lake. A tall fence protects the site from the public footpath that separates the site from the lakeside but there are frequent access gates. The entrance is very attractive and the work that Mme. Gicquaire puts into the preparation of the flower-beds is very evident. The terrace of the bar/restaurant is beautiful, featuring grape vines for welcome shade and a colourful array of spectacular flowers leading on to a landscaped waterfall area next to the three swimming pools and entertainment area. English is spoken. Used by tour operators (120 pitches).

**Facilities:** The latest sanitary block serving the lower pitches is well appointed with private cabins. Slightly older blocks serve the other terraces. Visitors with disabilities are advised to select a lower terrace where special facilities are provided. Washing machines and dryers. Bar. Restaurant. Pool complex, two pools heated. Good children's play area and children's club. Table tennis and volleyball. Watersports include windsurfing, pedaloes and small boats for hire. Organised programme in high season includes cycle tours, keep fit sessions and evening entertainment with disco twice weekly. **Off site:** Riding 3 km.

**Charges** 2002

| | |
|---|---|
| Per unit incl. 2 persons, electricity and water: lake pitch | € 14.00 - € 35.00 |
| standard pitch | € 14.00 - € 30.00 |
| extra person | € 4.50 |
| child (3-6 yrs) | € 3.00 |
| baby (0-2 yrs) | € 1.55 |
| dog | € 0.76 |
| local tax | € 0.30 |

**Tel:** 03 84 25 70 03. Fax: 03 84 25 75 96. E-mail: contact@lapergola.com. **Reservations:** Made with deposit (€ 122) and fee (€ 27,44). **Open** 10 May - 21 September.

**Directions:** Site is 2.5 km. north of Doucier on Lake Chalain road D27.

# Camping Fayolan

**3905** BP 52, 39130 Clairvaux-les-Lacs

This modern site, backed by wooded hills, is situated on the shores of Le Petit Lac about a mile from the town of Clairvaux-les-Lacs amid the lakes and forests of the Jura. Here one can relax, enjoy the peaceful countryside, explore the interesting villages, historic towns and museums of the area by car or cycle or take to the water where you can swim, windsurf and canoe. The neat, tidy site is in two parts, with pitches from 80-100 sq.m. either on terraces overlooking the lake or on the flatter area near the shore. There are electrical connections (6A) for those who want them and 200 pitches have electricity, water, drainage and sewage connections. The upper part has little shade until the young trees grow but there is some on the lower section. Used by tour operators (130 pitches).

**Facilities:** Four modern sanitary units spread around the site have warm water from push-button taps in washbasins and showers and hot water in sinks. Shop. Restaurant. Two good attractive swimming pools (heated from mid-May), one with a slide, and smaller one for children (trunks, not shorts, must be worn). Playground. Organised activities include archery, a fitness trail, walks, games, competitions, children's club and dancing. Fishing. Entertainment. **Off site:** Bicycle hire 800 m, riding 4 km.

**Charges** guide

| | |
|---|---|
| Per unit incl. 2 persons | € 9.45 - € 19.51 |
| extra person | € 4.42 - € 5.34 |
| child 11-14 yrs | € 2.29 - € 2.74 |
| child 4-10 yrs | € 1.52 - € 1.98 |
| animal | € 2.29 |
| electricity | € 2.44 - € 2.74 |
| serviced pitch | € 3.81 - € 4.57 |
| local tax | € 0.30 |

**Tel:** 03 84 25 26 19. Fax: 03 84 25 26 20. E-mail: Relais.Soleil.Jura@wanadoo.fr. **Reservations:** Contact site. **Open** 1 May - 30 September.

**Directions:** Clairvaux-les-Lacs is on the N78 between Lons-le-Saunier and Morez. In Clairvaux follow signs for 'Lacs Campings' and Fayolan.

## Camping La Marjorie

3906 | 640 Bvd. de l'Europe, 39000 Lons-le-Saunier

La Marjorie is a spacious site set on the outskirts of the spa town of Lons-le-Saunier. It is a former municipal site with 200 level pitches. Mainly on hardstanding, they are separated by well trimmed hedges interspersed with tall trees which gives privacy plus a little shade at some part of the day. Bordering one area of the site are open fields and woodlands. All pitches have electricity (6/10A) and a few are fully serviced. The site is 2.5 km. from the centre of the town which is the capital town of the Jura region. There is a bicycle path from the site into town and a mountain bike track behind the site. English is spoken.

**Facilities:** There are three well maintained toilet blocks, two modern and heated, with individual cubicles with washbasins and large showers. Baby baths, good facilities for disabled people, washing and ironing. Motorcaravan service point (€ 3,04 charge). Small shop. Small bar with reasonably priced takeaway meals (all 15/6-31/8). TV room, table tennis, small play area, boule pitch, volleyball and football field. Archery, canoeing and riding can be arranged (fee). **Off site:** Local swimming pool 200 m. Restaurants 500 m. Golf 5 km. Caves and waterfalls 17 km.

**Charges** 2002

| | |
|---|---|
| Per unit incl. 2 persons | € 9.30 - € 12.50 |
| with electricity (6A) | € 11.63 - € 13.95 |
| tent pitch incl. 2 persons | € 8.08 - € 11.00 |
| extra person | € 2.21 - € 3.00 |
| child (under 10 yrs) | € 1.40 - € 1.80 |
| dog | € 1.00 |
| double axle unit plus | € 30.00 |

**Tel:** 03 84 24 26 94. Fax: 03 84 24 08 40. E-mail: info@camping-marjorie.com. **Reservations:** Made with deposit (€ 130) and fee (€ 9,15). **Open** 1 April - 15 October.

**Directions:** Site is off the N83 Lons-le-Saunier - Besancon road. Approaching Lons on the D52 or the N78 or D471, site is signed from the first roundabout on the outskirts of the town.

## Camping International du Lac Vesoul

7002M | 70000 Vesoul

This is one of the better examples of a municipal site and is part of a leisure park around a large lake. A five kilometre path has been created around the lake for jogging, walking and cycling and there is a large open space for ball games or sunbathing, along with a good children's playground and bar/restaurant. A map at the entrance shows the water areas for swimming, boating and windsurfing. Watersports are organised by the Club Nautique Haut-Saonois Vesoul and there is also tennis, table tennis, archery, basketball and night-time carp fishing. The campsite does not have direct access to the lake as it is separated by a security fence, but access is possible at the site entrance. There are 160 good sized, level, grass pitches, all with electricity (10A). Access is from hard roads and pitches are separated by shrubs and bushes. There is a large hard area in the centre of the site brightened by flowers and young trees.

**Facilities:** Three good quality toilet blocks, one heated, are well spaced around the site. They have a mix of British and Turkish style WCs and free, premixed warm water from push-button taps in the washbasins and showers

**Charges** 2002

| | |
|---|---|
| Per person | € 3.00 |
| child (under 7 yrs) | € 1.30 |
| pitch | € 3.10 |
| pitch with electricity | € 5.10 |
| vehicle | € 2.10 |
| dog | € 1.60 |

**Tel:** 03 84 76 22 86. Fax: 03 84 75 74 93. **Reservations:** Contact site. **Open** 1 March - 31 October.

**Directions:** On road D474 to west of Vesoul on route to Besançon, well signed around the town.

# Savoy / Dauphiny Alpes

Map 9

Major city: Grenoble

D partements: 38 Is re, 73 Savoie, 74 Haute-Savoie

Lying between the Rhône Valley and the Alpine borders with Switzerland and Italy are the old provinces of Savoie and Dauphine. This is an area of enormous granite outcrops, deeply riven by spectacular glacier hewn and river etched valleys. It has become one of the world's leading wintersport playgrounds and in the summer provides a range of outdoor activities. From Chambéry, north to the shores of Lac Léman (Lake Geneva) are many towns and villages that, since Roman times, attracted visitors to take the waters. Aix-les-Bains, Evian and Annecy were three major lakeside spa resorts of the Victorians; while Chamonix, under Mont Blanc, and Grenoble, capital of Dauphine, attracted the more active (often British) 19th century travellers who pioneered modern ski-ing and 'alpinism'. Today's modern ski resorts are Tignes, Val d'Isère, Megeve and Courchevel, whilst Grenoble is a bustling town with academic eminence in high technology and industry. To the north is the region of Chartreuse famous for its monastery, and liqueur! Italy and Switzerland are within easy reach for day excursions.

## Cuisine of the region

'Plat gratine' applies to a wide varity of dishes; in the Alps this means cooked in breadcrumbs; gratins of all sorts show how well milk, cream and cheese combine together.

Farcement (Farçon Savoyard) – potatoes baked with cream, eggs, bacon, dried pears and prunes; a hearty stomach filler

Féra – a freshwater lake fish

Fondue – hot melted cheese and white wine; a classic of the region

Gratin Dauphinois – a classic potato dish with cream, cheese and garlic

Gratin Savoyard – another classic potato dish with cheese and butter

Lavaret – a freshwater lake fish, like salmon

Longeole – a country sausage

Lotte – a burbot, not unlike an eel

Omble chevalier – a char, it looks like a large salmon trout

Tartiflette – potato, bacon, onions and Reblochon cheese

## Places of interest

Aix-les-Bains – spa resort on the Lac du Bourget, boat excursions to the Royal Abbey of Hautecombe

Albertville – 1992 Winter Olympics, museum, now has an active night-life!

Annecy – canal-filled lakeside town, 12th century château, old quarter

Bourg-St-Maurice – centre of Savoie café society

Chambéry – old quarter, Dukes of Savoie château, Savoie museum.

Chamonix – site of first Winter Olympics in 1924; world capital of mountain climbing; Mont Blanc tunnel, 11.6 km. long (for many years the longest tunnel in the world – closed at present after a disastrous fire)

Evian-les-Bains – spa and casino on Lake Geneva, home of Evian water

Grenoble – University city; a cable car takes visitors across the River Isère and up to the Fort de la Bastille, from where there are panoramic views of the city and mountains beyond.

Mont Blanc – mountain visible 99 miles away in Lyon. Its sheer size explains why it still challenges climbers generations after it was first conquered

# Le Coin Tranquille

38490 Les Abrets

**the travel service**
**TO BOOK**

| | |
|---|---|
| Ferry | ✓ |
| Pitch | ✓ |
| Accommodation | ✓ |

01892 55 98 98

Set in the Dauphiny countryside north of Grenoble, Le Coin Tranquille is truly a 'quiet corner', especially outside school holiday times, although it is still popular with families in high season. Les Abrets is well placed for visits to the Savoy regions and the Alps. It is a neat, tidy and well maintained site of 192 grass pitches (160 for touring units), all with electricity. They are separated by well maintained hedges of hydrangea, flowering shrubs and a range of trees to make a lovely environment doubly enhanced by the rural aspect and marvellous views across to the mountains. This is a popular site with a warm welcome, that makes a wonderful base for exploring the area, especially in low season - the Chartreuse caves at Voiron are well worth a visit. Used by tour operators (14 pitches). A Sites et Paysages member.

**Facilities:** The central large sanitary block is of good quality and well kept, heated in low season. It includes washbasins in cabins, facilities for children and disabled people and a laundry room. Two other blocks on either edge of the site have been refurbished to a high standard. Busy shop. Excellent restaurant, open all year (closed two days weekly in low season) and attracting local clientele. Swimming pool and paddling pool (15/5-30/9; no bermuda shorts) with sunbathing areas. Play area. TV/video room with balcony, games room and quiet reading room. Supervised games for children, slide shows of the region's attractions and weekly entertainment for adults including live music (not discos) arranged in high season. Bicycle hire. **Off site:** Fishing 5 km. riding 6 km.

**Charges** 2002

| | |
|---|---|
| Per pitch incl. 2 persons | € 13.00 - € 24.00 |
| extra adult | € 3.80 - € 6.00 |
| child (2-7 yrs) | € 2.20 - € 4.00 |
| electricity (2-6A) | € 1.30 - € 3.00 |
| pet | € 1.00 |

**Tel:** 04 76 32 13 48. Fax: 04 76 37 40 67. E-mail: contact@coin-tranquille.com. **Reservations:** Write with deposit (€ 107) and fee (€ 15,24). **Open** 1 April - 31 October.

**Directions:** Site is northeast of Les Abrets. From the town take N6 towards Chambery, turning left after about 2 km (site signed) and site is about 1 km up a narrow road, on the right.

---

# Camping-Caravaning La Chabannerie

38930 St Martin-de-Clelles

Set amidst pine trees and glorious countryside, La Chabannerie is a former municipal site. Its English speaking, Belgian owner is working hard to upgrade the facilities. The 47 pitches are both varied and unusual, several of the caravan pitches having marvellous views of the mountains, whilst others, notably for tents, snuggle unobtrusively amongst the trees. Being small, it is friendly and unsophisticated, with no organised entertainment. The hills are all around for walking and there are mountain bike tracks to suit every level of ability. Sporting opportunities in the area range from rock climbing, paragliding, sailing, bungee jumping to donkey hire (for walking the mountain trails). Amateur botanists will appreciate the 38 different wild orchids that grow throughout the site and the owner's commitment to preserve the delicate naural environment required for them to thrive. No tour operators, no mobile homes or chalets.

**Facilities:** The main toilet block is new and heated in winter. Older, smaller blocks are only opened in July/Aug. WCs are mainly British style, washbasins are mainly in cubicles. A large unit containing WC, washbasin and shower has been adapted for disabled people and can also be used as a family shower room. A reader reports only one tap for drinking water. Reception doubles as a shop and carries quite a large selection of goods and fresh bread daily, but no gas. Small snack bar with food to either eat inside, take away or have delivered to your pitch. Small swimming pool (open June-Sept). Family room for reading or playing board games in inclement weather, small play area, table tennis and volleyball. **Off site:** Skiing or riding 8 km. Fishing or rafting 5 km

**Charges** 2002

| | |
|---|---|
| Per person | € 3.66 - € 4.42 |
| child (2-12 yrs) | € 1.98 - € 2.59 |
| caravan or large tent | € 1.98 - € 2.59 |
| car | € 1.22 - € 1.52 |
| motorcaravan | € 3.20 - € 4.12 |
| electricity (10A) | € 2.44 - € 2.74 |

**Tel:** 04 76 34 00 38. Fax: 04 76 34 43 54. E-mail: chabanne@infonie.fr. **Reservations:** Advised in July/Aug. **Open** all year.

**Directions:** Site is off the N75 south of Grenoble (approx. 48 km) and is signed approx. 11 km. south of Monestier de Clermont (east of N75).

## Camping Les Trois Lacs

La Plaine, 38460 Trept

Les Trois Lacs is situated on the edge of three lakes in flat, open country in the north of Dauphine. It is a pleasant and relaxing base to enjoy either the country-side, the historic places of the region or the programme of leisure activities provided by the site. The land around the lakes has been well landscaped with smooth lawns and a variety of shrubs and trees. The camping area is on one side of the largest lake with tall trees on one edge and views of distant mountains. The 166 good sized pitches, with 150 for tourists and 8 having water and a drain. They are in pairs between the hard access roads, each pair separated from the others by low hedges, but there is little shade. The small-est lake is kept for fishing and the others for boating and watersports with one section for swimming having a water slide (with lifeguard July/Aug).

**Facilities:** Good quality, fully equipped toilet blocks are in the centre of the camping area. Laundry room. Mobile shop calls in high season. Attractive bar/restaurant near reception serves drinks (all season) and simple snacks (June-Aug). Other snack bars are around the lakes. Two discos for teenagers and one for older people each week. Entertainment in July/Aug. Lakeside beach and water slide. Games room, tennis, table tennis, football, minigolf, beach volleyball, badminton, walking, and roller skating. **Off site:** Riding 500 m. Mountain bike hire 10 km. Shops at Trept 2 km.

**Charges 2002**

| | |
|---|---|
| Per person | € 5.00 |
| child (under 10 yrs) | € 3.00 |
| pitch | € 7.00 |
| animal | € 1.50 |
| electricity | € 3.00 |

**Tel:** 04 74 92 92 06. Fax: 04 74 92 93 35. E-mail: les3lacs@free.fr. **Reservations:** Made with deposit (€ 70) and fee (€ 15). **Open** 1 May - 10 September.

**Directions:** Leave N75 (Grenoble - Bourg-en-Bresse) road, at Morestel and travel west on D517. Site is well signed between Sablonnières and Trept.

## Camping-Caravaning Au Joyeux Réveil

Le Château, 38880 Autrans

The small town of Autrans is set on a plateau, 1,030 m. high, in the Vecors region. Au Joyeux Réveil is a simple site ideally situated for any of the activities that this wonderful area has to offer - from walking, mountain biking and pot-holing in summer to downhill and cross-country skiing in winter, it is all there for you in magnificent scenery. The site is on the outskirts of the town, set below a ski jump and short lift. The 100 pitches, mainly on grass, are reasonably level with a small tree to mark each corner. All have electric-ity (2/10A) and are in a sunny location with fantastic views. The D531 road and then the D106 look a little daunting on the map but they are good roads with very easy gradients. English is spoken.

**Facilities:** The new toilet block is very well appointed, with under-floor heating and all the expected facilities. Another new building houses a bar, snack bar and takeaway. Small, kidney-shaped swimming pool with sunbathing area. Small play area on grass. TV room. **Off site:** Short ski-lift is near the site and a shuttle bus runs regularly the 5 km. to the longer runs. Fishing or riding 300 m.

**Charges 2002**

| | |
|---|---|
| Per unit incl. 1 or 2 persons | € 11.89 - € 12.50 |
| extra person | € 4.27 |
| child (under 6 yrs) | € 3.20 |
| electricity (4A) | € 2.44 |

**Tel:** 04 76 95 33 44. Fax: 04 76 95 72 98. E-mail: camping-au-joyeux-reveil@wanadoo.fr. **Reservations:** Contact site. **Open** all year excl. Oct. and Nov.

**Directions:** Travelling south on A48 take exit for Veurey-Voroize on N532. Head south for about 7 km. to Sassenage, then turn on D531 to Autrans. Site is on the outskirts of the village.

# Camping La Cascade

route de l'Alpe d'Huez, 38520 Bourg-d'Oisans

La Cascade is close to and within sight and sound of the waterfall from which it takes its name. The friendly new owners keep this very pleasant site neat and tidy. Bourg d'Oisans lies in the Romanche valley 725 m. above sea level surrounded by high mountains. It is a real sun trap and gets very hot in summer. The ski resorts of Alpe d'Huez and Les Deux Alpes are close by. The Alpe d'Huez road past the campsite with its 21 hairpin bends is revered by serious cyclists as it is often used as the 'king of the mountain' stage for the Tour de France. La Cascade has 123 individual pitches, 111 for touring units on mainly flat ground. Of varying but quite adequate size with 16A electricity, many have little shade.

**Facilities:** Two heated sanitary blocks are of good quality with mainly British style toilets and washbasins in cabins. Washing machine. Bar and snack bar (1/7-31/8). Good sized, heated and sheltered swimming pool and paddling pool (15/5-30/9) surrounded by large, enclosed sunbathing area. Small playground. General room with TV. Games room. Table tennis, volleyball and boules. Evening entertainment and lots of activities organised in season. **Off site:** Supermarket 500 m. Bourg d'Oisans 1 km, with bars, restaurants, shops and banks etc. Ski resort of Alpe d'Huez 13 km. Bicycle hire 1 km, fishing 500 m.

**Charges** 2002

| | |
|---|---|
| Per unit incl. 2 persons | € 14.00 - € 21.00 |
| extra person (over 5 yrs) | € 3.50 - € 5.00 |
| electricity | € 3.00 |

**Tel:** 04 76 80 02 42. Fax: 04 76 80 22 63. E-mail: lacascade@wanadoo.fr. **Reservations:** Essential for July/Aug; made for any length with deposit (€ 64) and fee (€ 16). **Open** 20 December - 30 September.

**Directions:** Leave Bourg d'Oisans on the N91 towards Briançon. Shortly after crossing the river, on a sharp right hand bend, turn left onto the D211, signed Alpe d'Huez. Site is on right in 400 m.

---

# Camping La Rencontre du Soleil

route de l'Alpe d'Huez, 38520 Bourg-d'Oisans

Ferry ✓
Pitch ✓
Accommodation ✗
01892 55 98 98

This part of the Isère is an attractive region with some exceptional scenery for which this site proves a good base from which to explore. Pleasant, friendly and family run, it nestles between two impressive mountain ranges, at the base of France's largest National Park, Le Parc des Ecrins. Only 2 km. from Bourg d'Oisans, a regular staging point for the Tour de France, it offers some serious and exciting cycling. The site has 73 level pitches, most of a good size, with mature trees offering good shade. Canoeing, rafting, riding and many other activities are possible nearby. Some skiing is normally possible until mid-July at Les Deux Alpes (16 km). The site is used by tour operators (30 pitches). A 'Sites et Paysages' member.

**Facilities:** A large heated toilet block is of high quality and extremely clean and well maintained. Washing machine and dryer. Motorcaravan service point. Bread to order. Restaurant and takeaway (all season). Sitting room with TV. Small, sheltered swimming pool (15/6-15/9). Play area. Activities in high season include walking, mountain biking and a mini-club for children. **Off site:** Supermarket 1.5 km. Fishing and bicycle hire 2 km. Canoeing, rafting, riding and climbing nearby.

**Charges** 2002

| | |
|---|---|
| Per unit incl. 2 persons | € 14.30 - € 24.65 |
| extra person | € 4.80 - € 5.45 |
| child (2-5 yrs) | € 3.25 - € 3.85 |
| electricity (2/10A) | € 2.90 - € 4.00 |

**Tel:** 04 76 79 12 22. Fax: 04 76 80 26 37. E-mail: rencontre.soleil@wanadoo.fr. **Reservations:** Advised in high season and made for min. 1 week with deposit and fee. **Open** 11 May - 15 September.

**Directions:** Site is almost opposite no. 3803 on the Alpe d'Huez D211 road from the N91, just east of the town. Entrance is on a sharp bend - take care.

---

# Camping-Caravaning Belle Roche

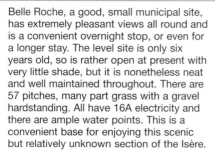

38390 Lalley

Belle Roche, a good, small municipal site, has extremely pleasant views all round and is a convenient overnight stop, or even for a longer stay. The level site is only six years old, so is rather open at present with very little shade, but it is nonetheless neat and well maintained throughout. There are 57 pitches, many part grass with a gravel hardstanding. All have 16A electricity and there are ample water points. This is a convenient base for enjoying this scenic but relatively unknown section of the Isère.

**Facilities:** Two sanitary blocks provide some washbasins in private cabins. Facilities for disabled visitors. Laundry and dishwashing. Good motorcaravan service point. Swimming pool (19 x 12 m; June-Sept.) with large sunbathing area, complete with sun beds. Bar and terrace serving simple, good value meals. Play area planned. Bread from reception. **Off site:** Village shop. Cycling, walking, climbing.

**Charges** guide

| | | |
|---|---|---|
| Per unit incl. 2 persons | 7,77 - | 10,82 |
| child (under 7 yrs) | | 1,37 |
| child (8-6 yrs) | | 2,74 |

**Tel:** (0)4.76.34.75.33. E-mail: camping-bellroche@joliefrance.com. **Reservations:** Advised for July/Aug. **Open** 1 May - 30 September.

**Directions:** Follow N75 south from Grenoble (about 65 km.) turn left on D66 and follow signs for site.

---

## Camping Belledonne

Rochetaillée, 38520 Bourg-d'Oisans

**3810**

Thoughtfully developed from agricultural land over the last 30 years by the Arnaud family, this extremely neat site takes its name from the nearby Belledonne mountain range, and one of the six valleys of the Oisan area. All are impressive, but there is something rather magnificent about the views surrounding this site; furthermore it enjoys sunshine for most of the day. Each of the 150 pitches are not only level and well drained, but also generously sized, with electricity. The site is divided into six areas, each named after one of the valleys, and high hedges and abundant mature trees provide ample privacy and shade. Adjacent to this is an attractive pool complex, comprising two swimming pools, one paddling pool and sunbathing space surrounded by well tended gardens and grass spaces. All in all this is a friendly and well run site, suitable for relaxing or as a base for exploring the interesting countryside around. There may be some noise from the nearby road. A 'Sites et Paysages' member.

**Facilities:** Two sanitary blocks include washbasins in cabins, a mixture of British and Turkish style toilets, washing up sinks, laundry, baby changing rooms and facilities for disabled visitors. Shop. Bar/restaurant (all season). Takeaway. TV room. Swimming and paddling pools. Tennis. Volleyball. Small children's play area and a large grass meadow with comprehensive fitness course. Bicycle hire.

**Charges** 2002

| | |
|---|---|
| Per pitch incl. 2 persons | € 14.40 - € 20.90 |
| 3 persons | € 17.00 - € 24.50 |
| extra person | € 3.80 - € 5.40 |
| child (under 7 yrs) | € 2.60 - € 3.60 |
| electricity (3-6A) | € 2.70 - € 3.70 |
| dog | € 0.90 |
| local tax | € 0.30 |

**Tel:** (0)4 76 80 07 18. **Fax:** (0)4 76 79 12 95. **E-mail:** belledon@club-internet.fr. **Reservations:** Made with € 14 fee; contact site. **Open** 24 May - 13 September.

**Directions:** From Grenoble take N85 to Vizille, then N91 towards Bourg d'Oisans. Branch left on D526 and site is approx. 250 m. on right.

## Camping Le Champ du Moulin

Bourg d'Arvd, 38520 Venosc

**3811**

With steep-sided mountains on all sides, Le Champ du Moulin nestles comfortably on the floor of the narrow Vénéon valley. Even though the bustling town of Le Bourg d'Oisans is only a 15 minute drive away, this peaceful campsite is enjoyed by visitors in both winter and summer. When we visited in early spring, it proved to be a good base for skiing. A cabin chairlift near the entrance transports visitors to Les 2 Alpes. This renowned resort lies out of sight over a sharp rise and offers miles of ski runs in season and extensive glacier skiing in summer. Watching over the site is the more traditional village of Venosc which clings to the hillside a short walk away. Its church, narrow streets, old buildings and notable craft shops are a delightful alternative to the more recently developed glitzy ski towns. On site, generous pitches and large trees are features to note. However, when the mountain snows starts to melt in late May/early June, the River Vénéon adjacent to the site changes from its winter trickle to an impressive torrent. Parents with small children need to be especially vigilant. With its location on the edge of the Ecrins National Park, this is a peaceful location with stunning mountain scenery and miles of marked cycling and walking trails. It is not really a suitable site for teenagers seeking late-night revelry and nightly disco dancing.

**Facilities:** A well heated toilet block is welcome after a day of winter sport, and clothes soon dry on the racks provided. Excellent baby room. Laundry. Motorcaravan service point planned. Chalet restaurant/bar with very good home cooking at easy-on-the-pocket prices. Small shop sharing reception with home baked fresh bread each morning. TV room. Computer room with internet access. Fishing. **Off site:** Municipal heated outdoor pools and flume next door open in summer, together with a children's playground, tennis courts and tree-top adventure park. White water rafting, paragliding, bungee jumping and hill walking available nearby. Discounted ski passes. Riding 0.5 km, golf 3 km (both summer only).

**Charges** 2002

| | |
|---|---|
| Per unit incl. 1 or 2 persons | € 10.50 - € 14.10 |
| extra person | € 3.60 - € 4.60 |
| child 2-6 yrs | € 3.10 - € 3.70 |
| electricity | € 3.10 |
| animal | € 1.60 |

**Tel:** (0)4 76 80 07 38. **Fax:** (0)4 76 80 24 44. **E-mail:** christian.avallet@wanadoo.fr. **Reservations:** Made with deposit and € 13 booking fee. **Open** 15 December - 30 September.

**Directions:** From Grenoble, leave on the southeast side of the city following signs for Oisans. At Bourg d'Oisans (40 km), go through village following signs for Les 2 Alpes and Briancon. After 3 km. turn right at sharp ben for Venosc. In 8 km. along the twisting valley road, pass the bottom ski station on the left. Site is on right after 400 m.

# Camping Le Bois Joli

73130 St Martin-sur-la-Chambre

the travel service TO BOOK

| | |
|---|---|
| Ferry | ✓ |
| Pitch | ✓ |
| Accommodation | ✗ |

01892 55 98 98

If you are looking for somewhere different off the beaten track where time can pass you by, or happen to be passing through on the N6 from Albertville to Modane and the Fréjus tunnel to Italy, this could be a good stopping place. Le Bois Joli (roughly speaking, 'pretty woodland', which it certainly is) is in wooded country in a most peaceful situation. Numerous trees provide good shade to all the pitches, although the natural layout of the site may not suit those who prefer uniformity and order. A minor road divides the site into two section, both with touring pitches. The 116 irregular shaped pitches vary in size from small to very large, some are grassy but most stony and some slope. They are in terraced clearings and all have electricity but water points are few and far between. There are two special pitches with water and drain for motorhomes. Access to some pitches is not easy. Every effort has been made to disturb the natural habitat as little as possible. The Savoy region is probably better known for its winter activities, but the beauty of the landscape and variety of plants existing beneath the winter snow means it is well worth visiting in summer.

**Facilities:** Two sanitary blocks, one refurbished and one with a newly built addition, provide basic facilities and the supply of hot water may be inadequate at peak times. British and Turkish style toilets, a room for disabled people, baby room, laundry and dishwashing sinks. Kiosk with terrace for drinks, takeaway food and basic food supplies. Bar (May to Sept) and rest room offering local cuisine form time to time and continental breakfasts daily (July/Aug). Heated swimming pool. Two play areas. Archery and table tennis. Very few organised activities. Off site: Several shops in Arves, 1 km. Fishing 2 km. Riding 4 km. Bicycle hire 10 km. Many mountain walks.

**Charges** 2002

| | |
|---|---|
| Per unit incl. 2 persons | € 10.00 - € 13.00 |
| extra person | € 3.05 - € 3.40 |
| child (under 7 yrs) | € 1.55 - € 2.30 |
| electricity 2-10A | € 2.30 - € 3.05 |
| animal | € 0.95 |
| local tax | € 0.17 |

**Tel:** 04 79 56 21 28. Fax: 04 79 56 29 95. E-mail: camping-le-bois-joli@wanadoo.fr. **Reservations:** Write to site. **Open** 1 April - 30 September.

**Directions:** Leave A43 autoroute at exit 26 signed La Chambre. At roundabout turn right on D927 and shortly, at next roundabout, turn left on D213 signed St Arve. In a few hundred metres turn right opposite the railway station (site signed). Site is just over 1 km. on the left.

---

# Camping-Caravaneige Le Versoyen

route des Arcs, 73700 Bourg-Saint-Maurice

Bourg-St-Maurice is on a small, level plain at an altitude of 830 m. on the River Isère, surrounded by high mountains. For many years a winter ski resort, it now caters for visitors all year round. The Parc national de la Vanoise is near, along with a wealth of interesting places. Le Versoyen itself attracts visitors all year round (except for a month when they close). The site's 200 unseparated, flat, grass pitches are marked by numbers on the tarmac roads and all have electrical connections (4/6A). Trees typically seen at this altitude give shade in some parts. although most pitches have almost none. Duckboards are provided for snow and wet weather and hardstanding pitches are available for motorcaravans. This is a good base for winter skiing, summer walking climbing, rafting or canoeing, or for car excursions.

**Facilities:** Two acceptable toilet blocks can be heated, although the provision may be hard pressed in high season. British and Turkish style WC's. Laundry. Motorcaravan service facilities. Heated restroom with TV. Small bar with takeaway in summer. Free shuttle to funicular railway. **Off site:** Commercial centre 300 m. away provides a variety of shops. Fishing or bicycle hire 200 m. Tennis and swimming pool 300 m. Riding 1 km. Bourg-st-Maurice 1.5 km. Les Arcs (15 minutes by funicular railway) with ski lifts, some for bikes, to wonderful mountain tracks for bikes and ramblers (15 km). Cross country ski track (up to 30 km. in winter) just behind the site.

**Charges** 2002

| | |
|---|---|
| Per unit incl. 1 person | € 8.15 - € 8.10 |
| extra person | € 4.30 - € 4.65 |
| child 2-7 yrs | € 2.25 - € 2.55 |
| child 7-12 yrs | € 4.00 - € 4.50 |
| dog | € 1.00 |
| electricity (4-12A) | € 3.55 - € 7.30 |
| cyclist or hiker's tent incl. 1 person | € 7.15 |
| local tax | € 0.17 |

**Tel:** 04 79 07 03 45. Fax: 04 79 07 25 41. E-mail: leversoyen@wanadoo.fr. **Reservations:** Write to site with deposit (€ 30) and fee (€ 10). **Open** all year except 7/11- 14/12 and 2/5-15/5.

**Directions:** Site is 1.5 km. east of Bourg-St-Maurice on CD119 Les Arcs road.

## Camping Les Lanchettes

73210 Peisey-Nancroix

This site is in the beautiful Vanoise National Park and at 1,470 m. is one of the highest campsites in this guide. The steep climb to the site, not recommended for underpowered units, through spectacular scenery is well worth the effort. This natural site is terraced and has 90 good size, reasonably level and well drained, grassy/stony pitches. With 80 used for touring units, all have electricity (3-10A). Because it is very cold in winter and quite cold on some spring and autumn evenings there are no outside taps. In winter about 30 pitches at the bottom of the site become part of a cross country ski run. For those who love wonderful scenery, flora and fauna and for those wanting a walking/biking summer holiday, this is the site for you.

**Facilities:** Comprehensive facilities are all in the basement of the house, very cosy in winter. Restaurant with takeaway (July/Aug. and mid Dec-mid April). Playground. Club/TV room. Large tent/marquee used in bad weather for a meeting place and as a dormitory by tenters. Motorcaravan service point. In winter a bus runs to all the hotels, bars, ski tows etc and calls at the site. Accompanied walks (one free) in the National Park. **Off site:** Riding next to site. Bicycle hire 6 km. Golf 8 km.

**Charges** 2002

| | |
|---|---|
| Per unit incl. 2 persons | € 10.80 - € 11.90 |
| electricity 3, 5 or 10A | € 2.90 - € 7.30 |

**Tel:** (0)4 79 07 93 07. Fax: (0)4 79 07 88 33. E-mail: lanchettes@free.fr. **Reservations:** Contact site. **Open** all year, 15 Oct - 15 Dec.

**Directions:** From Albertville take N90 towards Bourg-St-Maurice, through Moûtiers and Aime and about 5 km. further turn right, signed Landry and Peisey-Nancroix. Follow road down, then up a fairly wide, steep, winding hill (a few hairpin bends) for 10 km. Site on right in 1 km. beyond Nancroix.

## Camping Les Deux Glaciers

route des Tissiéres, Les Bossons, 74400 Chamonix

A pleasant and well kept, small mountain site for summer or winter use, Les Deux Glaciers lies between the two glaciers and is close to the well known resort of Chamonix. There are 135 individual pitches on terraces or single plots, levelled out of quite steeply rising ground, with electricity available in all areas. Access may be difficult for large outfits. The site is quietly situated with fine views of the surrounding high mountains but, being a northern slope, it loses the sun a little early and can be quite cold at night. It is pleasantly laid out with different trees and floral displays in their season. With a good position and commendable amenities and welcome, the site becomes full for much of July/Aug.

**Facilities:** Two small, clean sanitary blocks, both heated in cool weather, have modern facilities, at least half the washbasins in cabins. Facilities for disabled visitors. Washing machine and drying room. Snack restaurant (high season). Mobile traders call in season. General room (winter use only). Table tennis. **Off site:** Village shop 500 m. Fishing, bicycle hire or riding within 2 km, golf 4 km.

**Charges** 2002

| | |
|---|---|
| Per unit incl. 2 persons | € 11.60 |
| extra person | € 2.20 - € 4.40 |
| electricity (2-10A) | € 2.20 - 3.90 |

**Tel:** 04 50 53 13 84. Fax: 04 50 55 90 81. E-mail: glaciers@clubinternet.fr. **Reservations:** They are not keen but may make some for Britons, so try. In season, if not reserved, arrive early. **Open** all year.

**Directions:** From west turn right off N506 on second road for Les Bossons, which goes direct to site. From east turn right at sign for Les Bossons, then left at T-junction and pass under the main road to the site, on the right in few hundred metres.

## Camping L'Écureuil

490 route des Follieux, 74702 Sallanches

This spacious, family run site has a natural, country setting with magnificent mountain views. The 130 huge, grassy pitches (nearly all for touring) are well drained and marked out, but often have no other separation. All have some shade from a variety of mature trees and access is easy for all sizes of outfits. There are 100 electrical connections (10A) but some pitches may require very long leads. The site is close to Lac du Passy, a lake used for swimming, fishing and boating and to a large sports centre. There is some noise from the nearby autoroute. There is a little evening entertainment in high season but no on-site activities as all are available nearby.

**Facilities:** The four toilet blocks have all the usual, modern facilities, one block heated when it is cool. Motorcaravan service point. Shop, bar, restaurant and takeaway (all July and Aug). Small lake for swimming, fed from a spring. Bicycle hire. Volleyball, boules and ample space for children to play. Torches advised. **Off site:** Lac du Passy 700 m. Sports centre 700 m. Riding 1.5 km. Golf 13 km.

**Charges** 2002

| | |
|---|---|
| Per adult | € 4.15 |
| child under 12 yrs | € 2.12 |
| pitch and vehicle | € 4.50 - € 7.20 |
| electricity | € 2.50 |

**Tel:** (0)4 50 58 43 67. Fax: (0)4 50 58 44 61. E-mail: contact@camping-ecureuil.com. **Reservations:** Contact site. **Open** Easter - 30 September.

**Directions:** From A40 autoroute take exit 20 on N205 signed Sallanches. Go through town centre and at southern end turn left, just before garage. Straight on under railway bridge and fork right at restaurant. Site is 400 m. just past sports centre.

## Savoy / Dauphiny Alps
# Camping Les Rosières

**7408** 121 Clos des Rosières, 74400 Chamonix Mont-Blanc

This is one of the most spectacular settings imaginable for a campsite with the scenic grandeur of the Alps towering above and providing a perfect backdrop. Within walking distance (15 minutes) of Chamonix by way of a riverside path, this site attracts both summer and winter campers. Les Rosières offers a relaxing environment in the warm sunshine beneath the snow-capped peaks, or an ideal base for a winter skiing holiday. There are 147 level, numbered pitches, 115 for tourers, which are of average size on grass and separated by trees and shrubs. Electricity hook-ups (4/10A) are available on 60.

**Facilities:** The well planned, heated toilet block is maintained to high standards. Some washbasins are in cabins. En-suite provision for disabled people. Baby bath and shower. Laundry room. Dishwashing area. Motorcaravan service point. Gas supplies. Small bar, snacks and takeaway in July/Aug. Bicycle hire. **Off site:** Small shop next to site (closed 22/4-2/6). Sports centre 800 m. Fishing and riding 2 km.

**Charges 2002**

| | |
|---|---|
| Per person | € 4.50 - € 5.20 |
| pitch | € 4.20 - € 5.60 |
| electricity | € 2.60 - € 3.00 |

**Tel:** 04 50 53 10 42. **Fax:** 04 50 53 29 55. **E-mail:** info@campinglesrosieres.com. **Reservations:** Contact site. **Open** 7 February - 15 October.

**Directions:** From autoroute (Route Blanche) take N205 through Chamonix and, just after crossing the funicular railway, turn right at roundabout signed campsite and Les Praz. After 2 km turn left (site signed) and follow signs to site (about 1 km).

## Savoy / Dauphiny Alps
# Camping-Caravaning L'Escale

**7407** 74450 Le Grand-Bornand

the **travel service** TO BOOK

| | |
|---|---|
| Ferry | ✔ |
| Pitch | ✔ |
| Accommodation | ✔ |

01892 55 98 98

You are assured a good welcome from the Baur family at this beautifully maintained, picturesque site. Situated at the foot of the Aravis mountain range, beside the picture postcard ski resort of Le Grand-Bornand, L'Escale has wonderful views and is clearly popular all year round. The 149 fairly sunny pitches are of average size, clearly marked with a part gravel, part gravel surface and separated by trees and shrubs. All have electricity and 80 pitches are fully serviced. The village (200 m.) has all the facilities of a major resort for summer or winter holidays. In summer a variety of well signed footpaths provide forest or mountain walks. In winter the area provides superb facilities for down-hill and cross-country skiing. A 'Sites et Paysages' member.

**Facilities:** The toilet blocks (some heated when cold) have all the necessary facilities. Facilities can be under pressure during peak periods. Below the main building is a large drying room with sinks, tumble dryer and washing machines. Separate room for skis. Play area. Tennis. Table tennis. Torches advised. For summer 2003 a new complex will have indoor and outdoor pools and paddling pools, bar/restaurant and reception. **Off site:** Village 5 minutes walk. Bicycle hire 200 m. Riding, golf 3 km.

**Charges 2003**

| | |
|---|---|
| Per unit incl. 1 or 2 persons | € 13.20 - € 15.50 |
| extra person | € 3.90 - € 4.50 |
| electricity (2-10A) | € 3.10 - € 7.90 |

**Tel:** 04 50 02 20 69. **Fax:** 04 50 02 36 04. **E-mail:** contact@campinglesescale.com. **Reservations:** Made with deposit (€ 71) and fee (€ 10). **Open** all year excl. Oct and Nov.

**Directions:** Probably the best access is via Annecy following the D16 and D909 roads towards La Clusaz. Shortly before La Clusaz, at St Jean-de-Sixt, turn left on D4 signed Le Grand Bornand. Site is signed on the right, just before the village.

## Savoy / Dauphiny Alps
# Camping de la Plage

**7413** 304 rue de la garenne, 74500 Amphion-les-Bains

This very good, family run site is small, quiet and friendly. It has a very long season and is only a few hundred metres from Lake Geneva and the village of Amphion making it an excellent centre to relax and explore this wonderful region. Madame Frossard loves gardening and the site does her credit with its flowers, trees, hedges and beautifully mown grass. The 53 pitches, only a few used by mobile homes, are level, medium to large and separated by trees. They all have water points, drains and electricity. In addition to the very small pool on the site, there is a super water sports centre in the adjacent park, plus an excellent playground and plenty of space to enjoy.

**Facilities:** The ample, comprehensive facilities include facilities for disabled people, sinks for dish-washing and laundry. One toilet block is heated off season. Washing machine, dryer and iron. Small bar and takeaway in high season. Small heated pool, covered in cool weather. Small playground. Table tennis, boules. TV room. Well equipped exercise room. **Off site:** Shops, restaurants within walking distance. Hypermarket 1 km. Golf 3 km.

**Charges 2002**

| | |
|---|---|
| Per unit incl. 2 persons | € 13.70 - € 18.30 |
| extra person | € 3.00 - € 6.10 |
| electricity (2-10A) | € 1.52 - € 4.60 |

**Tel:** (0)4 50 70 00 46. **Fax:** (0)4 50 70 84 45. **E-mail:** info@camping-dela-plage.com. **Reservations:** Essential in high season; made with 25% deposit and € 11 fee. **Open** all year excl. 3 Nov - 24 Dec.

**Directions:** Site is between Thonon les Bains and Evian les Bains. Turn off the N5 at Amphion les Bains (at roundabout with statue and fountains) and follow site signs - site in a few hundred metres.

# Camping La Colombière

**7406** Saint-Julien-en-Genevois, 74160 Neydens

La Colombière, a small family owned site is on the edge of the small residential village of Neydens, a few minutes from the A40 autoroute and only a short drive from Geneva. It is an attractive,site with only 107 pitches, all reasonably level and separated by fruit trees, flowering shrubs and hedges. There are views to the east and west of the mountain ridges. M. Bussat owns a small vineyard close to the site, has the wine made in Switzerland and sells it by glass or bottle in the restaurant (a very nice rosé). One of France's long-distance footpaths (GR65) passes close to the site. The village of Neydens is the first stage for pilgrims from Northern Europe on the route to Santiago de Compostella on their way to cross the Pyrénées at St Pied de Port. The site has a dormitory with seven beds for pilgrims or for anyone else who may need a bed, for example, motorcyclists or a family en-route south. Neydens makes a good base for visiting Geneva and the Lac Leman region. It is a very pleasant, friendly site where you may drop in for a night stop - and stay for several days! English is spoken. A 'Sites et Paysages' member.

**Facilities:** Three good sanitary blocks (one can be heated) include washbasins in cubicles, a baby room and facilities for disabled people. Motorcaravan service point. Fridge hire. Gas supplies. Very good bar/restaurant (all season) and terrace overlooking the heated swimming pool (15/5-15/9). Low season organised visits of discovery, in high season one daily event including organised mountain walks and guided cycle tours (bicycle hire on site). Archery, volleyball and boules competitions. Children's playground. French country music evenings. **Off site:** Fishing or riding 1 km, golf 5 km. Geneva, the Lake and beautiful surrounding area.

**Charges** 2002

| | |
|---|---|
| Per unit incl. 2 persons | € 14.00 - € 18.00 |
| extra person | € 3.50 - € 4.50 |
| child (under 7 yrs) | € 3.00 - € 3.50 |
| dog | € 1.60 |
| electricity (5/6A) | € 3.50 |

**Tel:** 04 50 35 13 14. **Fax:** 04 50 35 13 40. **E-mail:** la.colombiere@wanadoo.fr. **Reservations:** Write to site. 8 days or more in high season gives free bicycle hire for 1 person, for 1 day. Less than 3 days - fee of € 15.24. **Open** 1 April - 30 September.

**Directions:** Take exit 13 from A40 autoroute south of Geneva, and then N201 towards Annecy. Turn into village of Neydens and follow campsite signs.

---

# Camping Le Plan du Fernuy

**7409** Route des Confins, 74220 La Clusaz

The pretty little village of La Clusaz (pop 1,800) is 32 km. east of Annecy at 1,200 m. above sea level in the heart of the Savoie Alps. Le Plan du Fernuy, 2 km. east of the village lies just to the north of the Avaris mountain range in a peaceful, scenic location. The neat, rectangular site has 53 of its 80 pitches available for tourists. Of reasonable size, all with electricity connections and 22 fully serviced, the pitches are arranged in rows on either side of hard access roads with good mountain views. Although surrounded by trees, there is little shade. The site's crowning glory is an excellent indoor heated pool with large windows looking out on to the mountains and sunbeds beside them. Reception is at the front of the pool building and, although the pool is not supervised, it can be seen from here. This is good ski-ing (free ski bus) in winter and walking country in summer with other sporting opportunities nearby. The pleasant owners speak good English.

**Facilities:** The large apartment building at entrance houses very good sanitary provision on the ground floor and is heated in cool weather. Some washbasins are in cabins. Baby room. Facilities for disabled visitors. Separate rooms for dishwashing and laundry with washing machine and dryer. Motorcaravan service point. Pleasant bar provides snacks, takeaway, basic food supplies, video games and a TV room. Heated indoor pool around 13 x 7 m. in size with separate paddling pool. **Off site:** Shops and restaurants in village.

**Charges** 2002

| | |
|---|---|
| Per pitch incl. 2 persons | € 15.00 - € 16.80 |
| with 4A electricity | € 18.10 - € 19.90 |
| 8A electricity | € 19.70 - € 21.50 |
| 13A electricity | € 21.20 - € 23.00 |
| extra person | € 4.57 |
| child (2-7 yrs) | € 3.05 |
| animal | € 1.50 |
| local tax (over 14 yrs) | € 0.40 |

**Tel:** 04 50 02 44 75. **Fax:** 04 50 32 67 02. **E-mail:** leplan.du.fernuy@wanadoo.fr. **Reservations:** Advised for mid-July - mid-Aug. and winter. **Open** 8 June - 19 September and 20 December - 28 April.

**Directions:** From Annecy take D909 to La Clusaz and turn towards Les Confins for site after 2 km. (well signed). Best to avoid using D909 from Flumat particularly with a caravan or motorhome.

## Village Camping Europa

**7410** 1444 Route Albertville, 74410 Saint-Jorioz

You will receive a friendly welcome at this quality, family run site. The flowers, shrubs, trees (giving some shade) and grassy pitches are lovely, in fact everything is neat and tidy. Of the 210 medium to large size, level pitches, 110 are for touring, all have electricity (6A) close by and a few have water and drain. The static units are separated from the touring section by high hedges giving the impression that you are on a small site. Europa should suit those families who like to make their own entertainment although there are some activities for children and a weekly soiree (high season) and it is a good base from which to tour the beautiful Lake Annecy area. They may be some noise from the adjacent main road.

**Facilities:** Two good toilet blocks, the one nearest the tourers recently modernised to a very high standard. They include some large cubicles with shower and washbasin. Motorcaravan service point. Good bar and restaurant (1/6-31/8). Pool complex with reasonably sized, heated swimming pool, paddling pool, jacuzzi, 5 slides and a cascade (jacuzzi, slides and cascade from mid June; entry braclet € 2 per week). Bicycle hire. Internet access. Barrier card deposit € 16. **Off site:** Fishing 300 m. Boat launching 500 m. Riding 3 km. Lakeside beach 2 km. Golf 8 km. 40 km long lakeside bike ride.

**Charges** 2002

| | |
|---|---|
| Per unit incl. 2 persons | € 14.00 - € 21.90 |
| with 6A electricity | € 17.10 - € 25.00 |
| extra person over 6 yrs | € 3.40 - € 5.10 |
| child 2-6 yrs | € 2.30 - € 4.00 |

**Tel:** (0)4 50 68 51 01. Fax: (0)4 50 68 55 20. E-mail: info@camping-europa.com. **Reservations:** Made with deposit (€ 94) and fee (€ 16). **Open** 3 May - 15 September.

**Directions:** From Annecy take N508 signed Albertville. Site is well signed on the right between Saint-Jorioz and Duingt.

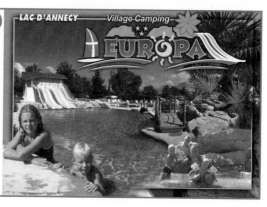

**Village Camping EUROPA**

Charming site, 400 meters from the lake of Annecy – 1 heated swiming pool, 1 water complex (with 5 water slides, waterfalls, children's games, jacuzzi, lagoon) – Restaurant with specialities of the Savoy region Quality installations – Chalets and mobile homes to let – Bikes for hire – Situated next to a cycling track.

**Village Camping EUROPA**
1444, route d'Albertville 74 410 ST – JORIOZ
Tel. 33 (0) 4 50 68 51 01 Fax. 33 (0) 4 50 68 55 20
E-mail : info@camping-europa.com
**www.camping-europa.com**

## Camping Belvédère

**7403M** 8 route du Semnoz, 74000 Annecy

Annecy is an attractive town in a beautiful setting at the head of the lake of the same name. The old centre is intersected by flower decked canals and also has historical interest. There is much to see and do in this region in both summer and winter, with Geneva near and the high Alps. Le Belvédère, as its name implies, overlooks the lake and is the nearest campsite to the town which can be reached by a quiet footpath. There are good part hardstanding terraces, with electricity (10A), water and drain, for 80 caravans and 50 grass pitches for tents. Space may be limited if the site is busy. One small area is reserved for groups. Tall pines and a steep hillside provide a backdrop to the site to the west and small trees provide decoration without giving much shade. This site is ideally placed for visiting Annecy but it is not suitable for large units.

**Facilities:** Three modern toilet blocks were clean when we visited. One is heated in cold weather, with a washroom for visitors with disabilities. Laundry facilities. Small shop, bar and restaurant (from June). Games room. Good playground. Swimming is possible in the lake. Bicycle hire. Communal barbecue. Sporting activities can be booked from the site. **Off site:** Boat launching 600 m. Lakeside beach 800 m.

**Charges** 2002

| | |
|---|---|
| Per unit incl. 2 persons | € 9.90 - € 17.55 |
| extra adult | € 3.80 - € 4.60 |
| child (2-10 yrs) | € 2.30 - € 2.75 |
| electricity (10A) | € 2.30 |

**Tel:** 04 50 45 48 30. Fax: 04 50 45 55 56. E-mail: camping@ville-annecy.fr. **Reservations:** Necessary for July/Aug. - write to Mairie d'Annecy, BP 2305, 74011 Annecy. **Open** 6 April - 15 October.

**Directions:** Leave A41 at Annecy Sud on N508 towards Albertville. Drive around the town and just after some traffic lights descend a hill looking out for hospital signs. Very soon after, on left hand bend, turn right up hill signed Le Semnoz. Keep right at fork. Take care at next junction - do not take right hand road signed Belvédère (this leads to a very steep hill back down to the lake. Turn left, signed Camping Belvédère.

# Camping Le Taillefer
**74111**
1530 Route de Chaparon, 74210 Doussard

This excellent, small site is family run and friendly. It is only 1.5 km. from Lake Annecy, yet it offers a quiet, very relaxing and beautiful environment all at a very good price. The views over the lakeside mountains are stunning. This site is terraced and abounds with flowers, shrubs and small trees. It only has 32 average to good sized, grassy, level and sunny pitches, 28 with electricity (6A). Those at the bottom of the site are reserved for tents. In high season the site is quiet as there are no organised events, although there are plenty on and around the lake close by.

**Facilities:** The modern toilet block has all the necessary facilities including for disabled visitors. Very small shop selling bread, drinks and ices etc. Small bar in high season. Playground, small club/TV room. Torches needed - no site lighting. **Off site:** Nearby village of Doussard has shops and a bank. Lake Annecy with beaches, restaurants, snack bars, fishing and many water sports. Minigolf, bicycle hire, boat launching, small nature reserve (all on Lake Annecy). Golf 5 km. Riding 7 km. 20 km cycle ride by the lake.

**Charges 2002**

| | |
|---|---|
| Per unit incl. 2 persons | € 11.00 - € 12.30 |
| extra person | € 2,20 - € 2.80 |
| electricity (6A) | 3.20 |

**Tel:** (0)4 50 44 30 30. **Reservations:** Made with € 30 booking fee. **Open** 1 May - 30 September.

**Directions:** From Annecy take N508 signed Albertville. At traffic lights in Bréddanaz turn right and then immediately left for 1.5 km. and site is on the left. Don't turn in by reception - this is a dead end. Wait in road until directions are received.

---

# Camp de la Ravoire
**7404**
Bout-du-Lac, route de la Ravoire, 74210 Doussard

the **travel service** TO BOOK

| | |
|---|---|
| Ferry | ✓ |
| Pitch | ✓ |
| Accommodation | ✗ |

01892 55 98 98

De la Ravoire is a quality site, some 800 m. from Lake Annecy, noted for its neat and tidy appearance and the quietness of its location in this popular tourist region. The 112 numbered pitches, on well mown grass and separated by small shrubs, have some shade, although there are trees on the lake side of the site. The 90 pitches for touring units (21 with water and drain) have electricity connections. Those looking for a quiet campsite in this most attractive region without the 'animation' programmes that so many French sites feel are necessary will find this a peaceful base, although disco noise from a site by the lake may drift across under some weather conditions. Used by a tour operator (18 pitches).

**Facilities:** The very good central toilet block includes washbasins in cabins, facilities for disabled people, and a laundry room with washing machines, dryers and irons. Bar and snack bar. Shop. Outdoor pool with separate water slide and paddling pool. Good young children's play area. Sports areas. **Off site:** Fishing, boat launching, bicycle hire 1 km, riding 6 km, golf 8 km. Good lakeside restaurant where the camp road leaves the main road, with others near, plus shops in Doussard village and Annecy.

**Charges 2002**

| | |
|---|---|
| Per unit incl. 2 adults and electricity (5A) | € 25.92 |
| extra person | € 2.44 - € 5.49 |

**Tel:** 04 50 44 37 80. Fax: 04 50 32 90 60. E-mail: info@camping-la-ravoire.fr. **Reservations:** Essential for July/Aug; made for min. 10 days. **Open** 15 May - 15 September.

**Directions:** Site is signed from the N508 Annecy - Albertville road, just north of Bout-du-Lac. At traffic lights in Bredannaz turn right and then immediately left. Site is on the left in about 1 km.

---

# Camping Municipal Saint Ferréol
**7405M**
74210 Saint Ferreol

This is a value-for-money site in a very popular area. Surrounded by glorious alpine scenery, it offers a relaxing environment away from the busy lakeside roads around Lake Annecy. Reception is located on the forecourt beside the security gate and also within this area is the St Ferréol village hall and boule club. The 114 grass pitches on the site are numbered and have electric hook-ups. The ground is level and there is some shade from the tall fir trees in the centre. This is an excellent base from which to explore the high mountain passes, visit Chamonix or linger by the turquoise coloured lake. In low season it is run with limited staff, with reception only open in the evening.

**Facilities:** Two spotlessly clean toilet blocks are fully tiled and equipped. Electronic barrier - campers are issued with a key. **Off site:** Two supermarkets, banks and post office at Faverges, a few minutes away by car.

**Charges 2002**

| | |
|---|---|
| Per unit incl. 2 persons | € 8.38 - € 10.67 |
| extra person | € 1.83 |
| animal | € 0.91 |
| electricity | € 1.83 |

**Tel:** 04 50 27 47 71. E-mail: st.ferreal@wanadoo.fr. **Reservations:** Are accepted - contact site. **Open** 15 June - 15 September.

**Directions:** From Annecy follow N508 towards Albertville to Faverges by-pass. Leave at second roundabout on N508 towards Albertville and site is clearly signed on left in 1 km.

# Atlantic Coast

Map 10

We have taken the coastal départements of the official French region of Aquitaine, stretching from Bordeaux in the north to the Pyrenees and the Spanish border in the south to make our 'tourist' region.

Major city: Bordeaux

Departements: 33 Gironde, 40 Landes, 64 Pyrenees Atlantiques

The Landes stretches north from Biarritz to Arcachon. The most notable features are the uninterrupted line of sandy beaches, over 100 miles long, and the giant pine forests in the hinterland. Water also plays a feature in the many 'etangs' which lie just behind the beaches and provide and attractive situation for many campsites. Dax on the banks of the Adour is a spa town.

The département of the Gironde covers the area from the Bassin d'Arcachon, famed for its oysters, and Europe's highest sand dune to the Gironde estuary and Bordeaux. The vineyards of Bordeaux are world famous and especially well known for their Medoc, Sauternes, and St Emilion wines.

The Pays Basque area (Pyrénées Atlantiques) in the south west corner is much influenced by Spain. The most famous Basque towns are Biarritz, Bayonne and the picturesque old port of St-Jean-de-Luz. Further inland and nearer the Pyrénées is the attractive town of St-Jean-Pied-de-Port on the pilgrims' route to northern Spain and Santiago de Compostela and only 20 km from the forest of Iraty with its lakes and ski runs. Look for the high, unusually shaped walls used for the Basque game of 'pelota'; St-Jean is one of the strongest centres of the sport.

Note: the site reports are arranged by département in numerical order.

## Cuisine of the region

*Foie Gras* – specially prepared livers of geese and ducks, seasoned and stuffed with truffles

*Confits* – (preserved goose and duck) are a key ingredient in a number of dishes

Fish and seafood – like carp stuffed with foie gras, mullet in red wine and besugo (sea bream)

*Chorizos* – spicy sausages

*Jambon de Bayonne* – raw ham, cured in salt and sliced paper thin

*Lamproie* – eel-like fish with leeks, onions and red Bordeaux wine

*Gâteau Basque* – shallow custard pastry, often with fruit fillings

*Cèpes* – fine, delicate mushrooms; sometimes dried

*Chou farci* – stuffed cabbage, sometimes aux marrons (with chestnuts)

## Wine

Three distinctive areas: Médoc, famous for fine red wines, Graves and Sauternes left of the Garonne and Saint-Emilion and its surroundings – for Entre-Deux-Mers and Côtes de Blaye

## Places of interest

*Bayonne* – old streets and fortifications; Basque Museum

*Bordeaux* – see the 14,000 piece Bohemian glass chandelier in the foyer of the Grand Theatre, and the 29 acre Esplanade des Quinconces

*Pau* – famous motor racing circuit on (closed) public highway; stadium for the Basque game of pelota

*St Emilion* – visit the castle ramparts or drink premier cru St Emilion at pavement cafés

*St Jean-de-Luz* – seaside resort and fishing village

*St Jean-Pied-de-Port* – ancient city with citadel; bright Basque houses in steep streets

## Atlantic Coast
# Sunêlia Camping La Pointe du Medoc
Route de la Pointe de Grave, 33123 Le Verdon-sur-Mer

**3321**

La Pointe du Medoc was established three years ago close to the tip of the Medoc peninsula and benefits from some excellent modern amenities. This site has 260 pitches, around half taken by mobile homes or chalets. It is roughly equi-distant between the sandy Atlantic beach (reached by a pleasant walk through the forest opposite the site) and that of the Gironde estuary, both around 1 km away. Pitches are generally large (100-150 sq.m), some are in full sun (the site lost many trees in the great storm of 1999) but those towards the rear of the site offer much more shade. All are equipped with electricity, and many have water and drainage. A little used railway line passes by the front of the site, as well as the main road to Le Verdon.

**Facilities:** Two modern toilet blocks are maintained to a high standard, with good hot showers and washbasins in private cabins. Pleasant bar and restaurant with take-away. In high season there is a wide range of organised entertainment and imaginative childrens' club. Sport and leisure facilities include a heated swimming pool with small waterfalls and split-level paddling pool. Massage room. Beach volleyball. Minigolf. **Off site:** Well located for excursions to the Medoc châteaux or marshland.

**Charges** 2002

| | |
|---|---|
| Per unit incl. 2 persons, electricity | € 20.00 |
| extra person (any age) | € 5.00 |

Less in low seasons. **Tel:** 05 56 73 39 99. Fax: 05 56 73 39 96. **Reservations:** Essential for high season - contact site. **Open** Easter - 30 September.

**Directions:** Site is located on the RN215 just south of Le Verdon and can be accessed either from the south (Bordeaux or the Blaye ferry), or from the north using the regular Royan - Pointe de Grave car ferry.

## Atlantic Coast
# Camping Palace
65 bvd Marsan de Montbrun, 33780 Soulac-sur-Mer

**3306**

Le Palace is close to the beach south of Royan across the estuary. It is a traditional site, large and level, with 535 good-sized pitches regularly laid out amongst a variety of trees which provide good shade. On the very sandy ground, pitches for caravans have hardened areas. Electricity is available, most pitches have water taps and some also have sewage connections. A wide range of amenities is arranged around a lush green roundabout with a fountain at the centre of the site. Dancing and concerts take place here in the main season. A wide, sandy beach is 400 m. from the site gates and swimming, said not to be dangerous in normal conditions, is controlled by lifeguards. English is spoken.

**Facilities:** Twelve toilet blocks, some smaller and more simple than others and some that open from the outside only, include washbasins in cabins. Baby rooms in four blocks, facilities for disabled people in one. Washing machines. Supermarket, other shops, restaurant and bar (all from 10/6). Swimming pool (20 x 10 m) with lifeguards. Supervised playground with paddling pool. Bicycle hire. Sports, entertainments and excursions in July/Aug. Winter caravan storage. **Off site:** Tennis courts adjacent, riding 400 m.

**Charges** 2002

| | |
|---|---|
| Per unit incl. 2 persons, 5A electricity and water | € 13.72 - € 19.16 |
| extra person (over 10 yrs) | € 2.74 - € 3.92 |

**Tel:** 05 56 09 80 22. Fax: 05 56 09 84 23. E-mail: campingpalace@libertysurf.fr. **Reservations:** Made for with deposit. **Open** 1 May - 15 September.

**Directions:** Site is 1 km. south of Soulac and well signed. The shortest and simplest way is via the ferry across the Gironde estuary from Royan to Pointe de Grave, but this is quite expensive with a caravan. Alternatively make the trip via Bordeaux.

## Atlantic Coast
# Camping Municipal Les Gabarreys
Route de la Rivière, 33250 Pauillac

**3315M**

An attractive, small site with well tended flower beds, Les Gabarreys is surrounded by the many vineyards of the Médoc region (reception provides a good map). An excellent site, it has 59 pitches, 41 with hardstanding for caravans or motorcaravans, 14 grass pitches for tents and 4 mobile homes, all with electricity (5/10A, some may require long leads). The 'Maison du Tourism and du Vin' should be your first port of call, the surrounding area is well supplied with wine caves, and being fairly level you could perhaps cycle to some of them. The site is popular with the grape pickers in September, but the warden always keeps some pitches for tourists.

**Facilities:** Two immaculate toilet blocks (with automatic perfume sprays) provide open and cubicle washbasins and excellent facilities for disabled people. Motorcaravan services. General room with satellite TV, fridge-freezer and a small library. Minigolf (free) and volleyball.

**Charges** 2002

| | |
|---|---|
| Per unit incl. 2 persons | € 10.52 |
| extra person | € 3.05 - € 3.66 |
| electricity (5/10A) | € 1.52 - € 4.57 |

**Tel:** (0)5 56 59 10 03. Fax: (0)5 56 73 30 68. E-mail: camping.les.gabarreys@wanadoo.fr. **Reservations:** Advisable for July-Sept. Open 4 April - 11 October.

**Directions:** Pauillac lies on the western side of the Gironde estuary, NNW of Bordeaux. From Bordeaux take the D1 to St Laurent, then the D206 to Pauillac where the site is signed to your right on entering the town. Alternatively if approaching from the north, you could use the ferry from Royan to Le Verdon, or Blaye to Lamarque (cheaper).

# Airotel Camping de la Côte d'Argent

**3311** 33990 Hourtin-Plage

the **travel service** TO BOOK

| | |
|---|---|
| Ferry | ✓ |
| Pitch | ✓ |
| Accommodation | ✗ |

01892 55 98 98

Spread over 20 hectares of undulating sand-based terrain and in the midst of a pine forest, this large site is well placed and well equipped for leisurely family holidays. It also makes an ideal base for walkers and cyclists, with over 100 km. of cycle lanes leading through the Medoc countryside. Hourtin-Plage is a pleasant invigorating resort on the Atlantic coast and a popular location for watersports enthusiasts, or those who prefer spending their days on the beach. More appealing though may be to stay on site, for Côte d'Argent's top attraction is its swimming pool complex with wooden bridges connecting the pools and islands, on which there are sunbathing patios and children's play areas. There are 750 touring pitches which are not clearly defined and in the trees, some on soft sand-based ground (night lighting provided). When we visited 48 hardstandings for motorcaravans were almost complete. Due to the work on the site the access roads were in a poor condition, but we were told would be repaired in the near future. A reader tells us that the site is well organised and ideal for children, akthough it can be noisy at night in high season.

**Facilities:** Five very clean sanitary blocks of various ages include provision for disabled visitors. Plenty of laundry machines. Motorcaravan service points. Large supermarket. Restaurant, takeaway and pizzeria bar. Four swimming pools, waterslides and flumes. Two tennis courts, pool tables and four play areas. Mini-club and organised entertainment in season. Charcoal barbecues are not permitted. **Off site:** Walkway to the beach.

**Charges** guide

| Per unit incl. 2 persons | € 18.60 - € 25.15 |
|---|---|
| extra person | € 2.74 - € 4.57 |
| child (2-10 yrs) | € 1.83 - € 3.35 |
| tent incl. 2 persons | € 15.24 - € 22.26 |
| electricity (6A) | € 3.81 |
| dog | € 1.68 - € 3.05 |
| local tax over 10 yrs | € 0.50 |

**Tel:** 05 56 09 10 25. Fax: 05 56 09 24 96. E-mail: info@camping-cote-dargent.com. **Reservations:** Necessary for July/August. **Open** 11 May - 15 September.

**Directions:** Turn off D101 Hourtin-Soulac road 3 km. north of Hourtin. Then join D101E signed Hourtin-Plage. Site is 300 m. from the beach.

# Camping Les Ourmes

**3305** avenue du Lac, 33990 Hourtin

Located only 500 metres from the largest freshwater lake in France, only 10 minutes drive from the beach and with its own pool, this is essentially a holiday site. Its 270 pitches, marked but in most cases not actually separated, are arranged amongst tall pines and other trees which give good shade. All have electricity connections. The site's amenities are arranged around a pleasant entrance courtyard with an evening entertainment programme in season. This site has a busy, cosmopolitan feel, with visitors of many different nationalities.

**Facilities:** Three purpose built toilet blocks are of a good standard including some washbasins in cabins. Washing machine in each block and dryer, with hot water taps for washing up. Small shop (1/6-15/9). Bar/restaurant with many outdoor tables serving snacks and takeaway meals (1/7-31/8). Medium sized swimming pool and new paddling pool (15/6-15/9). Separate large leisure area with children's play area, volleyball and basketball courts and table tennis tables (under cover). TV, games rooms and boules pitches. **Off site:** Watersports and fishing possible on the lake, with bicycle hire, tennis and riding within 500 m.

**Charges** 2002

| Per unit incl. 2 persons | € 11.00 - € 14.70 |
|---|---|
| with electricity | € 13.70 - € 17.70 |
| extra person (over 2 yrs) | € 1.80 - € 3.00 |
| dog | € 1.20 - € 1.50 |
| local tax (over 10 yrs) | € 0.17 |

**Tel:** 05 56 09 12 76. Fax: 05 56 09 23 90. E-mail: lesourmes@free.fr. **Reservations:** Necessary in high season. **Open** 1 April - 30 September.

**Directions:** Follow Route du Port (Ave du Lac) from the town centre and site is signed.

# Airotel Camping Caravaning de la Côte d'Argent

## 33990 Hourtin Plage

Tél :(+ 33)5.56.09.10.25 Fax :(+ 33)5.56.09.24.96
Internet : www.camping-cote-dargent.com

**Swimming pool complex of 3500 m² with water slides**

**Caravans and mobile homes to rent**

Camping de la Côte d'Argent occupies an area of 20 hectares situated in the heart of a pine forest, but only 300 m from a huge beach, and just 4 km away from one of the biggest natural lakes in the whole of the France. A characterful site, protected from the wind by the forest and nearby sand dunes, this site is natural surroundings also enjoys the benefit of an ideal climate.

ESF COMMUNICATION : 04 94 67 06 00

## Free brochures on request - Alan Rogers 2003

First Name(s)..............................................................................................................

Surname.....................................................................................................................

Address......................................................................................................................

Town...............................................................Post Code.........................................

## Atlantic Coast
# Camping Airotel de L'Océan

**33Z4**
33680 Lacanau-Océan

Its location on the Atlantic coast, only 600 metres from a lovely sandy beach makes this site extremely popular. Set in 10 hectares of wooded sand dunes, the site offers the total holiday experience with over 500 pitches set amongst pine trees with areas for peace and quiet and areas for those who want to be on top of it all. The pitches are quite spacious, some level and others requiring blocks. At the time of our visit everywhere was very dry and there was very little grass. There is a large swimming pool complex, a bar and disco (in a soundproof building). There are many cycle routes through the woods. Lacanau-Océan has many weekend visitors from Bordeaux and is popular for surfing.

**Facilities:** Six toilet blocks provide spacious facilities including washbasins in cabins, a room for disabled visitors in each block (although the site is quite hilly in places), baby rooms, washing machines and dishwashing. Motorcaravan service point. Supermarket. Bar, restaurant and takeaway. Large leisure pool complex. Various sports facilities. Fitness gym. TV and games rooms. Internet access. Bicycle hire. Barbecue area. **Off site:** Beach 600 m. Shops 1 km.

**Charges** 2002

| | |
|---|---|
| Per unit incl. 2 persons | € 11.00 - € 14.00 |
| with electricity | € 14.00 - € 17.00 |
| extra person | € 4.20 - € 7.00 |
| child (under 12 yrs) | free - € 5.50 |

**Tel:** 05 56 03 24 45. Fax: 05 57 70 01 87.
**Reservations:** Made with 25% deposit and € 28 fee. **Open** 1 May - 30 September.

**Directions:** From Bordeaux take D106 then onto D3 to Royan and through the wooded areas of the Atlantic coast. At Lacanau join D6 to Lacanau Ocean. At roundabout before village turn right and site is 800 m. on the right.

## Atlantic Coast
# Camping-Caravaning Les Grands Pins

**33I3**
33680 Lacanau-Océan

This Atlantic coast holiday site with direct access to fine sandy beach, is on undulating terrain amongst tall pine trees. A large site, it provides 570 pitches, with about 44 private and rental mobile homes, leaving around 525 pitches of varying sizes for touring units. The site is well served by tarmac access roads, and although not noticeably divided, one half of the site is a traffic free zone (except for arrival and departure day, caravans are placed on the pitch, with separate areas outside the zone for car parking). There is a good number of tent pitches, those in the centre of the site having some of the best views, and especially useful for tenters are safety deposit and fridge boxes which are available for rent. The large sandy beach is a 350 m. stroll from the gate at the back of the site.

**Facilities:** Five toilet blocks, including an excellent new one, include washbasins in cubicles, dishwashing and laundry sinks, a dog and wetsuit washing area, baby room and facilities for disabled people (not all units open in low season). Launderette. Motorcaravan services. Good supermarket, surf boutique. Bar, restaurant and snack bar with takeaway. Heated pool (20 x 10 m, from 1/5 with lifeguard in July/Aug). Jacuzzi. Games room. Fitness suite. Tennis (charge in July/Aug). Two playgrounds. Bicycle hire. Organised activities for children (July/Aug). Entrance barrier with keypad access. Only gas barbecues are permitted. **Off site:** Fishing, golf, riding and bicycle hire 5 km.

**Charges** 2002

| | |
|---|---|
| Per pitch incl. 2 persons, electricity | € 23.00 - € 30.00 |
| extra person | € 6.50 - € 8.50 |
| child (2-12 yrs) | free - € 4.00 |

**Tel:** (0)5 56 03 20 77. Fax: (0)5 57 70 03 89. E-mail: reception@lesgrandspins.com. **Reservations:** Essential for high season, made with deposit and reservation fee. Discounts for early booking. **Open** 19 April - 15 September, full facilities from 1/5.

**Directions:** From Bordeaux take N125/D6 west to Lacanau, continue on D6 to Lacanau Océan. Follow signs to camp sites, passing several other sites, and Les Grand Pins is signed to the right at the far end of the road. From northern France you could use the ferry from Royan to Le Verdon.

Camping and Mobile-homes 350m from the beach

# Camping Les Grands Pins ✳ ✳ ✳ ✳
F-33680 Lacanau Ocean  Tél : (33) 5 56 03 20 77    Fax (33) 5 57 70 03 89
E-mail : reception@lesgrandspins.com  www.lesgrandspins.com

## Atlantic Coast
# Camping La Cigale

Route de Lège, 33740 Arès

La Cigale is an attractive little site with charm and ambience where the owners extend a very warm welcome. Small and beautifully maintained, it is set amid pine trees and M. Pallet's floral displays. The 95 pitches, most with electricity and of 100 sq.m. in size, are level and grassy, divided by hedges and flower borders. The majority have shade from the pine trees. There are two small swimming pools in a pleasant setting and under the ample shade of a large plane tree, where drinks, meals and snacks are served on the bar terrace. This is an exceptional area for cycling, with designated routes. Across the bay lies bustling Arcachon and the enormous Dune de Pilat, easily reached by ferry from Cap Ferret. Used by tour operators (18%).

**Facilities:** The central, flower-bedecked, unisex toilet block includes a family room with two showers, facilities for disabled visitors and a laundry with a washing machine and dryer. All is meticulously maintained. Motorcaravan services. Simple shop. Bar terrace with meals and snacks. Two small swimming pools. Small children's play area. Full-time entertainers for children and adults in July/Aug. **Off site:** Site is convenient for a wide choice of beaches. Fishing or riding 1 km. Village centre 800 m.

**Charges** guide

| | |
|---|---|
| Per unit incl. 1 or 2 persons | € 13.72 - € 17.53 |
| extra person | € 3.81 |
| child (7 yrs) | € 2.29 |
| electricity (4/6A) | € 3.66 |
| local tax (1/6-30/9) | € 0.17 |

**Tel:** 05 56 60 22 59. Fax: 05 57 70 41 66. E-mail: campinglacigaleares@wanadoo.fr. **Reservations:** Advised for July/Aug. and made with deposit (€ 79) and fee (€ 16). **Open** 15 May - 15 September.

**Directions:** Leave Bordeaux ring-road at exit 10 (D213) or exit 11 (D106) and continue on good roads direct to Arès. Turn into Arès following road to church square. Turn right following signs for Lège/Cap Ferret. Site is 800 m. on right.

## Atlantic Coast
# Camping-Caravaning Le Truc Vert

Route du Truc-Vert, 33905 Lège Cap Ferret

Relaxing amidst the tall pines of this 10 hectare hillside site is pleasant, but if you are looking for more activity there are many cycle ways and walks around the site to enjoy. There are over 400 pitches (200 with 6A electricity) with trees giving shade. Some pitches are level but for many you will need levelling blocks. Some of the site roads are very steep so care is needed. The entrance area is decked with flowers and very welcoming. There are tables and chairs outside the reception and bar where you can sit in the evening sun. Care needs to be taken while travelling on the main roads through the woods (keep to speed limits) as the occasional wild boar ventures out onto the roads. The beach is only 300 metres and is quite secluded (with lifeguards).

**Facilities:** Seven toilet blocks spread well around the site offer good facilities with good showers and washbasins in cubicles, facilities for disabled people (although some may find the roads on site very steep). Motorcaravan service area. Laundry and dishwashing. Bar and restaurant. Supermarket. Play area. TV/games room. Various activities on site, evening entertainment in season. **Off site:** Fishing 300 m. Beach 300 m. Riding 500 m.

**Charges** 2002

| | |
|---|---|
| Per pitch | € 9.45 |
| person over 2 yrs | € 4.11 |
| electricity (5A) | € 3.95 |
| local tax | € 0.21 - € 0.42 |

**Tel:** (0)5 56 60 89 55. Fax: (0)5 56 60 99 47. E-mail: camping.truc-vert@worldonline.fr. **Reservations:** Contact site. **Open** 1 April - 30 September.

**Directions:** From Bordeaux take D106 heading for Lège Cap Ferret. Just before village sign turn right (large billboard for the site above hedge) and follow through woods for about 2 km. site on your left.

# Camping-Caravaning Fontaine-Vieille
4 boulevard du Colonel Wurtz, 33510 Andernos-les-Bains

**3302**

Fontaine-Vieille is a large, traditional site that recently celebrated its 50th anniversary. The site stretches along the eastern edge of the Bassin d'Arcachon under light woodland in the residential area of the small town of Andernos. Popular with the French, it has 800 individual pitches, some with views and 600 with electricity connections. On flat grassy ground, they are marked by stones in the ground or young trees. A beach runs alongside the tidal Bassin which can be used for boating when the tide is in. When it is out, there is sand and mud but it is claimed that bathing in the channels is still possible.

**Facilities:** Seven sanitary blocks, of rather unusual design, provide adequate number of hot showers, plus facilities for people with disabilities and children. Maintenance can be variable. Shop (15/5-15/9). Bar with terrace. Restaurant with takeaway (all season). Communal barbecue (only gas individual barbecues may be used). Swimming pool complex. Four tennis courts. TV room. Two children's play areas for little ones and adventure area for older children. Minigolf. Boats, sailboards for hire. Bicycle hire. Sports are organised. Caravan storage. **Off site:** Riding 5 km, golf 3 km. Town shops near.

**Charges** guide

| | |
|---|---|
| Per unit incl. 2 persons | € 14.50 |
| with electricity (5A) | € 17.50 |
| extra person | € 3.05 |
| child (2-7 yrs) | € 2.30 |
| local tax | € 0.17 |

**Tel:** 05 56 82 01 67. Fax: 05 56 82 09 81.
**Reservations:** Made for any length with deposit (€ 80) and fee (€ 20). **Open** 1 April - 30 September.

**Directions:** Turn off the D3 at southern end of Andernos towards Bassin at camp sign.

4, Boulevard du Colonel Wurtz - 33510 Andernos-les-bains - Tél. 05 56 82 01 67 - Fax. 05 56 82 09 81
Internet:http://www.fontaine-vieille.com

## Atlantic Coast
# Domaine de la Barbanne

**3308** route de Montagne, 33330 Saint Emilion

the travel service
TO BOOK
erry ✓
itch ✓
ccommodation ✗
1892 55 98 98

La Barbanne is a pleasant, friendly, family-owned site in the heart of the Bordeaux wine region, only 2.5 km. from St Emilion. With 160 pitches, the owners have transformed it into a carefully maintained, well equipped site. The original parts of the site bordering the lake have tarred roads, good shade and pleasant surroundings, whilst the newer area has younger trees, some shade and gravel access roads. The pitches are being re-numbered and are all large, level and grassy with dividing hedges and electricity connections. La Barbanne has an attractive entrance and reception area with ample space for parking or turning. The site owners run a free minibus service to St Emilion and also organise excursions to local places of interest. A 'Sites et Paysages' member.

**Facilities:** Two toilet blocks, the original one fully refurbished, the other in the newer area being very modern. Most washbasins are in cabins. Visitors with disabilities are well catered for. Motorcaravan service point. Small, well stocked shop. Bar with terrace, takeaway and restaurant (1/7-31/8). Two swimming pools, one heated with cork-screw water slide. Play area. Children's club (from 1/7). Tennis, boules, volleyball, table tennis and minigolf. The lake provides free fishing, pedaloes, canoes and lakeside walks. Bicycle hire. **Off site:** Riding 8 km.

**Charges** 2002

| | |
|---|---|
| Per pitch | € 5.50 - € 7.00 |
| adult | € 3.50 - € 5.50 |
| child under 7 yrs | € 2.00 - € 4.20 |
| electricity (6A) | € 3.00 - € 4.00 |

**Tel:** 05 57 24 75 80. Fax: 05 57 24 69 68. E-mail: barbanne@wanadoo.fr. **Reservations:** Made for min. 4 days. **Open** 1 April - 22 September.

**Directions:** At St Emilion take D122 for 2.5 km. Turn right just before Montagne and site is on left after 400 m. Caravans and motorhomes must approach the site by taking the D243 from Libourne or from Castillon on the D936 via D130/D243.

## Atlantic Coast
# Camping Le Pressoir

**3309** Petit Palais et Cornemps, 33570 Lussac

the travel service
TO BOOK
erry ✓
itch ✓
ccommodation ✗
1892 55 98 98

Buried in the famous wine producing countryside of the Lussac, Pomerol and St Emilion area north of Bordeaux, Le Pressoir is surrounded by fields of vines. With a manicured entrance featuring attractive trees, shrubs and flowers, together with preserved equipment from its former role as a wine farm, it is a neat site with good quality facilities. The 100 large pitches are arranged on either side of a gravel road leading up a slight hill and many are shaded by attractive trees. They are over 100 sq.m. and equipped with electricity (blue EC plugs) and interspersed with five Trigano type tents for hire. The old barn has been converted into a stylish bar and a really charming, separate restaurant. A quiet, family site, Le Pressoir provides a comfortable base for a holiday in this area famous for good food and wine.

**Facilities:** Very good fully equipped toilet facilities in purpose built block near the farmhouse include hair and make-up area for ladies, facilities for disabled visitors, and washing machine. Bar. Restaurant (all season) and snack bar with takeaway. Swimming pool (14 x 7 m; 15/5-15/9, no bermuda shorts). Children's playground with timber equipment. Petanque, volleyball and table tennis. Gates locked 22.00 - 08.00 hrs. **Off site:** Tennis nearby. Fishing 5 km, riding and bicycle hire 10 km.

**Charges** guide

| | |
|---|---|
| Per standard pitch | € 6.40 |
| with 6A electricity | € 9.15 |
| person | € 5.34 |
| child (2-6 yrs) | € 3.05 |
| dog | € 1.50 |

**Tel:** 05 57 69 73 25. Fax: 05 57 69 77 36. E-mail: camping.le.pressoir@wanadoo.fr. **Reservations:** Advised for July/Aug. and made with deposit and 12 fee. **Open** April - 3 October.

**Directions:** From N89 Bordeaux - Périgueux turn at Saint Médard de Guizières towards Lussac on the D21. Site is signed here and also from Lussac.

## Atlantic Coast
# Camping de L'Eyre

**3320M** Allée de la Plage, 33380 Mios

This well kept municipal site is close to Bordeaux, Arcachon and the Dune de Pilat and only 8 km from the A63 autoroute. It has 107 marked pitches, 50 for touring units, some on flat ground, others more sloping. Many are well shaded and have water and electricity connections. The site abuts an extensive sports complex and it is possible to swim or fish in the Eyre river, which runs alongside the site.

**Facilities:** Good basic facilities. Bicycle hire. Height barrier at entrance - arrive when reception is open, 09.00-13.00 and 15.00-19.00 hrs. Double axle vans are not accepted. **Off site:** Shops, restaurants, etc. are to be found in Mios village. Riding 3 km.

**Charges** guide

| | |
|---|---|
| Per unit incl. 2 persons | € 10.52 |
| extra person | € 3.05 |
| electricity (6A) | € 2.90 |

**Tel:** 05 56 26 42 04. Fax: 05 56 26 42 04. **Reservations:** Advised for July/Aug. **Open** all year.

**Directions:** From A63 south of Bordeaux take exit 22 onto A660 signed Arcachon. After 5 km. at junction 1 take D216 to Mios. Mios is on the D3 and site is on the western end of the village, well signed.

For latest information visit www.alanrogers.com **179**

## Camping de la Dune

3301 route de Biscarrosse, 33115 La Pyla-sur-Mer

La Dune is a good example of a busy French family site. It is informal, friendly and lively, with a comprehensive range of amenities. From its situation at the foot of the enormous dune (the highest in Europe) you can reach the beach either by climbing over the dune - a ladder goes up nearly to the top - or driving round. The 325 marked pitches, some sloping, some terraced but level, vary somewhat in size but all are hedged with shade from pine trees. Nearly half are caravan pitches with electricity, water and drainaway. Some of the site roads are quite narrow and parts are quite sandy. English spoken. No tour operators. A busy site with good security.

**Facilities:** Modern sanitary blocks include one that can be heated in cool weather and has roomy showers and washbasins en-suite. WCs are of British and Turkish types, many washbasins are in cabins. Some blocks may be closed at night. Motorcaravan service point. Small supermarket. Bar and restaurant with takeaway (from June). Swimming pool. Playground with mini-club. Sports and tournaments organised in July/Aug. Only gas barbecues are allowed. Fridge hire. **Off site:** Riding 2 km, fishing 3 km, golf 10 km.

**Charges** 2002

| | |
|---|---|
| Per tent incl. 2 persons with tent | € 11.00 - € 21.50 |
| caravan incl. electricity and water | € 14.00 - € 24.50 |
| extra person | € 3.50 - € 7.50 |

**Tel:** 05 56 22 72 17. Fax: 05 56 22 72 17. E-mail: campingdeladune@wanadoo.fr. **Reservations:** Made for min. 1 week in high season with 25% deposit and fee (€ 22,87). **Open** 1 May - 30 September.

**Directions:** The D259, signed from the N250 to Biscarrosse and Dune du Pilat, just before La Teste, avoids Pyla-sur-Mer. At end of new road turn left at roundabout onto D218 coast road. La Dune is second site on right.

---

## Camping Panorama

3331 Route de Biscarosse, Pyla sur Mer, 33115 Arcachon

Many campsites set amongst pine trees have a rather untidy look, but Panorama is different. Here the entrance is very inviting with well tended flower beds and a pleasant, airy reception. From the entrance there is a climb up to the pitches, passing the swimming pool and play area. The touring pitches are set amongst the tall pines, all with electricity, and these outnumber the mobile home pitches. Many activities and entertainments are organised in high season, even classical concerts. A track leads down to the beach with a staircase. The area is a maze of cycle tracks. A Yelloh Village member.

**Facilities:** Toilet blocks of varying ages and quality are clean and well maintained with baby rooms and facilities for disabled people. Brown tiles make them appear a little dark. Fridge hire. Laundry facilities. Motorcaravan service point. Bar/restaurant with panoramic view of the ocean. Attractive pool area with three heated pools and jacuzzi (115-3019). Play area. Tennis. Minigolf. Table tennis. Entertainment in high season. Off site: Riding 1 km. Golf 10 km.

**Charges** 2002

| | |
|---|---|
| Per pitch | € 9.00 - € 18.00 |
| person | € 3.00 - € 6.00 |
| child (under 12 yrs) | € 1.00 - € 2.50 |
| electricity (3-6A) | € 3.00 - € 5.00 |

**Tel:** (0)5 5622 1044. Fax: (0)5 5622 10 12. E-mail: mail@camping-panorama.com. **Reservations:** Made with deposit and fee. **Open** 1 May -30 September.

**Directions:** The new D259, signed from the N250 to Biscarrosse and Dune du Pilate, just before La Teste, avoids Pyla-sur-Mer. At roundabout at end of road, turn left on D218 coast road. Site is 4 km.

---

## Sunêlia Camping Le Petit Nice

3322 Route de Biscarrosse, 33115 Pyla-sur-Mer

**the travel service TO BOOK**

| Ferry | ✔ |
|---|---|
| Pitch | ✔ |
| Accommodation | ✔ |

01892 55 98 98

Le Petit Nice is a traditional seaside site, just south of the great Dune de Pyla (Europe's largest sand dune, and a genuinely remarkable sight). It is a friendly, if relatively unsophisticated, site with direct (steep) access to an excellent sandy beach. The 225 pitches are for the most part terraced, descending towards the sea. Many are quite small, with larger pitches generally occupied by mobile homes. For this reason it is likely to appeal more to campers and motorcaravanners than caravaners. Most pitches are shaded by pine trees but those closest to the sea are unshaded. Unusually, the site also has a private hang gliding and paragliding take-off strip (very popular activities here).

**Facilities:** Two refurbished toilet blocks include washbasins in cubicles. Bar/restaurant at front of site, along with well-stocked shop and games room. Attractive swimming pool with small slide, children's pool and jacuzzi. Tennis, table tennis and boules.

**Charges** 2002

| | |
|---|---|
| Per pitch | € 12.00 |
| adult | € 5.00 |
| child | € 2.50 - € 3.50 |
| electricity | € 4.50 |

Reductions for other dates. **Tel:** 05 56 22 74 03. Fax: 05 56 22 14 31. **Reservations:** Essential for high season; contact site. **Open** 1 April - 30 September.

**Directions:** Site is located on the D218 (Arcachon - Biscarrosse) road to the south of the Dune de Pyla and is the fifth site you pass after the Dune.

---

## Camping Le Grand Pré

**3314** Route de Casteljaloux, 33430 Bazas

In a rural position, this is a developing site with only 30 pitches at present. The pitches are on grass, and will be separated by low shrubs and bushes which have yet to mature. All have electricity hook-ups (6-16A). Reception facilities and a bar are in a very tastefully converted old barn, where you may have breakfast or collect bread if ordered the day before. There is a traffic free footpath direct from the site to the town, which we can recommend. The fortified town is notable for the magnificent Cathedral (illuminated at night), the annual festival of the Bazardais cattle, the bonfires of St. Jean, and the weekly Saturday market, and is on the Pilgrims Route. Reservation is advisable for July and August especially during the Uzeste Music Festival (20-27 August approx).

**Facilities:** The single, high quality toilet block should be adequate for current demand, but will be supplemented by more units as the site expands. It includes open and cubicle washbasins, washing machine and dryer, dishwashing and laundry sinks, a mother and baby room, and facilities for disabled persons. Motorcaravan service point. Unusual swimming pool and paddling pool. Small children's playground.

**Charges** 2003

| | |
|---|---|
| Per unit incl. 1 or 2 persons | € 7.65 - € 18.30 |
| incl. 3 persons | € 9.20 - € 21.35 |
| electricity 6-16A | € 3.10 - € 4.60 |
| extra person over 10 yrs | € 2.30 - € 3.82 |
| dog | free - € 1.53 |

**Tel:** (0)5 56 65 13 17. Fax: (0)5 56 25 90 52. E-mail: legrandpre@wanadoo.fr. **Reservations:** Advisable for July and August. **Open** 1 April - 31 October.

**Directions:** Bazas is about 55 km. SE of Bordeaux, and 15 km. south of Langon. From Bazas centre take the D655 east towards Casteljaloux, and the site entrance is 1 km. on right (well signed).

---

## Haven Camping La Réserve

**4017** Gastés, 40160 Parentis-en-Born

La Resérve was featured in this guide until it was sold a few years ago. It has now been taken over by Haven Europe. A big site set in a pine wood, it has access to a large lake with a beach and small harbour (Atlantic beaches are nearby). The lake shelves very gradually so provides good bathing for children and good facilities for windsurfing and sailing; powered boats for water ski-ing are also permitted here. The 700 numbered pitches are of above average size (mostly 120 sq.m.), set on mainly flat ground and marked by stones in the ground. Most have electricity. Much organised entertainment and sports activities for children and adults in the Haven Europe tradition.

**Facilities:** Five toilet blocks, with en-suite facilities in one, include washbasins in cabins. Washing machines. When visited they were in need of care and maintenance - this is being addressed by the company. Well stocked supermarket. Restaurant and large bar where entertainment is organised all season. Heated swimming pool, another unheated outdoor pool (350 sq.m), with water slides and paddling pool (lifeguards on duty). Children's club for all ages. Two tennis courts (floodlit in the evening), minigolf, table tennis and volleyball. Boat hire (including powered ones), windsurfing courses and water ski-ing. TV room, general room and amusement machines. Fishing. Bicycle hire. **Off site:** The Atlantic beaches are nearby.

**Charges** 2002

| | |
|---|---|
| Per pitch incl. up to 6 persons | € 9.00 - € 30.00 |
| with electricity | € 10.00 - € 35.00 |

**Tel:** (0)5 58 09 75 96. Fax: (0)5 58 09 78 71. **Reservations:** Accepted at any time for min. 4 days; no booking fee. Contact site or Haven Europe in the UK on 0870 242 7777 for information or reservation. **Open** 1 May - 28 September.

**Directions:** Turn west off D652 Gastes - Mimizan road 3 km. south of Gastes by camp sign.

---

# Camping du Domaine de la Rive

route de Bordeaux, 40600 Biscarosse

**4010**

Set in pine woods, La Rive has a superb beach-side loaction on Lac de Sanguient. It provides mostly level, numbered and clearly defined pitches of 100 sq.m. All have electricity connections (6A) and there is good shade. The swimming pool complex is wonderful, with various pools linked by water channels and bridges, the four-slide pool having a wide staircase to the top to speed up enjoyment. There is also a jacuzzi, paddling pool and two large, unusually shaped swimming pools, all surrounded by paved sunbathing areas and decorated with palm trees. An indoor pool is planned. The beach is excellent, shelving gently to provide safe bathing for all ages. There are windsurfers and small craft can be launched from the site's slip-way. This is a friendly site with a good mix of nationalities and lots of activities for the family, although it can be noisy at night in high season.

**Facilities:** Five modern, very good quality toilet blocks have washbasins in cabins and mainly British style toilets. Visitors with disabilities well catered for in three blocks. Baby baths. We found the facilities very clean. Motorcaravan service point. Well stocked shop with gas (15/5-15/9). Bar serving snacks and takeaway. Games room. Restaurant with reasonably priced family meals (1/6-15/9). Swimming pool complex supervised July/Aug (15/5-15/9). Play area. Two tennis courts. Bicycle hire. Basketball court, table tennis, boules, archery and football. Fishing. Water skiing. Watersports equipment hire. Tournaments in various sports arranged June-Aug. Discos and karaoke evenings organised outside bar with stage and tiered seating. Mini-club for children. Charcoal barbecues not permitted on pitches (central area available). Caravan storage. **Off site:** Riding 5 km, golf 10 km.

**Charges** 2002

| Per pitch incl. 2 persons, | |
|---|---|
| electricity | € 20.00 - € 30.00 |
| with water and drainage | € 23.00 - € 33.00 |
| extra person | € 3.40 - € 5.00 |
| child (3-10 yrs) | € 2.30 - €.50 |
| dog | € 2.10 - € 3.30 |
| local tax | € 0.50 |

**Tel:** 05 58 78 12 33. Fax: 05 58 78 12 92. E-mail: info@camping-de-la-rive.fr. **Reservations:** Advised for July/Aug; write or fax site. (deposit 100) **Open** 1 April - 30 September.

**Directions:** Take D652 from Sanguinet to Biscarrosse and site signed on the right in 6 km.

---

# Camping Les Ecureuils

Port Navarrosse, 40600 Biscarosse

**4015**

Les Ecureuils is a pretty site within 200 m. of Lake Sanguinet. A pleasant entrance, new reception area and well tended flower beds at the very attractive restaurant lead into this neat, well cared for site with its buildings in the style of Alpine chalets. With only 130 touring pitches it is quite small in comparison with many sites in the area. The level pitches are mostly shaded on sand or gravel ground. All are at least 100 sq.m. and have 10A electricity connections (long leads may be required). There are 40 mobile homes, 30 privately owned (these made very attractive with masses of flowers around them). This is a quiet, family oriented site, well maintained and reasonably priced, with night security.

**Facilities:** High quality toilet blocks have washbasins in cabins, and apart from one Turkish style toilet in each block, British type WCs. Restaurant and terrace overlooking the medium sized pool (l/5-30/9) and paddling pool. Takeaway where bread and milk also available. Games room with pool and video games. Children's play area. Minigolf, boules, volleyball, basketball and table tennis. Tennis (charged). Bicycle hire (the area is a maze of cycle tracks). Only gas barbecues are permitted. **Off site:** Supermarket 3 km. Lake 200 m. for all types of water sports.

**Charges** 2002

| Per unit incl. 1 or 2 persons | €15.10 - € 25.80 |
|---|---|
| extra adult | € 3.35 - € 4.45 |
| child (under 10 yrs) | € 3.05 - € 3.70 |
| electricity | € 3.35 |
| tent or car | € 2.30 |
| dog | € 3.80 |
| local tax (over 9 yrs) | € 0.50 |

**Tel:** 05 58 09 80 00. Fax: 05 58 09 81 21. E-mail: camping.les.ecureuils@biscarros.com. **Reservations:** Made with deposit ( 91,47) and fee ( 22,87); contact site. **Open** 15 April - 30 September.

**Directions:** Heading south on D652 Bordeaux - Biscarrosse road, bear right on D305 signed 'Navarrosse Port & Plage'. Take second right signed 'Port' and site is on right.

---

## Atlantic Coast
# Camping Municipal Lou Broustaricq
route de Langeot, 40460 Sanguinet

**4009M**

This is a good municipal site, if lacking a little in atmosphere, with some 555 individual pitches on flat ground in light woodland, partly shaded by high trees. Some pitches are now separated by newly planted shrubs and trees. Caravan pitches are 110 sq.m. with hardstanding (20 for motorcaravans), electricity and water, pitches for tents average 100 sq.m. A path of about 200 m. leads to the big lake (no cars this way, but access for cars with boats 2 km). A very reliable site, there is always a chance of finding space. There may be some aircraft noise at times from a nearby army base. The site is used by a British tour operator.

**Facilities:** Eight unisex toilet blocks, one new, modern and heated (not all open in winter) have washbasins in cabins and facilities for disabled people and babies. Washing machines. Commercial centre by the entrance with supermarket and other shops, snack bar and takeaway, mostly opening mid-June and a restaurant in July/Aug. Swimming pool complex with slide and extra pools (mid-May - mid-Sept, lifeguards in July/Aug). Two good tennis courts. Bicycle hire. Minigolf, table tennis, volleyball, basketball. Playgrounds. Area for barbecues. Entrance barrier (deposit for card).

**Charges** guide

| | |
|---|---|
| Per unit incl. 1 or 2 persons | € 8.54 - € 21.04 |
| extra person | € 2.44 |
| electricity (6A) | € 2.59 |

**Tel:** 05 58 82 74 82. Fax: 05 58 82 10 74. **Reservations:** Made for any length with deposit (25%) and fee ( 22,87). **Open** all year.

**Directions:** Turn to northwest off the D46 at campsite sign, 1 km. northeast of Sanguinet.

## Atlantic Coast
# Camping Lous Seurrots
Contis Plage, 40170 St-Julien-en-Born

**4007**

Lous Seurrots is only a short 300 metre walk from the beach and parts of the site have views across the estuary. There are 610 pitches, mainly in pine woods on sandy undulating ground. They are numbered but only roughly marked out, most have good shade and over 80% have electrical hook-ups. The site's pool complex is in a superb setting of palm trees and flower beds and the paved sunbathing areas have wonderful views out to the estuary and the sea. Used by tour operators. For all its size, Lous Seurrots is a family site with the emphasis on peace and tranquillity (no discos).

**Facilities:** Six well kept, modern toilet blocks include some washbasins in cabins. Baby rooms and good facilities for disabled people. Laundry and dishwashing sinks. Washing machines. Motorcaravan service point. Large shop (1/6-15/9). Bar, takeaway and restaurant (15/5-15/9). Swimming pool complex (15/5-30/9). Tennis, table tennis, archery, volleyball and minigolf. Canoeing. Bicycle hire. Fishing. Mini-club. Evening entertainment in high season in open-air auditorium. Only gas barbecues are permitted. **Off site:** Riding 3 km.

**Charges** 2002

| | | |
|---|---|---|
| Per unit incl. 2 adults | 15.00 - | 24.00 |
| extra person | 3.00 - | 5.00 |
| electricity (6A) | | 3.50 |

**Tel:** 05 58 42 85 82. Fax: 05 58 42 49 11. E-mail: info@lous-seurrots.com. **Reservations:** Made with deposit ( 46) and fee ( 18,29). **Open** 1 April - 30 September.

**Directions:** Turn off D652 on D41 (15 km. south of Mimizan) to Contis-Plage and site on left.

## Atlantic Coast
# Camping-Caravaning Sen Yan
Le Village Tropical, 40170 Mézos

**4011**

This exotic familysite is about 12 kilometres from the Atlantic coast in the Landes forest area and set just outside the village. There are 310 pitches marked with hedges, 190 with electricity (6A), and with ample water points. Some mobile homes and tour operator pitches are in a separate 'village'. The reception, bar and pool area is almost tropical with the luxuriant greenery of its banana trees, palm trees, tropical flowers and its straw sunshades.

**Facilities:** Three toilet blocks with good quality fittings have showers and washbasins in cabins and some British style WCs. The newest block has a section for babies, plus facilities for disabled people. Shop (from 15/6). Bar, restaurant and snacks (1/7-31/8). Swimming pools (1/6-30/9), one of which can be covered. Archery. Practice golf. Activities and evening entertainment including a disco twice a week in high season. Only gas barbecues are permitted. **Off site:** Fishing 500 m, riding 6 km.

**Charges** 2002

| | | |
|---|---|---|
| Per pitch incl. 2 persons | 11.90 - | 17.00 |
| with 5A electricity | 14.00 - | 20.00 |
| extra person | 2.90 - | 3.90 |
| twin axle caravan plus | | 15.25 |

**Tel:** 05 58 42 60 05. Fax: 05 58 42 64 56. E-mail: reception@sen-yan.com. **Reservations:** Made with deposit ( 84) and fee ( 26). **Open** 1 June - 15 September.

**Directions:** From N10 exit 14 (Onesse-Laharie), take D38 Bias/Mimizan road. After 13 km. turn south to Mézos from where site is signed.

## Atlantic Coast
## Camping Les Vignes

**4016** Route de la Plage du Cap de L'Homy, 40170 Lit-et-Mixe

Les Vignes is a large holiday site close to the Atlantic coast with 420 pitches, of which 240 are occupied by a mix of mobile homes, bungalows and tents, most of which are for rent. The 180 tourist pitches are relatively level on a sandy base, all serviced with electricity (10A) and water, some with waste water drains. The site's amenities, including a supermarket, restaurant and bar, are located at the entrance to the site. The rather stylish swimming pool complex includes a six lane water slide. A wide range of activities is provided and during July and August a great variety of entertainment options for both adults and children, some of which takes place in the new entertainment 'Big Top'.

**Facilities:** Four virtually identical sanitary units (not all open in low season) provide combined washbasin and shower cubicles, dishwashing and laundry sinks, washing machines and dryers, facilities for babies and disabled people. Large supermarket. Restaurant, bar and takeaway (all from mid-June). Swimming pool complex (1/6-15/9, large pool from 21/6). Tennis. Table tennis. Golf driving range. Minigolf. Volleyball, basketball. Pétanque. Kids' club and playground. Bicycle hire. **Off site:** Golf course, canoeing, kayaking, surfing, riding. Many cycle tracks.

**Charges** 2002

| | |
|---|---|
| Per pitch incl. 2 persons | € 12.00 - € 27.50 |
| water and electricity (mandatory) | € 2.50 - € 5.00 |
| extra person (over 5 yrs ) | € 4.00 - € 5.00 |
| child (under 5 yrs) | € 1.50 - € 3.00 |
| animal | € 3.00 |

**Tel:** (0)5 58 42 85 60. Fax: (0)5 58 42 74 36. E-mail: contact@les-vignes.com. **Reservations:** Advisable for high season, made with deposit and fee. **Open** 1 June - 15 September.

**Directions:** Lit-et-Mixe is 20 km. south of Mimizan. From Lit-et-Mixe take D652 south for 1 km., then turn west on D88 towards Cap de l'Homy for 1.5 km. where site entrance is on left.

**★★★★ Grand Confort**

**AIROTEL CAMPING CARAVANING**
Route de la plage du Cap de l'Homy
**40170 LIT-ET-MIXE**
Tél : 05 58 42 85 60  Fax : 05 58 42 74 36
www.les-vignes.com
E-mail : contact@les-vignes.com

Aquatic space with slides, lagoon and exotic gardens, Multisport ground, mini-golf, play area, game of bowls. July and August :managerial staff : sport and activities, Miniclub, evening parties, Television. Nearby : cycle track, surf, Canoeing kayaking and Horse riding.

Accommodation : canvas bungalows, caravans, Mobil-homes, chalets and Apartments "luxury"

Open from 01/06 to 15/09

## Atlantic Coast
## Camping Eurosol

**4006** route de la Plage, 40560 Vielle-St-Girons

The sandy beach 700 metres from Eurosol has supervised bathing in high season. The site also has its own swimming pool with paved sunbathing areas which are planted with palm trees giving quite a tropical feel. The site itself is on undulating ground amongst mature pine trees giving good shade and the pitches on the slopes are mainly only suitable for tents. The 417 pitches for touring units are numbered (although with nothing to separate them, there is little privacy) and 259 have electricity with 120 fully serviced (86 with mobile homes). A family site with entertainers who speak many languages, many games and tournaments are organised and a beach volleyball competition is held each evening in front of the bar.

**Facilities:** There are four main toilet blocks all refurbished to include washbasins in cabins. Two smaller blocks have facilities for babies and disabled people. Motorcaravan service point. Fridge rental. Well stocked shop (11/5-21/9). Bar, restaurant and takeaway (all 1/7-31/8). Raised deck area and a stage for live shows (mainly performed by the very versatile staff) arranged in July/Aug. and mainly finishing by midnight. Swimming pool (from 1/6). Tennis. Multisport court for basketball, handball and football. Charcoal barbecues are not permitted. **Off site:** Riding school opposite. Fishing 700 m.

**Charges** 2002

| | |
|---|---|
| Per unit incl. 1 or 2 persons | € 10.00 - € 19.50 |
| with electricity | € 11.50 - € 24.00 |
| with water and drainage | € 11.5 - € 26.00 |
| extra person over 4 years | € 4.00 - € 8.00 |
| dog | € 2.50 |
| local tax | € 0.42 |

**Tel:** 05 58 47 90 14. Fax: 05 58 47 76 74. E-mail: contact@camping-eurosol.com. **Reservations:** Made for min. 1 week with deposit (€ 92) and fee (€ 22,87). **Open** 11 May - 21 September.

**Directions:** Turn off D652 at St Girons on D42 towards St Girons-Plage. Site is on left before coming to beach (4.5 km).

## Yelloh Village La Paillotte

**4004** 40140 Azur

La Paillotte, in the Landes area of south-west France, is a site with a character of its own. The campsite buildings (reception, shop, restaurant, even sanitary blocks) are all Tahitian in style, circular and constructed from local woods with the typical straw roof (and layer of waterproof material underneath). Some are now being replaced but still in character. It lies right beside the Soustons lake, 1.5 km. from Azur village, and has its own sandy beach. This is particularly suitable for young children because the lake is shallow and slopes extremely gradually. For boating the site has a small private harbour where you can keep your own non-powered boat (of shallow draught). All 310 pitches at La Paillotte are marked, individual ones and are mostly shady with shrubs and trees planted. The 150 pitches for touring units vary in price according to size, position and whether they are equipped with electricity, water, etc. La Paillotte is an unusual site with its own atmosphere which appeals to many regular clients. Used by tour operators (45 pitches). Member 'Sites et Paysages' and 'Yelloh Village'.

**Facilities:** Circular rustic-style toilet blocks are rather different from the usual campsite amenities, but are modern and fully tiled. They include individual wash-basins, partly enclosed, some toilets and basins en-suite and separate 'mini' facilities for children. Outside washing-up sinks. Washing machines and dryers. Motorcaravan service points. Shop (1/6-6/9). Good restaurant with pleasant terrace overlooking the lake and bar (all 12/5-10/9). Takeaway (high season). New swimming pool complex (from 1/5, no bermuda style shorts). Sports, games and activities organised for children and adults. 'Mini-club' room, with 'mini' equipment. TV room, library and amuse-ment room with juke box .Fishing. Bicycle hire. Table tennis. Sailing, windsurfing (with lessons), rowing boats and pedaloes for hire. Torches useful. No dogs are accepted. **Off site:** Riding 5 km, golf 10 km. Atlantic beaches 10 km.

**Charges** 2002

| Per unit incl. 2 persons | € 15.00 - € 26.00 |
| --- | --- |
| with 6A electricity | € 15.00 - € 31.00 |
| with electricity and water | € 19.00 - € 33.00 |
| pitch by the lake | € 22.00 - € 40.00 |
| extra person (over 3 yrs) | € 3.50 - € 5.50 |
| local tax in July/Aug. (over 10 yrs) | € 0.34 |

**Tel:** 05 58 48 12 12. Fax: 05 58 48 10 73. E-mail: info@paillotte.com. **Reservations:** Advised for high season; made for Sat. to Sat. only 2/7- 27/8, with deposit ( € 38,11 per week) and fee ( € 25). **Open** April - September.

**Directions:** Coming from the north along N10, turn west on D150 at Magescq. From south go via Soustons. In Azur turn left before church (site signed).

---

## Sunêlia Le Col-Vert

**4005** Lac de Leon, 40560 Vielle-St-Girons

the travel service
TO BOOK
Ferry ✓
Pitch ✓
Accommodation ✓
01892 55 98 98

This extensive but natural site edges a nature reserve and stretches right along the Lac de Léon, a conservation area, for 1 km. on a narrow frontage. This makes it particularly suitable for those who want to practise water sports such as sailing and windsurfing. Bathing is also possible (although there are pools on site as well) as the lake bed shelves gently making it easy for children. The site has a supervised beach, sail-boarding courses are arranged and there are some boats and boards for hire. There are some 800 pitches in total, the 380 pitches for touring units being flat and covered by light pinewood, most with good shade. They are of around 100 sq.m, only partly separated and some 72 have water and electricity points. Much 'anima-tion' is organised in season: children's games, tournaments, etc. by day and dancing or shows in the evenings. Used by tour operators (80 pitches).

**Facilities:** The four toilet blocks include a very large one towards the far end of the site. Not all are open in low season. Cleaning can be variable and the hot water supply is not reliable. Mostly British WCs, washbasins in cabins. Dishwashing sinks (mainly cold water but with hot tap to draw from). Washing machines, dryer and dishwasher. Good facilities for disabled people. Motorcaravan services. Shops (15/5-15/9). Good bar/restaurant by the lake (open to all). Simple takeaway. Two heated pools (all season and supervised), one open air with whirl pool and a covered one, with sunbathing areas. Children's play-ground. TV room, table tennis, amusement machines. Sports area with tennis and volleyball. Fitness centre and sauna/solarium. Two jogging tracks. Safety deposit boxes. Note: An overall charge is made for the leisure activities but this excludes certain facilities, eg. riding, bicycle hire, sauna, tennis, minigolf. Fishing (lessons for children). Riding. Sailing school (15/6-15/9). Several areas for barbe-cues. **Off site:** Walking and cycle ways in the forest. Golf 10 km. Atlantic beaches 5 km.

**Charges** 2002

| Per unit incl. 2 persons | |
| --- | --- |
| acc to season, type and location | € 8.50 - €28.50 |
| extra person | € 2.00 - € 4.50 |
| child (3-7 yrs) | € 1.50 - € 3.50 |
| dog | € 1.00 - € 3.00 |
| electricity (3/10A) | € 3.35 - € 5.00 |
| local tax | € 0.41 |

**Tel:** 05 58 42 94 06. Fax: 05 58 42 91 88. E-mail: contact@colvert.com. **Reservations:** Any length with UK£42 deposit per week booked and £25 fee. **Open** Easter - 15 September.

**Directions:** Roads to lake and site lead off D652 St Girons - Léon road at Vielle-St-Girons (signed).

# Yelloh Village Camping Airotel Saint Martin

avenue de l'Océan, 40660 Moliets-Plage

A family site aimed mainly at couples and young families, Airotel St Martin is a welcome change to most of the sites in this area in that it has only a small number of mobile homes (77) compared to the number of touring pitches (583). First impressions are of a neat, tidy, well cared for site and the direct access to the beach is an added bonus. The pitches are mainly typically French in style with low hedges separating them plus some shade. There is also a 'free and easy' area under tall trees. Electric hook ups are 5-10A and a number of pitches also have water and drainage. Entertainment in high season is low key (with the emphasis on quiet nights). Daytime competitions and a 'mini-club' are organised. The occasional evening entertainment is well away from the pitches with no discos or karaoke. A Yelloh Village member.

**Facilities:** The six toilet blocks are of a high standard and very well maintained with washbasins in cabins, large showers, baby rooms and facilities for disabled customers. Motorcaravan service point. Washing machines and dryers. Fridge rental. Very good supermarket and various bars, restaurants and takeaways are all at the entrance, owned by the site and mostly open all season. Attractive new indoor pool, jacuzzi and sauna (charged for in July/Aug), open all season. Large outdoor pool area with pools, jacuzzi and paddling pool (mid June - mid Sept). Multi sports pitch. Small play area. Internet access. **Off site:** Tennis or golf 700 m. Riding 7 km. This is an excellent area for cycling.

**Charges** 2002

| Per unit incl. 1 or 2 persons | € 16.00 - € 24.50 |
|---|---|
| with electricity | € 18.00 - € 27.50 |
| family pitch - no electricity | € 18.00 - € 30.00 |
| with electricity | € 20.00 - € 33.00 |

**Tel:** 05 58 48 52 30. Fax: 05 58 48 50 73. E-mail: contact@camping-saint-martin.fr. **Reservations:** Contact site. **Open** Easter - 15 October.

**Directions:** From the N10 take D142 to Lèon, then D652 to Moliets-et-Mar. Follow signs to Moliets-Plage, site is well signed.

# Camping Yelloh Village Sylvamar

avenue de l'Océan, 40530 Labenne Océan

Camping Village Sylvamar is situated less than a kilometre from the long sandy beach of Labenne Ocean. The large, light and airy reception area with its internet access point is very welcoming. The 500 pitches (320 for touring units) are level, numbered and mostly separated by low hedges. All have electricity (10A), many also have water and waste water points and there is welcoming shade. The swimming pool complex is absolutely superb, set in a sunny location. There are pools of various sizes with a very large one for paddling. The four toboggans are very popular and there is a fast flowing channel that youngsters find very exciting, sailing down in the inflatable boats and rubber rings provided. There is ample room for sunbathing and all is overlooked by the bar/restaurant and its terrace. A Yelloh! Village member.

**Facilities:** Three modern toilet blocks with good quality fittings have washbasins in cabins, and facilities for babies and disabled visitors. Washing machines at each block. No shop on site but a large supermarket is only 500 m. Bar/restaurant (all season) sells bread and takeaway and has a comprehensive menu for adults and children. Play area for young children. Mini-club in July/Aug. with painting, games etc. Fitness centre (charged). Tennis (charged in July/Aug). Bicycle hire. Table tennis. Badminton. Library with comfortable seating. Extensive entertainment programme for all ages, incl. evening shows in the outdoor amphitheatre from folklore, cabaret, concerts to karaoke. Fridges hire. Barbecues are not permitted (communal ones provided).

**Charges** 2002

| Per unit incl. 1. 2 persons, electricity | € 12.00 - € 25.00 |
|---|---|
| extra person (over 7 yrs) | € 3.00 - € 6.00 |
| dog | free - € 4.00 |

**Tel:** (0)5 59 45 75 16. Fax: (0)5 59 45 46 39. E-mail: camping@sylvamar.fr. **Reservations:** Made with deposit ( € 124), fee ( € 30) and cancellation insurance ( € 16). **Open** 24 April - 28 September.

**Directions:** Labenne is on the N10. In Labenne, head west on D126 signed Labenne Océan and site is on right in 4 km.

# Camping Les Chênes

4002 Bois de Boulogne, 40100 Dax

Dax is not a place that springs at once to mind as a holiday town but, as well as being a 'spa', it has a comprehensive programme of events and shows during the summer season. Les Chênes is well established site, popular with the French, situated on the edge of town amongst park-land (also near the river) and close to the spa for the thermal treatments. The 183 touring pitches are of two types, some large and traditional with hedges, water and electricity connections, and others more informal, set amongst tall pines with electricity if required. This is a reliable, well run site, with a little of something for everyone, but probably most popular for adults taking the 'treatments'.

**Facilities:** Two very different toilet blocks, one new and very modern with heating, washbasins in cubicles, facilities for disabled people and good provision for babies and young children. The older block has been refurbished. Fully equipped laundry room. Ample laundry and dishwashing sinks. Shop also providing takeaway (31/3-27/10). Unusual and attractive swimming and paddling pools (28/4-15/9). Good play area. Large field for ball games, table tennis and boule pitch. Bicycle hire. Mini-club (July/Aug). Occasional evenings for adults with meals and dancing. Charcoal barbecues are not permitted. **Off site:** Restaurant opposite the site entrance. Fishing 100 m, riding and golf 300 m. Beaches 28 km.

**Charges** 2002

| | |
|---|---|
| Per pitch incl. 1 or 2 persons and electricity (5A) | € 12.50 - € 17.50 |
| extra person | € 4.00 |
| child (2-10 yrs) | € 2.00 |
| local tax (high season) | € 0.30 |

**Tel:** 05 58 90 05 53. Fax: 05 58 90 42 43. E-mail: camping-chenes@wanadoo.fr. **Reservations:** Made with deposit (€ 46) and fee (€ 7,62); contact site. **Open** 25 March - 2 November.

**Directions:** Site is west of town, south of the river, signed after main river bridge and at many junctions in town - Bois de Boulogne (1.5 km). In very wet weather the access road may flood (but not site).

Camping Les Chênes ★★★★

Hôtel de plein air du Bois de Boulogne
40100 DAX
Tel. 0033 558 90 05 53
Fax 0033 558 90 42 43

# Camping Les Pins du Soleil

4003 Départementale 459, 40990 St-Paul-lès-Dax

the travel service
TO BOOK
Ferry ✔
Pitch ✔
Accommodation ✔
01892 55 98 98

This site will appeal to families, particularly those with younger children, or those who prefer to be some way back from the coast within easy reach of shops, cultural activities, etc. and well placed for touring the area. Dax is a busy spa town with many attractions - Les Pins du Soleil is actually at St Paul lès Dax, some 3 km. from Dax itself. The site has 145 good sized pitches, 99 for touring units of which 59 have electricity and drainage. The site benefits from being developed in light woodland so there is a fair amount of shade from the many small trees. A range of excursions is possible by bus to St Sebastian, Lourdes, etc. English is spoken. The nearby Calicéo aquatic centre is recommended.

**Facilities:** Modern sanitary facilities include facilities for babies, disabled visitors and laundry. Small supermarket. Bar. Takeaway (from June). Attractive, medium sized pool with café (both 2/6-15/9). Children's playground and mini-club in high season. Volleyball, table tennis and bicycle hire. **Off site:** Fishing 1 km, riding 3 km. Bus to the thermal baths.

**Charges** 2002

| | |
|---|---|
| Per pitch incl. 2 persons | € 8.00 - € 16.00 |
| with electricity, water and drainage | € 15.00 - € 21.00 |
| extra person | € 6.00 |
| child (4-10 yrs) | € 3.50 |
| animal | € 1.50 |
| local tax | € 0.27 |

**Tel:** 05 58 91 37 91. Fax: 05 58 91 00 24. E-mail: pinsoleil@aol.com. **Reservations:** Made with deposit (€ 35) and fee (€ 6). **Open** 7 April - 27 October.

**Directions:** From the west on N124, avoid bypass and follow signs for Dax and St. Paul. Almost immediately turn right at roundabout on D459 and follow signs. Site is a little way along on left. It is also well

## Camping Le Vieux Port

Plage sud, 40660 Messanges

The area to the north of Bayonne is heavily forested and a number of very large campsites are attractively located close to the superb Atlantic beaches. Le Vieux Port is probably the largest and certainly one of the most impressive of these. Appealing particularly to families with teenagers, this lively site has no fewer than 1,406 open pitches of mixed size, most with electricity and some with water and drainage. Sprawling beneath the pines, the camping area is well shaded and pitches are generally of a good size, attractively grouped around the toilet blocks. At least a third of the site is taken up with mobile homes and there are a large number of tour operators here (30%). The heated pool complex is exceptional boasting no less than five outdoor pools and three large water slides. There is also a heated indoor pool. At the back of the site a path leads across the dunes to a superb beach. A little train also trundles to the beach on a fairly regular basis in high season. All in all, a lively site with a great deal to offer an active family.

**Facilities:** Nine well appointed toilet blocks are all of modern design and well maintained. Facilities for disabled people. Motorcaravan service point. Good shopping facilities, including a well stocked supermarket and various smaller shops. Several restaurants (including takeaway service) and bars (all open throughout the season). Large swimming pool complex (no bermuda shorts). Three tennis courts, two football pitches, a multi-sport pitch, minigolf etc. Bicycle hire. Well run and popular riding centre. Large animation team organise a wide range of activities in high season including frequent discos and karaoke evenings. Only communal barbecues are allowed.

**Charges** 2002

| | |
|---|---|
| Per unit incl. 2 persons | € 11.00 - € 26.00 |
| extra person over 10 yrs | € 2.50 - € 5.00 |
| child under 10 yrs | € 1.50 - € 3.00 |
| electricity (6/10A) | € 2.50 - € 6.00 |
| local tax (June-Sept) | € 0.42 |
| animal | € 1.25 - € 2.50 |

**Tel:** 05 58 48 22 00. Fax: 05 58 48 01 69. E-mail: levieuxport@wanadoo.fr. **Reservations:** Essential in high season. **Open** 1 April - 30 September.

**Directions:** Leave RN 10 at Magescq exit heading for Soustons. Pass through Soustons following signs for Vieux-Boucau. Bypass this town and site is clearly signed to the left at second roundabout.

HOLIDAYS CLUB — *Le Vieux Port* AIROTEL ★★★★ — Information and bookings — www.levieuxport.com — DIRECT ACCESS BEACH

MESSANGES — South atlantic coast — Tél. 00 33 5 58 48 22 00 — Fax 00 33 5 58 48 01 69

## Camping-Caravaning Lou P'tit Poun

110 avenue du Quartier Neuf, 40390 St Martin de Seignanx

The manicured grounds surrounding Lou P'tit Poun give it a well kept appearance, a theme carried out throughout this very pleasing site. It is only after arriving at the car park that you feel confident it is not a private estate. Beyond this point the site unfolds to reveal an abundance of thoughtfully positioned shrubs and trees. The avenues around the site are wide and the 168 pitches are spacious. All have electricity (6/10A), 30 are fully serviced and some are separated by low hedges. The jovial owners make their guests welcome and organise weekly entertainment for young and old in high season. The sandy beaches of the Basque coast are a ten minute drive. A Sites et Paysages member.

**Facilities:** Two unisex sanitary blocks, maintained to a high standard and kept clean, include washbasins in cabins, baby bath and provision for disabled people. Dishwashing sinks and laundry facilities with washing machine and dryer. Motorcaravan service point. Café, bread and bar (1/7-31/8). Swimming pool (1/6-15/9). Play area. Games room, TV. Half court tennis. Table tennis. Bicycle hire. Caravan storage. **Off site:** Fishing or riding 7 km, golf 10 km.

**Charges** 2002

| | |
|---|---|
| Per pitch incl. 1 or 2 persons | € 9.00 - € 20.00 |
| with 4A electricity | € 11.50 - € 23.50 |
| extra person | € 4.00 - € 5.50 |
| child (under 7 yrs) | € 2.00 - € 3.50 |

**Tel:** 05 59 56 55 79. Fax: 05 59 56 53 71. E-mail: ptitpoun@club-internet.fr. **Reservations:** Made with deposit and fee. **Open** 1 June - 15 September.

**Directions:** From A63 exit 6 join N117 towards Pau. Site signed at Leclerc supermarket. Continue on N117 for 5.5 km. and site is clearly signed on right.

## Atlantic Coast
# Camping de la Côte
40660 Messanges

A peaceful family site, surrounded by pine forests near the beaches of the Landes, has large, level pitches edged with newly planted trees and shrubs. A number of the 142 touring pitches are set among trees that provide shade, 118 have electricity connections (6/10A) and some also have water. The beach and the dunes are 20 minutes walk. M. and Mme. Moresmau are very proud of their site and do their utmost to maintain a quiet family atmosphere with customers who return year after year.

**Facilities:** Two modern toilet blocks built in the Landes style are of excellent quality and very well maintained. Facilities include washbasins in cabins, a baby room and provision for disabled people. Washing machines and dryer with sinks for laundry and dishes. Motorcaravan service point. Reception sells bread and milk, a few basic supplies and gas (1/7-31/8). Barbecues only permitted at designated areas. Games room, play area, football, volleyball, table tennis and boules. **Off site:** Fishing or riding within 1 km, bicycle hire 1.5 km, golf 2 km. Supermarket and the resort of Vieux-Boucau near.

**Charges 2002**

| | |
|---|---|
| Per unit incl. 2 persons | € 8.40 - €11.50 |
| extra person | € 2.30 - € 2.90 |
| child (under 7 yrs) | € 1.60 - € 2.10 |
| electricity (6/10A) | € 2.20 - € 3.90 |

**Tel:** 05 58 48 94 94. Fax: 05 58 48 94 44. E-mail: lacote@wanadoo.fr. **Reservations:** Advised and made with deposit ( € 45,73). **Open** 1 April - 30 September.

**Directions:** Site is signed off the D652, 1.5 km. north of Vieux-Boucau.

## Atlantic Coast
# Camping Airotel La Chêneraie
chemin Cazenave, 64100 Bayonne

La Chêneraie is only 8 km. from the coast at Anglet with its long sandy beach and large car park, but you would think you were much further away from all the hustle and bustle of the coast. The distant views of the Pyrénées from various points all add to the feeling of peace. The 210 pitches are arranged on neat grass, with most partially divided by trees and shrubs, so quite well shaded. Many have electricity connections, some with water and drainage. One area is very sloping but it has been terraced to give level pitches. Wooded walks lead to a small lake which can be used for inflatables or fishing (no swimming). A tour operator uses 20 pitches. English is spoken.

**Facilities:** The large, central sanitary block includes washbasins in cabins, with three smaller blocks around the site providing additional facilities. In high season these facilities may be under pressure and maintenance and cleaning could be variable. Dishwashing and laundry sinks. Washing machine and dryers, baby baths, and facilities for disabled people. Shop, restaurant with all day snacks and a takeaway (all main season). Medium sized swimming pool open June - end August (longer if the weather is good). Children's playground. Tennis courts (free outside July/Aug). TV room. Table tennis. **Off site:** Bicycle hire 5 km, riding 6 km, golf 7 km.

**Charges 2002**

| | |
|---|---|
| Per pitch | € 9.45 - € 11.43 |
| with water and electricity | € 10.67 - € 16.01 |
| person | € 3.66 - € 4.27 |
| child (under 10 yrs) | € 2.13 - € 2.74 |
| dog | € 2.29 |
| local tax (over 18s) | € 0.17 |

**Tel:** 05 59 55 01 31. Fax: 05 59 55 11 17. **Reservations:** Made for min. 1 week with deposit (€ 62) and fee (€ 15,24). **Open** Easter - 30 September (full services 1/6-15/9).

**Directions:** Site is 4 km. northeast of Bayonne just off main N117 road to Pau, signed at traffic lights. From new autoroute A63 take exit 6 marked 'Bayonne St Esprit'.

## Camping Le Pavillon Royal

**6406** avenue du Prince de Galles, 64210 Bidart

Le Pavillon Royal has an excellent situation on raised ground overlooking the sea, with good views along the coast to the south and to the north coast of Spain beyond. Beneath the site - and only a very short walk down - stretches a wide sandy beach. This is the Atlantic with its breakers and a central marked-out section of the beach is supervised by lifeguards (mid-June - 25 Sept). There is also a section with rocks and pools. If the sea is rough, the site has a large swimming pool and sunbathing area. The site is divided up into 303 marked, level pitches, many of a good size. Connected by asphalt roads, all have electricity and some are serviced with electricity, water and drainage. Much of the campsite is in full sun, although one area is shaded. Reservation in high season is advisable.

**Facilities:** The toilet blocks are of highest quality with mainly British style WCs, washbasins in cabins, sinks and baby baths and good units for disabled people, all thoroughly cleaned twice daily. Washing facilities are closed at night except for night units. Washing machines and dryers. Motorcaravan services. Well stocked shop (including gas). Restaurant with takeaway (all season). Swimming and paddling pools. Sauna. Children's playground. General room, TV room and games room with table tennis, also used for films. Fishing. Surf school. Dogs are not accepted. Barrier card with deposit. **Off site:** Bicycle hire 3 km, riding 1 km.

**Charges 2003**

| Per unit incl. 2 persons, | | |
|---|---|---|
| electricity and water | € 23.00 - | € 35.00 |
| tent pitch incl. 1 or 2 persons | € 17.00 - | € 27.00 |
| child (under 4 yrs) | € 6.00 - | € 6.50 |
| local tax | | € 0.50 |

**Tel:** 05 59 23 00 54. Fax: 05 59 23 44 47. E-mail: info@pavillon-royal.com. **Reservations:** Made for exact dates with deposit and fee. **Open** 15 May - 25 September.

**Directions:** Don't go into Bidart as the site is on the Biarritz side. From the north, keep on main N10 bypassing Biarritz, then turn sharp back right on D911 (last possible road leading to Biarritz). After 600 m. turn left at camp sign (easy to miss). From A63 autoroute take C4 exit.

## Camping Les Tamaris Plage

**6408** Quartier Acotz, 64500 Saint-Jean-de-Luz

This is a small, pleasant and well kept site. It is situated well outside the town but just across the road from a sandy beach with 79 numbered pitches, 45 with electricity, including some mobile homes and bungalows. They are of very good size and separated by hedges, on slightly sloping ground with some shade. It becomes full for nearly all July and August with families on long stays, so reservation then is advisable. No shop, bread daily across the road

**Facilities:** Single toilet block of superb quality and unusual design should be an ample provision. Washbasins and showers in private cabins, mainly British style WCs, dishwashing sinks, facilities for disabled people. Washing machine. Covered terrace with views of the sea. Adult TV room and children's room with TV and games. Playground. **Off site:** Fishing 30 m, bicycle hire, golf 4 km, riding 7 km.

**Charges 2002**

| Per unit (100 sq.m. pitch) incl. 2 persons | | |
|---|---|---|
| and electricity (5A) | € 21.00 - | € 27.50 |
| tent pitch (80 sq.m.) | | |
| incl. 2 persons | € 16.50 - | € 23.00 |
| extra person (over 2 yrs) | € 3.50 - | € 5.00 |

**Tel:** 05 59 26 55 90. Fax: 05 59 47 70 15. E-mail: tamaris1@clubinternet.fr. **Reservations:** Made with 20% deposit and fee (€ 18.30). **Open** 1 April - 30 September.

**Directions:** Proceed south on N10 and 1.5 km. after Guethary take first road on right (before access to the motorway and Carrefour centre commercial) and follow camp signs.

## Atlantic Coast
# Sunêlia Village Camping Bérrua
64210 Bidart

**6414**

the travel service
TO BOOK
Ferry ✓
Pitch ✓
Accommodation ✓
01892 55 98 98

Bérrua Village Camping, set only one kilometre from the sea, is an ideal location for visiting the beaches here in southwest France. A neat and tidy site, it has 274 level pitches (174 for touring units) set amongst trees. Most have electricity (6A) and some are fully serviced. The swimming pool is a little on the plain side but has sunbeds around for sunbathing and a paddling pool. There is some animation organised in high season for both adults and children, for example guided walks, dances, sporting competitions, bingo and karaoke. A member of the Sunêlia group.

**Facilities:** Toilet facilities are good (unisex) consisting of two blocks with washbasins in cabins, baby rooms, facilities for disabled visitors, washing machines and dishwashing sinks (cold water only). Shop (July/Aug). Bar/restaurant and takeaway (15/4-15/9). Swimming pool. Games room. Play area (3-10yrs only). Bicycle hire. Archery and boule. **Off site:** Fishing 1 km. Golf or riding 3 km.

**Charges** 2002

| Per unit incl. 2 persons | € 12.00 - € 21.00 |
| extra person | € 1.70 - € 4.70 |
| electricity (6A) | € 1.90 - € 3.50 |
| animal | free - € 2.70 |

**Tel:** 05 59 54 96 66. **Fax:** 05 59 54 78 30. **E-mail:** contact@berrua.com. **Reservations:** Contact site. **Open** 6 April - 5 October.

**Directions:** Site is east of Bidart on Route d'Arbonne. From autoroute exit 4 take N10 south towards St Jean de Luz and at first traffic lights turn left. Site is signed and is on right in 500 m.

## Atlantic Coast
# Camping Le Ruisseau
route d'Arbonne, 64210 Bidart

**6407**

the travel service
TO BOOK
Ferry ✓
Pitch ✓
Accommodation ✓
01892 55 98 98

This pleasant, busy site, just behind the coast, is about 2 km. from Bidart and 2.5 km. from a sandy beach. It has two swimming pools - one 1,100 sq.m. pool complex with slides on the main site and an indoor heated pool on the newer area opposite. There is also a little lake, where boating is possible, in the area at the bottom of the site. Pitches on the main site are individual, marked and of a good size, either on flat terraces or around the lake. The terrain is wooded so the great majority of them have some shade. There are 330 here with a further 110 on a second area where shade has developed and which has its own good toilet block. Electrical connections are available throughout. Animation is provided in the main season, with day-time sports and evening entertainment. The site is popular with tour operators and has its own mobile homes.

**Facilities:** Toilet facilities (unisex) in two main blocks and some extra smaller units have washbasins in cabins and are regularly refurbished and maintained. Washing machines. Shop. Large self-service restaurant with takeaway and separate bar with terraces, and TV. Outdoor swimming pools and indoor pool. Sauna and solarium. Large play area. Two tennis courts. Volleyball, table tennis. Fitness track. TV and games rooms. Minigolf. Fitness room. Bicycle hire. Surf board hire. **Off site:** Riding or golf 2 km.

**Charges** 2002

| Per unit incl. 2 persons | € 15.00 - € 23.00 |
| extra person | € 4.30 - € 5.35 |
| child (under 7) | € 2.15 - € 3.00 |
| electricity | € 2.90 - € 3.80 |

**Tel:** 05 59 41 94 50. **Fax:** 05 59 41 95 73. **E-mail:** francoise.dumont3@wanadoo.fr. **Reservations:** Made for exact dates with deposit, fee and cancellation insurance. **Open** 1 May - 15 September.

**Directions:** Site is east of Bidart on a minor road towards Arbonne. From autoroute take Biarritz exit, turn towards St Jean-de-Luz on N10, take first left at traffic lights and follow camp signs for 1.5 km. Travelling south on N10 the turn is the first after the autoroute No.4 entry point, at new roundabout. The next exit is the traffic lights as mentioned before.

## Atlantic Coast
# Camping Municipal Chibaou-Berria
64500 St Jean-de-Luz

**6421M**

The first impression of this large site beside the beach is one of neatness. From the entrance tarmac roads lead to spacious pitches which are divided by hedges with plenty of room for awnings. Pitches to the left hand side beyond reception are placed at different levels, whilst those to the right have a sea view. There are 221 pitches in all, all with electrical hook-ups. There is direct access to the beach for surfing and windsurfing. Nearby are discos, tennis courts and often Basque folk festivities or Corridas with Landes cows.

**Facilities:** Toilet facilities, spotlessly clean when visited, include some showers with washbasins and individual wash cabins. Toilets are a mix of British and Turkish style. Dishwashing sinks in open position. Laundry facilities including washing machines.

**Charges** 2002

| Per person | € 4.90 |
| child (under 10 yrs) | € 2.70 - € 2.80 |
| pitch | € 5.10 |
| electricity | € 2.70 |

**Tel:** 05 59 26 11 94. **Reservations:** Contact site. **Open** 1 June - 15 September.

**Directions:** From A63 (St Jean de Luz Nord) take N10 towards Bayonne. Take 2nd left signed Acotz Campings. Site signed in about 1 km (1st left at Carrefour has a low bridge). From north, 1.5 km after Geutherey on N10 turn right at supermarket.

## Camping du Col d'Ibardin

64122 Urrugne

This family owned site at the foot of the Basque Pyrénées is highly recommended. It is well run with emphasis on personal attention, the smiling Madame, her staff and family ensuring that all are made welcome and is attractively set in the middle of an oak wood. Behind the forecourt, with its brightly coloured shrubs and modern reception area, various roadways lead to the 193 pitches. These are individual, spacious and enjoy the benefit of the shade (if preferred a more open aspect can be found). There are electricity hook-ups (4/10A) and adequate water points. From this site you can enjoy the mountain scenery, be on the beach at Socoa within minutes or cross the border into Spain approximately 14 km. down the road. Used by tour operators (20 pitches).

**Facilities:** Two toilet blocks, one rebuilt to a high specification, are kept very clean. WC for disabled people. Dishwashing facilities in separate open areas. Laundry unit with washing machine and dryer. Motorcaravan service point. Small shop selling basic foodstuffs and gas, with orders taken for bread (1/5-15/9). Catering and takeaway service in July/Aug. Bar and occasional evening entertainment which includes Flamenco dancing. Swimming pool and paddling pool. Children's playground and club with adult supervision. Tennis courts, boules, table tennis, video games. Bicycle hire. **Off site:** Fishing 5 km, riding 2 km, golf 7 km. Large supermarket and shopping centre 5 km.

**Charges** 2002

| | |
|---|---|
| Per unit incl. 2 persons | € 12.00 - € 18.00 |
| extra adult | € 2.60 - € 4.00 |
| child (2-7 yrs) | € 1.55 - € 2.50 |
| electricity (4/10A) | € 2.75 - € 4.85 |
| animal | € 1.00 - € 1.60 |
| local tax (high season) | € 0.25 |

**Tel:** 05 59 54 31 21. Fax: 05 59 54 62 28. E-mail: info@col-ibardin.com. **Reservations:** Are accepted - contact site. **Open** 1 April - 30 September.

**Directions:** Leave A63 autoroute at St Jean-de-Luz sud, exit no. 2 and join the RN10 in the direction of Urrugne. Turn left at roundabout (signed Col d'Ibardin) on the D4 and site is on right after 5 km. Do not turn off to the Col itself, but carry on towards Ascain.

## Atlantic Coast
# Camping Municipal de Mosqueros
64270 Salies de Bearn

**6423M**

In scenic surroundings convenient for the A64, this 3 star municipal site is worthy of its grading and is attractively located in a parkland situation 1 km. from the pretty little town of Salies de Béarn. It has an immaculate appearance, welcoming wardens and very clean facilities. Tarmac roads lead from the entrance barrier (locked at night), past reception to spacious, numbered pitches. Most have electricity (10A), many have water taps and all are separated by tall shrubs and hedges giving privacy. Salies de Béarn, with its old houses overhanging the river and its thermal baths, is only minutes away.

**Facilities:** The fully equipped toilet block is in a central position and maintained to a high standard. Dishwashing and laundry area with sinks, washing machine, dryer and iron. TV and recreation room. Swimming pool. Tennis court adjacent. **Off site:** Golf and riding 2 km.

**Charges** 2002

| | |
|---|---|
| Per person | € 2.45 |
| child (1-7 yrs) | € 1.50 |
| caravan pitch | € 5.00 |
| tent pitch | € 2.50 |
| electricity | € 2.40 |
| local tax | € 0.28 |

**Tel:** 05 59 38 12 94. **Reservations:** Advisable for July/Aug. Contact site. **Open** 15 March - 15 October.

**Directions:** Site is well signed in the town and is on the D17 Bayonne road, west of the town.

## Atlantic Coast
# Europ Camping
Ascarat, 64220 St Jean-Pied-de-Port

**6401**

Europ Camping is a neat and orderly, family run site with wonderful views of the vine-covered closer hills and the distant high Pyrénées. Each of the 93 pitches is clearly marked and separated by shrubs and all have electricity (6A), water and drainage. The area is good for walking or mountain biking and there is rafting on a local river. The site is only 20 km. from the forest of Iraty with its lakes and ski-runs, and the Spanish border on the route de St Jacques-de-Compostelle, is 8 km.

**Facilities:** The central, modern and well appointed toilet block includes washbasins in cubicles and facilities for disabled visitors. Two washing machines, dryer. Laundry and dishwashing sinks outside, but under cover. Motorcaravan service point. Small shop. Bar/restaurant with takeaway. Swimming pool with children's pool and sauna. Play area. Volleyball and petanque. Barbecue area. **Off site:** St Jean-Pied-de-Port 2 km. Tennis near, fishing 200 m, bicycle hire 2 km, riding 10 km.

**Charges** 2002

| | |
|---|---|
| Per adult | € 5.40 |
| child (under 7 yrs) | € 2.70 |
| pitch and car | € 7.50 |
| electricity (6A) | € 3.80 |
| local tax | € 0.23 |

**Tel:** 05 59 37 12 78. Fax: 05 59 37 29 82. **Reservations:** Made in writing with 30% deposit and 21,34 fee. **Open** Easter - 30 September.

**Directions:** Site is 2 km. northwest of St Jean-Pied-de-Port in the hamlet of Ascarat and is signed from the D918 Bayonne road.

## Atlantic Coast
# Camping Les Gaves
64440 Laruns

**6404**

Des Gaves is a clean, small and well managed site, open all year, with very friendly owners and staff. It is set high in Pyrennean walking country on the route to Spain. Laruns is only 25 km. from the Spanish border. There are 101 pitches including 38 level touring pitches, most fully serviced, numbered and separated (the remainder are used for private or site rental). The river runs alongside the site (well fenced) and fishing is possible and the busy little tourist town of Laruns is only a short walk. Tourist information here will suggest many and varied things to do in the area.

**Facilities:** The toilet block is rather reminiscent of a school dormitory but can be heated in cool weather and has plenty of hot water and fairly modern fittings. Washbasins for ladies in curtained cubicles. Dishwashing and laundry sinks. Laundry room. No shop but the baker calls daily. Small bar with a large screen TV, pool and video games (July/Aug). Larger bar with three table tennis tables. Small play area. Boules. Volleyball. Fishing. Card operated barrier (€ 15,24 deposit). **Off site:** Bicycle hire 800 m.

**Charges** 2002

| | |
|---|---|
| Per pitch | € 5.64 - € 9.15 |
| person | € 2.90 - € 3.51 |
| child (under 10 yrs) | € 1.83 - € 2.29 |
| electricity 3-10A | € 2.44 - € 3.96 |
| local tax | € 0.15 |

**Tel:** 05 59 05 32 37. Fax: 05 59 05 47 14. **Reservations:** Advised for July/Aug. and winter sports season. **Open** all year.

**Directions:** Take N134 from Pau towards Olorons and branch left on D934 at Gan. Follow to Laruns and just after town, turn left following signs to site.

# Dordogne / Aveyron

Map 11

We have again rearranged the French départements and regions to give us what we believe the British think of as 'the Dordogne' and have lifted the following départements from these official French regions:

| Aquitaine | Midi-Pyrénées | Poitou-Charentes |
|---|---|---|
| Départements:<br>24 Dordogne<br>47 Lot et Garonne | Départements:<br>12 Aveyron, 46 Lot | Département:<br>16 Charente |

The history of the Dordogne goes back many thousands of years when man lived in the caves of the Périgord and left cave paintings at sites such as Les Eyzies and Lascaux. The ancient dukedom of Aquitaine was ruled by the English for 300 years following the marriage of Eleanor of Aquitaine to Henry Plantagenet, who became King of England in 1154. The fortified villages and castles of the area bear evidence of the resulting conflict between the French and English for control of Aquitaine, and today add charm and character to the countryside. Monpazier is the best surviving example of the bastides (fortified towns). It is a diverse region of mountains, vineyards, and fertile river valleys, rolling grasslands and dense forests. Within its boundaries are the beautiful valleys of the Dordogne and Vézère.

To the south of the cultivated fields and cliff-side villages beside the river Lot lie the higher, stony lands of the Quercy Causse and the rocky gorges of the Rivers Aveyron and Tarn. Centred around Millau, there are tortuous gorges and valleys, spectacular rivers, underground caves and grottes, and thickly forested mountains. This is the home of Roquefort cheese.

To the north west is the old province of Poitou, or Charente, heartland of the domains of Eleanor, Duchess of Aquitaine, where the river Charente was once a busy industrial waterway bringing armaments from Angoulême to the naval shipyards of Rochefort. Today it is Cognac beside the River Charente which springs to mind. Untouched by any recession 80% of the production is exported. The Remy Martin tastings are worth a visit.

Note: Reports are laid out by département in numerical order not by region.

## Cuisine of the region

*Cagouilles* – snails from Charentes
*Foie Gras* – specially prepared livers of geese and ducks, seasoned and stuffed with truffles
*Cassoulet* – a hearty stew of duck, sausages and beans
*Confit de Canard (d'oie)* – preserved duck meat (goose)
*Magret de canard* – duck breast fillets
*Confits* – (preserved goose and duck) are a key ingredient in a number of dishes
Fish and seafood – like carp stuffed with foie gras, mullet in red wine and besugo (sea bream)
*Chorizos* – spicy sausages
*Cèpes* – fine, delicate mushrooms; sometimes dried
*Chou farci* – stuffed cabbage, sometimes aux marrons (with chestnuts)
*Huile de noix* (walnut oil) – many magnificent walnut trees in the Dordogne area
*Mouclade* – mussels cooked in wine, egg yolks and cream, served with Pineau des Charentes

## Places of interest

*Agen* – rich agricultural area, famous for its prunes
*Angoulême* – Hill-top town surrouded by ramparts; cathedral, Renaissance château
*Cognac* – the most celebrated 'eau de vie' in the world, cellars, Valois Castle
*Cordes* – medieval walled hilltop village
*Monflanquin* – well preserved fortified village
*Rocamadour* – cliffside medieval pilgrimage site
*Saint Cirq-La Popie* – medieval village perched on a cliff
*Sarlat* – the Saturday market is wonderful (arrive by 9.30 to find a parking space!)

## Dordogne/Aveyron
# Camping Marmotel
12130 Saint Geniez d'Olt

**1215**

The road into Marmotel passes various industrial buildings and is a little off-putting - persevere, they are soon left behind. The campsite itself is a mixture of old and new. The old part provides many pitches with lots of shade and separated by hedges. The new area is sunny until the trees grow. These pitches each have a personal sanitary unit, with shower, WC, washbasin and dishwashing. New and very well designed, they are reasonably priced for such luxury. All pitches have electricity (10A). A lovely new restaurant with terrace overlooks the new heated swimming and paddling pools which have fountains, a toboggan and sun beds on either grass or the tiled surrounds. The bar/reception area is also new with comfortable seating and internet access.

**Facilities:** Good sanitary facilities include baby baths and facilities for disabled visitors. Washing machines. Bar/restaurant and takeaway (all season). Swimming pools. Fishing. Bicycle hire. Tennis. Small play area. Entertainment for all ages in July/Aug. including a disco under the bar, cinema screen, karaoke, dances and a mini club for 4-10 yr olds. **Off site:** Large supermarket 500 m. Riding 500 m. Bicycle tours and canoe trips on the Lot and rafting on the Tarn.

**Charges 2002**

| | |
|---|---|
| Per unit incl. 1 or 2 persons, 10A electricity | € 21.50 |
| with sanitary unit | € 24.50 |
| extra person | € 3.80 - € 4.50 |
| child under 3 yrs | € 2.30 |
| animal | € 1.00 |

**Tel:** 05 65 70 46 51. Fax: 05 65 47 41 38. E-mail: info@marmotel.com. **Reservations:** Made with deposit (€ 100) and fee (€ 15). **Open** 7 May - 21 September.

**Directions:** Heading south on autoroute A75 (free) take exit 40 and follow signs for St Geniez d'Olt. Site is at western end of village. Site is signed onto D19 to Prades d'Aubrac, then 500 m. on left.

## Dordogne/Aveyron
# Camping La Boissiere
route de la Cascade, 12130 Saint Geniez d'Olt

**1209**

With trout in the river and carp in the lakes, La Boissière is a fisherman's paradise. Situated on the banks of the River Lot, surrounded by wooded hills, walking, swimming, canoeing or cycling are alternative pursuits. Mature trees provide plenty of shade on the generous, partly hedged, grassy pitches, all of which have electricity connections (6A) and frequently placed water points. Reception is housed in an old, converted farmhouse. There is direct access through the site to the river, which is suitable for swimming and canoeing. The nearby old town of St Geniez d'Olt should satisfy all shopping needs, and day or longer fishing licences can be obtained there (the helpful site staff will advise).

**Facilities:** Two modern sanitary blocks offer all the necessary facilities at a high standard, including washbasins in cubicles, plus the novel luxury of 'litter flaps' for dry waste. Washing machine and dryer. Basic provisions are stocked (milk and bread in high season only). Bar with terrace. Large, heated swimming pool (no Bermuda style shorts) and paddling pool. Bouncy castle and children's playground. Entertainment is organised in July/Aug.

**Charges guide**

| | |
|---|---|
| Per unit incl. 2 adults | € 8.84 - € 14.94 |
| extra person | € 3.20 - € 4.73 |
| child (2-7 yrs) | € 1.98 - € 3.05 |
| electricity | € 3.05 |

**Tel:** 05 65 70 40 43. Fax: 05 65 47 56 39. **Reservations:** Contact site. **Open** 20 April - 30 September.

**Directions:** Site is off the D988 east of Saint Geniez d'Olt.

## Dordogne/Aveyron
# Camping du Rouergue
Avenue de Fondiès, 12200 Villefranche-de-Rouergue

**1212**

A spacious, well appointed and shady site in the Vallée de L'Aveyron, Camping du Rouergue is adjacent to the municipal sports facilities and run by the Rouergue Tourisme Service. The site has 98 grassy individual pitches of varying sizes, served by tarmac roads, and virtually all serviced with electricity (16A), water and waste water drain. There are reduced rates for campers at the municipal pool and shops and restaurants are within walking distance along the riverside footpath. Villefranche-de-Rouergue is one of the larger bastide towns of the region and is on the pilgrim route to Santiago de Compostela. The site is also ideally placed for exploring.

**Facilities:** The modern spacious sanitary unit includes mainly washbasins in cubicles, dishwashing and laundry sinks and facilities for babies and for disabled persons. With two identical sections to the block, only one is open during low season. Motorcaravan service point outside campsite entrance. TV room. Well equipped playground.

**Charges 2002**

| | |
|---|---|
| Per pitch incl. 2 persons | € 10.50 - € 13.50 |
| extra person (over 10 yrs) | € 2.30 |
| child (4-10 yrs) | € 1.50 |
| electricity | € 2.50 |

**Tel:** (0)5 65 45 16 24. Fax: (0)5 65 45 55 58. E-mail: infos@villefranche.com. **Reservations:** Advisable for high season, made with 20% deposit. Open 20 April - 30 September.

**Directions:** Villefranche de Rouergue is about midway between Cahors and Rodez. Site is 1 km. southwest of town on D47 towards Monteils, follow signs from D911 to campsite and 'stade'.

## Dordogne/Aveyron
## Camping Les Tours
12460 Saint Amans-des-Cots

**1204**

This is an impressive campsite set in beautiful countryside very close to the Truyère Gorges, Upper Lot valley and the Aubrac Plateau. Efficiently run, it is situated on the shores of the Lac de la Selves providing 250 pitches. Of around 100 sq.m. and with 5A electrical connections, some border the lake, the rest are terraced and hedged with views of the lake. About 100 pitches also have individual water points. The site has a spacious feel, enhanced by the thoughtfully planned terraced layout, and seemed to be in an excellent state of repair and very clean. The owner and his staff are friendly and helpful. Used by tour operators (75 pitches). There is some up and down walking to the facilities, especially from the upper terraces.

**Facilities:** Four good toilet blocks including two excellent new ones, one of an unusual round design, are fully equipped including individual washing cubicles and are more than adequate. Attractive central complex housing the amenities. Restaurant, bar. Swimming pools (650 and 40 sq.m.). Shop (with gas), Takeaway. Modern play area. Volleyball, tennis courts, football area and table tennis. Varied programme of daytime and evening activities, with mini-club, archery and tree climbing (all supervised). Lake activities include canoeing, pedaloes, windsurfing, water ski-ing and provision for launching small boats. Internet point. **Off site:** Riding and golf 8 km.

**Charges** 2002

| | |
|---|---|
| Per unit incl. 2 persons | € 24.00 |
| extra person | € 5.00 |
| child (under 7 yrs) | € 3.50 |
| electricity | € 3.00 |

**Tel:** 05 65 44 88 10. Fax: 05 65 44 83 07. E-mail: camping-les-tours@wanadoo.fr. **Reservations:** Made and are advisable for July/Aug. - write for details. **Open** 18 May - 8 September.

**Directions:** Take D34 from Entraygues-sur-Truyère to St Amans-des-Cots (14 km). In St Amans take the D97 to Colombez and then the D599 to Lac de la Selves (site is signed). Site is 5 km. from St Amans. Alternatively, if using autoroute A75, take St Flour exit and follow D921 south for 41 km. Go 1.5 km. past Lacalm and turn right on D34 signed St Amans-des-Cots. Follow signs for 23 km.

## Dordogne/Aveyron
## Camping Municipal du Lauradiol
12460 Campouriez

**1210M**

A strikingly neat and pretty little site, tucked into a wooded gorge in the Aveyron hills, Lauradiol is alongside the La Selves river (fishing possible), 500 m. from the Cambeyra barrage. The 34 pitches, 21 with electricity, are arranged on flat grass, neatly separated by trim hedges. Many are quite large, although those actually along the river bank are somewhat smaller. There is quite good shade from a variety of trees. Surprisingly for such a small site, there is even a swimming pool and a well kept tennis court - both free to campers. There is not much else by way of facilities, but there are several villages within 5 or 6 km. for restaurants, shopping, etc.

**Facilities:** The toilet block was recently refurbished and very clean when inspected. It includes washbasins in private cabins and a room for disabled visitors (WC, basin and shower). Swimming pool. Tennis

**Charges** 2002

| Per caravan incl. electricity | |
|---|---|
| with 1 or 2 persons | € 12.65 |
| 3 or 4 persons | € 14.18 |
| tent incl. 1 or 2 persons | € 9.60 |
| tent incl. 3 or 4 persons | € 11.13 |
| child under 5 yrs | free |

**Tel:** 05 65 44 53 95. **Reservations:** Advised for July/Aug. Write or phone La Mairie de Campouriez. Open 20 June - 10 September.

**Directions:** Site is between Entraygues sur Truyère and Campouriez on the D34 at the hamlet of Lauradiol, about 5 km. from Entraygues. Site entrance is by the river bridge at junction of D34 and D572.

## Camping Les Terrasses du Lac
route du Vibal, 12290 Pont-de-Salars

1205

At an altitude of some 2,000 ft. on the plateau of Le Lévézou, this outlying site enjoys attractive views over Lac de Pont de Salars. The site seems largely undiscovered by the British, perhaps as it is only open for a short season. A terraced site, it provides 180 good sized, level pitches with or without shade, all with electricity (130 for touring). There are good views over the lake which has direct access from the site at two places - one for pedestrians and swimmers, the other for cars and trailers for launching small boats. This site is well placed for excursions into the Gorges du Tarn, Caves du Roquefort and nearby historic towns and villages.

**Facilities:** Four toilet blocks of varying ages include some washbasins in private cabins, plus washing up areas under cover and laundry facilities. Fridge hire. Shop. Large bar/restaurant with a lively French ambience serving full meals in high season and snacks at other times, with takeaway (all1/7-31/8). Heated swimming pool (200 sq.m.) and children`s pool (1/6-30/9). Solarium. Children`s playground. Volleyball, pétanque, table tennis, billiards. Games and TV rooms. Entertainment and activities organised in high season. Barbecue area. **Off site:** Tennis 3 km.

**Charges** 2003

| Per pitch incl. 2 persons | € 11.00 - € 18.00 |
| --- | --- |
| extra person | € 3.30 - € 4.00 |
| child (2-7 yrs) | € 3.00 |
| electricity (6A) | € 3.30 - € 4.50 |
| local tax | € 0.15 |

**Tel:** 05 65 46 88 18. **Fax:** 05 65 46 85 38. **E-mail:** terrasses12@aol.com. **Reservations:** Made with deposit (€ 61) and fee (€ 15,24). **Open** 1 June - 30 September.

**Directions:** Using D911 Millau - Rodez road, turn north at Pont de Salars towards the lake on the D523. Follow camp signs. Ignore first site and continue following lake until Les Terraces (approx. 5-6 km).

In overhanging of the lake, discover an exceptional place for your relaxation and your escape.Chalets and Mobile homes to rent. A 200 m² heated swimming pool.
Special animations for the 20th anniversary.

### LES TERRASSES
#### DU LAC ★★★★

Route de Vibal 12 290 PONT DE SALARS
Tel : 0033 565 46 88 18
Fax : 0033 565 46 85 38
w w w . t e r r a s s e s . f r . s t
Email : TERRASSES12@aol.com

## Camping Soleil-Levant
Lac de Pareloup, 12290 Canet-de-Salars

1214

Soleil Levant has a superb lakeside beach right on the site, with shady grassy banks for picnicking. Very reasonably priced, this is a site for lovers of nature, peace and quiet. There are competitions and games for all ages in July and Aug, but at other times there is just the sound of the birds. The level pitches all have electricity (3-10A) and water. Many have some shade but the newer ones will have to wait for the trees to grow. There is a boat ramp so many kinds of water activities are possible. This is a good area for walking and biking.

**Facilities:** The toilet blocks include one very old one (due to be re-built), one good, refurbished one, and a new excellent one. Half the WCs are British style, the rest Turkish style. Showers are pre-set and most washbasins are in cubicles. There are superb facilities for disabled visitors and a baby room with bath, shower and child's WC. Dishwashing and laundry sinks with cold water, washing machines. No shop, bread at the bar July/Aug, plus gas. Bar with TV and video games. Takeaway in July and Aug. **Off site:** Watersports equipment hire 300 m. Riding 4 km.

**Charges** 2002

| Per unit incl. 2 persons, electricity | € 11.50 - € 16.00 |
| --- | --- |
| extra person | € 3.00 - € 3.80 |
| child (2-6 yrs) | free - € 2.50 |
| dog | € free - € 1.55 |

**Tel:** 05 65 46 03 65. **Fax:** 05 65 46 03 62. **E-mail:** contact@camping-le-soleil-levant.com. **Reservations:** Contact site. **Open** 1 April - 31 October.

**Directions:** From Rodez take N88 south, then D911 towards Millau. 2.5 km. after Pont de Salars turn south on D993 signed Salles Curan. Site is on left in approx. 7 km.

# Camping Club Les Genêts

Lac de Pareloup, 12410 Salles Curan

This family run site is on the shores of Lac de Pareloup and offers both family holiday and watersports facilities. The 162 pitches include 102 grassy, mostly individual pitches for touring units. These are in two areas, one on each side of the entrance lane, and are divided by hedges, shrubs and trees. Most have electricity (6A) and many also have water and waste water drain. The site slopes gently down to the beach and lake with facilities for all watersports including waterskiing. A full animation and activities programme is organised in high season, and there is much to see and do in this very attractive corner of Aveyron. Used by tour operators (40 pitches). A `Sites et Paysages' member.

**Facilities:** Two main sanitary units include washbasins in cubicles and a suite for disabled people. Refurbishment of the older unit is planned, whilst the other unit is new. Baby room. Dishwashing and laundry sinks. Laundry room. Very well stocked shop. Bar and restaurant. Snack bar serving pizzas and other snacks in main season. Swimming pool and spa pool (both 1/6-15/9; unsupervised). Children's playground. Minigolf, volleyball and boules. Bicycle hire. Red Indian style tee-pees. Hire of pedaloes, windsurfers and kayaks. Fishing licences available.

**Charges** 2002

| Per unit incl. 1 or 2 persons and 6A electricity | € 11.00 - € 24.00 |
|---|---|
| lakeside pitch | € 11.00 - € 32.00 |
| extra person over 7 yrs | € 3.00 - € 5.50 |
| child 2-7 yrs | free - € 5.50 |
| pet | € 3.00 - € 4.00 |

**Tel:** 05 65 46 35 34. Fax: 05 65 78 00 72. E-mail: contact@camping-les-genets.fr. **Reservations:** Advised for July/Aug. and made with deposit (€155) and fee (€29). **Open** 25 May - 15 September.

**Directions:** From Salles-Curan take D577 for about 4 km. and turn right into a narrow lane immediately after a sharp right hand bend. Site is signed at junction.

the travel service
TO BOOK

| | |
|---|---|
| Ferry | ✔ |
| Pitch | ✔ |
| Accommodation | ✗ |

01892 55 98 98

Les Rivages is a large site on the outskirts of the town. It is well organised and well situated, being close to the high limestone Causses and the dramatic gorges of the Tarn and Dourbie, the latter of which runs past the back of the site. Smaller pitches, used for tents and small units, abut a pleasant riverside space suitable for sunbathing, fishing or picnics. Most of the 314 pitches are large, 100 sq.m. or more, and well shaded. A newer part of the site (on the right as you enter) has less shade but pitches are larger. All pitches have electricity (6A), and 100 have water and drainage. The site offers a very wide range of sporting activities close to 30 in all (see facilities). Millau is a bustling and pleasant town. Don't miss the night markets, but don't eat before you get there - there are thousands of things to taste, many of them grilled or spit roasted. The gates are shut 10 pm.- 8 am, with night-watchman.

**Facilities:** Four well kept modern toilet blocks have all necessary facilities. A special block for children includes baby baths, small showers, children's toilets as well as ironing facilities. Shop for most essentials (20/5-15/9). Terrace restaurant and bar overlooking a good-sized main swimming pool and children's pool (from 10/5). Children's play area. Much evening entertainment, largely for children, along with child-minding and a mini-club. Tennis (indoor and outdoor). Squash (can be viewed from the bar). Table tennis. Floodlit petanque. Many river activities, walking, bird watching and fishing. **Off site:** Rafting and canoeing arranged. Bicycle hire 1 km, riding 10 km, golf 40 km. Hypermarket in Millau.

**Charges** 2002

| | |
|---|---|
| Per pitch incl. 2 persons | € 12.50 - € 19.50 |
| with electricity | € 14.50 - € 22.50 |
| with water and drainage | € 16.50 - € 24.50 |
| extra person (over 3 yrs) | € 3.00 - € 4.00 |
| pet | € 2.50 - € 3.00 |
| local tax (15/6-15/9) | € 0.30 |

**Tel:** 05 65 61 01 07. Fax: 05 65 59 03 56. E-mail: campinglesrivages@wanadoo.fr. **Reservations:** Advisable for Jul/Aug. with deposit (€ 61) and fee (€ 15,24). **Open** 1 May - 30 September.

**Directions:** From Millau, take D991 road south towards Nant. Site is about 400 m. on the right.

Airotel ★★★★
Les Rivages
camping · caravaning · mobil-home · tentes

GORGES DU TARN • MILLAU • AVEYRON
Avenue de l'Aigoual - 12100 MILLAU - France
Tél. 00 33 (0)5 65 61 01 07 • Fax 00 33 (0)5 65 59 03 56

www.campinglesrivages.com
e-mail : campinglesrivages@wanadoo.fr

## Camping-Caravaning de Peyrelade

**1200** route des Gorges du Tarn, 12640 Rivière-sur-Tarn

Situated at the foot of the Tarn gorges on the banks of the river, this attractive site is dominated by the ruins of the Château de Peyrelade. Bathing from the pebble beach is safe and the water is clean. The 130 touring pitches are terraced, level and shady with 6A electricity hook-ups (long leads may be required for riverside pitches) and nearby water points. The site is ideally placed for visiting the Tarn, Jonte and Dourbie gorges, and centres for rafting and canoeing are a short drive up the river. Other nearby attractions include the Caves of Aven Armand, the Chaos de Montpellier, Roquefort (of cheese fame) and the pleasant town of Millau. Many of the roads along and between the Gorges are breathtaking for passengers, but scary for drivers who don't like looking down!

**Facilities:** The two toilet blocks have been refurbished. Young children are catered for, also people with disabilities. Washing machines and dryer. Bar, restaurant, pizzeria and takeaway (all from 1/6). Paddling pool and attractively designed swimming pool (proper swimming trunks, no shorts). Good playground. Games room and mini-club. Fishing. **Off site:** Bicycle hire 100 m, riding 3 km. Facilities in the adjacent leisure centre can be booked at reception at reduced charges. Millau nearby with hypermarket, shops and night markets but note road to/from Millau can be jammed at peak hours.

**Charges** 2002

| Per unit incl. 2 persons | € 13.00 - € 18.00 |
|---|---|
| extra adult | € 3.00 - € 4.00 |
| child (under 5 yrs) | € 2.00 - € 2.50 |
| dog | € 1.50 |
| electricity (6A) | € 3.00 |
| local tax | € 0.15 |

**Tel:** 05 65 62 62 54. Fax: 05 65 62 65 61. E-mail: campingpeyrelade@wanadoo.fr. **Reservations:** Made with deposit (€ 70) and fee (€ 15,24). **Open** 15 May - 15 September.

**Directions:** Take autoroute A75 to Séverac. From N9 Séverac - Millau road, turn east from Aguessac on D907 (Gorges du Tarn signs). Site is 2 km. past Rivière sur Tarn on right - access is quite steep.

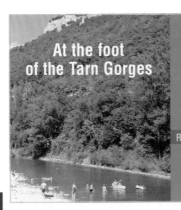

## Camping-Caravaning Les Peupliers

**1216** 12640 Rivière-sur-Tarn

Les Peupiers is a friendly, family site on the banks of the Tarn river. Most of the good-sized pitches have shade, and all have electricity, water and a waste water point. The river has a landing place for canoes, but no beach. In a lovely, sunny situation is the swimming pool with a paddling pool and sun beds, all protected by a beautifully clipped hedge and with a super view to the surrounding hills and the Château du Preylarde perched above the village. The site has its own canoes and qualified instructors will take visitors by minibus down-river for 10 or 20 km. to canoe back.

**Facilities:** Toilet facilities are large, light and airy give a good provision with washbasins in cubicles and mainly British style WCs. Good facilities for disabled visitors. Washing machines. Basics incl. bread kept in July/Aug. Bar with TV and video games. Snack bar and takeaway (1/5-30/9). Games organised in July/Aug. Fishing. Volleyball, football, badminton. Play area. Above reception is a balcony with fitness equipment. Weekly dances organised in July/Aug. **Off site:** Village with shops and restaurant 300 m.

**Charges** 2002

| Per pitch | € 3.00 - € 5.00 |
|---|---|
| person | € 4.00 - € 6.00 |
| child (under 5 yrs) | € 2.00 - € 3.00 |
| electricity (6A) | € 3.00 |

**Tel:** 05 65 59 85 17. Fax: 05 65 61 09 03. **Reservations:** Made with deposit (€ 125) and fee (€ 25). **Open** 1 May - 30 September.

**Directions:** Heading south from Clermont-Ferrand to Millau, the A75 turns into the N9. Then in about 14.5 km. at village of Aguessac, Rivière du Tarn and the Tarn Gorge are signed to the left at traffic lights. Site is about 4 km. at entrance of Rivière-sur-Tarn.

the **travel service**
TO BOOK

| Ferry | ✓ |
| Pitch | ✓ |
| Accommodation | ✗ |

01892 55 98 98

This pleasant terraced site has been imaginatively and tastefully developed by the Dupond family over a 25 year period. In particular, the magnificent carved features in the bar create a delightful ambience. True, the ground is hard in summer but reception staff supply robust nails if your awning pegs prove a problem. Most of the 200 pitches (all with electricity and water) are peaceful, generous in size and with views of the valley. The pools are bedecked by flowers and crowned by a large urn which dispenses water into the paddling pool. But it is the activity programme that is unique at Val de Cantobre, supervised by qualified instructors, some arranged by the owners and some at a fair distance from the site. Passive recreationists appreciate the scenery, especially Cantobre, a medieval village that clings to a cliff in view of the site. Nature lovers will be delighted to see the vultures wheeling in the Tarn gorge. Butterflies in profusion, orchids, huge edible snails, glow worms, beavers and the natterjack toad all live here. It is easy to see why - the place is magnificent. Although tour operators occupy around 40% of the pitches, the terrace design provides some peace and privacy, especially on the upper levels and a warm welcome awaits from the Dupond family.

**Facilities:** The fully equipped impressive toilet block is beautifully appointed with a huge indoor dishwashing area. Shop, although small, offers a wide variety of provisions; including many regional specialities (comparing well with local shops and markets). Attractive new bar, restaurant, pizzeria and takeaway facility. Three adjoining swimming pools. Around 15 types of activity including river rafting, white water canoeing, rock climbing or jumps from Millau's hill tops on twin seater steerable parachutes. All weather sports pitch. Fishing. Torch useful.

**Charges 2002**

| Per unit incl. 2 persons and 4A electricity | € 18.00 - € 26.00 |
| extra person (4 yrs and over) | € 3.00 - € 6.00 |
| dog | free - € 3.00 |

**Tel:** 05 65 58 43 00. Fax: 05 65 62 10 36. **Reservations:** Made for any length with 25% deposit, fee (€ 18,29) and optional cancellation insurance. **Open** 18 May - 15 September, with all facilities.

**Directions:** Site is 4 km. north of Nant, on D991 road to Millau. From Millau direction take D991 signed Gorge du Dourbie.

Camping Cheque

## Dordogne/Aveyron
# Camping La Grange de Monteillac
12310 Sévérac-l'Eglise

**1207**

La Grange de Monteillac is a modern, well equipped site in the beautiful, well preserved small village of Sévérac L'Église. A spacious site, it provides 95 individual pitches on gently sloping grass, separated by low wooden rails and attractive new planting. All pitches have access to electricity (6A), water and waste water connections. They include 21 chalets and tents for rent. The friendly owner and his welcoming staff will advise about the visits to a château evening with candlelight banquet, an angora farm, and a local pottery that are run weekly in main season. An evening stroll around this delightful village is a must, and Sévérac Le Château (21 km), Rodez (28 km), and the many other pretty towns and villages in the region should satisfy all shopping, sightseeing and cultural needs.

**Facilities:** The central sanitary building is modern, spacious and clean, with all washbasins in cubicles. Facilities for babies and disabled people. Dishwashing and laundry sinks. Washing machine and dryer. Shop at reception (1/7-31/8). Pool-side snack-bar serving pizzas, grills etc. in high season. Music or groups feature in the bar. Original swimming pool with toilets and changing rooms below and a further new pool. Large well equipped children's playground plus plenty of grassy space for ball games. Organised activities include children's club, bicycle hire and archery lessons. **Off site:** Fishing 2 km. Riding 9 km.

**Charges** 2003

| | |
|---|---|
| Per unit incl. 2 persons and electricity | € 20.00 |
| extra adult | € 3.50 |
| child (under 7 yrs) | € 2.80 |
| dog | € 1.30 |

**Tel:** 05 65 70 21 00. Fax: 05 65 70 21 01. E-mail: info@la-grange-de-monteillac.com. **Reservations:** Contact site. **Open** 1 May - 15 September.

**Directions:** Site is on the edge of Sévérac L'Église village, just off N88 Rodez - Sévérac Le Château road. From A75 use exit 42.

## Dordogne/Aveyron
# Camping Marco de Bignac
Lieudit 'Les Sablons', 16170 Bignac

**1606**

The small village of Bignac is set in peaceful countryside not too far from the N10 road, north of Angoulême. Since buying the campsite in 1994, the Marshall family have worked hard to improve this tranquil site which is arranged along one side of an attractive lake on a level, grassy meadow. The 89 pitches are marked at each corner by a tree so there is shade, and electricity (3/6A) is available. At the far end of the site is a hedged swimming pool and plenty of grassy space for ball games. The lake shores are home to ducks and the lake itself is used for fishing and small boats. The reception office is part of the owner's home and near here is a bar and snack bar with tables outside and views across the lake. This site is popular with British visitors and is a peaceful, relaxing location for couples or young families. There is no noisy entertainment and all the activities are free of charge.

**Facilities:** Two traditional French style toilet blocks have functional facilities all in cabins opening from the outside. Dishwashing or laundry sinks at either end of each block. Washing machine. Bar and snack bar (1/6-31/8; closed Mon. until high season). Essentials kept in the bar and baker calls daily (high season). Swimming pool (15/6-31/8, unsupervised). Football field, badminton, tennis, table tennis, pedaloes, minigolf and boule pitch (boules provided), all free. Play area. Pets corner. Fishing. Special evenings, outings and competitions organised in high season. A torch may be useful. **Off site:** Local markets. Riding 5 km.

**Charges** guide

| | |
|---|---|
| Per pitch incl. 2 persons | € 10.67 - € 14.48 |
| extra person | € 2.29 - € 3.81 |
| child (2-7 yrs) | free - € 2.29 |
| electricity 3-6A | € 2.29 - € 3.81 |

**Tel:** 05 45 21 78 41. Fax: 05 45 21 52 37. **Reservations:** Made with deposit. **Open** 15 May - 15 September.

**Directions:** From N10 south of Poitiers, 14 km. north of Angoulême, take D11 west for Vars and Basse. Go through Vars to Basse where turn right onto D117 to Bignac. Site is signed at several junctions and in village (Camping Bignac).

the travel service
TO BOOK

| Ferry | ✓ |
| Pitch | ✓ |
| Accommodation | ✓ |

01892 55 98 98

## The Alan Rogers' Travel Service

This unique service enables our readers to reserve their holidays as well as ferry crossings and comprehensive insurance cover at extremely competitive rates. The majority of participating sites are in France and we are able to offer a selection of some of the very best sites in this country.

Share our experience and let us help
to ensure that your holiday will be a complete success.

Alan Rogers Travel Service 01892 55 98 98 or www.alanrogers.com

the **travel service**
TO BOOK
Ferry ✔
Pitch ✔
Accommodation ✘
01892 55 98 98

A welcoming and friendly, family site in pretty, rolling Périgord Vert countryside, Gorges du Chambon is arranged around a restored Charente farmhouse and its outbuildings. It provides an attractive, spacious setting with 120 large, marked pitches with electrical connections. On gently sloping grass and enjoying extensive views over the countryside, the pitches are arranged in two circular groups with a sanitary block at the centre of each. The site also offers canoe hire on the river and a footpath has been created to the river. A converted barn provides an interesting gallery arrangement in the restaurant/bar. The site owners are very helpful and readers rate the site highly - 'a beautiful, well kept, spacious site'.

**Facilities:** Traditional style, unisex blocks include washbasins in cabins, facilities for disabled people, a baby bath, laundry sinks, washing machine and dryer, and good dishwashing rooms. Reception stocks some basic supplies and bread can be ordered. Bar and restaurant plus takeaway including pizzas (1/7-31/8). Swimming pool (18 x 7 m) and children's pool. Play area. Games room, TV and table tennis. Tennis, archery and minigolf. Bicycle and canoe hire. Animation in July/Aug. includes a children's club, youth disco and teenagers' corner. Dogs are not accepted. **Off site:** Fishing and riding within 200 m. Golf 4 km. Visits are organised to local producers and day trips (low season).

**Charges** 2002

| | |
|---|---|
| Per pitch | € 5.60 - € 6.70 |
| person | € 4.30 - € 5.30 |
| child (1-7 yrs) | € 1.95 - € 2.29 |
| vehicle | € 1.95 |
| electricity (6A) | € 3.20 |

**Tel:** 05 45 70 71 70. Fax: 05 45 70 80 02. E-mail: gorges.chambon@wanadoo.fr. **Reservations:** Necessary for July/Aug; contact site. **Open** 27 April - 14 September.

**Directions:** From N141 Angoulême - Limoges road at Rochefoucauld take D6 to Montbron village. Follow D6 in direction of Piegut-Pluviers and site is signed down country road past holiday complex.

## Dordogne/Aveyron
# Camping Municipal de Bourgines
1601M Ile de Bourgines, 16000 Angoulême

This municipal site on flat grassy terrain provides a convenient and satisfactory night halt close to the town and to the main routes to the southwest. With the municipal swimming pool complex next door, you might even stay an extra day or so. There are 160 neat, flat pitches, most separated by bushes and trees, 100 with electricity (5/15A) and 11 with drainage. There is good security (gates locked from 8 pm. in low season with parking outside). The river runs close by and is used for fishing, canoeing and boat trips.

**Facilities:** The two toilet blocks can be heated and are a satisfactory supply with mostly Turkish style WCs, washbasins in cubicles, free hot showers, chain operated in the newer block, with taps in the old block by reception. Motorcaravan service point (drive-over). Bread and basic supplies are available from reception. Playground and table tennis. **Off site:** Bicycle hire 100 m. riding or golf 5 km

**Charges** guide

| | |
|---|---|
| Per pitch incl. 2 adults | € 9.15 |
| extra person | € 1.52 - € 2.74 |
| electricity 5-15A | € 2.59 - € 4.12 |

**Tel:** 05 45 92 83 22. Fax: 05 45 95 91 76. E-mail: campingangouleme@wanadoo.fr. **Reservations:** Write to site or Office de Tourisme, 7B Rue du Chat, Place des Halles, 16007 Angoulême-Cedex. **Tel:** 05 45 95 16 84. **Open** 1 April - 30 September.

**Directions:** From N10 (town by-pass) west of Angoulême, turn towards centre of town at junction with N141 (Cognac road). At first roundabout turn left (site signed) and continue round inner ring. Turn right again where site is signed.

## Camping Municipal de Cognac

boulevard de Châtenay, route de Ste-Sévère, 16100 Cognac

**1605M**

If you are a lover of brandy this area is a must, with abundant vineyards and little roadside chalets offering tastings of Pineau (a Cognac based aperitif) and a vast range of Cognacs. This municipal site by the Charente river is convenient as a night stop or longer stay to visit the area, and for sleeping off the effects of the 'tastings' - you probably won't even notice the slight noise from the nearby road! The 160 large pitches, all with electricity (5/6A), are neatly laid out and separated by shrubs and trees. The famous Cognac Houses (Pineau, Hennessy, Hine, Martell, Remy Martin, etc.) and the Cognac Museum may be visited. There is public transport to the town centre (daily July/Aug; Saturdays only at other times).

**Facilities:** Two fairly modern toilet blocks have mixed British and Turkish style WCs, including children's toilets, washbasins in cabins, dishwashing and laundry sinks and a washing machine. Cleaning can be variable. Motorcaravan services. Small swimming pool on site (municipal pool nearby). Snack bar and entertainment (15/6-15/9). Fishing. Volleyball. Table tennis. Children's play area on grass. **Off site:** Riverside walks. Restaurants, bars and shops in the town (2.3 km). Bicycle hire 2 km, riding 6 km, golf 5 km.

**Charges** 2002

| | |
|---|---|
| Per pitch incl. 2 persons | € 9.91 - € 12.20 |
| extra person | € 2.74 |
| child (0-7 yrs) | € 1.83 |

**Tel:** 05 45 32 13 32. Fax: 05 45 36 55 29.
**Reservations:** Advised in high season. Write for more information to Office de Tourisme de Cognac, 16 Rue du 14 Juillet, 16100 Cognac. Tel: 05 45 82 10 71. Fax: 05 45 82 34 47. **Open** 1 May - 15 October.

**Directions:** Site is signed from N141 Saintes - Angoulême road following signs for town centre. It is to the north of the town beside the river on the D24 to Boutiers and Ste-Sévère.

## VISIT THE 'PAYS DU COGNAC'

On the banks of the Charente, just a few hundred metres from the prestigious Cognac Houses

Open 1 May - 15 October, in very attractive surroundings - 160 pitches, perfectly equipped, (snack - shop - swimming pool - volley-ball - entertainment, etc) - 5 mobile homes to rent
And only a few kilometres from the Gulf of Cognac at SAINT-BRICE, the Riding Centre at CHERVES-RICHEMONT, the Tennis Centre at SAINT-BRICE

we suggest **Camping de COGNAC** ★★★

*For information and reservations contact:*
Office de Tourisme, 16 rue du XIV Juillet, 16100 COGNAC.
Tel: 0033 545.82.10.71 - Fax: 0033 545.82.34.47
or Communauté de Communes de COGNAC, 16108 COGNAC-Cedex.
Tel: 0033 545.36.55.36. Fax: 0033 545.36.55.29

## Camping Municipal Le Champion

16230 Mansle

**1603M**

Le Champion is a convenient stop-over from the N10 or a good base to explore the northern Charente area. Beside the Charente river, the site has a cool, relaxing atmosphere created by its attractive location. The site, with 120 average size, separated pitches, is mostly open with little shade. All pitches have electricity (16A) and water points. Two privately owned restaurants are at the site entrance. One is attractively canopied and has 'al fresco' facilities and snack bar priced food. Information on opportunities for cycling, walking, canoeing or fishing is available from the local Syndicate d'Initiative (500 m). There is some road noise from the N10.

**Facilities:** The main modern sanitary block is well maintained and provides some washbasins in cabins and facilities for disabled people. Dishwashing and laundry areas and a small washing machine. An additional smaller, older block in the tenting area at the rear of the site. Motorcaravan service point at entrance. Minigolf. **Off site:** Town and shops 200 m. Swimming pool in town (discount for campers), recreational area next to the site.

**Charges** guide

| | |
|---|---|
| Per pitch | € 2.44 |
| adult | € 1.83 |
| child (under 7 yrs) | € 0.91 |
| caravan or tent | € 1.68 |
| vehicle | € 1.68 |
| electricity | € 2.44 |
| motorcaravan incl. 2 persons | € 9.15 |

**Tel:** 05 45 20 31 41. Fax: 05 45 22 86 30.
**Reservations:** Bookings accepted without deposit, although not usually necessary. **Open** 15 May - 15 September.

**Directions:** Site is well signed off the N10 (in the town of Mansle), 30 km. north of Angoulême.

# Camping de L'Etang Bleu
24340 Vieux-Mareuil

Set halfway between the historic towns of Perigueux and Angoulême, this tranquil countryside site in a mature woodland setting has recently been acquired by enthusiastic British owners Mark and Jo Finch. The site has 169 pitches, with 108 available to touring units. The remainder are taken up by two small tour operators and site owned mobile homes and ready erected tents for rent. The pitches are of a good size, flat and grassy, with mature hedging and trees providing privacy and plenty of shade. All pitches have water and 90 have electricity (10/16A). At the bottom of the site is a fishing lake stocked with carp (no permit required), and various woodland walks start from the campsite grounds. The bright and cheerful 'bistro bar' provides good value food and drinks, and becomes a focal point for evening socialising on site. This site is ideal for couples or families with young children who are looking for a quiet and relaxing holiday away from the hustle and bustle of the busiest tourist areas, but still within reach of some of the area's major towns.

**Facilities:** Two old-fashioned but scrupulously clean and well maintained toilet blocks provide mostly British style toilets, washbasins (some in cubicles), pre-set pushbutton showers, laundry and dishwashing sinks. Two washing machines, dryer, ironing board and baby room planned for 2003. Small playground with paddling pool. Swimming pool (20m x 10m) with sun terrace and loungers. Pleasant bar and terrace with 'bistro' food (all season), Takeaway. Small shop (items not stocked can be ordered on request). Table tennis, boules. Canoe and bicycle hire. Various entertainments, sporting activities and excursions organised in high season. (Floodlit tennis court, minigolf and adventure type playground are planned for summer 2003). **Off site:** Restaurant - Auberge de L'Etang Bleu - adjacent to campsite, small supermarket, post office etc. in Mareuil (7 km).

**Charges** 2003
Not yet decided - contact site

**Tel:** 05 53 60 92 70. Fax: 05 53 56 66 66.
**Reservations:** Advisable for high season. **Open** 1 April - 30 September.

**Directions:** From Angoulême take D939 south, from Perigueux take D939 north. From either direction after about 45 km. the village of Vieux Mareuil is signed on north side of the road. Turn here on D93, and follow narrow road through the village. Just after leaving village site is signed on right, just past Auberge de L'Etang Bleu. Follow signs down long gravel drive to site entrance. Note: American-style motorhomes and larger caravans may find it easier to access site by taking the D708 Mareuil - Nontron road, and turning south on the D93, avoiding the narrow access roads in Vieux Mareuil village.

*L'Etang Bleu* Dordogne

Tel : 0033 553 609 270
Fax : 0033 553 566 666
www.letangbleu.com

A warm welcome
All the usual facilities of a high quality campsite
Discover the hidden jewel of the Dordogne.

# Castel Camping Château Le Verdoyer

Champs Romain, 24470 St-Pardoux

2401

travel
service
'O BOOK
rry ✔
tch ✔
ccommodation ✔
1892 55 98 98

Le Verdoyer is a Dutch, family- owned site developed in the park of a restored château. We particularly like this site for its beautiful buildings and lovely surroundings. It is situated in this lesser known area of the Dordogne sometimes referred to as the Périgord Vert, with its green forests and small lakes. The 37 acre estate has two such lakes, one in front of the Château for fishing and one accessed by a footpath, with sandy beach and safe swimming area where canoeing and windsurfing for beginners are also possible. There are 150 marked, level, terraced pitches (some a little rocky). Mostly of a good size (100-150 sq.m), all have electricity (5/10A), with a choice of wooded area or open field, where hedges have been planted and have grown well; 120 are 'confort' pitches with more planned. There is a swimming pool complex and in high season activities are organised for children (5-13 yrs) but there is definitely no disco! The courtyard area between reception and the bar is home to evening activities, and provides a pleasant place to enjoy drinks and relax. The Château itself has rooms to let and its excellent lakeside restaurant is also open to the public. Used by a Dutch tour operator (15 pitches).

**Facilities:** Recently completely renewed, three very well appointed toilet blocks include washbasins in cabins, facilities for disabled people and baby baths. Serviced launderette. Motorcaravan service point. Fridge rental. Multi-purpose shop with gas. Bar with snacks and takeaway facilities. Good value bistro serves meals in July/Aug. Restaurant open to public. Two pools (25 x 10 m. and 10 x 7 m; the smaller one can be covered in low season) and paddling pool. Children's play areas. All-weather tennis court. Volleyball, basketball and badminton. Table tennis. Minigolf. Bicycle hire (tennis and bicycles free in low season). Small library. **Off site:** Riding 3 km.

**Charges** guide

| | |
|---|---|
| Per unit incl. 2 persons | € 22.90 |
| extra adult | € 6.10 |
| child (2-7 yrs) | € 4.60 |
| full services | free - € 4.40 |
| without electricity | € 2.60 |
| dog | free - € 3.05 |

**Tel:** 05 53 56 94 64. Fax: 05 53 56 38 70. E-mail: chateau@verdoyer.fr. **Reservations:** Write to site. **Open** 1 May - 30 September.

**Directions:** Site is 2 km. from the Limoges (N21) - Chalus (D6bis-D85) - Nontron road, 20 km. south of Chalus and is well signed from the main road. Site is on the D96 about 4 km. north of village of Champs Romain.

# Camping Municipal Le Repaire

24800 Thiviers

2421M

This attractive and peaceful municipal site in the heart of the Périgord Vert was completely refurbished and thoughtfully redeveloped in 1995 and is maturing nicely. The 94 pitches are divided by shrubs and a variety of trees have been planted to provide some shade in parts. There is plenty of space for all units, some pitches being very large and most have access to electrical connections (6A). There are a few pitches in the woods.

**Facilities:** Two modern toilet blocks kept clean, provide washbasins in cabins, cubicles for disabled visitors, washing machines and drying facilities. One unit is shut in low season. No chemical disposal point. Reception area with small shop. Terrace bar and snack/takeaway service (all July/Aug). Swimming pool (unheated) and adjacent shallow pool. Small fishing lake. Children's playground. Tennis. Boules, petanque, table tennis, exercise track and volleyball. Bicycle hire. Barbecue area.

**Charges** 2002

| | |
|---|---|
| Per pitch | € 3.81 - € 5.34 |
| adult | € 3.05 - € 3.81 |
| child (2-12 yrs) | € 1.83 - € 2.39 |
| electricity | € 2.59 |

**Tel:** 05 53 52 69 75. Fax: 05 53 52 69 75. **Reservations:** Not normally necessary, but possible with a 25% deposit. **Open** 1 May - 30 September.

**Directions:** From N21 Limoges - Perigueux road, turn off at traffic lights in centre of Thiviers. Site is signed to left from a quite complex junction, and is about 2 km from the town on the D707 east towards Lanouaille.

## Dordogne/Aveyron
# Camping Les Tourterelles
24390 Tourtoirac

**2425**

This is a site with its own equestrian centre that will appeal to lovers of the countryside, in an area that is ideal for walking or horse riding. The adjacent riding stables with 30 horses is run by the owner's daughter Angélique. The horses have been selected to be ideal for the local terrain, and to be safe and dependable. There are 125 pitches in total, but the site has some chalets, bungalows and mobile homes which leaves around 87 grassy pitches for tourists. These are on several different levels most with good shade from mature trees, and all have electricity hook-ups (6A). In low season the site can organise tours to local walnut farms, dairies etc.

**Facilities:** Three good, fully equipped toilet blocks, one new provide a baby unit. Laundry. Bread can be ordered. Bar/restaurant serving good value meals, with takeaway. Freezer pack service. Swimming pool (20 x 10 m.) and paddling pool. Riding. Tennis, volleyball, badminton, table tennis. Animation programme in main season. **Off site:** Shop at Tourtoirac (1 km.), supermarket at Excideuil.

**Charges** guide

| | |
|---|---|
| Per adult | € 3.60 |
| child (under 9 yrs) | € 3.00 |
| pitch | € 8.60 - € 9.15 |
| electricity | € 3.35 |

**Tel:** 05 53 51 11 17. Fax: 05 53 50 53 44. E-mail: les-tourterelles@wanadoo.fr. **Reservations:** Advised for July/Aug. **Open** 30 April - 30 September

**Directions:** From Limoges take D704 to St Yrieux (70 km. south), Lanouaille and Cherveix-Cubas. Just after Cherveix-Cubas turn right in village on D5 to Tourtoirac. Turn right in village and fork left on D73 towards Coulaures; site is on left in 1 km.

## Dordogne/Aveyron
# Camping de Barnabé
rue des Bains, 24750 Perigeux

**2428**

A memorable site in a unique setting, Barnabé has a special ambience. A distinctive 1936 Art Deco style building houses the reception, bar, restaurant and games room, complete with an attractive terrace overlooking the River L'Isle. The bar has its own Wurlitzer juke box. This site has 56 pitches all for touring vans and with access to electricity (4/6A) in four areas, with 14 pitches in an annexe on the opposite side of the river. Pedestrian access between the two parts of the site is provided by an old fashioned, passenger operated ferry boat, which is a delightful way to cross the river. The entrance and access roads are a little narrow, and larger units will need to take great care. The ground may be rather firm for tent pegs.

**Facilities:** Six sanitary buildings around the site (one on the far side of the river). Not modern, but functional, simple and clean with spacious shower cubicles. Unisex facilities, with both British and Turkish style toilets (no paper). One heated block is open in winter. **Off site:** Périgeux town centre 2 km.

**Charges** 2002

| | |
|---|---|
| Per adult | € 2.85 |
| child (under 7 yrs) | € 1.70 |
| pitch | € 4.40 |
| electricity (4/6A) | € 2.30 |

**Tel:** 05 53 53 41 45. Fax: 05 53 54 16 62. **Reservations:** Contact site. **Open** all year.

**Directions:** From N2089 on outskirts of Boulazac, turn towards Périgeux at the 'Memoire' roundabout. Go under railway bridge, round a double bend (right hand lane) and turn right. Continue on to site signed to the right. We suggest continuing to the far end of Rue des Bains using the car park opposite the Barnabé entrance until you locate your pitch.

## Dordogne/Aveyron
# Camping Le Grand Dague
Atur, 24750 Périgueux

**2416**

Le Grand Dague is a good quality site on the outskirts of Périgueux. Having negotiated the narrow access road, the site is found to be very spacious, clean and attractive. There are 93 good sized, slightly sloping pitches, 66 of which are for touring units. All have electricity (6A). The site is approximately 6 km. from Périgueux and also close to hypermarkets and tennis. There are no tour operators. A 'Sites et Paysages' member.

**Facilities:** Excellent sanitary facilities in four centrally located, inter-linking units, one heated in colder months, provide mostly unisex facilities which include washbasins in cubicles, a baby room and facilities for disabled people. Small shop (15/5-30/9). Attractive restaurant, bar and takeaway (all from June). Swimming pool, slide and paddling pool (from early May). Football, volleyball, badminton, petanque, minigolf and table tennis. Fishing. Bicycle hire. Rally field. **Off site:** Riding 5 km, golf 10 km.

**Charges** 2002

| | |
|---|---|
| Per pitch | € 5.00 - € 7.50 |
| person | € 4.20 - € 5.75 |
| electricity (6A) | € 3.70 |

**Tel:** 05 53 04 21 01. Fax: 05 53 04 22 01. E-mail: info@legranddague.fr. **Reservations:** Advised for high season and made with deposit (€ 76,22) and fee (€ 15,24). **Open** Easter - 30 September.

**Directions:** Site is signed from N89 south of Périgueux. From centre of Périgueux take Brive road, then road to Atur. Site is well signed.

## Dordogne/Aveyron
# Camping La Tuilière
2400

St Rémy-sur-Lidoire, 24700 Montpon Ménestérol

La Tuilière is a tradional and spacious site, run by a family with lots of activities for children. With a small lake, 100 pitches are arranged on a gently sloping hillside. Most pitches are reasonably level with some shade and there are 75 with electricity connections (6/10A), although long leads may be needed. The entrance building houses a small reception. The small unfenced lake can be used for fishing and water games. This is a typical French site with very friendly owners (who encourage British rallies). St Rémy is in the western Dordogne (less crowded with tourists), not far from Ste Foy la Grande, and well positioned to visit the wine areas of St Emilion, Pomerol and Bergerac.

**Facilities:** Two modern toilet blocks are very clean and include some washbasins in cubicles. Baby room and unit for disabled visitors. Laundry facilities. Small shop and attractive bar/restaurant (all 1/7-31/8). Swimming pool and paddling pool. Jacuzzi. Good play area and tennis court. Bicycle hire. Archery, minigolf, table tennis and pool tables. Dances, tournaments and karaoke nights arranged in July/Aug. **Off site:** Supermarket 5 km. Riding 3 km.

**Charges** guide

| | |
|---|---|
| Per pitch | € 4.27 |
| person | € 3.05 |
| child (under 7 yrs) | € 1.83 |
| electricity (3-10A) | € 1.91 - € 3.05 |

**Tel:** 05 53 82 47 29. Fax: 05 53 82 47 29. E-mail: la.tuilliere@wanadoo.fr. **Reservations:** Made with € 10 deposit. **Open** 1 June - 15 September.

**Directions:** From the north on D708 Montpon-Ménestérol to St Foy-la-Grande road, site is 5 km. south of Montpon on the right. From south, site is 1.5 km. north of St Rémy on the D708 (on the left).

## Dordogne/Aveyron
# Camping La Rivière Fleurie
2430

Saint-Aulaye de Breuilh, 24230 Saint-Antoine de Breuilh

This is the St Aulaye on the Dordogne, not the one on the Dronne. It is situated on the north bank at the wider end of the river, where it rolls majestically towards Bordeaux. Close to the vineyards of Pomerol and St Emilion, it is not far from the extensive shopping of St Foy la Grande and Bergerac. The site is small in that it has only 60 pitches, but all are spacious, divided by shrubs and shade is steadily developing. There are no tour operators, but 8 pitches are used for cabins or mobile homes. We were impressed by the quiet, family-oriented ambience of this site, with its flavour of traditional French camping in a modern, safe environment.

**Facilities:** Sanitary facilities are plentiful and modern. Bar and terrace restaurant (open all season) serving a range of basic meals. Swimming pool (100 sq.m) and toddlers' pool. Football and volleyball. Table tennis. Weekly 'soirées', where the owners host an evening of French food and entertainment. Bicycle hire. Canoe trips arranged. **Off site:** Municipal tennis court adjacent (free to campers). Fishing 100 m. Riding 4 km. Bicycle hire 8 km.

**Charges** 2002

| | | |
|---|---|---|
| Per unit incl. 2 persons | | € 12.95 |
| extra person | € 2.30 - | € 3.80 |
| electricity | € 3.05 - | € 3.05 |

**Tel:** (0)5 53 24 82 80. Fax: (0)5 53 24 82 80. E-mail: info@la-riviere-fleurie.com. **Reservations:** Not normally required, but write to site to be sure for high season. **Open** 1 April - 30 September.

**Directions:** Travelling west along D936, take 2nd road signed to St Aulaye after about 10 km. (the first, after 6 km. at St Antoine, has bends). Follow road until reaching the river, and site is signed.

## Dordogne/Aveyron
# Camping Lestaubière
2407

Pont St Mamet, 24140 Douville

Just off the main N21 road near Pont St Mamet, mid-way between Bergerac and Perigueux, one thinks first of Camping Lestaubière as a useful transit site but in fact most people stay for a while. It takes 90 units, mostly on fairly flat, shaded wooded ground at the top of the site, with some on more sloping open meadow with views. Pitches are marked and all have electricity (4A) although long leads may be necessary. The swimming pool and small lake with diving platform and beach encourage longer stays. A general room with a bar is reached via a pleasant, shaded patio terrace under vines and maples. There are many British and Dutch visitors, but no tour operators. Good English is spoken by the Dutch owners

**Facilities:** Two toilet blocks include some washbasins in private cabins in the larger block. Baby baths and large family shower room. Ample dishwashing and laundry sinks. No facilities for disabled visitors. Small shop. Bar. Library. Swimming pool (unsupervised) and paddling pool. Good children's play equipment. Volleyball, boules and fishing. Occasional organised activities. **Off site:** Tennis near.

**Charges** 2002

| | |
|---|---|
| Per person | € 4.90 |
| child (under 7) | € 3.20 |
| pitch | € 5.50 |
| electricity (4A) | € 2.60 |

**Tel:** 05 53 82 98 15. Fax: 05 53 28 90 17. E-mail: lestaubiere@cs.com. **Reservations:** Made for exact dates (min. 1 week) without deposit to guarantee admission. **Open** 1 May - 1 October.

**Directions:** From N21 take exit for Pont St Mamet and site is 500 m. north of the village.

## Camping Le Paradis

**2406** St Léon-sur-Vézère, 24290 Montignac

Le Paradis is an exceptionally attractive riverside site, halfway between Les Eyzies and Montignac. Well placed for exploring the Dordogne and its prehistoric grottos and other sites, the site is very well kept and laid out with mature shrubs and bushes of different types. It has 200 individual pitches of good size on flat grass, divided by trees and shrubs (164 for touring units). All have electricity, water and drainage, and there are some special pitches for motorcaravans. Canoeing on the Vézère river starts from steps which give comfortable access to the riverside, adjacent to a small beach. The site welcomes a good quota of British and Dutch clients, many through a tour operator. Organised games, competitions and evening events are aimed at maintaining a true French flavour. English is spoken. This is a site of real quality, which we thoroughly recommend.

**Facilities:** Two unisex toilet blocks are of outstanding quality and fully equipped, although shower cubicles are small. They can be heated, have baby baths and toilets, extensive laundry facilities and even outside showers for those who have just had a swim or romp in the sand-pit! Well stocked shop (with gas). Restaurant with extensive choice of menu with good takeaway service. Very good pool complex heated in low season, with one deep pool (25 x 10 m), another shallower one (17 x 7 m), plus a paddling pool. Two tennis courts. Football, BMX track, volleyball, table tennis and pool activities. Fishing. Bicycle hire. Well designed children's playground. **Off site:** Riding 2 km. Various trips organised to surrounding area.

**Charges 2002**

| | |
|---|---|
| Per person | € 4.31 - € 6.17 |
| pitch | € 6.72 - € 9.60 |
| electricity (6A) | € 2.97 |
| local tax (1/7-31/8) | € 0.23 |

**Tel:** 05 53 50 72 64. Fax: 05 53 50 75 90. E-mail: le-paradis@perigord.com. **Reservations:** Made for any length with deposit (€ 79,27) and fee (€ 19,82). **Open** 1 April - 25 October.

**Directions:** Site is by the D706, 10 km. north of Les Eyzies near the village of St Léon-sur-Vézère, or south of Montignac (13 km).

## Camping Le Moulin du Bleufond

**2429** ave. Aristide Briand, 24290 Montignac

Built on flat ground around a 17th century mill, this converted and improved former municipal site has its own pool as well as adjacent town facilities for various sports. The 84 pitches are marked and divided by mature hedges, and almost all have electricity and some shade. Some are quite small, so it is best to ensure when booking that you ask for one of the larger ones (in excess of 100 sq.m). Owners of the very largest caravans or motorhomes may need to think again. Montignac is at the head of what is to become a World Heritage site - the Vezère valley houses some of the planet's most important prehistoric caves and grottoes, and the Lascaux complex is minutes away and, although the original cave is now closed to the public, the replica Lascaux II is nearby. A third major cave system was discovered earlier this year. The site is separated from the river by a reasonably quiet road, but there is a sizeable bank for fishing. This is an ideal base from which to visit a fascinating and beautiful part of the Perigord.

**Facilities:** Good quality, clean sanitary facilities are well cared for by the energetic new owners and can be heated. Small shop catering for bread and emergencies. Bar and snack bar (all season). Heated swimming pool (140 sq.m) and paddling pool. Games room with table football, pool and table tennis. Canoe trips and bicycle hire can be arranged at reception. Musical evenings weekly in high season. **Off site:** Shops and a range of interesting restaurants in the town.

**Charges 2003**

| | |
|---|---|
| Per pitch | € 3.50 - € 5.10 |
| adult | € 3.30 - € 4.26 |
| child (3-8 yrs) | € 2.13 - € 2.28 |
| electricity (-10A) | € 2.80 - € 3.00 |
| animal | € 1.52 |

**Tel:** (0)5 53 51 83 95. Fax: (0)5 53 51 19 92. E-mail: le.moulin.du.bleufond@wanadoo.fr. **Reservations:** Advised for July/Aug. **Open** 1 April - 15 October.

**Directions:** Travelling west along N89 from Brive, turn left after 22 km. on D704. Montignac is 9 km. further. Drive into the centre of the town and turn sharp right after the town bridge (allow for a wide sweep!) The site is 150 m. on the left.

## Dordogne/Aveyron
# Camping-Caravaning Saint Avit Loisirs
Le Bugue, 24260 Saint-Avit-de-Vialard

**2418**

the travel service
TO BOOK

| | |
|---|---|
| Ferry | ✔ |
| Pitch | ✔ |
| Accommodation | ✗ |

01892 55 98 98

Although St Avit Loisirs is set in the middle of rolling countryside, far from the hustle and bustle of the main tourist areas of the Dordogne, the facilities are first class, providing virtually everything you could possibly want without the need to leave the site. This makes it ideal for families with children of all ages. The site is divided into two sections. One smaller part is dedicated to chalets and mobile homes, whilst the main section of the site contains 199 flat and mainly grassy pitches, all a minimum of 100 sq.m and with electricity (6A), arranged in cul-de-sacs off a main access road. Tour operator tents and mobile homes (with lots of British visitors) occupy around half the pitches, leaving 99 for touring units. Three modern unisex toilet blocks provide high quality facilites, but could possibly become overstretched (particularly laundry and dishwashing sinks) in high season. The café (highly recommended), shop and bar open onto a large terrace with pergola and hanging baskets, which overlooks the excellent pool complex. In high season activities and entertainments are organised. The site is ideally situated for visits to Les Eyzies and Lascaux as well as many other places of interest in the Dordogne region. English is spoken.

**Facilities:** Modern toilet blocks include washbasins in cabins, full laundry facilities and baby changing areas. Well stocked shop, bar, restaurant, good-value cafeteria and takeaway are housed in a recently built, but traditional-style stone building. Outdoor swimming pool (200 sq.m), children's pool, water slide, 'crazy river' and heated indoor pool with jacuzzi and adjacent fitness room. Disco behind bar, soundproofed. Table tennis. Floodlit minigolf and boules area and dirt bike track. Good quality tennis court, volleyball and extensive play area. Canoe trips on the Dordogne, and other sporting activities organised. Good walks direct from the site. **Off site:** Sarlat and Perigeux within range for markets and hypermarkets.

**Charges** 2002

| | |
|---|---|
| Per pitch | € 5.50 - € 10.50 |
| with electricity | € 9.00 - € 14.00 |
| with water and drainage | € 11.50 - € 17.00 |
| adult or child over 4 yrs | € 3.50 - € 7.00 |
| child under 4 yrs | free |
| dog | € 2.00 - € 3.50 |
| local tax (over 9 yrs) | € 0.30 |

**Tel:** 05 53 02 64 00. Fax: 05 53 02 64 39. E-mail: contact@saint-avit-loisirs.com. **Reservations:** Made with deposit (€ 46 per week) and fee (€ 15). **Open** 1 April - 30 September.

**Directions:** Site is 6 km. north of Le Bugue. From D710 Le Bugue - Perigueux road, turn west on C201 (about 2.5 km. from Le Bugue), toward St Avit de Vialard. Follow road around and through hamlet of St Avit, bearing right -site is about 1.5 km. past here, on the right. Note: the road to St Avit is narrow and bumpy in places.

## Dordogne/Aveyron
# Camping Les Bo-Bains
24150 Badefoils-sur-Dordogne

**2424**

Well placed for exploring this rather wider section of the Dordogne, Les Bö-Bains is very well kept and is laid out with mature trees and neat pitches along a 700 m. stretch of the south bank. The 97 good-sized pitches are separated by hedges, shrubs and bushes of different types, on flat grass terraces accessed by tarmac roads. All pitches have electricity, with water taps and drainaway points between each pair. There are one or two extra large pitches for big motorhomes, and two with hardstanding. The riverside terrace is particularly pleasant, and perfect for anglers, though families with very young children may prefer to be in the next terrace up. River bathing is possible and a rock shelf makes access to the river more amenable, though further out the current can be quite strong. Canoeing on the Dordogne or Vézère can be arranged from reception and there are places to launch one's own small craft. The site welcomes a good quota of French and Dutch clients, but not many British as yet. There are no tour operators.

**Facilities:** The two main toilet blocks are of good quality with baby rooms and laundry facilities. Small shop. Restaurant with a choice of menu and comprehensive takeaway service. Swimming pool complex with a main pool (18 x 9 m), another shallower one (5 x 5 m), plus a slide and landing pool (14 x 7 m). Several small children's play areas. TV room. Tennis court, small football field, minigolf, boules, trampoline, volleyball, table tennis and pool activities. Games, competitions and evening events are organised by the site, who try to maintain a French flavour.

**Charges** 2002

| | |
|---|---|
| Per pitch incl. 2 persons and electricity (5A) | € 14.48 - € 26.68 |
| extra person over 4 yrs | € 3.05 - € 5.34 |

**Tel:** 05 53 73 52 52. Fax: 05 53 73 52 55.
**Reservations:** Made for any length with deposit.
**Open** 15 April - 30 September.

**Directions:** Site is on D29 between Lalinde and Badefols, 27 km. east of Bergerac, 35 km. west of Sarlat.

## Dordogne/Aveyron
# Camping Le Port de Limeuil

24480 Allés-sur-Dordogne

At the confluence of Dordogne and Vézère rivers, opposite the picturesque village of Limieul, this delightful family site has a peaceful and relaxed ambience. There are 90 marked, grassy, flat and numbered pitches, some very spacious and all with electricity (5A). The buildings are in traditional Périgourdine style and surrounded with flowers and shrubs - it is a very pretty site. A large open grassy space between the river bank and the main camping area adds to the feeling of space (there are unmarked pitches for tents and camper vans along the bank). This is an ideal location for visiting the west central part of the Dordogne département, and is recommended for long stays.

**Facilities:** The two toilet blocks are very well appointed. Friendly bar/restaurant with snacks and takeaway (all 25/5-5/9). Swimming pool with jacuzzi, paddling pool and children's slide (1/5-15/9). Badminton, football, boules and volleyball. Mountain bike hire. Canoe hire - launched from the site's own pebble beach.

**Charges 2002**

| | |
|---|---|
| Per pitch incl. 2 persons | € 18.30 |
| extra person | € 2.75 - € 3.80 |
| electricity (5A) | € 3.05 |

**Tel:** 05 53 63 29 76. Fax: 05 53 63 04 19. E-mail: didierbonvallet@aol.com. **Reservations:** Advised for mid July - end Aug. **Open** 1 May - 30 September.

**Directions:** Site is about 7 km south of Le Bugue. From D51/D31E Le Buisson to Le Bugue road turn west onto D51 towards Limeuil. Just before you cross the bridge into the village of Limeuil, turn left (site signed here), across another bridge. Site is about 100 m. along this road on the right.

## Dordogne/Aveyron
# Camping-Caravaning La Linotte

24260 Le Bugue

La Linotte is a well designed, family run site where the camping area is well separated (about 150 m. away) from the activities. There are stunning views of the surrounding countryside from the terrace and the excellent pool complex. From reception an access road takes you to the camping area, which has 98 pitches, 52 of which are for caravans and tents. The pitches are hedged, level, and on grass, with 6A electric hook-ups, some having good views across the valley. Out of season the site is very quiet and relaxed, with few facilities available, whilst during July and August it becomes more lively, with regular pétanque tournaments, canoeing and walking outings, dancing and pool evenings organised.

**Facilities:** A smart sanitary unit with a bright and cheerful interior provides a mix of British and Turkish style WCs and washbasins in cubicles. Facilities for babies and disabled people. Bar/restaurant with takeaway (1/7-30/8). Small shop and bread to order (1/7-30/8). Pool complex (15/5-15/9) with 200 sq.m. main pool, two slides, paddling pool (both heated), and jacuzzi. Small playground with trampolines. Volleyball, football and table tennis.

**Charges 2002**

| | | |
|---|---|---|
| Per pitch | € 3.96 - | € 6.86 |
| person | € 2.90 - | € 5.34 |
| electricity (6-10A) | € 2.44 - | € 3.81 |

**Tel:** 05 53 07 17 61. Fax: 05 53 54 16 96. E-mail: infos@campinglalinotte.com. **Reservations:** Made for July/August with deposit (€ 76.23) and fee (€ 15.24). **Open** 1 April - 30 September.

**Directions:** From Le Bugue follow signs for Perigueux along the D710. Just on outskirts of Le Bugue turn right on D32E where site is signed. After approx. 1.5 km. turn right (site signed) on to minor road for a further 1 km. to site entrance on right.

## Dordogne/Aveyron
# Camping Le Mas
Sireuil, 24620 Les Eyzies

A quiet and unpretentious site, Le Mas is situated at the top of the hill above the Beune valley, in the popular Périgord Noir region with its many castles, grottoes and tourist towns. There are tantalising glimpses over the surrounding countryside from the site, which has a total of 136 pitches, with some mobile homes and chalets, leaving around 70 tourist pitches. The individual hedged and grassy pitches have good shade from mature trees and all have electric hook-ups (6A).

**Facilities:** Two functional unisex sanitary blocks, one slightly more modern than the other, include British and Turkish style WCs (with paper) and washbasins in cubicles. Dishwashing and laundry sinks. Shop, bar, snack bar and takeaway. Swimming pool (16 x 7 m) and paddling pool. All facilities fully open 15/5-15/9. Tennis, volleyball, pétanque and woodland fitness circuit. Activities for children in the main season. **Off site:** The adjacent Auberge du Mas (run by the site owner's sister) serves local specialities.

**Charges 2002**

| | | |
|---|---|---|
| Per pitch | | € 8.00 |
| person | € 3.70 - | € 4.50 |
| electricity | | € 2.80 |

**Tel:** 05 53 29 68 06. Fax: 05 53 31 12 73. E-mail: camping-le-mas@wanadoo.fr. **Reservations:** Made for min. of 1 week. **Open** 15 May - 15 September.

**Directions:** From D47 between Sarlat and Les Eyzies, turn on to C2 towards Sireuil village. Turn right after approx. 2 km. (site well signed here), to site in about 500 m. on the right.

# Castel Camping Le Moulin du Roch

route des Eyzies, D47, 24200 Sarlat

**2404**

the travel service TO BOOK

| | |
|---|---|
| Ferry | ✓ |
| Pitch | ✓ |
| Accommodation | ✓ |

01892 55 98 98

Set on natural sloping woodland in the grounds of a former water mill, the Dutreux family have ensured that Le Moulin du Roch is an attractive and well run family campsite. The site has 199 pitches, of which 104 are available for touring units. Pitches are mostly flat (some slope slightly) and grassy, and all have electricity (6A). Pitches on the upper levels have plenty of shade, whilst those on the lower level near the amenities and the fishing lake are more open. Entertainment and activities are organised from June to September, with something for everyone from craft workshops and sports tournaments to canoeing and caving for the more adventurous. An excellent multi-lingual children's club runs in July and August. Walking and cycle routes lead from the site through surrounding woodland.

**Facilities:** Three modern toilet blocks provide excellent facilities. Washing machines and dryers. Shop (18/05-07/09) stocks a good range of groceries and fresh food, and is very reasonably priced. Bar with terrace, takeaway and superb restaurant (all 18/05-07/09, closed Mondays). Newly built swimming pool with adjoining paddling pool (01/05-15/09). Fishing lake (carp and roach - no charge), tennis, table tennis, boules area, volleyball pitch, playground, discos twice weekly in high season. Dogs and other animals are not accepted. **Off site:** Medieval town of Sarlat with all amenities is 10 km. Bicycle hire and riding both 10 km, golf 15 km.

**Charges** 2002

| | |
|---|---|
| Per pitch incl. 2 persons | € 12.00 - € 22.00 |
| with electricity | € 15.00 - € 25.00 |
| with full services | € 17.00 - € 28.00 |
| extra person (over 9 yrs) | € 3.00 - € 6.00 |
| child (4-9 yrs) | free - € 2.50 |
| local tax | € 3.00 |

**Tel:** 05 53 59 20 27. **Fax:** 05 53 59 20 95. **E-mail:** moulin.du.roch@wanadoo.fr. **Reservations:** Essential from June - August, with deposit (20%) and fee (€ 19 in July/Aug). **Open** 1 May - 14 September.

**Directions:** Site is on south side of the D47, 10 km. from Sarlat and 11 km. from Les Eyzies.

---

# Sunêlia Le Moulinal

24540 Biron

**2410**

the travel service TO BOOK

| | |
|---|---|
| Ferry | ✓ |
| Pitch | ✓ |
| Accommodation | ✓ |

01892 55 98 98

A lakeside site with a wide range of activities, not only does Le Moulinal provide a good base for exploring the southern Dordogne, but it also has extensive wooded grounds to explore with picnic areas. The 280 grassy pitches (60 for touring units), all with electricity (3/6A), are level but of varying size. Some are a little cramped where access may be difficult for larger units. The five-acre lake has a sandy beach and is suitable for boating (canoes available), swimming and fishing. Ambitious, well organised animation is run as a series of programmes; the 'baby club' (ages 2-6) offering amongst other things, ball games, painting and pottery; there is a 'kid's club' for 6-12 year olds; the 'junior club' for 12-15, and a 'sport-club' for active young people or adults - pot-holing and rock climbing feature. A 'tourist club' and 'art club' add to the variety of programmes. The site is also popular with tour operators (80 pitches), although the owner has reduced their presence.

**Facilities:** Toilet facilities, built to harmonise with the surroundings, include British and Turkish style toilets (most in one block), some washbasins in cabins, and dishwashing sinks. Facilities for disabled people and babies. Laundry with washing machines and dryers. Motorcaravan service point. Excellent restaurant serving regional meals. Bar serving snacks and light meals (all season). Snack bar/takeaway on the other side of the lake. Large, heated swimming pool with jacuzzi and children's pool. Rustic children's play area on grass. Canoeing, potholing, tennis, diving and archery (small charges), volleyball, table tennis, fishing, dance, football and hockey (all free). Bicycle hire. Excursions organised on foot, on horseback, by car or bicycle. Full programme of evening entertainment in high season.

**Charges** 2002

| | |
|---|---|
| Per standard pitch incl. 2 persons | € 12.00 - € 29.00 |
| pitch near lake with electricity | € 17.00 - € 37.00 |
| with electricity, water and drainage | € 19.00 - € 39.00 |
| extra person (over 7 yrs) | € 3.00 - € 8.20 |
| child (2-7 yrs) | free - € 7.80 |
| animal | free - € 3.00 |
| local tax | € 0.16 |

**Tel:** 05 53 40 84 60. **Fax:** 05 53 40 81 49. **E-mail:** lemoulinal@perigord.com. **Reservations:** Made with deposit (€ 42) and for high season, fee (€ 34). **Open** 5 April - 14 September with all services.

**Directions:** Biron is 53 km. southeast of Bergerac. From Biron take D53/D150 south to Lacapelle Biron (4.5 km). Site is 1.5 km. west of the village beside the D255 to Villeréal.

## Dordogne/Aveyron
### Camping Les Hauts de Ratebout
Sainte Foy de Belvès, 24170 Belvès

**2405**

Situated southwest of Sarlat, there are some stunning views of the surrounding countryside from many of the 200 pitches at this pretty hilltop campsite. The terraced pitches vary in size (80-130 sq.m), with some more level than others. All have electricity (6A) and water. Housed in an older building, the restaurant/bar has plenty of atmosphere and is interestingly furnished. The swimming pool complex includes a 200 sq.m. unheated pool with slide, a shallow 100 sq.m. pool which is covered and heated as necessary, a fun pool with another slide and a small paddling pool. The site is used by tour operators (55 pitches). The walled town of Belvès is worth a visit.

**Facilities:** Four high standard toilet blocks offer the usual amenities including private washbasins and facilities for disabled people. Washing machines and dryers in each block. Small shop (with gas) and take-away. Restaurant, bars and terrace. Swimming pool complex (proper trunks). Gravel based adventure playground. General room with pool and football tables and TV. Volleyball, table tennis. Bicycle hire. Two tennis courts. Activities in season. **Off site:** Fishing 6 km. Riding 7 km. Golf 8 km.

**Charges** 2002

| Per unit incl. 2 adults, water and electricity | € 17.00 - € 26.00 |
|---|---|
| with drainage | € 17.00 - € 28.00 |
| extra person | € 3.50 - € 5.50 |
| child (3-7 yrs) | € 1.60 - € 4.00 |

**Tel:** 05 53 29 02 10. Fax: 05 53 29 08 28. E-mail: camping@hauts-ratebout.fr. **Reservations:** Made for a few days or more, with deposit and fee. **Open** 26 April - 6 September.

**Directions:** From Belvès, take D710 southwards for 2 km. then left on D54 at camp sign and follow through to site.

## Dordogne/Aveyron
### Camping-Caravaning Le Moulin de David
Gaugeac, 24540 Monpazier

**2408**

Owned and run by a French family who continually seek to improve it, this pleasant and attractive site is one for those who enjoy peace, away from the hustle and bustle of the main Dordogne attractions, yet sufficiently close for them to be accessible. Set in a 14 ha. wooded valley, it has 160 pitches split into two sections; 108 are for touring vans - 35 below the central reception complex in a shaded situation, and 73 above on partly terraced ground with varying degrees of shade. All pitches have electricity. Spacing is good and there is no crowding. The site has been attractively planted with a pleasing variety of shrubs and trees, and combined with the small stream that runs through the centre of the site they create a beautiful and tranquil setting. There is a delightful wooded walk via a long distance footpath (GR 36) to Château Biron (2-3 km), and the Bastide town of Monpazier is also within walking distance. A `Sites et Paysages' member.

**Facilities:** All three sanitary blocks are of a good standard, including washbasins in cabins, facilities for disabled visitors and babies in each. Adequate dishwashing and laundry sinks. Laundry room. Good shop. Bar/restaurant with shaded patio and take-away. Swimming pool and children's paddling pool, plus freshwater pool with waterslide. Play area. Boules, half-court tennis, table tennis, volleyball, basketball, trampolining and football area. Library. Bicycle hire. Events, games and canoe trips organised (1/7-31/8).

**Charges** 2002

| Per normal pitch | € 4.90 - € 9.00 |
|---|---|
| large pitch incl. water and drainage | € 7.85 - € 11.70 |
| person (over 2 yrs) | € 3.55 - € 6.20 |
| electricity (3/10A) | € 3.25 - € 5.50 |
| animal | € 1.30 - € 2.45 |
| local tax (over 13 yrs) | € 0.23 |

**Tel:** 05 53 22 65 25. Fax: 05 53 23 99 76. E-mail: courrier@moulin-de-david.com. **Reservations:** Advisable for Jul/Aug, with deposit (€ 61 per week reserved) and booking fee (€ 19) for stays between 29/06 and 24/08). **Open** 18 May - 7 September.

**Directions:** From Monpazier take the D2 Villeréal road. Take third turning left (after about 2 km), signed to Moulin de David and 'Gaugeac mairie'. Site is about 500 m. along this road on the left.

MOULIN DE DAVID ****
A good Campsite !

CAMPINGS SITES PAYSAGES

Web: moulin-de-david.com Mail: courrier@moulin-de-david.com
England: Kay SALE, 40 Lindale Mount, Wakefield, West Yorkshire WF2 0BH, Tel: 01924 781503

## Camping Les Périères

route Ste Nathalène, 24203 Sarlat

**2403**

Les Périères is a good quality small site in an attractive setting on the outskirts of the town of Sarlat. It has 100 pitches arranged on wide terraces around the semi-circle of a fairly steep valley, overlooking central leisure areas that include indoor and outdoor pools and tennis courts. The pitches are of a very good size, all equipped with electricity (6A), water and drainage. Attractive trees provide dappled shade in many areas. The site becomes full in high season when reservation is advisable, but a proportion of the site is not reserved, so you may find space if you arrive early. The site has a refreshingly spacious and open air, quite free from overcrowding, and is one of the most thoughtfully improved sites we have visited.

**Facilities:** The toilet blocks of varying styles and sizes should be quite sufficient, including wash-basins in cabins, facilities for disabled visitors, a good baby bathroom in one block and washing machines and dryers. Motorcaravan service point. Small shop. Pleasant bar. Outdoor terrace restaurant with takeaway (15/6-15/9). Swimming pool (no shorts), paddling pool and new indoor spa pool and sauna. Two tennis courts. Table tennis (indoors or out), football pitch and fitness track with exercise halts. **Off site:** Bicycle hire 1 km, fishing 5 km, riding or golf 7 km.

**Charges** 2002

| | |
|---|---|
| Per unit incl. 2 persons | € 18.00 - € 24.00 |
| with electricity | € 21.70 -€ 27.80 |
| extra person | € 5.80 |
| child (under 7 yrs) | € 3.60 |

**Tel:** 05 53 59 05 84. Fax: 05 53 28 57 51. E-mail: les-perieres@wanadoo.fr. **Reservations:** Advised for high season and made for min. 1 week with deposit (€ 100 p/week) and fee (€ 15). **Open** Easter - 30 September.

**Directions:** Site is east of the town on D47 Ste Nathalene road towards 'Sous-Préfecture' and Croix d'Alon.

Camping Les Périères

24200 SARLAT, DORDOGNE - PÉRIGORD

*The 4-star site in a natural amphitheatre of woods and meadows. A peaceful oasis in the heart of Black Périgord, yet only half a mile from the medieval town and gastronomic centre of Sarlat.*

**LARGE INDIVIDUAL PITCHES**
**EXCELLENT TOILET BLOCKS**
**SWIMMING POOLS, one covered and heated**
**SAUNA - TENNIS COURTS**
**VOLLEYBALL - TABLE TENNIS**
**LOUNGE BAR - SHOP - LIBRARY**

## Camping Les Grottes de Roffy

Sainte Nathalène, 24200 Sarlat

**2413**

A well organised site, some 5 km. east of Sarlat, Les Grottes de Roffy has 164 clearly marked pitches, some very large. Set on very well kept grass terraces, they have easy access and good views across an attractive valley. Some have plentiful shade, although others are more open, and all have electricity (6A). The reception, bar, restaurant and shop are located within converted farm buildings surrounding a semi-courtyard. We were very impressed with the shop, well stocked with a variety of goods and a tempting charcuterie section (prepared on site) with plenty of ideas for the barbecue. Adding to the musical talent of the site owners, a variety of music groups perform throughout the season. Conveniently located for Sarlat, this is a pleasant place to stay. It a good site for families. Used by tour operators (73 pitches).

**Facilities:** Two toilet blocks with modern facilities are more than adequate. Well stocked shop bar. Restaurant with imaginative and sensibly priced menu. Takeaway (all amenities from 6/5). Good swimming pool complex comprising two deep pools (one heated), a fountain, children's pool and heated jacuzzi. Concrete play space for roller skating. Children's play area. **Off site:** Fishing 2 km, bicycle hire 7 km, riding 10 km, golf 15 km.

**Charges** 2002

| | |
|---|---|
| Per pitch | € 6.50 - € 8.00 |
| with electricity | € 8.85 - € 11.00 |
| with full services | € 10.00 - € 12.50 |
| adult | € 5.00 - € 6.20 |
| child (2-7 yrs) | € 3.60 - € 4.40 |
| animal | € 1.80 |
| local tax (over 7 yrs) | € 0.25 |

**Tel:** 05 53 59 15 61. Fax: 05 53 31 09 11. E-mail: roffy@perigord.com. **Reservations:** Made with deposit. **Open** 1 May - 21 September.

**Directions:** Take D47 east from Sarlat to Ste Nathalène. Site is well signed just before the village.

## Dordogne/Aveyron

# Camping-Caravaning Aqua Viva

**2411**

route Sarlac-Souillac, Carsac-Aillac, 24200 Sarlat

This site is divided into two sections, separated by the access road. One side is very quiet and spacious with 186 pitches (some very large) and 32 chalets terraced in woodland. The other half contains pitches on flat grass. Canoe lessons and guided trips on the Dordogne are organised by the site, as are many other sporting activities. The site is ideally situated for visits to Rocamadour and Padirac, as well as the many places of interest in the Dordogne region. It is also close to Sarlat for markets and hypermarkets. The site is very popular with families, especially those with pre-teen and younger teenage children. English is spoken. There are no tour operators.

**Facilities:** Each part of the site has a very modern, very clean and heated toilet block, with facilities for disabled people, laundry and baby areas. Small shop and takeaway. Small restaurant. Bar and terrace with evening entertainment in season. Excellent, heated swimming pool and children's pool. Small lake (for fishing). Table tennis. Floodlit basketball and boules area. High quality minigolf. Children's tennis court and under 7s play park. Multi-sports area. Bicycle hire. **Off site:** Riding and golf 5 km.

**Charges** 2003

| | |
|---|---|
| Per pitch | € 4.20 - € 9.50 |
| person | € 3.10 - € 6.20 |
| child (2-7 yrs) | € 1.80 - € 4.00 |
| electricity (3/10A) | € 3.50 - € 4.50 |

**Tel:** 05 53 31 46 00. **Fax:** 05 53 29 36 37. **E-mail:** aqua_viva@perigord.com. **Reservations:** Made with 50% deposit and € 20 fee. **Open** Easter - 30 September.

**Directions:** Site is 6 km. from Sarlat on the D704 road from Sarlat to Souillac. Coming from Sarlat, the entrance on the left is not easy to see.

## Dordogne/Aveyron

# Camping Soleil Plage

**2409**

Vitrac, 24200 Sarlat

This spacious site is in one of the most attractive sections of the Dordogne valley, right on the riverside. The site has a total of 199 pitches, divided into two sections, of which around 95 are for touring units. The smaller section surrounds the main reception and other facilities, which are housed in a renovated farmhouse, whilst the larger section of the site is about 250 m. from the reception and pool areas, and offers river bathing from a sizeable pebble bank. All pitches are bounded by hedges and are of good size, and in the larger section there are a few giant pitches for large families. Most pitches have some shade. Various activities are organised in high season including walks and sports tournaments, and canoe hire is possible. Once a week there is a 'soirée' usually involving a barbecue or paella, with band and lots of free wine - worth catching! The site is becoming increasingly popular, though in late August it begins to empty. Used by tour operators (80 pitches).

**Facilities:** Toilet facilities are provided by two modern unisex blocks. Washing machines. Motorcaravan service point. Friendly bar with good takeaway menu, restaurant serving excellent Périgourdine menus, and well stocked shop (all 12/5-15/9). Very impressive pool complex includes main pool, paddling pool, spa pool and two water slides. Tennis court, devilish minigolf, table tennis, volleyball and football pitches. TV room. Playground. Fishing. Canoe and kayak hire. **Off site:** Bicycle hire 2 km, golf 1 km, riding 5 km.

**Charges** 2002

| | |
|---|---|
| Per person over 10 yrs | € 3.80 - € 6.00 |
| child (2-10 yrs) | € 2.30 - € 3.50 |
| pitch | € 5.80 - € 10.05 |
| with electricity | € 8.20 - € 13.30 |
| with full services | € 11.00 - € 18.00 |
| local tax (high season, over 10 yrs) | € 0.30 |

**Tel:** 05 53 28 33 33. **Fax:** 05 53 28 30 24. **E-mail:** soleil.plage@wanadoo.fr. **Reservations:** Made for exact dates: min. 1 week with deposit (€ 65) and fee (€ 35); send for booking form. **Open** 1 May - 30 September.

**Directions:** Site is 8 km south of Sarlat. From D703 Vitrac - Carsac-Aillac road turn southeast at 'Domaine de Rochebois' golf course (site signed here). Follow road to the end, turn right at T-junction, and follow the road along and around to the left. Site is on left just after turning the corner.

## Dordogne/Aveyron
# Camping Domaine des Chênes Verts
route de Sarlat, 24370 Calviac en Périgord

**2422**

the **travel service**
TO BOOK

| | |
|---|---|
| ferry | ✓ |
| pitch | ✓ |
| Accommodation | ✗ |

01892 55 98 98

This peaceful countryside family campsite is set in a beautiful area of the Dordogne valley, and is complemented by the renovated Périgordian farm buildings which house the amenities at the centre of the site. The spacious grounds which contain many trees provide 143 pitches on either side of the main buildings, of which 63 are for touring units. Most of the good sized, grassy pitches are shaded, and all are separated by hedging. There is electricity (6A) to all pitches, and water points nearby. The majority of pitches are level but some are gently sloping. The owners, who speak some English, are very helpful and friendly, and in high season they organise a range of entertainments and activities from wine tasting to canoeing expeditions.

**Facilities:** Two fully equipped unisex toilet blocks include washbasins in cabins, dishwashing and laundry areas. Washing machine. Shop (1/7-30/8, but bread, milk, etc, from reception in low season). Motorcaravan service point. Fridge hire. Gas supplies. Bar, restaurant and takeaway (15/6-15/9). Medium sized swimming pool with large sunbathing area (15/6-15/9), covered, heated pool (1/4-20/9) and paddling pool. Play area. Large grass area for ball games, volleyball, basketball and tennis courts. TV and games room.

**Charges 2002**

| | |
|---|---|
| Per pitch | € 5.60 - € 7.00 |
| person | € 2.00 - € 4.50 |
| electricity (6A) | € 2.80 - € 3.50 |

**Tel:** 05 53 59 21 07. **Fax:** 05 53 31 05 51. **E-mail:** chenes-verts@wanadoo.fr. **Reservations:** Advised in July/Aug. **Open** 1 May - 28 September.

**Directions:** From D704 Sarlat - Gourdon road turn east on D704A towards Souillac and Calviac (this turning is about 3.5 km. from Sarlat). Site is about 5 km. along this road on the left.

## Dordogne/Aveyron
# Camping Bel Ombrage
24250 St-Cybranet

**2414**

Bel Ombrage is a quiet, clean site located in a pretty location by the little River Céou, with a pebble beach onto a backwater that is safe and clean for bathing. The site has a good pool complex, but otherwise there are few on site facilities. The 180 well shaded, grass pitches are flat and of a good size, marked out by trees and bushes. Bel Ombrage is very close to Domme and Castelnaud and would make an ideal and inexpensive base for touring the southern Dordogne area. It is a short walk to the village of St Cybranet, with restaurants and a well stocked store. A short drive takes you to the beautifully restored village of Daglan.

**Facilities:** Two modern toilet blocks are kept spotlessly clean, with facilities for disabled visitors and babies. Laundry. Bread van calls each morning. Good pool complex. Fishing. **Off site:** Pizzeria next door. Excursions can be booked at reception. Tennis courts and canoeing close. Riding or bicycle hire 3 km, golf 6 km.

**Charges 2002**

| | |
|---|---|
| Per pitch | € 6.00 |
| person | € 2.50 - € 4.60 |
| electricity (10A) | € 3.10 |
| local tax | € 0.25 |

**Tel:** 05 53 28 34 14. **Fax:** 05 53 59 64 64. **E-mail:** belombrage@wanadoo.fr. **Reservations:** Write to site. **Open** 1 June - 5 September.

**Directions:** Site is about 14 km south of Sarlat, on the east side of the D57 Castelnaud-la-chapelle - St Cybranet road, about 1 km. before the junction with the D50.

## Camping Les Deux Vallées

24220 Vézac

**2415**

This site is enviably situated almost under the shadow of Beynac castle in the heart of the Dordogne. There are 100 flat marked touring pitches, including a newly established and more open section. The pitches are of a good size, some generous, and are divided by trees and shrubs, all with electricity (6A). There is plenty of shade and the general feel is of unspoilt but well managed woodland. There is a small fishing lake on site, and it is only a short distance to the Dordogne river for bathing or canoeing. The site is being steadily upgraded with more pitches planned by its Dutch owners, who provide a friendly welcome. A single track railway runs along the eastern boundary of the site (trains are relatively infrequent). English is spoken. This site would be ideal for those wanting a quiet and relatively inexpensive base from which to visit the Dordogne region.

**Facilities:** The main unisex toilet block is modern and very clean, and gives an ample provision, with good access for disabled people. A second smaller recently refurbished block can be heated for off-season use. Shop and bar/restaurant (both 1/06-30/9) serving good value snacks and more ambitious meals to take away, eat inside or on the terrace. Good sized pool (1.6 m. deep) and children's pool (from mid May). Bicycle hire. Volleyball, basketball, small minigolf, boules area, table tennis, table football. Quiz nights and barbecues are a regular feature in the main season. **Off site:** Riding 2 km, golf 8 km.

**Charges** 2002

| | |
|---|---|
| Per pitch | € 4.00 - € 6.50 |
| person over 3 yrs | € 3.00 - € 5.00 |
| electricity (6A) | € 3.00 |
| animal | € 0.60 - € 1.00 |

**Tel:** 05 53 29 53 55. Fax: 05 53 31 09 81. E-mail: les2v@perigord.fr. **Reservations:** Advised for July/Aug. and made with deposit (€ 100) and fee (€ 15). **Open** all year.

**Directions:** Site is on the northwest side of the D57 Beynac-et-Cazenac - Sarlat road, about 8 km from Sarlat and 2 km. from Beynac. From Beynac direction follow the D57, pass under a railway bridge and then take the second turning left (site signed here). Go across a level crossing, follow the road around and take the first turn left. Site is about 200 m. From Sarlat direction this turning will be on your right, just past a detatched stone house.

## Camping-Caravaning Les Granges

**2402** 24250 Grolejac-en-Perigord

Situated only 500 metres from the village of Groléjac, Les Granges is a lively and well maintained campsite set on sloping ground in woodland. There are 192 pitches, of which 96 are available for touring units. The pitches are marked and numbered on level terraces, and most receive good shade from mature trees and shrubs. All pitches have electricity (6A), and water either on the pitch or close by. The site has a good sized swimming pool and a large shallow pool for children. A bridge connects these to a fun pool with water slides. Regular entertainment is organised in high season, along with a children's club every weekday morning. About 80 pitches are used by tour operators.

**Facilities:** The toilet blocks are of a very high standard with good facilities for disabled visitors. Bar/restaurant and snack bar with takeaway (15/05-15/09). No shop, but bread and milk can be ordered. Play area. Table tennis, volleyball, basketball, minigolf, climbing wall. Canoe and bicycle hire. **Off site:** Shops and restaurants in Groléjac.

**Charges 2002**

| | |
|---|---|
| Per unit incl. 2 persons | € 14.30 - € 21.30 |
| extra person over 2 yrs | € 6.00 |
| electricity | € 3.20 |

**Tel:** 05 53 28 11 15. Fax: 05 53 28 57 13. E-mail: lesueur.francine@wanadoo.fr. **Reservations:** Made for exact dates with deposit (€ 121.96) and fee (€ 18.29). **Open** 1 May - 25 Spetember.

**Directions:** In the centre of the village of Groléjac on main D704 road. Site is signed through a gravel parking area on the west side of the road. Drive through this area and follow road around to T-junction. Turn right, under railway bridge, and immediately left (site is signed here). Site is just along this road on the left.

## Camping Les Peneyrals

**2432** Le Poujol, St Crépin-Carlucet, 24590 Salignac-Eyvigues

Set within easy reach of all the attractions of the Périgord region, M. and Mme. Havel have created an attractive and friendly family campsite at Les Peneyrals. Set on a wooded hillside, with flowers in abundance (thanks to the dedication of Mme. Havel's mother), the site has 199 pitches, of which 87 are available for touring units. The pitches at the bottom of the hill tend to be quieter as they are further from the main facilities, but are all level and grassy (some on terraces), with electricity (5/10A), and most have some shade. An attractive bar and restaurant with terrace overlook the excellent pool complex. The site is used fairly unobtrusively by two tour operators (71 pitches).

**Facilities:** Two modern, unisex toilet blocks provide good quality facilities, including provision for babies and disabled visitors. Motorcaravan service point. Good value shop, restaurant and takeaway. Pool complex with two large pools (one heated), paddling pool and four water slides. Bicycle hire. Minigolf, tennis court (charged). Football. Badminton, volleyball and table tennis. Play area. Fishing lake. Activities organised in season.

**Charges 2002**

| | |
|---|---|
| Per pitch | € 8.70 |
| person | € 6.10 |
| child under 7 yrs | free - € 3.80 |
| electricity (5/10A) | € 2.75 - € 3.21 |

**Tel:** (0)5 53 28 85 71. Fax: (0)5 53 28 80 99. E-mail: camping.peneyrals@wanadoo.fr. **Reservations:** Made with deposit (€ 70) and booking fee (€ 17). **Open** 15 May - 13 September.

**Directions:** Site is 11 km. north of Sarlat. From D704 Sarlat - Montignac road turn east on D60 towards Salignac-Eyvigues. After 4 km. turn south on D56 towards St Crépin-Carlucet. Site is 500 m.

## Camping-Caravaning La Bouquerie

**2431** 24590 St Geniès-en-Périgord

La Bouquerie is a lively site, situated within easy reach of the main road network in the Dordogne, but without any associated traffic noise. The main complex is based around some beautifully restored traditional Périgordin buildings. It includes a shop, and a bar and restaurant overlooking the pool complex, with a large outdoor terrace for fine weather. Only 37 of the 185 pitches are used for touring units, Of varying size (80-120 sq.m.), these are flat and grassy, some with shade, and all have electrical connections (5A). La Bouquerie is ideally situated for exploring the Périgord region, and has something to offer families with children of all ages.

**Facilities:** The three unisex toilet blocks contain a mixture of new and older facilities, but are all clean and well maintained. Two blocks provide facilities for disabled visitors and baby rooms. Shop (15/05-15/09) with takeaway food. Bar and restaurant (both 15/05-15/09). Pool complex (all season) with paddling pool. Activities organised in high season.

**Charges 2002**

| | |
|---|---|
| Per adult | € 6.11 |
| child under 7 yrs | € 4.22 |
| pitch | € 8.60 |
| with electricity | 1€ 1.33 |

**Tel:** (0)5 53 28 98 22. Fax: (0)5 53 29 19 75. E-mail: labouquerie@wanadoo.fr. **Reservations:** Advised for high season. **Open** Easter - 28 September.

**Directions:** Site is signed just off D704 Sarlat - Montignac road, about 500 m. north of junction with D64 St Geniès road. Turn off D704 at sign and take first left signed La Bouquerie - site is straight ahead.

## Dordogne/Aveyron
# Camping Le Moulin de Paulhiac
24520 Daglan

**2423**

Daglan is a very pretty village that is undergoing a complete renovation and it is becoming something of a tourist centre for this quieter area of the Dordogne. It is very close to Domme and La Roque-Gajeac. We were very impressed with the friendly welcome from the Armagnac family, who are justifiably proud of their well-kept and attractive site, built in the grounds surrounding an old mill. The 150 numbered pitches are separated by hedges and shrubs, all have electricity, and there is plenty of shade. Many pitches are next to a stream that runs through the site, and joins the River Ceou along its far edge. A tent field slopes gently down to the river, which is well marked and quite shallow. This site will appeal especially to families with younger children, and is a place where we feel the parents would be able to relax and have a holiday too!

**Facilities:** Two clean toilet blocks are large enough to be adequate for the site. Well-stocked site shop - you can buy the owner's home-grown walnuts (delicious!). Good value restaurant and takeaway. Modern pool complex (no bermuda style shorts) with a main pool (15 x 7.5 m), children's pool (7.5 x 7.5 m), a further small pool and two slides with landing pool. Volleyball, table tennis, badminton and boules. Canoe trips are organised on the Dordogne. Evening activities organised. Children's club. **Off site:** Municipal tennis courts adjoining.

**Charges** 2002

| | |
|---|---|
| Per pitch | € 8.00 |
| person | € 5.50 |
| child under 10 yrs | € 2.00 - € 4.00 |
| dog | € 1.50 |
| electricity (6A) | € 3.00 |
| water and drainage | € 1.50 |

**Tel:** 05 53 28 20 88. **Fax:** 05 53 29 33 45. **E-mail:** Francis.Armagnac@wanadoo.fr. **Reservations:** Made for any length with deposit (€ 20) and fee (€ 10). **Open** 15 May - 15 September.

**Directions:** Crossing the Cenac (near Domme), take D46 south for 6 km, turn right on D60 to Daglan. Turn right on D57, and the site is about 5 km. on the right.

## Dordogne/Aveyron
# Camping Château de Lacomté
46500 Carlucet

**4608**

| the **travel service** | |
|---|---|
| **TO BOOK** | |
| Ferry | ✔ |
| Pitch | ✔ |
| Accommodation | ✗ |
| 01892 55 98 98 | |

Château de Lacomté is the closest site in this guide to Rocamadour; just a 15 minute drive along a back road. A little further on is the Gouffre de Padirac with its underground rivers and concretions. The site is run by an English family, Sheila and Stuart Coe and their children, who have worked hard developing the site and provide a warm welcome. The restaurant and bar make up part of the converted outbuildings of the château. The views from the terrace over mature woodland are memorable, and the pool and terrace are beautifully lit at night. The Coes try to retain as much of the meadowland as possible for wildlife and flowers. The main camping field is quietly located down a slope to one side of the bar area. The first section contains pitches marked out on slightly sloping ground, most with flat areas, and six with hardstanding. The majority of pitches on this upper terrace have good shade, although most pitches on the extensive lower field are still relatively open. All pitches have electricity, water and drainage. The site is very popular with British visitors and it is advisable to reserve if you want one of the best places. Perhaps a little more out of the way than other Dordogne sites and out of season you may have to travel to the nearest town for bread and other supplies. A novel service, aimed at people with large motorhomes, cyclists and backpackers, offers the use of a small car included in the cost of the pitch (drivers over 25 yrs).

**Facilities:** The good, clean toilet block is well equipped and includes laundry facilities. Fridge hire. Small shop (15/6-15/9). Restaurant (with a good reputation). Bar. Large swimming pool (from 1/6) with children's paddling area. Children's playground, tennis court and table tennis. Torches useful. **Off site:** Fishing 6-10 km. Close to Gramat and Cahors for supermarkets and other shops.

**Charges** 2002

| | |
|---|---|
| Per pitch | € 7.35 |
| person | € 5.80 |
| child (under 12 yrs) | € 3.35 |
| dog | € 3.05 |
| electricity | € 4.30 |

**Tel:** 05 65 38 75 46. **Fax:** 05 65 33 17 68. **E-mail:** chateaulacomte@wanadoo.fr. **Reservations:** Made with 25% deposit and fee (€ 7,62). **Open** 15 May - 15 October.

**Directions:** From N20, 8 km. south of Peyrac, take D1 towards Gramat. After 12 km. turn left on D677, then after 1.5 km. left on D323 to Carlucet where site is signed. The D32 (Rocamadour - Carlucet) is not advised for caravans or large motorcaravans.

# Camping Domaine de la Paille Basse

46200 Souillac-sur-Dordogne

**4601**

Lying some 8 km. from Souillac, this family owned, high quality site is easily accessible from the N20 and well placed to take advantage of excursions into the Dordogne. It is part of a large domaine of 80 hectares, which is available to campers for walks and recreation. The site is quite high up and there are excellent views over the surrounding countryside. The 250 pitches are in two main areas - one is level in cleared woodland with good shade, and the other on grass in open ground without shade. Numbered and marked, the pitches are a minimum 100 sq.m. and often considerably more. About 80 have individual electricity, water and drainage, and electricity is available to all the others. Activities and entertainment are organised in season (animation was of a very high standard when we stayed). For good reason, the site can get very busy in high season and is popular with tour operators (20%), but there is more space available from mid August.

**Facilities:** The main toilet facilities are in three different sections, all centrally located close to reception (there is also a small night unit at one end of site). All have modern equipment and are kept very clean. Laundry facilities. Shop for essentials. Good restaurant, bar with terrace and takeaway. Crêperie. Good swimming pool complex, with main pool (25 x 10 m), second one (10 x 6 m) and paddling pool (unheated). Solarium. Sound-proofed disco room (twice weekly in season). TV rooms (with satellite). Cinema room below swimming pool area. Archery, tennis (charged), football, volleyball and table tennis. Children's playground. **Off site:** Golf 4 km.

**Charges** 2002

| | |
|---|---|
| Per person | € 5.50 |
| child (under 7) | € 3.50 |
| pitch | € 8.50 |
| electricity (3A) | € 3.50 |
| local tax | € 0.15 |

**Tel:** 05 65 37 85 48. Fax: 05 65 37 09 58. E-mail: paille.basse@wanadoo.fr. **Reservations:** Advised mid-July - mid-Aug. and made for min. 1 week with deposit and € 18,29 booking fee. **Open** 15 May - 15 September.

**Directions:** From Souillac take D15 road leading northwest towards Salignac-Eyvignes and after 6 km. turn right at camp sign and follow steep and narrow approach road for 2 km.

## Dordogne/Aveyron
# Camping Le Soulhol
**4610M** quai Auguste Salesse, 46400 Saint-Céré

Saint-Céré is an interesting small town, overlooked by the old château of the same name. It is actually situated in the département of Lot but is still in that area considered by the British to be the 'Dordogne'. This municipal site is now under privatised management, an increasingly popular system in France. It is neatly and attractively arranged with 180 large, flat pitches of which half have 10A electrical connections. They are marked by rose bushes and have quite a lot of shade from the avenues of mature trees which extend down the sides and middle of the site. A further separate area is used mainly for rallies, etc. with its own elderly sanitary block.

**Facilities:** Two main sanitary blocks, a new one opened in '99 and a refurbished, more central unit, are fully equipped including washbasins in private cabins. Dishwashing sinks. Washing machine. Ices and gas at reception. Bread can be ordered. Snack bar and takeaway. Boules. Fishing. Bicycle hire. **Off site:** Municipal swimming pool open July/Aug, free for campers and tennis courts both adjacent (100 m). Shops and restaurants 300 m.

**Charges** 2002

| | |
|---|---|
| Per person | € 3.05 |
| child (4-7 yrs) | € 1.52 |
| pitch | € 2.59 |
| electricity (5/10A) | € 2.29 - € 3.05 |

**Tel:** 05 65 38 12 37. Fax: 05 65 10 61 75.
**Reservations:** Made with deposit (€ 39) and fee (€ 13,72). **Open** 1 April - 30 September.

**Directions:** Site is off the D48 road towards Lacapelle and is well signed.

## Dordogne/Aveyron
# Camping Le Rêve
**4605** 46300 Le Vigan

Le Rêve is a very peaceful site situated in the heart of rolling countryside where the Perigord runs into Quercy. There is plenty of space for all units. Pitches are divided by shrubs, all have access to electricity (6A) and a variety of attractive trees have grown well to provide some shade. Some of the 56 pitches are very large and there are now 13 pitches in the woods. Le Rêve continues to impress us with its tranquillity and the young Dutch owners are keen to develop the site in such a way that this will not be lost. This site is particularly suitable for families with very young children

**Facilities:** The modern toilet block has been extended to include a heated enclosed area. Washbasins in cabins, cubicles for disabled people and a baby room. Washing machine and dryers. Small shop, pleasant bar, restaurant and takeaway (all open all season). Small, clean, solar heated swimming pool and large paddling pool. Shaded playground. Boules. Bicycle hire. Table tennis and volleyball. **Off site:** Fishing 5 km, riding 2 km.

**Charges** 2002

| | |
|---|---|
| Per adult | € 3.80 |
| child (under 7 yrs) | € 2.00 |
| pitch | € 5.00 |
| electricity (6A) | € 2.50 |

**Tel:** 05 65 41 25 20. Fax: 05 65 41 68 52. E-mail: info@campinglereve.fr. **Reservations:** Advised for high season and made for any length with deposit (€ 61) and fee (€ 4,57). **Open** 25 April - 15 September.

**Directions:** From A20 exit 55 Souillac, follow N20 from Souillac towards Cahors. About 3 km. south of Payrac, turn right on D673 (Le Vigan and Gourdon). After 2 km, site signed on right down a small lane and is some 3 km. further on.

## Dordogne/Aveyron
# Camping Les Pins
**4603** 46350 Payrac-en-Quercy

Camping Les Pins is suitable for a Dordogne holiday or overnight stop on way south. It is named after its magnificent pine trees and also has impressive views. There are 125 clearly marked, level pitches (100 sq.m), of which 55 are for touring units (some mobile homes on site). Many pitches are shady although there is a fair number of sunny places, and all have electricity, most also with water and drainage. There is a good restaurant and bar and in season, some entertainment includes weekly family discos. The site is used by tour operators.

Fcilities: Three toilet blocks are well maintained and include washbasins in cabins and good baby bath facilities. Dishwashing and laundry sinks, washing machines and dryers. Motorcaravan service point. Bread available. Good value bar/restaurant and takeaway (1/6-31/8). Pool complex with swimming pool (15 x 17 m.), three new water slides and smaller paddling pool (15/5-15/9). Good quality tennis court. Table tennis, pétanque and volleyball. TV and library. **Off site:** Fishing 7 km, riding 10 km.

**Charges** 2002

| | |
|---|---|
| Per person | € 3.05 - € 4.88 |
| pitch | € 7.32 |
| with electricity | € 9.91 |

**Tel:** 05 65 37 96 32. Fax: 05 65 37 91 08. E-mail: info@les-pins-camping.com. **Reservations:** Made for min. 1 week with deposit (25%) plus fee (€ 15,24). **Open** 1 April - 15 September.

**Directions:** Entrance is on western carriageway of the N20 just south of Payrac-en-Quercy, 16 km. from Souillac.

## Dordogne/Aveyron
## Camping Moulin de Laborde

**4604** 46700 Montcabrier

The watermill and its outbuildings at Moulin de Laborde have been sympathetically developed and provide for the site facilities with a courtyard and terrace. Bordered by woods, hills and a small river, there are 90 pitches of at least 100 sq.m on level grass. Well marked out by shrubs and trees, all have electricity. A gate at the back of the site leads walkers onto a 'Grand Randonée'. The Château of Bonaguil and towns of Fumel and Villefranche du Perigord are close. The friendly Dutch owners speak good English and French.

**Facilities:** The good toilet block has well designed showers and washbasins in cabins. Covered area provides sinks for dishwashing and laundry. Unit for disabled people. Washing machine and dryer. Shop stocks basics and gas (all season). Small bar, restaurant and takeaway. Swimming pool with sunbathing area and paddling pool (15/5-15/9). Rustic children's play area. Small lake for recreation. Volleyball, badminton court, boules, recreation room and table tennis. Mountain bike hire. Fishing. Rock climbing lessons plus organised activities every day. Dogs are not accepted. **Off site:** Riding 5 km, golf 8 km, tennis near and canoeing on the Lot.

**Charges** 2002

| | |
|---|---|
| Per person | € 5.50 |
| child (under 7) | € 2.75 |
| pitch | € 7.00 |
| electricity (4A) | € 2.25 |
| local tax (over 10 yrs) | € 0.30 |

**Tel:** 05 65 24 62 06. Fax: 05 65 36 51 33. E-mail: moulindelaborde@wanadoo.fr. **Reservations:** Write to site with deposit (€ 7 per night booked). **Open** 1 May - 15 September.

**Directions:** Site is near Montcabrier, which is just south of the D673, 12 km. from Fumel. Follow D673 north for 1 km. towards Gourdon, and site is on the left.

## Dordogne/Aveyron
## Camping de la Plage

**4607** 46330 Saint-Cirq-Lapopie

Due to its unusual position adjacent to the River Lot, this site is a good base for those who want an active holiday, with many sporting activities available either on site or in the immediate area. It does attract organised groups of young people and can be quite lively at times. The site is a rental base for canoeing and kayaking (lifejackets and all equipment included in hire charge). The campsite has 120 pitches with electricity (6/10A) available to all, a few fully serviced pitches and some hardstandings. Most are on a very slight slope and have good shade from mature trees and bushes. This site is open all year and may be subject to flooding in the winter months - contact site before travelling.

**Facilities:** Two practical sanitary units include washbasins in cubicles and both have dishwashing and laundry sinks. Unit for disabled people, although the local terrain is not ideal. Washing machine and dryer. Motorcaravan service point (usual services and toilet block, charged for) outside at the rear of site on the river bank. Bar/café at entrance with internet terminal. Canoeing, kayaking and swimming from beach at the rear of the site (lifeguard July/Aug). **Off site:** Riding, rock climbing, caving and canyoning all near by.

**Charges** 2002

| | |
|---|---|
| Per adult | € 5.00 |
| child (under 7 yrs) | € 3.00 |
| pitch incl. 2 persons and electricity | € 17.00 - € 18.00 |
| electricity 6A/10A | € 3.00 - € 4.00 |
| dog | € 1.00 |

**Tel:** 05 65 30 29 51. Fax: 05 65 30 23 33. E-mail: camping.laplage@wanadoo.fr. **Reservations:** Advised for high season. **Open** all year.

**Directions:** From Cahors take D653 east to Vers, then take D662 for 17 km. to Tour de Faure. Cross river on narrow bridge and site entrance is on right by bar/restaurant. Do not approach via Saint-Cirq-Lapopie.

## The Alan Rogers' Travel Service

This unique service enables our readers to reserve their holidays as well as ferry crossings and comprehensive insurance cover at extremely competitive rates. The majority of participating sites are in France and we are able to offer a selection of some of the very best sites in this country.

Share our experience and let us help
to ensure that your holiday will be a complete success.

**Alan Rogers Travel Service 01892 55 98 98 or www.alanrogers.com**

# Dordogne/Aveyron
## Camping-Caravaning Moulin du Périé
47500 Sauveterre-la-Lemance

**the travel service TO BOOK**

| | |
|---|---|
| Ferry | ✔ |
| Pitch | ✔ |
| Accommodation | ✗ |

01892 55 98 98

Set in a quiet area and surrounded by woodlands this peaceful little site is well away from much of the tourist bustle. Its 125 grass pitches, divided by mixed trees and bushes, are reasonably sized and extremely well kept, as indeed is the entire site. All pitches have electricity (6A) and most enjoy good shade, with younger trees and shrubs rapidly filling out in the new area. The picturesque old mill buildings, adorned with flowers and creepers, now home to the restaurant etc. and the food is to be recommended as is the owner's extensive knowledge of wine that he is pleased to share with visitors. The attractive front courtyard is complemented by an equally pleasant terrace at the rear. A quiet, friendly site with regular visitors - reservation is advised for July/Aug. A 'Sites et Paysages' member.

**Facilities:** Three clean, modern and well maintained toilet blocks incorporate facilities for disabled visitors, babies and laundry. Motorcaravan service facilities. Shop for essentials (with gas). Bar/reception and restaurant (including takeaway). Two small, clean swimming pools (no bermuda-style shorts) overlook a shallow, spring water lake, ideal for inflatable boats and paddling. Bordering the lake, a large grass field is popular for football and volleyball. Boules, table tennis, outdoor chess. New children's playground and trampoline. Small, indoor play area. Bicycle hire. In season various activities, on and off site are arranged; including canoeing, riding, wine tasting visits, sight seeing trips plus weekly barbecues and gastronomic meals. Winter caravan storage. **Off site:** Fishing 1 km. Small supermarket in village and larger stores in Fumel.

**Charges** 2002

| | |
|---|---|
| Per unit incl. 2 persons | € 11.00 - € 18.80 |
| with electricity | € 14.30 - € 22.10 |
| extra person | € 3.55 - € 5.60 |
| child (under 7 yrs) | € 1.50 - € 3.00 |
| animal | € 1.80 - € 3.40 |

**Tel:** 05 53 40 67 26. **Fax:** 05 53 40 62 46. **E-mail:** moulinduperie@wanadoo.fr. **Reservations:** Advised for July/Aug. and made with deposit (€ 130) and fee (€ 18). **Open** 4 May - 24 September.

**Directions:** Sauveterre-la -Lémance lies by the Fumel - Périgueux (D710) road, midway between the Dordogne and Lot rivers. From D710, cross railway line, straight through village and turn left (north east) at far end on C201 minor road signed Château Sauveterre, Loubejec and site. Site is 3 km. up this road on right.

# MOULIN DU PÉRIÉ ★★★★
## Camping - Caravanning

**CAMPING - CARAVANING Open from 03/05/2003 to 20/09/2003**

All services open during the opening:
- restaurant, bar, take away, shop, swimming pool.

During the high season:
- sports, children's activities, music, camp fire, circus
- organised day trip by bus: wine tasting, canoeing on the Dordogne river.

Comfortable accommodation for hire are available at the site: chalets, mobile homes, caravans and large bungalow tents.

**Special Inclusive Holidays**
Two weeks holiday discovering the natural and scenic Perigord / Dordogne area.
Interesting & Complete Programmes
Local wine and food tasting in June

For more information and free brochure, write and phone to:
**France: Henri or Anne-Marie BAUDOT**
**tel: 0033 553 40 67 26**
**fax: 0033 553 40 62 46**
**Moulin du Périé**
**47500 Sauveterre la Lémance France**
**www.camping-moulin-perie.com**
**E-mail: MOULINDUPERIE@wanadoo.fr**

# DORDOGNE - PÉRIGORD

## Castel Camping Le Château de Fonrives

**4703** Rives, 47210 Villeréal

This is one of those very pleasant Dordogne sites set in pretty part-farmed, part-wooded countryside, close to the delightful old town of Villeréal. The neat, orderly site is a mixture of hazelnut orchards, woodland with lake, château (mostly 16th century) and camping areas. An attractive avenue leads to the barns adjacent to the château which have been tastefully converted (the restaurant particularly so). There are 200 pitches, 140 for touring units. Of 100-150 sq.m. in size, all have electricity (4, 6 or 10A) and 60 have water taps also. Pitches near the woodland receive moderate shade, but elsewhere there is light shade from hedges and young trees. Some 'wild' camping is possible in one or two areas. The lake can be used for fishing or boating.

**Facilities:** Two main sanitary units are clean and adequate including washbasins in well appointed cabins and some private bathrooms (for hire by the week). Facilities for children and babies. Laundry rooms. Motorcaravan services. Shop. Elegant restaurant, plus bar, snacks and takeaway meals (all 10/6-10/9). Swimming pool (no bermuda style shorts) and paddling pool. Children's play areas. Small field for volleyball and football. Trampolines. Reading room. Minigolf. Bicycle hire. Activities organised for children and adults in season, including excursions and walks. Caravan storage. **Off site:** Riding 8 km.

**Charges** guide

| Per unit incl. 2 persons | € 13.11 - € 20.58 |
|---|---|
| extra person | € 3.81 - € 5.03 |
| child (under 7 yrs) | € 2.29 - € 3.05 |
| electricity (4-10A) | € 2.74 - € 3.81 |

**Tel:** 05 53 36 63 38. **Fax:** 05 53 36 09 98. **E-mail:** chateau.de.fonrives@wanadoo.fr. **Reservations:** Advisable for July/Aug. **Open** 4 May - 14 September.

**Directions:** Site is about 2 km. northwest of Villeréal, on the Bergerac road (D14/D207).

CASTEL - CAMPING du CHATEAU de FONRIVES
★ ★ ★ ★
LES CASTELS

Peace and Quiet. Comfort and spacious surroundings, 20 hectares of natural parkland. Bed and breakfast. Mobile homes, Bungalows, Chalet available for hire

47210 Rives, Villeréal - Tel: 0033 553.36.63.38  Fax: 0033 553.36.09.98

## Camping Fontaine du Roc

**4707** Devillac, 47210 Villeréal

This small site, which is approached up a narrow access road, has wonderful views over the surrounding countryside. The 50 grassy pitches are all of a good size (120 sq.m) and are positioned around the perimeter of the site, with the children's playground and swimming pool elevated in the centre. A small bar, snack bar and terrace overlook the pool. This a quiet and peaceful site without tour operators.

**Facilities:** The single sanitary block provides washbasins in cabins and facilities for disabled people. Dishwashing and laundry sinks. Bar with TV. Snack bar. Free fishing in pool on adjoining land. Bicycle hire can be arranged. Play area. **Off site:** Riding 5 km. Golf 15 km. Fishing 200 km.

**Charges** 2002

| Per pitch | € 4.70 - € 6.00 |
|---|---|
| person | € 4.00 |
| child (under 7 yrs) | € 2.60 |
| electricity (5/10A) | € 2.00 - € 3.20 |
| animal | € 1.25 |

**Tel:** 05 53 36 08 16. **E-mail:** fontaine-du-roc@wanadoo.fr. **Reservations:** Advised for high season. **Open** 1 April - 31 October.

**Directions:** Site is 12 km. southwest of Monpazier. From Monpazier take D104 to Villeréal and turn left to Vergt-de-Biron and Devillac on D2E/D272. Site is signed right off this road.

## Dordogne/Aveyron
# Camping Moulin de Campech

47160 Villefranche-de-Queyran

**4705**

This site is run by Sue and George Thomas along with Sue's parents, Dot and Bob Dunn. A cheery welcome and a free drink awaits you and a determination to ensure that you enjoy your stay. A fabulous view also awaits as you descend the drive from the entrance. The trout lake with graceful weeping willows feeds under the restored mill house which is home to the owners, the main administration area alongside and the bar and restaurant. Enjoy the fare produced by Sue on the pretty terrace as the trout jump (fresh trout is a menu option). The river continues through one side of the site. Children will need supervision around the lake and at the pool which is on an elevated area above the mill house. The 60 pitches are mostly divided by hedges, with electricity available (2/6A, long leads may be necessary in places).

**Facilities:** The single, rather ordinary toilet unit has modern fittings, can be heated and includes both British and Turkish style WCs, some washbasins in cubicles with hot water, or open washbasins (cold only in men's section). Covered dishwashing and laundry sinks. Two washing machines and a dryer. Bar and restaurant. Terraced swimming pool and baby pool. Open grassy area for volleyball and other games. Table tennis and baby-foot in tent outside. Board games, boules and small library. Barbecue and gourmet nights organised in high season. Fishing (discounted rate for campers). Torch useful. **Off site:** Watersports, bicycle hire, golf or riding 10 km. Markets every day in villages and towns around the region.

**Charges** 2002

| | |
|---|---|
| Per pitch | € 6.25 - € 7.85 |
| adult | € 3.20 - € 4.50 |
| child (under 7 yrs) | € 2.40 - € 3.00 |
| electricity (2/6A) | € 2.30 - € 3.80 |
| dog | € 2.30 |

**Tel:** 05 53 88 72 43. Fax: 05 53 88 06 52. E-mail: campech@wanadoo.fr. **Reservations:** Advised for July/Aug. Open 25 March - 1 November.

**Directions:** Take A10 south to Bordeaux. Join A62 for Toulouse and take exit 6 for Damazan. Follow D8 to Mont de Marsan, at Cap du Bosc turn right onto D11 for Casteljaloux. The site is 10 km on the right and signed.

## Dordogne/Aveyron
# Camping Municipal Tonneins

47400 Tonneins

**4710M**

Close to the River Garonne, this small site has a rather formal charm with neat flower beds, well mown lawns and a generally extremely well cared for appearance. With a small reception, the Guardien based on site and a security barrier, it only has 40 pitches (a few occupied by seasonal units) plus a meadow for additional camping. All with electricity (15A), the pitches are of a reasonable size, partly separated by hedges and shrubs. The site is on the southern outskirts of the town with a fair choice of shops, restaurants, etc and only a 15 minute drive from the charming old riverside town of Port Ste Marie. There is some road and rail noise at times. This is a good stopping off point.

**Facilities:** Sanitary facilities, very clean when seen in high season, provide British style WCs, washbasins in cabins and dishwashing sinks (H&C) under cover. Purpose built and roomy but of fairly old design, they are adequate rather than luxurious. Washing machine. No proper chemical disposal point. Ice and cold drinks available. Under cover area with fridge and freezer and tables and chairs. Small children's play area, sandpit and table tennis. Torch useful.

**Charges** 2002

| | |
|---|---|
| Per unit incl. 1 person | € 5.10 |
| incl. 2 persons | € 7.24 |
| extra person | € 2.35 |
| electricity | € 3.00 |

**Tel:** 05 53 79 02 28. **Reservations:** Contact site. **Open** 1 June - 30 September.

**Directions:** Take either exit 5 from autoroute to Marmande then the N113 south or exit 6 to Aiguillon (avoid town) and follow N113 north. Site off N113 just south of Tonneins.

# go as you please

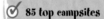

# Limousin/Auvergne

Map 12

We have combined two of the French official regions for our Tourist region:

| Limousin | Auvergne |
|---|---|
| Major cities: Limoges, Brive-la-Gaillarde<br>Départements: 19 Corrèze<br>23 Creuse, 87 Haute-Vienne | Major city: Clermont-Ferrand<br>Départements: 03 Allier, 15 Cantal<br>43 Haute-Loire, 63 Puy-de-Dôme |

We have also included département **48 Lozère** which is actually part
of the offical French region of Languedoc-Roussillon

Limousin is an unspoilt, thinly populated region on the western side of the Massif Central. With hills and gorges and lush green meadows grazed on by the Limousin breed of cattle, numerous ancient village churches dot the landscape as well as more imposing abbey churches and fortresses. Its moorland has made the region popular with horse breeders. The Anglo-Arab horse originated from the famous studs at Pompadour. The city of Limoges, synonymous with porcelain, produced the finest painted enamelware of Europe in the 16th and 17th centuries and today remains the porcelain capital of France, and Aubusson is known for beautiful and intricate tapestries.

The Auvergne, set in the heart of the Massif Central, is a dramatic region of awe-inspiring non-active volcanoes, lakes, rivers and forests. It is a wonderful destination for nature lovers, those who enjoy active outdoor pursuits or for people who want to 'take the waters' at the spa resorts. The 'Parc Naturel Régional des Volcans d'Auvergne' – the Auvergne Volcano Park – is the largest natural park in France and is a protected environment for exceptional flora and fauna. An area once fairly isolated and inward looking, it is now realising its potential as a holiday area. Note: site reports are laid out by département in numerical order not by region.

## Cuisine of the region

Limousin is known for a soup called 'bréjaude', eaten with rye bread, and so thick with cabbage and other vegetables that a spoon will stand up in it. Also for traditional dishes which include a varity of stews such as potée, cassoulet, beans and pork and sauced dishes accompanied by chestnuts or rye pancakes.

The beef (Limousin) of the region is extremely tender and full of flavour

Desserts include thick home-made cakes, almond cake of the Creuse, galette Corrézienne

Local specialties in the Auvergne include ham and andouille sausages, stuffed cabbage, and bacon with lentil and cèpes (mushrooms) and fresh river fish such as trout and pike are much used

*Aligot* – purée of potatoes with Tomme de Cantal cheese, cream, garlic and butter

*Friand Sanflorin* – pork meat and herbs in pastry

*Jambon d'Auvergne* – a tasty mountain ham

*Perdrix à l'Auvergnate* – partridge stewed in white wine

*Potée Auvergnate* – a stew of vegetables, cabbage, pork and sausage

Le Puy is famed for its lentils and Vereine du Velay – yellow and green liqueurs made from over 30 mountain plants

## Places of interest

*Aubusson* – long tradition of tapestry making, Hotel de Ville tapestry collections

*Clermont-Ferrand* – old city centre, 11th and 12th century Notre Dame du Port Basilica,13th century cathedral; known as 'ville noire' for its houses built in local black volcanic rock

*Limoges* – porcelain, enamel and faience work, château, church of St Michel-de-Lions, cathedral of St Etienne

*Vichy* – spa, natural spring park, seat of the collaborationist government in 1940

# Limousin/Auvergne
## Camping de la Filature

**0301** Ile de Nieres, 03450 Ebreuil

the **travel service**
TO BOOK
Ferry ✓
Pitch ✓
Accommodation ✗
01892 55 98 98

Near to the spa town of Vichy and beside a fine fly fishing river that borders the Massif Central region, this site makes a good base to explore the Auvergne. Developed on the site of a spinning mill (hot water is still produced by wood burning - note the chimney), this rural setting is home to peacocks (including some white ones). It has an individuality that is unusual in French sites which is being perpetuated by its English owners. There are 80 spacious, grassy pitches, most with shade from mature trees and many directly on the river bank. In summer the river is clean, shallow and pleasant to play in. There is a deeper swimming area 500 m. away. Most pitches have electricity (3/6A). The area is ideal for walking and cycling, especially mountain biking. Bird watching and wild flowers are additional attractions.

**Facilities:** Very clean sanitary facilities are in individual cubicles (a little on the dark side). Fully equipped, they include mostly British type toilets, bathroom, a washing machine and ironing facilities. Small shop for essentials (1/5-30/9). Baker calls. Bar (1/6-30/9). Excellent takeaway (15/5-30/9). Barbecues and pizza nights organised in high season. River bathing and fishing. Play area and children's club. Bicycle hire. Minigolf, table football, table tennis. **Off site:** Riding, canoeing and tennis nearby.

**Charges** 2002

| | |
|---|---|
| Per unit incl. 2 persons | € 14.00 |
| extra adult | € 4.00 |
| child (under 16 yrs) | € 2.00 |
| electricity (3/6A) | € 2.00 - € 3.00 |

**Tel:** 04 70 90 72 01. **Fax:** 04 70 90 79 48. **E-mail:** camping.filature@libertysurf.fr. **Reservations:** Made with deposit (€ 30 per week of stay or full amount if stay costs less). **Open** 31 March - 1 October.

**Directions:** Site is well signed from exit 12 of A71 autoroute to Clermont Ferrand in the direction of Ébreuil. It is about 6 km. from the A71 and 1 km. west of Ébreuil beside the river on the D915 towards the Chouvigny gorges.

*Don't wait to die to go to heaven, come to:* ★★★★

CAMPING DE LA FILATURE DE LA SIOULE
03450 EBREUIL, FRANCE
*See us on website www.campingfilature.com*

- Very clean facilities and a bathroom
- Really hot water ● Excellent take away with pizza and barbecue evenings in high season ● Bar and terrace
- Low season bargains for long stays
- Children up to 16 charged child rate
- Near to exit 12 of A71 for stopover or long stay

**Tel: 0033 (0)4 70 90 72 01 Fax: 0033 (0)4 70 90 79 48**
E-mail: camping.filature@libertysurf.fr

# Limousin/Auvergne
## Camping Château de Chazeuil

**0302** 03150 Varennes-sur-Allier

Set amongst parkland, this site is set on level lawns in front of the château. The 60 marked pitches all have electricity (although long leads may be necessary). Mature trees provide some pitches with shade. Although the entrance is adjacent to the main N7, traffic noise should be no problem as the site is set well back from the road. A one-way road system operates to ensure a safe exit from the site. The site provides a pleasant night's stop or short stay. There are walks from the campsite and the surrounding area has several interesting towns such as Vichy and St Pourçain with its vineyards.

**Facilities:** The modern sanitary block provides washbasins and showers in cabins, a washing machine and dishwashing and laundry sinks. It is maintained to a satisfactory level. Very pleasant unheated swimming pool and sunbathing area. Play area. Table tennis. Reading room. **Off site:** Shops, restaurants, etc. in Varennes (2 km). Fishing in River Allier (2 km).

**Charges** 2002

| | |
|---|---|
| Per person | € 4.27 |
| child (under 7 yrs) | € 2.74 |
| pitch | € 4.27 |
| vehicle | € 1.68 - € 2.74 |
| electricity (6A) | € 2.74 |

**Tel:** 04 70 45 00 10. **Fax:** 04 70 45 00 10. **E-mail:** camping-de-chazeuil@ifrance.com. **Reservations:** Made for min. 3 days with € 46 deposit. **Open** 15 April - 15 October.

**Directions:** Site is 25 km south of Moulins and just north of Varennes on the eastern side of the main N7 at the traffic lights (D46 turning for St Pourcain).

## Camping Champ de la Chapelle

**0304** 03360 Braize

Champ de la Chapelle is a small, quiet site in the 10,500 hectare Forest of Troncais. It is the perfect answer for those who want to get away from it all. With only 80 pitches set in 5.6 hectares, they are large (up to 250 sq.m.) with plenty of shade and open space. It is the policy of the owner to keep the site small, quiet and unsophisticated. The reward is the wealth of wild life here - you may see red squirrels, deer, bee-eaters or hoopoes. Of the 80 pitches, 62 have electricity (16A) and water. There are many lakes in the area, the museum at nearby St Armand-Montrond traces 100,000 years of local history and at Ainay-le-Viel you can visit 'Little Carcassone'.

**Facilities:** The modern, well appointed sanitary block includes washbasins in cabins. Low toilets for children. Good dishwashing facilities. Washing machine and dryer. Small snack kiosk sells croque monsieur, pizza, quiche, soft drinks, ices, etc. Bread is sometimes available. Small pool (from 15/5). Children's play area. Courts for volleyball, flip-ball and petanque. **Off site:** Nearest supermarket is 5 km. at St Bonnet. Lake at 5 km. offers fishing, bathing, pedaloes, canoes, sail-boarding, minigolf, volleyball, tennis and, in high season, organised rambles every day. Riding 6 km. The whole area is a paradise for nature lovers, cyclists and walkers.

**Charges** 2002

| | |
|---|---|
| Per unit incl. 1 person | € 7.32 |
| extra person over 5 yrs | € 2.44 |
| child (under 5 yrs) | € 1.07 |
| pet | € 1.00 |
| electricity | € 2.44 |

**Tel:** 04 70 06 15 45. Fax: 04 73 33 19 62. E-mail: ccdlp@aol.com. **Reservations:** Made for any period with non-returnable fee (€ 9,15). **Open** 12 April - 14 September.

**Directions**: From N144 Bourges-Montlucon road take D978A eastward and at roundabout take D28 signed Braize. Site signed in approx. 3 km. on right with sign for church and campsite. Then follow site signs for approx. 3 km. (single track with passing places).

## Camping-Caravaning La Petite Valette

**0305** Sazeret, 03390 Montmarault

Originally a working farm, La Petite Valette has been transformed over eight years by its hard working Dutch and German owners into a very attractive and peaceful campsite. There are 55 level grassy pitches, many with rural views, each with an electricity point (6A) and separated by young bushes and trees. There is some shade on most pitches. A small lake in one of the lower fields is stocked with fish for anglers. Ponies and small livestock (rabbits, chickens and ducks) keep the farm feeling alive and restaurant tables in the cottage garden overflowing with flowers provide a tranquil atmosphere.

**Facilities:** Toilet facilities are housed in original outbuildings, each block having very good quality, modern fittings. A large separate room has full facilities for disabled people, families and babies. Laundry. Bread can be ordered. Meals and snacks served in the farmhouse restaurant (to order only). New swimming and paddling pools. Small fenced play area with a seat and 'brolly' for Mum will keep toddlers happy, whilst older children have table tennis in one of the barns, mountain bike hire and organised activities in July/Aug. **Off site:** Tennis, riding and sailing in the area. Montmarault 4 km. for shopping needs.

**Charges** 2002

| | |
|---|---|
| Per adult | € 3.55 - € 4.19 |
| child (0-8 yrs) | € 2.45 - € 2.86 |
| pitch | € 5.95 - € 7.00 |
| dog | € 1.68 |
| electricity (6A) | € 2.85 |
| surcharge for 1 night stay | € 4.00 - € 5.50 |

**Tel:** 04 70 07 64 57. Fax: 04 70 07 25 48. E-mail: la.petite.valette@wanadoo.fr. **Reservations:** Essential for July/Aug. and made with 50% deposit. **Open** 1 April - 30 October.

**Directions**: From N145 Montmarault - Moulins road, turn right at first roundabout onto D46 signed St Pourcain. Turn left at next roundabout onto unclassified road signed Deux-Chaises and La Valette. After 2.5 km. turn left at site sign (La Valette) and site is approx. 1 km.

## Limousin/Auvergne
# Camping Deneuvre

**0306** Les Graves - RN9, 03500 Châtel de Neuvre

Anyone looking for a quiet, unsophisticated family site need look no further. Its situation on the banks of the Allier and alongside a nature reserve makes this the ideal spot for both bird-watchers and water lovers alike. The site hires out canoes and takes parties of canoeists on the river. The fish are very wily by all accounts and are not easily caught - what a challenge! The 75 pitches are about 80 sq.m, some a little larger, and all are on grass. The ones overlooking the river are naturally the most popular. Most pitches have some shade and 52 pitches have electricity (4A). English is spoken by the Dutch family owners.

**Facilities:** Unisex toilet blocks include some washbasins in cabins, a baby room with bath and a good unit for disabled people. Reception doubles as the bar and restaurant with a few essential groceries. Small pool, table tennis, darts and children's play area. Boule competitions and games for children organised in July/Aug. Bicycle hire. **Off site:** Riding 8 km, golf 12 km.

**Charges** 2002

| | |
|---|---|
| Per person | € 3.00 - € 3.75 |
| child (2-10 yrs) | € 2.00 - € 2.75 |
| pitch | € 3.00 - € 4.75 |
| dog | € 1.00 |
| electricity (4A) | € 2.25 |

**Tel:** 04 70 42 04 51. Fax: 04 70 42 04 51. E-mail: campingdeneuvre@wanadoo.fr. **Reservations:** Made with deposit; contact site. **Open** 1 April - 1 October.

**Directions:** Site is at northern end of Châtel de Neuvre on RN9 Moulins - St Pourcain road, signed from the main road. Site is 500 m.

---

## Limousin/Auvergne
# Camping Municipal Dompierre-sur-Besbre

**0317M** 03290 Dompierre-sur-Besbre

Popular with a cosmopolitan clientele, this very attractive, floral site has large, individually hedged, grassy pitches. It is located adjacent to the municipal sports fields, and within easy walking distance of the town centre and supermarket (700 m). There are 70 pitches with only a few long stay units, leaving about 65 for tourists; 60 have electricity (10A) and most have full service facilities. The warden is very proud of his efficiently run, value for money site. The Canal Latéral de la Loire is good for boating - do visit the nearby vertical boat lift.

**Facilities:** The toilet block is kept very clean and includes some washbasins in curtained cubicles for ladies, Turkish and British style WCs, dishwashing and laundry sinks plus a washing machine. Motorcaravan service point. **Off site:** The Vallée de la Besbre has a wealth of activities, with tennis and a swimming pool close by. Several small lakes in local villages are suitable for fishing. Cycle tracks and footpaths, and equestrian centres in the area.

**Charges** 2002

| | |
|---|---|
| Per adult | € 1.75 |
| child (5-14 yrs) | € 0.90 |
| pitch | € 1.40 - € 1.70 |
| electricity | € 1.60 |

No credit cards. **Tel:** 04 70 34 55 57. **Reservations:** Advised for high season. **Open** 15 May - 15 September.

**Directions:** Site is southeast of town centre just before the junction of N79 and D55, close to the river bridge.

---

## Limousin/Auvergne
# Camping Municipal du Lac

**0320M** avenue Mark Dormoy, 03310 Neris-les-Bains

This is a modern site on the edge of a very attractive, small spa town. It is actually a combination of two smaller sites now offering 135 mainly flat pitches. Those on the upper level are part-hardstanding in small bays and of only average size. Those on the lower level are in a very pleasant woodland setting with the pitches on either side of a babbling brook and close to a small ornamental lake. All have 10A electrical connections and a few on the lower level have water and drainage.

**Facilities:** There are three sanitary blocks, one on the upper level and two new ones on the lower level. They provide mostly British type WCs, washbasins in cabins, washing machine and dryer. New motorcaravan service point. Snack bar. **Off site:** The town's many and varied facilities are close

**Charges** guide

| | |
|---|---|
| Per unit incl. electricity and 1 person | € 8.43 |
| double axle caravan | € 16.01 |
| extra person (over 10 yrs) | € 3.20 |
| child (4-10 yrs) | € 1.56 |
| dog | € 0.91 |
| local tax (over 10 yrs) | € 0.35 |

**Tel:** 04 70 03 17 69. Fax: 04 70 03 79 99. **Reservations:** Contact site. **Open** 7 April - 28 October.

**Directions:** At roundabout in town centre, adjacent to Tourist Office take exit towards Villebret. Take first right and then first left into Avenue Marx Dormoy. Site is on the right in 500 m.

---

## Camping-Caravaning Le Val Saint Jean

**1503** 15200 Mauriac

La Val Saint-Jean is part of a typical, newly developed 'Centre de Loisirs' which the French do so well, set beside a lake in the heart of the département of Cantal. The campsite is situated at a height of 700 m. and provides 100 generously sized touring pitches (with 10A electricity), terraced with good views and organised for the maximum of privacy, on a hill above the lake. The site is well planned so that you are never far from a sanitary block and it has an impressive number of good quality facilities. Most of the activities are situated by the lake where you can use all the facilities of the leisure club including canoeing, kayaking and pedalos. The lake has a sandy beach and an area for swimming. There is a large swimming pool, plus one for children on the campsite with sunbathing areas (free to campers). Both the pool and the lake have lifeguards most of the time and can get very busy in the main season. This less well known region is well worth exploring and the local gastronomy can be experienced in the village of Mauriac with its attractive architecture typical of the area.

**Facilities:** The two sanitary blocks (4 and 6 years old) are well equipped with hot water throughout, providing some washbasins in cabins, dishwashing sinks and a laundry room with washing machine and dryer. Facilities for people with disabilities. Limited shop. Bar, snack bar and restaurant (all May - Sept). Swimming and paddling pools (1/6-15/9). Children's play area, playing field and table tennis. Watersports. Fishing. Activities organised for children (8-16 yrs) in July/Aug. **Off site:** A nine-hole golf course is next to site. Mauriac village 600 m. Riding 2 km.

**Charges** 2002

| | |
|---|---|
| Per unit incl. 2 persons | € 7.80 - € 15.00 |
| extra adult | € 3.00 - € 4.50 |
| child 10-18 yrs | € 3.00 - € 3.80 |
| child under 10 yrs | free - € 1.60 |
| dog | € 1.50 |
| electricity (10A) | € 3.00 |

**Tel:** 04 71 67 31 13. Fax: 04 71 68 17 34. E-mail: sogeval@wanadoo.fr. **Reservations:** Contact site. **Open** 11 May - 15 September.

**Directions:** From Clermont-Ferrand take RN 89 towards Bordeaux, then D922 towards Bort-les-Orgues-Mauriac. Site is well signed in Mauriac.

Camping Val St-Jean ★ ★ ★
Mauriac          Auvergne

Tel: 0033 471 67 31 13 - Fax: 0033 471 68 17 34
E-mail: SOGEVAL@wanadoo.fr
Website: www.camping-massifcentral.com

## Limousin/Auvergne
# Camping Intercommunal de l'Abeille
**1901** Village de Vacances VAL, L'Abeille, 19340 Eygurande

L'Abeille is situated between Clermont-Ferrand and Brive, in the grounds of and part of a 'village de vacances' complex. Most of the 75 pitches are large and separated by hedges, the 36 with electric hook-up (10A) being the largest (long leads may be needed for some hook-ups). All pitches are numbered, some are on gravel and some on grass. The manager was happy to point out that all the facilities of the Village are available to campers.

**Facilities:** Two small, well appointed toilet blocks include washbasins in cubicles and really large showers. Dishwashing and laundry sinks. Washing machines in each block, a dryer in one. Bar and restaurant. Very pleasant swimming pool and sunbathing area. Gym and jacuzzi (charged). Play areas. In season games and competitions are organised for adults and children. Tennis (free). Bicycles, pedaloes and boats for hire. Riding. Fishing permits. **Off site:** Village for bread is 1 km. Supermarket at Bourg-Lastic (9 km).

**Charges** guide

| | |
|---|---|
| Per pitch incl. 4 persons | € 9.91 - € 12.96 |
| extra adult | € 2.74 - € 3.20 |
| child (over 7 yrs) | € 1.52 - € 1.68 |
| electricity | € 2.40 |

**Tel:** 05 55 94 31 39. **Fax:** 05 55 94 41 98.
**Reservations:** Write to Village VAL 'L'Abeille', 19340 Eygurande or phone (0)4.73.43.00.43 (head office in Clermont-Ferrand) or site in season. Probably easiest just to turn up. **Open** 7 June - 13 September.

**Directions:** Site is signed (VAL) on the eastern edge of the village of Merlines which is 20 km. northeast of Ussel on the N89 road.

## Limousin/Auvergne
# Camping La Rivière
**1905** route de Brive, 19270 Donzenac

The Corrèze is not nearly as well known as the Dordogne to the immediate south, but it is, in fact, a beautiful area deserving of more attention. Donzenac itself is an attractive small town with a variety of shops, restaurants, etc. This former municipal site is situated on the outskirts, somewhat less than a mile from the centre (an uphill walk). The site is quite small with 77 fairly large pitches on level grass, the majority with electricity and many with shade from tall trees. It is next door to the town tennis courts and swimming pool (July/Aug. only; free to campers).

**Facilities:** Modernised sanitary facilities are very good and include a laundry room. Small takeaway. Baker calls at site in July/Aug. Table tennis, boules and minigolf. Fishing. Bicycle hire. **Off site:** Riding 4 km, golf 10 km.

**Charges** guide

| | |
|---|---|
| Per person | € 3.35 - € 3.81 |
| pitch | € 3.66 - € 4.12 |
| electricity (5A) | € 2.29 |
| dog | € 1.22 |

**Tel:** 05 55 85 63 95. **Fax:** 05 55 85 63 95.
**Reservations:** Probably unnecessary, but if in doubt 'phone. **Open** 1 April - 30 September.

**Directions:** Site is signed 'Village de Vacances', off the D920 at the bottom of the hill 2 km. south of Donzenac (7 km. north of Brive).

## Limousin/Auvergne
# Camping Le Mialaret
**1906** route d'Egletons, 19160 Neuvic

Mialaret is 4 km. from the village of Neuvic and only 14 km. from the river Dordogne. It is set in the grounds of a 19th century château, now a hotel with a good reputation for fresh lobster and with a special evening menu for campers. Most pitches are set in a sunny, gently sloping meadow type situation. Some are level and separated by small bushes, most have 6A electricity. In low season there are cooking courses with the chefs of the hotel, also at that time of the year the owner has time to take customers on a conducted tour of the 8 hectare estate in his 4x4 . Entertainment in high season is quite low key with some games, tournaments or an evening sing-along around a campfire, also musical evenings by both professionals and of the do-it-yourself type.

**Facilities:** Three refurbished sanitary blocks give an adequate provision, one heated. Washbasins in cabins, baby baths, facilities for disabled people, washing machines and dishwashing sinks. Motorcaravan service point. Shop at reception with bread daily. Bar with snacks and takeaway. Dinner at the hotel at special rate for campers. Play areas. Tennis. Fishing. Volleyball, football. Bicycle hire. The swimming pool is virtually a national monument as it is an original art-deco example. **Off site:** Village with shops and lake 4 km.

**Charges** 2002

| | |
|---|---|
| Per pitch | € 4.00 - € 5.00 |
| person | € 4.00 - € 5.00 |
| electricity | € 3.00 |

**Tel:** 05 55 46 02 50. **Fax:** 05 55 46 02 65. **E-mail:** info@lemialaret.com. **Reservations:** Contact site. **Open** 1 May - 31 October.

**Directions:** From Clermont-Ferrand take N89 southwest, and at Ussel take D982 to Neuvic. In Neuvic follow signs for Egleton and signs for site. Site is 4 km. on right. The D991 Egleton - Neuvic road is only suitable for cars or small motorhomes.

# Camping Le Château de Poinsouze

route de la Châtre, BP 12, 23600 Boussac-Bourg

Le Château de Poinsouze is a recently developed site with 136 pitches arranged on the open, gently sloping, grassy park to one side of the château's main drive - a beautiful plane tree avenue. It is a well designed, high quality site. The 94 touring pitches, some with lake frontage, all have electricity (6, 10 or 16A), with water, waste water and sewage connections to many. The château (not open to the public) lies across the lake from the site. The exceptionally well restored outbuildings on the opposite side of the drive house a new restaurant, other facilities and the pool area. The site has a friendly family atmosphere, there are organised activities in main season including dances, children's games and crafts, family triathlons, and there are marked walks around the park and woods. All facilities are open all season, though times may vary. This is a top class site with a formula which should ensure a stress-free, enjoyable family holiday. Boussac (2.5 km) has a market every Thursday morning. The massive 12/15th century fortress, Château de Boussac, is open daily all year.

**Facilities:** The high quality, double glazed sanitary unit is entered via a large utility area equipped with dishwashing and laundry sinks, foot-pedal operated taps, sinks accessible for wheelchair users, drinks machine and two smaller rooms with washing machines, dryer and ironing. Four spacious rooms are very well equipped including some washbasins in cubicles, baby baths, changing mats and child's WC, and two suites for disabled people. Good motorcaravan service point. Well stocked shop. Takeaway, Comfortable bar with games, TV and library room above. New restaurant. Well fenced swimming pool with slide, children's pool (children wear colour coded bracelets, deposit required). Fenced playground designed with safety in mind. Table tennis, petanque, pool table and table football games. Bicycle hire. Free fishing in the lake (if you put the fish back); boats and lifejackets can be hired. Football, volleyball, basketball, badminton and other games. Dogs are not accepted in high season (6/7-23/8).

**Charges** 2003

| | |
|---|---|
| Per pitch incl. 2 persons | € 12.00 - € 19.00 |
| with electricity (6A), water, drain | € 19.00 - € 25.00 |
| with electricity (10A), water, waste water, sewage connection | € 21.00 - € 26.00 |
| extra adult | € 3.50 - € 5.50 |
| child (2-7 yrs) | € 2.00 - € 4.00 |
| electricity 10-25A | € 2.00 - € 4.50 |
| dog (low and mid-season only) | € 3.00 |

**Tel:** 05 55 65 02 21. Fax: 05 55 65 86 49. E-mail: info.camping-de.poinsouze@wanadoo.fr.
**Reservations:** Advisable during July/Aug; made with 30% deposit and € 18,29 fee. **Open** 16 May - 14 September.

**Directions:** Site entrance is 2.5 km north of Boussac on D917 (towards La Châtre).

## Limousin/Auvergne
# Camping du Plan d'Eau de Courtille
**2305M** | 23000 Gueret

On gently sloping ground set in parkland beside a lake, this small site is just over 2 km from the centre of Guéret itself. Although there are few facilities on site there is a restaurant within walking distance. The lake offers some water sports and swimming is possible from the small beaches. There are footpaths and cycle tracks around the lake and in the park. The site has 70 good sized, individual pitches, all slightly sloping and with willow hedging. Most have some shade and all have electricity (3/10A). They are arranged in six circular clusters around the two toilet blocks.

**Facilities:** Purpose built sanitary units provide a mix of Turkish and British style WCs, washbasins in cubicles, facilities for disabled people, plus dishwashing and laundry sinks. Good motorcaravan service point. **Off site:** Swimming, riding, forest walks, cycling and canoeing near.

**Charges** guide

| | |
|---|---|
| Per pitch incl. electricity | € 5.49 |
| person (over 7 yrs) | € 1.83 |
| child (2-7 yrs) | € 0.84 |
| car | € 1.14 |
| animal | € 0.84 |

**Tel:** 05 55 81 92 24. **Reservations:** Probably unnecessary but are made - details from site. **Open** 1 June - 30 September.

**Directions:** Site is well signed from the town centre and is beside the Etang de Courtille, south west of the town.

## Limousin/Auvergne
# Camping La Fressange
**4301M** | 43140 St-Didier-en-Velay

This pretty site in rolling Haute-Loire countryside is worth considering as a base for touring this area or as a night-stop to visit St Didier. It has the advantage of being situated some 1 km southeast of the town, opposite the municipal swimming pool complex, which includes one pool of Olympic size. The sheltered site is attractively laid out on a series of grassy terraces - despite this, many pitches are on quite a slope and are difficult for motorcaravans. The 140 or so pitches (some occupied by long stay units) all have electricity (5A). There is some shade from the trees that border the site and further shade from smaller trees within it. There are no tour operators and the site is extensively used by the French.

**Facilities:** Two modern sanitary blocks include washbasins in cabins (warm water), dishwashing sinks, washing machine and facilities for disabled visitors. Barrier card (deposit). **Off site:** Town 5-10 minutes walk. Fishing, tennis 200 m. Municipal pool complex (July/Aug). Tennis courts 2 km

**Charges** 2003

| | |
|---|---|
| Per unit incl. 2 adults | € 10.00 |
| extra adult | € 2.150 |
| child (0-10 yrs) | free - € 1.50 |
| electricity | € 3.00 |

**Tel:** 04 71 66 25 28 (low season 04 73 34 75 53). E-mail; sogeval@wanadoo.fr. **Reservations:** Advised in high season. **Open** 1 May - 30 September.

**Directions:** Site is signed from the N88 via La Séauve, southwest of Semène. Alternatively from Firminy, southwest of St Etienne, take the D500 to St Didier.

## Limousin/Auvergne
# Camping du Puy-en-Velay
**4302** | avenue d'Aiguilhe, 43000 Le Puy-en-Velay

Formerly known as Camping Bouthezard, this busy urban site has a good security barrier and a warden who lives on site. Tarmac roads lead to around 70 grassy pitches with 6A electricity. A motorcaravan service point is adjacent with its own security barrier - apply to campsite reception for a barrier key to use the services, or for an overnight stop (reception opens 08.00-21.00 hrs). The town of Le Puy with its very interesting historic sector is within ten minutes walk and is well worth the trip. The Office de Tourisme is on the southern side in Place du Breuil.

**Facilities:** The main sanitary unit, recently refurbished and extended, includes some washbasins in cubicles. Facilities for disabled persons. Dishwashing and laundry sinks. An older unit at the rear of the site is only used in peak season. The facilities may be stretched in high season. Motorcaravan service point - see above. Table tennis, boule, volleyball and badminton.

**Charges** 2002

| | |
|---|---|
| Per unit incl. 2 persons incl. tax | € 8.10 |
| 4 persons incl. tax | € 12.80 |
| child (2-10 yrs) | € 1.10 |
| electricity | € 2.90 |

No credit cards. **Tel:** 04 71 09 55 09. **Reservations:** Contact site. **Open** mid-April - 1 October.

**Directions:** Site is northwest of the town centre, close to where N102 crosses the River Borne, and the Rocher St Michel d'Aiguilhe (a church on a rocky pinnacle). Site well signed around the town.

## Camping du Vaubarlet

**4303** Vaubarlet, 43600 Sainte-Sigolène

This peacefully located, spacious riverside family site has 130 marked, level, grassy and open pitches, with perimeter shade and electricity (6A). With 109 pitches for tourists, the remainder are occupied by site owned tents or mobile homes. Those who really like to get away from it all can use a small 'wild camping' area on the opposite side of the river with its own very basic facilities. This area is reached either by footbridge or a separate road access. The main site is separated from the river (unfenced) by a large field used for sports activities. This is also an attractive site for those seeking a quieter late break in September when it can be warm and sunny and with the pool, rooftop sun-deck, delightful modern bar with covered terrace all open. Tourist attractions in and around the region include a textile museum in Sainte Sigolène, an 'escargot' farm in nearby Grazac, the stunning scenery, chateaux and churches of the Haute-Loire, and the annual medieval festival in Le Puy each September. A 'Sites et Paysages' member.

**Facilities:** Two toilet units have British and Turkish style WCs, some washbasins in cubicles for ladies, baby room, laundry with washing machine and dryer and dishwashing sinks. Two new family bathrooms (WC, basin, shower) behind the bar, are also suitable for disabled people. Basic sanitary unit and campers' kitchen with cooker in 'wild' area. Small shop (bread to order). Takeaway in main season. Bar. Fenced swimming pool with children's pool. Bicycle hire. Table tennis, boule, volleyball and space for ball games. Children's playground. Organised activities in main season include camp fire and music evenings, canoe lessons for children, pony riding and mini-motorbike motocross (possibly noisy). Trout fishing (licenses available). Birdwatching, walking. Barbecues on loan. **Off site:** Two supermarkets in Ste Sigolène (6 km). Three golf courses nearby.

**Charges** 2002

| Per unit incl. 2 persons | € 14.00 |
|---|---|
| extra adult | € 3.00 |
| child (2-7 yrs) | € 2.00 |
| electricity | € 3.00 |
| pet | € 1.00 |

**Tel:** 04 71 66 64 95. Fax: 04 71 66 11 98. E-mail: vaubarlet@aol.com. **Reservations:** Advised for high season and made with 25% deposit and fee (€ 19,82). **Open** 1 May - 30 September.

**Directions:** Site is 6 km. southwest of Ste Sigolène on the D43 signed Grazac. Turn off this road by river bridge and follow signs.

## Camping-Caravaning Le Champ d'Ayres

**4800** route de la Brèze, 48150 Meyrueis

The road to Meyrueis is not for the faint-hearted, although we managed in quite a large motorhome with only a few stretches being a little on the narrow side, and the return seemed even easier. This is a tradi-tionally French style site with a modern feel to it, set in the heart of the Cevennes. Very neat, tidy and well kept, Le Champ d'Ayres is run by a young family with young fami-lies in mind (teenagers might be bored). The site is slightly sloping with 70 grass pitches, the majority hedged with well trimmed bushes and most with some shade. All have electricity (6/10A) but may require long leads. The area is surrounded by mountains and gorges but the river Jonte is not a canoeing river so a trip to the Tarn would be needed for that. The Gorges de Jonte has an observatory from which vultures can be observed flying the thermals. Being very central there are many attractions in the area - wild horses have been introduced on the causses a few miles to the north, the observatory at the top of Mt Aigoual is well worth a visit and there are many caves in the region.

**Facilities:** The central sanitary block, kept excep-tionally clean, includes mainly British style WCs and some washbasins in cabins. Family sized shower room, room with facilities for disabled visitors and baby room. Laundry and dishwashing sinks. Washing machine and dryer. Reception incorporates a small bar (1/6-15/9) which also sells ices and bread. Swimming and paddling pools (25/5-15/9). Play area on grass (5-10 yrs), small games room, table tennis, basketball, netball and a boules pitch. In July/Aug. activities are arranged for children, also paella evenings with music and activities such as walking and caving. **Off site:** The pretty small town of Meyrueis has many good restaurants.

**Charges** 2003

| Per unit incl. 2 persons | € 10.00 - € 14.00 |
|---|---|
| extra person | € 2.50 - € 3.30 |
| child (under 7 yrs) | € 1.60 - € 2.30 |
| electricity (6A) | € 2.50 |
| local tax (15/6-15/9) | € 0.25 |

**Tel:** 04 66 45 60 51. Fax: 04 66 45 60 51. E-mail: campinglechampdayres@wanadoo.fr. **Reservations:** Contact site. **Open** 1 April - 30 September.

**Directions:** From N9 at Aquessac (5 km. north of Millau) take D907 signed Gorge du Tarn. At Rozier turn right on D996 signed Meyrueis and Gorges de la Jonte. In Meyrueis follow signs for Château d'Ayres and campsite signs. Site is 500 m.

## Limousin/Auvergne
# Camping Municipal Les Prades
43160 La Chaise Dieu

**4311M**

This very attractive, rural municipal site is 1.5 km. north of the town, situated in pleasant countryside next to woodland and a lake with public footpaths adjacent. The site provides 100 pitches, some with electricity (10A), arranged on well cut grass which is landscaped with numerous pine trees (mature and with character) and tarmac roads. All is well tended and rather park-like. A spacious and well run site, the guardian Mme. Delorme, lives on site.

**Facilities:** Two modern sanitary blocks have wash-basins in cubicles, toilets (Turkish type for men) and plenty of hot water; finding a cold water tap is a different matter - try the laundry sink. Only one block is open in low season. Play area. **Off site:** Fishing and windsurfing facilities near.

**Charges** 2002

| | |
|---|---|
| Per person | € 2.74 |
| child (under 7) | € 1.83 |
| pitch | € 2,29 - € 2.74 |
| electricity | € 2.74 |
| local tax | € 0.15 |

**Tel:** 04 71 00 07 88. **Reservations:** Advised - contact site. **Open** 1 June - 30 September.

**Directions:** La Chaise-Dieu is approx. 40 km. north of Le Puy on the D906. Site is signed 1.5 km. north of the town.

## Limousin/Auvergne
# Château Camping La Grange Fort
Les Pradeaux, 63500 Issoire

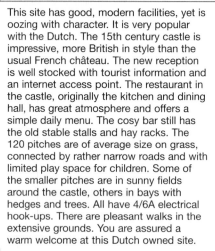

**6304**

This site has good, modern facilities, yet is oozing with character. It is very popular with the Dutch. The 15th century castle is impressive, more British in style than the usual French château. The new reception is well stocked with tourist information and an internet access point. The restaurant in the castle, originally the kitchen and dining hall, has great atmosphere and offers a simple daily menu. The cosy bar still has the old stable stalls and hay racks. The 120 pitches are of average size on grass, connected by rather narrow roads and with limited play space for children. Some of the smaller pitches are in sunny fields around the castle, others in bays with hedges and trees. All have 4/6A electrical hook-ups. There are pleasant walks in the extensive grounds. You are assured a warm welcome at this Dutch owned site.

**Facilities:** The main toilet facilities in the old stable buildings are modern and heated but hot water is only available morning and early evening. Baby rooms. The men's has facilities for disabled visitors and a 'hydra shower'. Laundry room. Reception has a few groceries (bread to order). Restaurant and bar (1/6-15/9) with takeaway. Indoor pool with sliding glass doors, sauna and massage table (15/4-15/10). Two outdoor pools (15/6-1/10). Play area and games room. Tennis, minigolf, table tennis, volleyball, football field and boules. Organised activities in season include archery, canoeing, riding and cycling (horses and bikes provided). **Off site:** Fishing 250 m.

**Charges** 2002

| | |
|---|---|
| Per adult | € 4.10 |
| child (under 7 yrs) | € 2.50 |
| pitch | € 6.90 |
| electricity | € 2.50 |

**Tel:** 04 73 71 02 43. **Fax:** 04 73 71 07 69. **E-mail:** chateau@grangefort.com. **Reservations:** Contact site for details. **Open** 1 March - 1 November.

**Directions:** From A75 autoroute take exit 13 at Issoire. Travel east on D996 to Parentignat and in village turn right (D999) and after 200 m. right again on D34 signed Nonette. Site is 3 km.

## Limousin/Auvergne
# Camping Municipal du Mas
avenue du Docteur Bienfait, 63500 Issoire

**6310M**

This site is located a few hundred metres from exit 12 (Issoire) on the A75 autoroute - there could be some road noise, but it was not intrusive when we visited in late June. The very spacious site is on fairly level grass, with most of the 140 pitches arranged in bays of two or three. Most are fully serviced and have some shade. A useful grassy area beside a lake is immediately opposite the site for sunbathing or picnicking under the trees. The lake is used for fishing and is probably unsuitable for swimming.

**Facilities:** Sanitary facilities in three blocks, one heated in cool weather, are quite adequate with mostly Turkish style WCs and some washbasins ine cabins. Dishwashing and laundry sinks (cold water only) and two washing machines. Not all blocks are open in low season. Good motorcaravan service point. General room with TV and cold drinks machine. Play area. Minigolf and table tennis. **Off site:** Hypermarket just the other side of the motor-way. Sports complex nearby.

**Charges** 2002

| | |
|---|---|
| Per person | € 3.00 |
| child (under 7 yrs) | € 1.50 |
| pitch and vehicle | € 2.50 - € 3.50 |
| electricity (6A) | € 2.00 |

**Tel:** 04 73 89 03 59. **Reservations:** Seldom required and discouraged. **Open** 1 April - 31 October.

**Directions:** Take exit 12 from the A75 towards Orbeil. At roundabout take first exit (site signed) and site is a few hundred metres.

## Camping La Ribeyre

**6305** Jassat, 63790 Murol

About a kilometre from the centre of Murol, La Ribeyre has a charm about it which is quite unique. The owners, Mme Pommier and her two sons, originally farmers, have put much personal effort in constructing the site and its buildings, even the pool. Many young trees have been planted to add to those already on site and a man-made lake at one end provides facilities for water sports. There is a picturesque reception area, with a fountain and tastefully laid-out floral decorations. The site now provides 400 level, grassy pitches, of which 300 have electricity (3/6A) and 64 have individual electricity, water and drainage. Although not normally advertised, there are 10A outlets for those who take the trouble to ask. The surrounding area is very much worth a visit. From mountains rising to over 6,000 ft, to lakes, cavernes and many local craft centres, this site is a superb centre. It is only 5 or 6 km. from St Nectaire, about 10 km from Besse and about 20 km from Le Mont Dore, which is a starting point for the Puy de Sancy, the highest peak in the area. This is a wonderful walking and cycling area and the flowers in May and June are a joy to behold. Supervised by the owners, the atmosphere on site is extremely friendly.

**Facilities:** Six excellent, very clean modern toilet blocks provide British and Turkish style WCs and some washbasins in cubicles. Snack bar in peak season (20/6-1/9). Heated swimming pool 200 sq.m.(1/5-1/9). TV and games room. Tennis, volleyball and fishing. New play area. Lake providing swimming, canoeing and surf boarding (lifeguard in July/Aug). Facilities are limited in early season. **Off site:** Bicycle hire 1 km.

**Charges** 2002

| | |
|---|---|
| Per unit incl. 1 adult | € 7.60 - € 11.00 |
| extra person | € 3.10 - € 4.40 |
| child (under 5 yrs) | € 2.30 - € 3.40 |
| electricity (6A) | € 3.10 - € 3.80 |
| pitch with full services plus | € 6.10 |
| local tax (child 5-16 yrs 0.15) | € 0.38 |

**Tel:** 04 73 88 64 29. Fax: 04 73 88 64 41.
**Reservations:** Contact site. **Open** 1 May - 15 September.

**Directions:** From A75 autoroute, take exit 6, signed St Nectaire and carry on to Murol. Several sites are signed as you go into the town. Turn left and then, opposite Syndicat d'Initiative, turn right. La Ribeyre is the second site on the left, just after the entrance to Jassat and is well marked on left.

## Camping Le Pré Bas

Lac Chambon, 63790 Murol

**6307**

In the heart of the Parc des Volcans d'Auvergne. almost on the edge of Lac Chambon, Le Pre Bas is especially suitable for families with younger children and those seeking the watersports opportunities that the lake provides. Large, level, grassy pitches are divided up by mature hedging and trees and, with 50 mobile homes for rent, around 130 pitches are available for tourists, all with electricity (4A). Close by is a gate which leads on to the lakeside, where there is windsurfing, pedaloes, canoes or fishing, and 50 m. away is a beach with supervised bathing. The site has a new pool complex with heated swimming pools (one covered), a slide and a paddling pool.

**Facilities:** There is one large central toilet building with four smaller units spread around site. These include some washbasins in cubicles, facilities for disabled guests and dishwashing sinks. Laundry with sinks, washing machines, dryers and ironing facilities, and baby room. Motorcaravan service point. Snack bar with a small terrace (10/6-10/9 and some weekends in low season). Pool complex (10/6-10/9) has three pools of different depths (lifeguard in July/Aug). Watersports and fishing. Games room with table tennis, table football, etc, large 'salle' with giant TV screen, library and adventure style playground. Organised activities (late June - early Sept) include local visits, guided walks, riding, archery and climbing.

**Charges** 2002

| | |
|---|---|
| Per pitch incl. 1 person | € 7.60 - € 12.00 |
| extra person | € 3.10 - € 4.50 |
| child (1-5 yrs) | free - € 3.00 |
| child (5-10 yrs) | € 2.30 - € 4.00 |
| electricity (6A) | € 3.10 - € 3.85 |
| local tax | € 0.30 |

**Tel:** 04 73 88 63 04. Fax: 04 73 88 65 93. E-mail: prebas@lac-chambon.com. **Reservations:** Essential for high season, made with € 39 p/week deposit. **Open** 1 May - 30 September.

**Directions:** Site is located on the D966, 3 km. west of Murol towards Le Mont Dore.

In the middle of the Auvergne Volcanoes Park, on the banks of Lake Chambon

## Camping du Pré Bas ☆☆☆

❤ Heated and covered Swimming pool and waterslide complex
❤ Static caravans and pitches
❤ Snack bar - Billiard and television room
❤ Leisure and many sports on site and in the vicinity
❤ Hiking from the camp site
❤ 35km from the European Park of Volcanism " Vulcania

Member of the national Charter of " Camping Qualité "

Camping Qualité

**63790 Lac Chambon**
**Tel : 0033 4-73-88-63-04**
**Fax : 0033 4-73-88-65-93**
**www.campingauvergne.com**

## Limousin/Auvergne
# Camping Le Clos Auroy

**6306** Rue de la Narse, 63670 Orcet

Orcet is a typical Auvergne village just south of Clermont Ferrand and, being fairly close (3 km) to the A75, it makes an excellent stopping off point on the journey south (the A75 is free of charge from here, southwards to Montpellier). Le Clos Auroy is a new and popular site, 300 m. from the village. The 90 good size pitches are on level grass, separated by high hedges, all with electricity (5A), and many fully serviced. In winter only 20 pitches are available.

**Facilities:** Two good quality sanitary units include washbasins in cubicles. Dishwashing and laundry sinks. Washing machine and dryer. A smaller, heated unit at reception is used mainly for the winter season. Chemical disposal is at the motorcaravan service point, close to the site entrance (a long walk from some pitches, as is the fresh water tap). Small shop and takeaway (both 1/7-15/9). Well fenced, heated swimming pool (12 x 6 m; 15/5-30/9). Playground. Coffee mornings. Tennis. **Off site:** Boule 50 m. Fishing and canoeing 500 m. Village with shops and three wine 'caves' 300 m. Very large children's playground nearby and riverside walk just outside gate.

**Charges 2003**

| | |
|---|---|
| Per unit incl. 2 persons | € 14.00 |
| extra person | € 3.60 |
| child (1-7 yrs) | € 2.50 |
| animal | € 1.50 |
| electricity (5/10A) | € 2.60 - € 4.20 |
| local tax | € 0.14 - € 0.27 |
| extra for 1 or 2 night stays | € 1.00 - € 2.00 |

**Tel:** 04 73 84 26 97. **Fax:** 04 73 84 26 97. **E-mail:** camping.Le.Clos.Auroy@wanadoo.fr. **Reservations:** Advised for July/August. **Open** all year.

**Directions:** From A75 take exit 4 or 5 towards Orcet and follow campsite signs.

---

## Limousin/Auvergne
# Camping du Château de Leychoisier

**8702** Domaine de Leychoisier, 87270 Bonnac-la-Côte

the travel service
TO BOOK

| | |
|---|---|
| Ferry | ✓ |
| Pitch | ✓ |
| Accommodation | ✗ |

01892 55 98 98

This well-established chataeu site offers peace and quiet in superb surroundings and the large estate offers the opportunity to explore the grounds and to walk down to the four hectare lake. It is ideally situated only 2 km. from the A20/N20 and 10 km. north of Limoges. There are 90 large grass pitches, some partly sloping with a mixture of sun and shade, and 76 having electricity (10A). The lake provides free fishing, boating, canoeing and a marked off area for swimming. Perhaps a little expensive for the facilities provided, this is, however, a quiet site where you have plenty of space and where there are no letting units and many people like it for these reasons.

**Facilities:** The partially refurbished sanitary block is in an old building. Very clean, but rather cramped it needs extending and updating to cope with demand at busy times. Some washbasins in private cabins and provision for disabled visitors. Washing machine. Basic food provisions sold from reception (order bread the night before). Restaurant (from 20/6), snack bar and bar housed in open-ended barn, partly protected by a canopy and attractive gazebo. Swimming pool (proper swimming trunks, no shorts). Lake. Children's play area. Table tennis, tennis and boules courts (both in need of repair when we visited), volleyball and bar billiards. Torch useful. Winter caravan storage. **Off site:** Mini-market 2 km, supermarket 5 km. Golf 20 km, riding 7 km.

**Charges 2002**

| | |
|---|---|
| Per pitch | € 7.00 - € 8.00 |
| motorcaravan plus | € 1.50 - € 3.00 |
| person | € 4.50 - € 6.00 |
| child (under 7) | € 3.00 - € 4.00 |
| electricity | € 3.50 - € 4.00 |
| local tax | € 0.50 - € 1.00 |

**Tel:** 05 55 39 93 43. **Fax:** 05 55 39 93 43. **E-mail:** leychoisier@wanadoo.fr. **Reservations:** Made with deposit (€ 15,24) and fee (€ 12,20), although short reservations accepted without charge in low season. **Open** 15 April - 20 September.

**Directions:** From A20 take exit 27 (west) signed Bonnac-La-Côte. Site is well signed from the village.

# Rhône Valley

Map 13

Major city: Lyon

Départements: 01 Ain, 07 Ardèche, 26 Drôme, 42 Loire, 69 Rhône

The Rhône Valley is one of Europe's main arteries – this traditional route carries millions of travellers and millions of tons of freight by rail (TGV), by autoroute and by water to the Mediterranean. However, either side of this busy corridor are areas of great interest and natural beauty. From the sun-baked Drôme, with its ever-changing landscapes, culminating in the isolated mountains of the Vercors; the deep gorges and high plateaux of the Ardèche, studded with prehistoric caves to lush valleys filled with orchards and the vineyards of the Beaujolais and the Rhône Valley.

The region's 2,000 year history as a cultural crossroads has blessed the area with a rich blend of customs, architecture and sights of interest. The city of Lyon was developed by the Romans as a trading centre, and was once the capital. It is now the second largest city of France. Although heavily industrialised, it has a charming old quarter and is renowned for its gastronomy. The Place de la Terreur in the centre of the city is where the guillotine was placed during the French revolution – until it wore out through over-use. There are also reminders of the city's role in World War 2 as a resistance centre.

Not far from Lyon lies the Dombes, the 'land of a thousand lakes', the medieval village of Pérouges and the Roman ruins of Vienne with its yearly jazz festival.

Note: the site reports are laid out by département in numerical order not by region.

## Cuisine of the region

From Lyon to Bresse and Bugey by way of the Dombes, food is an art and a science. The poultry, cheese, freshwater fish, mushrooms and wines are superb

*Bresse (Poulet, Poularde, Volaille de)* – the best French poultry, fed on corn and when killed bathed in milk; flesh is white and delicate

*Gras-double* – ox tripe, served with onions

*Poulet demi-deuil* (half-mourning) – called this because of thin slices of truffle placed under the chicken breast

*Poulet au vinaigre* – chicken, shallots, tomatoes, white wine, wine vinegar and a cream sauce

*Rosette* – a large pork sausage

*Sabodet* – Lyonnais sausage of pig's head, pork and beef, served hot

Wine

Beaujolais, Côte Rotie, St Julien, Condrieu, Tain-Hermitage, Chiroubles and Julienas are some of the wines produced in this region

## Places of interest

*Beaujolais* – vineyards and golden-stone villages

*Bourg-en-Bresse* – 16th/17th century church of Notre-Dame, craft shops, museum of Ain; also famous for its yellow, corn-fed chickens

*Dombes* – land of a thousand lakes, ornithological park

*Lyon* – Gallo-Roman artifacts, Renaissance quarter, historical Fabric Museum, silk museum.

*Montélimar* – nougat capital of France

*Pérouges* – lovely medieval village, Galette de Pérouges

*St Etienne* – museum of Modern Art

*Vallon-Pont d'Arc* – base from which to visit Gorges de l'Ardèche; canoe and rafting centre

*Vienne* – Roman remains, Gothic style cathedral, 6th century church St Pierre

## Rhône Valley
# Camping La Plaine Tonique
Base de Plein Air, 01340 Montrevel-en-Bresse

This site belongs to a syndicate of several local villages. It is a very well maintained, large site with 560 marked and numbered pitches, all with 10A electricity. The majority are of a good size, hedged and on flat grass, with reasonable shade in most parts. Although large, the site is spacious and certainly does not feel so as it is broken up into smaller sections by trees and hedges. The site is on the edge of a large, 320-acre lake with its own beach and adjacent public beach. A variety of watersports includes sailing, windsurfing, swimming, canoeing and, on other parts of the lake, water-skiing and fishing. Campers may bring their own boats, but not motor boats. A separate area of the site is used by Dutch tour operators (100 pitches).

**Facilities:** The eleven blocks have mostly been renovated to a very high standard with some washbasins in cabins, baby rooms and washing machines. Motorcaravan service point. Restaurant, bar (all season) and shop (July/Aug) are adjacent to the site. 'Aquatonic' centre with five pools (reduced charge for campers). Watersports and fishing. Minigolf and tennis courts. Adventure play area on beach. Games room. Archery, bicycle hire and new roller skating area. **Off site:** Riding 2 km. Montrevel 300 m. walk.

**Charges 2003**

| | |
|---|---|
| Per unit incl. electricity | € 6.90 - € 10.60 |
| person | € 2.60 - € 4.30 |
| child (3-7 yrs) | € 1.40 - € 2.10 |

**Tel:** 04 74 30 80 52. **Fax:** 04 74 30 80 77. **E-mail:** plaine.tonique@wanadoo.fr. **Reservations:** Required mid July - end Aug; write with 25% deposit. **Open** 14 April - 28 September.

**Directions:** Site is 20 km. north of Bourg-en-Bresse and 25 km. east of Macon. Montrevel is on the D975; site signed in the town centre on road towards Etrez on D28.

## Rhône Valley
# Camping de L'Ile Chambod
01250 Hautecourt

Anyone looking for a quiet, unsophisticated, family run and rurally situated site need look no further. This small site is being completely redeveloped to a high standard by its enthusiastic young English-speaking owners, including two new toilet blocks and a swimming pool. The 110 good-sized pitches (about 100 sq m) are separated by small hedges and most have some shade. They all have access to electricity (5A but a few with 10A) although some may need long leads, with plenty of water points. A lakeside beach is only 300 m. away (small charge in July/August) offers simple watersports and minigolf. Bourg-en-Bresse offers a wealth of shops, restaurants, museums etc.

**Facilities:** Two new and well appointed toilet blocks include some washbasins in cabins, dishwashing and laundry sinks. Washing machine and dryer. Both blocks have facilities suitable for disabled visitors and one has a baby room. Bread to order. Small shop and takeaway (June, July and Aug). Small play area. Activities organised in high season for children.

**Charges 2002**

| | |
|---|---|
| Per person | € 3.50 |
| child (up to 12 yrs) | € 2.50 |
| pitch | € 2.50 |
| vehicle | € 2.00 |
| electricity 5-10A | € 2.50 - € 3.50 |
| animal | € 1.00 |

**Tel:** (0)4 74 37 25 41. **Fax:** (0)4 74 37 28 28. **E-mail:** camping.chambod@free.fr. **Reservations:** Advised for July/Aug. **Open** 1 May - 30 September.

**Directions:** Site is approx. 23 km. southeast of Bourg-en-Bresse via the D979. It is well signed from the crossroad in Hautecourt, and is a further 4 km. down the lane.

## Rhône Valley
# Camping La Garenne
chemin de la Garenne, 07800 St-Laurent-du-Pape

This spacious, family orientated site is within easy reach of the A7/N7 south of Valence. Owned and run by Dutchman Tim Martojo, guests are predominantly Dutch but all are made welcome and English is widely spoken. Visitors' pursuits have been carefully considered resulting in a variety of family activities. People with diverse interests are therefore attracted throughout the season - for example, bridge evenings are organised in May, June and September. The 116 grassy/stony pitches (rock pegs advised), some terraced and some sloping, are of 80-100 sq.m, some separated by hedges. All have electricity but only 4A (some need long leads). The amount of shade varies from none to quite heavy.

**Facilities:** It is a short stroll to the village where most necessities are catered for. Fishing 1 km, riding 2 km. Walking, biking, canoeing, canyoning and exploring the Ardèche region. Some off site activities run from site. **Off site:** The village is a short stroll. Fishing 1 km, riding 2 km.

**Charges 2002**

| | |
|---|---|
| Per unit incl. 1 or 2 persons | € 11.00 - € 23.00 |
| with electricity | € 14.00 - € 23.00 |
| extra person (over 3 yrs) | € 4.50 |

**Tel:** 04 75 62 24 62. **Fax:** 04 75 62 24 62. **Reservations:** Advised and made with deposit (€ 75) and fee (€ 15). **Open** 1 March - 1 November.

**Directions:** From A7 exit 16 Loriol south of Valence take N304 west over the Rhône to Le Pouzin. Turn right immediately on N86 to la Voulte sur Rhône. Go through Voulte following signs for St Laurent du Pape and then left on D120. In St Laurent cross the river and turn left. Shortly, just before La Poste, turn right and site is shortly on the left.

# Domaine des Plantas

,07360 Les Ollières-sur-Eyrieux

**the travel service**

TO BOOK

| Ferry | ✔ |
| Pitch | ✔ |
| Accommodation | ✔ |

01892 55 98 98

A good quality site in a spectacular setting on the steep banks of the Eyrieux river, Domaine des Plantas offers an attractive alternative to those in the more popular southern parts of the Ardèche. The Eyrieux valley is less well known, but arguably just as attractive as those further south and a good deal less crowded, particularly in the main season. Perhaps the only drawback to this site is the narrow twisting three kilometre approach road which, although by no means frightening, may present something of a challenge to those with large outfits - however, the helpful owners have an ingenious convoy system designed to assist campers on departure. There is a sandy beach beside the quite fast-flowing, but fairly shallow, river (used for bathing) and a swimming pool and paddling pool with tiled surrounds for sunbathing. Facilities are housed in an original building which is quite impressive with its Protestant history and visible from the main road across the river long before you reach it. The restaurant terrace provides a stunning viewpoint. The 162 pitches (35 new in 2002, with electricity, water and drain) are terraced and shaded, so some up and down walking is required. They have electricity connections (10A, long leads may be needed) and water points are very accessible.

**Facilities:** One large, modern toilet block, centrally situated in courtyard style, is well equipped with washbasins in cubicles and good facilities for children with small toilets and baby baths. An additional smaller block serves the higher terraces. Dishwashing and laundry sinks. Washing machine. Motorcaravan service point. Small shop (bread to order). Bar, restaurant and disco. Heated kidney shaped swimming pool and paddling pool. Adventure play area beside river. Mountain biking, canoeing, canyoning, riding and 'randonnées pedestres' (sounds better in French!). In high season animation for children organised six days a week, and discos for 14-18 year olds held in cellar twice weekly (strictly no alcohol). Many activities are possible and are arranged according to the campers' motivations, including excursions. Only gas barbecues are allowed. **Off site:** Riding 15 km.

**Charges** 2002

| Per unit incl. 2 persons, electricity | € 18.00 - € 26.00 |
| extra person over 4 yrs | € 4.00 - € 6.00 |
| animal | € 2.00 |
| local tax | € 0.31 |

**Tel:** 04 75 66 21 53. Fax: 04 75 66 23 65. E-mail: plantas.ardeche@wanadoo.fr. **Reservations:** Made with deposit (€ 110) and fee (€ 20). **Open** 15 June - 15 September.

**Directions:** From A7 take exit 15 (Valence Sud). Immediately after the péage turn right to Valence centre, then follow signs to Montélimar via the N7 for 7 km. Turn right towards Charmes sur Rhône, thence to Beauchastel. On leaving Beauchastel follow signs to Ollieres sur Eyrieux.

# Camping-Caravaning L'Ardéchois

Le Chambon, Gluiras, 07190 St-Sauveur-de-Montagut

0702

This attractive site is quite a way off the beaten track and the approach road is winding and narrow in places. However, it is worth the effort, to find in such a spectacular setting, a hillside site offering a range of amenities. There are several different types of pitch, varying in size (85-140 sq.m) and with many separated by trees and plants. Some are alongside the small, fast-flowing river, while the rest (60%) are on higher, sloping ground nearer the restaurant/bar. All 83 touring pitches have electricity (6A). The main site access roads are tarmac but are quite steep and larger units may find access to some terraces difficult. The amenities have been created by the careful conversion of old buildings which provide modern facilities in an attractive style (all from Easter). The new friendly Dutch owners have developed an extensive excursion programme for exploring this attractive area on foot or by car. The site is popular with the Dutch. A Sites et Paysages member.

**Facilities:** Two good sanitary blocks provide washbasins in private cabins, baths and showers for babies and facilities for people with disabilities. Maintenance can be variable. Dishwashing and laundry rooms. Motorcaravan service point. Shop. Bar/restaurant. TV room. Table tennis. Volleyball. Bicycle hire, archery and fishing. Swimming pool (heated in low season; no bermuda style shorts) with adjacent bar, snack bar and terrace, plus a paddling pool for children. **Off site:** Canyoning, climbing, and canoeing trips organised.

**Charges** 2003

| | |
|---|---|
| Per unit incl. 2 persons | € 18.00 - € 24.00 |
| extra person | € 4.00 |
| animal | € 3.00 - € 4.00 |
| extra car | € 7.00 |

**Tel:** 04 75 66 61 87. Fax: 04 75 66 63 67. E-mail: ardechois.camping@wanadoo.fr. **Reservations:** Write with deposit (€ 69) and fee (€ 23); min. 10 days 6/7-24/8. **Open** Easter - 31 October.

**Directions:** From Valence take N86 south for 12 km, turn right onto D120 to St Sauveur de Montagut, then take D102 towards Mézilhac for 8 km. to site.

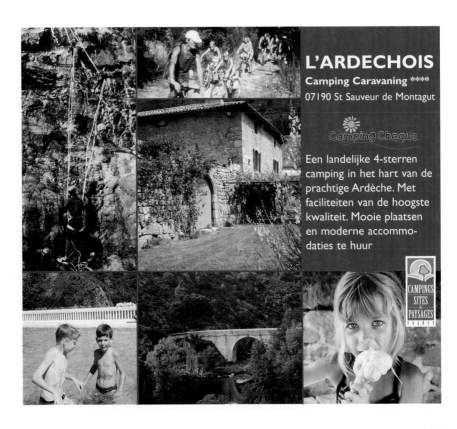

Domaine Le Pommier is an extremely spacious Dutch owned site of 10 hectares in 32 hectares of wooded grounds. It has first class facilities, including the most up-to-date toilet blocks, a very good bar/restaurant and one of the best swimming pool complexes we have seen - ideal for all the family. The site is steeply terraced (a tractor is available for assistance) and has wonderful views over the Ardèche mountains and beyond. There are 400 pitches with 275 for tourists. They are grassy/stony, of good size and well spaced. Separated by young trees and hedges, some have little or no shade. All have access to electricity and water is close by.

**Facilities:** Four new toilet blocks, one with under floor heating, provide all the necessary facilities. Comprehensive shop. Bar/restaurant. Heated pool complex with water slides, a flowing 'river', several good, unusual paddling pools and a conventional pool for serious swimming. Large fitness room. Everything opens from the end of April. Boules, football, minigolf, badminton, games in the woods, table tennis, archery, water polo, tug of war, volleyball, tennis etc. Sound-proof disco. Very extensive programme of events on and off site. Off season excursions to vineyards, wine tasting, museums, nougat factory and old villages. Also bridge and water colour classes. **Off site:** Villeneuve de Berg 1.5 km. River Ardèche 12 km. Potholing, rock climbing, canoeing, canyoning, mountain biking, walking or horse riding. Touring the many old villages and the Ardèche Gorge.

**Charges** 2002

| | |
|---|---|
| Per unit incl. 2 persons | € 12.20 - € 25.00 |
| extra person over 4 yrs | € 3.05 - € 5.35 |
| electricity | € 3.05 |
| dog | € 1.25 |
| local tax | € 0.50 |

**Tel:** (0)4 75 94 82 81. Fax: (0)4 75 94 83 90. E-mail: info@campinglepommier.com. **Reservations:** Made with booking fee (€ 20) and cancellation insurance (4.5%). **Open** 1 April - 15 October.

**Directions:** Site is west of Montélimar on the N102. The entrance is adjacent to the roundabout at the eastern end of the Villeneuve de Berg bypass.

## Rhône Valley
## Camping Nature Parc L'Ardéchois

route touristique des Gorges, 07150 Vallon-Pont-d'Arc

This very high quality, family run site is within walking distance of Vallon Pont d'Arc. It borders the River Ardèche and canoe trips are run, professionally, direct from the site. This campsite is ideal for families with younger children seeking an active holiday. The facilities are comprehensive and of an extremely high standard, particularly the new (2002) central toilet block. Of the 244 pitches, there are 225 medium to large grass pitches for tourers, separated by trees and individual shrubs. All have electricity and about half have full services. The focal point of the site is the bar and restaurant with terrace and stage overlooking the attractive heated pool. Access to the site is easy and suitable for large outfits.

**Facilities:** Two well equipped toilet blocks, one superb with 'everything' working automatically. Facilities are of the highest standard, very clean and include good facilities for babies, those with disabilities, washing up and laundry. Four private bathrooms to hire. Washing machines. Well stocked shop. Bar/restaurant. Swimming pool and paddling pool (no Bermuda shorts). Football, tennis and table tennis. Play area. Internet point. Organised activities, canoe trips. **Off site:** Vallon Pont d'Arc 800 m.

**Charges** 2002

| | |
|---|---|
| Per pitch incl. 2 persons | € 21.50 - € 27.50 |
| with water and drainage | € 27.50 - € 34.00 |
| extra person (any age) | € 5.00 - € 6.50 |
| electricity | € 4.00 |

**Tel:** (0)4 75 88 06 63. Fax: (0)4 75 37 14 97. E-mail: ardecamp@aol.com. **Reservations:** Made with deposit (€ 94) and fee (€ 31). **Open** 15 April - 22 September.

**Directions:** From Vallon Pont d'Arc (western end of the Ardèche Gorge) go east on the D290. Site entrance is shortly on the right.

## Rhône Valley
## Camping La Rouveyrolle

Casteljau, 07460 Berrias et Casteljau

Le Rouveyrolle's very friendly (English speaking) French owners run a site ideally suited for families. This is a very tranquil and relaxed site by the river Chassezac in attractive countryside surrounded by vineyards and orchards. The focal point is the lovely pool, paddling pool (with fountain) and sunbathing area, all overlooked by the bar/restaurant and terrace. Of the 100 good sized pitches, 40 are available for tourists. These are on flat grass separated by shrubs and hedges with some shade and all have electricity (5A). Pot-holing and rock climbing (with guides) are possible nearby and excursions can be arranged.

**Facilities:** Toilet facilities in two modern blocks include some British style WCs, although the majority are Turkish type. Facilities for disabled people are by the pool. Washing machine. Shop. Bar/restaurant (June - mid Sept) and takeaway. Family entertainment in July/Aug. Swimming pool with waterfall and rock feature. River beach nearby with swimming and canoeing in July/Aug. Fishing. Playground. Tennis. Bicycle hire. **Off site:** Village 500 m. Riding 4 km.

**Charges** 2002

| | |
|---|---|
| Per unit incl. 2 persons | € 11.00 - € 21.00 |
| extra person | € 3.00 - € 5.80 |
| electricity | € 3.60 |

**Tel:** 04 75 39 00 67. Fax: 04 75 39 07 28. E-mail: rouv@club-internet.fr. **Reservations:** Write to site. **Open** 1 April - 30 September.

**Directions:** From A7 at Montelimar, take D102 west to Aubenas. Cross river and turn left on D104, south through Joyeuse and Chandolas/Maison-Neuve. Turn right after bridge on D252, right after 1.75 km. (site signed) then right at next crossroads. Site is 1 km. signed right (don't turn into Rouveyrolle village).

## Rhône Valley
## Camping Les Coudoulets

Pradons, 07120 Ruoms

For those who prefer a more intimate, peaceful campsite beside the river Ardèche, only a short distance away from the main centre, then this well cared for site is for you. It is run by a very enthusiastic and friendly family who have developed this site from their farm. They have a small vineyard and their wine is on sale in the bar, we fully recommend it. There are 125 grassy, level and well shaded pitches, separated by trees and shrubs. With 112 for touring, all have 6A electricity. There is an area for bathing in the river and it is an ideal spot for canoeists, etc.

**Facilities:** The very good, clean toilet block has all the necessary facilities including excellent facilities for disabled people. Motorcaravan service point. Small bar with TV and terrace, also selling bread. Small heated swimming pool and paddling pool. Fishing, football, volleyball and table tennis. Organised events in July/Aug. **Off site:** Shop 300 m.

**Charges** 2002

| | |
|---|---|
| Per unit incl. 2 persons | € 12.20 - € 15.40 |
| extra person | € 2.44 - € 3.20 |
| electricity (6A) | € 3.10 |

**Tel:** (0)4 75 93 94 95. Fax: (0)4 75 39 65 89. E-mail: camping@coudoulets.com. **Reservations:** Made with deposit (€ 70) but no booking fee. Max. 6 persons and 1 car per pitch. **Open** 1 May - 12 September.

**Directions:** Leave Montélimar going west on N192 towards Aubenas. Shortly after passing Villeneuve de Berg turn left on D103 towards Vogüé for 5 km. Turn left on D579 towards Ruoms and site is on right in 10 km. on entering the village of Pradons.

## Castel Camping Domaine de la Bastide

**0708** RD111, route de Gros-Pierres, Sampzon, 07120 Ruoms

The Cargnelutti family are very keen to maintain high standards on their site near Vallon-Pont-d'Arc and this is evident as soon as you drive in, with its neat and tidy appearance and flowers everywhere. On driving down to your pitch, it seems that there are lots of mobile homes. Actually there are only 46 mobile homes, 25 small chalets plus another 16 pitches used by a tour operator, which out of 300 pitches is really not many. Once past these, the site opens up to reveal pleasant, good sized pitches, all with some shade and bordered by flowering trees and bushes. All have electricity (3/5A) and 86 are fully serviced. Canoe trips are arranged down the Gorge d'Ardèche and in mid-June each year a large section of the river bank adjacent to the site is cleared of boulders and sand put down - just the job for children.

**Facilities:** Two toilet blocks, the newest with very high quality fittings including washbasins in cubicles, a baby room and facilities for disabled people. The older block is only open in high season and has mainly Turkish style WCs, plus showers, etc. Shop. Attractive restaurant, pizzeria and bar (mid June to end Aug). Heated swimming pool with pleasant sunbathing area. Free sauna and gym with a resident instructor. Play area. Table tennis, boules, volleyball, football, basketball and tennis courts. Fishing. Games and competitions are organised in July/Aug. plus discos in a soundproof cellar. Security patrols ensure quiet nights. Doctor calls daily (July/Aug) and hairdresser weekly (July/Aug). Only gas barbecues are permitted. **Off site:** Riding and bicycle hire 3 km. Golf 6 km. The small town of Ruoms is 4 km, Vallon-Pont-d'Arc 7 km.

**Charges** 2002

| | |
|---|---|
| Per unit incl. 2 persons, electricity | € 20.00 - € 30.00 |
| with water and drainage | € 24.00 - € 33.00 |
| extra person over 3 yrs | € 4.50 - € 6.00 |
| dog | free - € 4.00 |
| local tax (over 10 yrs) | € 0.30 |

**Tel:** 04 75 39 64 72. Fax: 04 75 39 73 28. E-mail: camping.bastide@wanadoo.fr. **Reservations:** Made with deposit (€ 100) and booking fee (€ 30). **Open** 1 April - 30 September.

**Directions:** Going south from Ruoms on the D579, bear right on D111 signed Ales. Cross Chassezac river bridge and site is 200 m. on the left.

## Sunêlia Le Ranc Davaine

**0705** St Alban-Auriolles, 07120 Ruoms

the **travel service** TO BOOK

Ferry ✓
Pitch ✓
Accommodation ✓

01892 55 98 98

Le Ranc Davine is a quite large, busy, family oriented site set in two areas separated by a reasonably quiet road. The larger area provides all the entertainment facilities and most of the 430 pitches. The 113 touring pitches are mostly scattered between static caravan and tour operator pitches and are on fairly flat, rather stony ground under a variety of trees giving much needed shade. All are supplied with electricity (6/10A), some needing very long leads which may cross tarmac roads. The lower part is beside the river (unfenced). Sunbathing areas surround the pool complex, overlooked by the terrace of the restaurant, providing very pleasant surroundings, especially attractive with evening floodlighting. A lively entertainment programme (July/Aug) is aimed at young children and teenagers. The site is popular with tour operators (113 pitches) and there are 162 mobile homes. It can get very busy for much of the season. A Sites et Paysages member.

**Facilities:** Five toilet blocks are fully equipped with many washbasins in cabins. Not all blocks are opened outside the main season, in high season they get very busy. The lower area has a new, unisex block. Full facilities for disabled visitors. Dishwashing and laundry sinks, washing machines, dryers and irons. Large shop catering for most needs. Cash point. Internet point in reception. Bar/restaurant serving good range of meals. Pizzeria and takeaway. Attractive large, irregularly shaped swimming pool (no bermuda-style shorts or shirts) heated in cool weather, supplemented by two small square pools. Children's play area. Tennis, table tennis, basketball, football, archery and minigolf. Fishing. Extensive programme of sports in the pools, clubs for youngsters and teenagers, many other organised activities including discos (until 3 am four times a week in high season). **Off site:** Canoe hire nearby for excursions down the River Ardèche. Riding 2 km. Karting.

**Charges** 2002

| | |
|---|---|
| Per unit incl. 2 persons | € 17.00 - € 28.00 |
| with electricity | € 21.00 - € 32.00 |
| extra person over 10 yrs | € 5.00 - € 7.00 |
| child 2-10 yrs | free - € 7.00 |
| animal | free - € 3.00 |

**Tel:** 04 75 39 60 55. Fax: 04 75 39 38 50. E-mail: camping-ranc-davaine@wanadoo.fr. **Reservations:** Made with deposit (€ 100) and fee (€ 30). **Open** 23 March - 14 September.

**Directions:** From Ruoms go south on the D111. Just before Grospierres turn right onto D246, cross the river bridge (2.5 m. width restriction) and then left on D208 towards Chandolas and site.

# Camping Soleil Vivarais

Sampzon, 07120 Ruoms

A large, quality site bordering the River Ardèche, complete with beach, Soleil Vivarais offers much to visitors, particularly families with children. A popular feature is the 'barrage' with its canoe ramp, used by children with rubber boats more than canoeists, and providing an invigorating shower for bathers. Water is shallow in high season, but swimming is then best attempted in one of the pools. Of the 270 pitches, 50 generously sized, level pitches are for tourers, all with 10A electricity. Many are shaded and 30 have full services. During the day the proximity of the swimming pools to the terraces of the bar and restaurant make it a pleasantly social area. In the evening the purpose built stage, with professional lighting and sound system, provides an ideal platform for a regular family entertainment programme, mostly mimed musical shows. A new section beyond the beach houses good quality chalets, and an very attractive new pool complex, which all may use. Used by tour operators (80 pitches). A 'Sites et Paysages' and 'Yelloh Village' member.

**Facilities:** Three fairly modern and one very modern toilet block are clean and cope adequately with demands placed upon them. Baby and child room and four units for people with disabilities. Washing machines and dryers. Small supermarket, well stocked and sensibly priced. Bright, modern bar/restaurant complex with takeaway and occasional pizzas. Sound-proof disco adjacent to the bar (capacity 100-120), popular with teenagers. Heated main pool and paddling pool (no bermuda style shorts). Water polo, aqua-aerobics, pool games. Tennis (charged). Basketball, volleyball and football. Fishing. Petanque, table tennis and archery. Bicycle hire. Extensive animation programme for all ages in June, July and August. **Off site:** Activities nearby, many with qualified instruction and supervision, include mountain biking, walking, canoeing, rafting, climbing and caving. Riding 2 km, golf 10 km.

**Charges** 2002

| | |
|---|---|
| Per unit incl. 2 persons, electricity | € 19.00 - € 34.00 |
| extra person | € 4.00 - € 7.00 |
| child (1-10 yrs) | free - € 6.50 |
| pet | free - € 3.00 |
| local tax (over 10s) | € 0.30 |

**Tel:** 04 75 39 67 56. Fax: 04 75 39 64 69. E-mail: camping-soleil-vivarais@wanadoo.fr. **Reservations:** Made by fax and credit card or write to site with deposit (€ 92) and fee (€ 30). **Open** week before Easter - 20 September.

**Directions:** From Le Teil, just west of Montelimar, turn off the N86 and take the N102 westwards through Villeneuve-de-Berg. Disregard the first sign for Vallon-Pont-d'Arc and continue for about 5 km. on N102 before turning left on D103, toward Vogue, then left on D579 and through Ruoms. Still on the D579, follow Vallon Pont D'Arc signs towards Sampzon. Site is on right via a bridge across the river controlled by lights.

A river all around... and all around the open air.

Chalets, mobiles homes and canvas bungalows to rent.

800 m beach bordering the Ardèche.

Open from 05/04 to 15/09/2003.

Your children (under 16 years old) are our guests From 05/04 to 31/05/03.

INFORMATION RESERVATIONS

Tel. +33 475 39 67 56 - Fax: +33 475 39 64 69
07120 SAMPZON - FRANCE
www-soleil-vivarais.com
E-mail : info@soleil-vivarais.com

ADAC

Camping Club
★ ★ ★ ★

SOLEIL VIVARAIS

Ardèche du Sud

yelloh! VILLAGE

DDB nouveau monde LE TOURISME

# Camping Les Ranchisses

route de Valgorge, Chassiers, 07110 Largentière

Combining farming, wine-making, running an Auberge and a friendly family campsite is no simple task, but the Chevalier family seem to manage it quite effortlessly. Well run and with the emphasis on personal attention, this site is highly recommended. In a somewhat lesser known area of the Ardèche at Chassiers, in a peaceful location on the Route de Valgorge (there may be some road noise), the site has developed from an original 'camping à la ferme' into a very well equipped modern campsite. There are 150 good-sized, level, grassy pitches, 88 for tourists with electricity and including 42 serviced pitches (electricity, water, waste water). Pitches are in two distinct areas - the original site which is well shaded, and the lower part which is more open. There is an unfenced frontage onto a small lake connected to the river, providing opportunities for bathing, fishing or canoeing (free life jackets) with one part of the bathing area quite safe for youngsters (supervision essential). The site's own Auberge is set in a room of the original 1824 building that once used to house silk worms. You may dine either inside the cave-like restaurant or outside on the attractive, shaded terrace. The traditional food is recommended, being both reasonably priced and of extremely good quality. A reader reports some noise until midnight.

**Facilities:** Two modern, comprehensively equipped toilet buildings include washbasins in cubicles, dishwashing and laundry sinks and facilities for babies and disabled persons. It is an excellent provision, kept immaculate. Laundry in separate building. Motorcaravan service point. Small shop, takeaway and bar with terrace (all 20/4-22/9). Excellent pool complex with two large pools (20 x 10 m. and 15 x 7.5 m, both heated and open all season) and paddling pool. Adventure style playground. Organised amusements for children in high season. Bicycle hire. Tennis court. Minigolf. Table tennis. Boules. Canoeing. **Off site:** Medieval village of Largentière (1.5 km.) with Tuesday market and medieval festival in July. Canoe and kayaking on the Ardèche arranged from the site each Wednesday (mid -June - end Aug).

**Charges** 2002

| | |
|---|---|
| Per unit incl. 2 persons | € 18.00 - € 22.50 |
| serviced pitch | € 23.00 - € 28.50 |
| extra person | € 4.00 - € 5.50 |
| child (1-10 yrs) | € 3.00 - € 4.40 |
| dog | free - € 2.00 |
| electricity | € 4.00 |
| local tax | € 0.15 |

**Tel:** 04 75 88 31 97. Fax: 04 75 88 32 73. E-mail: reception@lesranchisses.fr. **Reservations:** Made with 30% deposit plus booking/insurance fee (€ 30). **Open** 14 April - end September.

**Directions:** Largentière is southwest of Aubenas and is best approached using the D104. 16 km. south of Aubenas turn northwest on the D5 and, immediately, on leaving Largentière, fork left signed Valgorge. Site is first on left, in about 1.8 km.

# Sunêlia Le Grand Lierne

BP 8, 26120 Chabeuil

2603

In addition to its obvious attraction as an overnight stop, fairly convenient for the A7 autoroute, this site provides a pleasant base to explore this little known area (worth discovering) between the Ardèche and the Vercors mountains and the Côte du Rhône wine area. It has 140 marked pitches, 76 for touring units, mainly separated by developing hedges or oak trees. They have good shade, some are on flat ground and all have electricity (6/10A). A more open area exists for those who prefer less shade and a view of the mountains. A varied entertainment programme has a particular emphasis on activities for children, with a range of activities and excursions. The owners wish to keep a balance between nationalities and are also keen to encourage rallies and will arrange visit programmes. English spoken. Used by tour operators (30%). A 'Sites et Paysages' member.

**Facilities:** Two sanitary blocks include washbasins in cabins, facilities for disabled people and a small WC for children. Dishwashing under cover. Washing machines (powder provided), dryers and outdoor lines by the blocks. Motorcaravan services. Shop. Bar/snack bar with terrace for eating in and take-away (all season). Fridge rental. Two swimming pools, one covered and heated in low season (no bermuda shorts), paddling pool and 50 m. water slide. Children's playgrounds and trampoline. Mini-tennis, minigolf, table tennis, volleyball, archery and football field. Bicycle hire. Library. Barbecues are permitted in special areas. Dogs and other pets are not accepted in high season (6/7-24/8). Caravan storage. **Off site:** Fishing 3 km, riding 7 km, golf 3 km, canoe/kayak near.

**Charges** 2002

| | |
|---|---|
| Per unit incl. 2 adults | € 15.00 - € 24.00 |
| extra person | € 6.00 - € 7.00 |
| child (2-7 yrs) | € 3.00 - € 5.00 |
| electricity (6/10A) | € 4.00 - € 5.50 |
| animal | € 2.50 |
| local tax | € 0.20 |

**Tel:** 04 75 59 83 14. Fax: 04 75 59 87 95. E-mail: contact@grandlierne.com. **Reservations:** Accepted with deposit (€ 92) and fee (€ 27,50). **Open** 27 April - 7 September, with all services.

**Directions:** Site signed in Chabeuil about 11 km. east of Valence (18 km. from autoroute). It is best to approach Chabeuil from the south side of Valence via the Valence ring road, thence onto the D68 to Chabeuil itself. Site is off the D125 to Charpey, 5 km. from Chabeuil, but well signed.

# Castel Camping du Château de Senaud

26140 Albon

Château du Sénaud, near the N7 south of Vienne, makes a useful stopover on the way south, but one could enjoy a longer stay to explore the surrounding villages and mountains. It is one of the original sites in the Castel chain and is still run with character and hands-on attention by Mme. Comtesse d'Armagnac. There are a fair number of permanent caravans used at weekends, but it also has some 85 pitches in tourist areas. Some have shade, some have views across the Rhône valley, and electricity and water connections are available on all pitches. There may be some noise from the autoroute.

**Facilities:** Four toilet blocks include British and one Turkish style toilets, washbasins in cabins, some en-suite with shower in one block. Facilities for babies. Washing machines. Motorcaravan service point. Shop (15/5-15/9). Bar, takeaway and good value small restaurant with simple menu (all 15/6-15/9). Swimming pool with water toboggan (1/5-15/9, depending on the weather) and new jacuzzi. Tennis court. Fishing. Bicycle hire. Table tennis, bowling alley and minigolf. **Off site:** Riding 10 km. Golf course and walks adjacent.

**Charges** guide

| | |
|---|---|
| Per person | € 3.96 - € 4.88 |
| child (under 7) | € 2.44 |
| pitch | € 6.10 |
| dog | € 1.52 |
| electricity (10A) | € 3.20 - € 3.66 |

**Tel:** 04 75 03 11 31. Fax: 04 75 03 08 06. E-mail: camping.de.senaud@libertysurf.fr. **Reservations:** Made with deposit for min. 3 nights. **Open** 15 March - 31 October.

**Directions:** Leave autoroute at Chanas exit, proceed south on N7 for 8 km. then east on D301 from Le Creux de la Thine to site. From south, exit autoroute for Tain-Tournon and proceed north, approaching site on D122 through St Vallier then D132 towards Anneyron to site.

26140 ALBON
Tel: 0033 475 03 11 31
Fax: 0033 475 03 08 06
www.chateau.de.senaud.com
camping.de.senaud@libertysurf.fr

LES CASTELS

*At the gateway to the Drome, the "Château de Senaud" offers you a rare treasure in a beautiful green country setting: a XVIIth century castle with its numerous annexes and outbuildings.*
*It contains a small water leisure complexae with toboggan, swimming pool and paddling pool.*
*Its geographic location offers a variety of walks and visits: Parc du Vercors, Palais du Facteur Cheval. 18 holes golfcourses.*

## Camping Le Couspeau

**2604** 26460 Le Poet Célard

The approach to this site is via a steep road, and with several hairpin bends to negotiate, care is required - underpowered units should not attempt this hill. However, for others the views are reward enough as a magnificent landscape of mountains and valleys unfolds. The overall impression of beauty and tranquillity is reflected in the amiable attitude of the owners, who maintain a helpful, yet low profile, relaxed presence. Access to the 67 touring pitches (all with 6A electricity) on the older section of the site is reasonably easy; levelling blocks may be handy as some of the terraced pitches are slightly sloping. Mature trees provide shade and there are adequate water points around the site. The 20 pitches on the new lower section of the site are very large (150 sq.m) and all have electricity, water and a drain. They are separated by small hedges and some small trees but have little shade. Access is via a steep road but tractor assistance is available. The site has a good restaurant and bar and a terrace with panoramic views. In July and August on one evening each week there is live music, on another a themed meal. Those seeking to unwind and relax should appreciate the delightful scenery and setting of this medium sized site.

**Facilities:** Three sanitary blocks, two in the old section and one in the new, are kept very clean. Laundry and dishwashing sinks, washing machines and dryer. Facilities for disabled campers (on the older section), but the site is not ideal due steep roads and steps. Well stocked shop (15/6-30/9). Restaurant/bar and takeaway (15/6-30/9). Main pool (1/6-30/9) and smaller, covered one (1/5-30/9 and heated in low seasons) plus a toddlers' pool. Children's play area and organised activities in high season. Tennis, table tennis and volleyball. Guided hill walks and cycle trips. Rafting, canoe trips (on the River Drôme), riding and paragliding arranged. **Off site:** Riding and fishing 5 km. Canoeing, rafting and paragliding. Ideal area for the serious cyclists, mountain bikers and hikers.

**Charges** 2002

| | |
|---|---|
| Per unit incl. 2 persons | € 12.00 - € 20.00 |
| extra large pitch | € 32.00 |
| extra person | € 4.00 - € 6.00 |
| child under 7 yrs | free - € 4.00 |
| animal | free - € 1.00 |
| electricity (6A) | € 3.00 |
| local tax (over 12 yrs) | € 0.30 |

**Tel:** 04 75 53 30 14. Fax: 04 75 53 37 23. E-mail: info@couspeau.com. **Reservations:** Advised for July/Aug. and made with deposit (€ 75) and fee (€ 23). **Open** 1 May - 26 September.

**Directions:** From A7 autoroute exit 16 take D104 to Crest. At traffic lights, on the Crest bypass, turn hard right on D538 south towards Bourdeaux. Shortly before Bourdeaux turn right over small river bridge onto D328B, signed Le Poët Célard. After climbing for about 1.5 km, at T-junction, turn right on D328 and just before Le Poët Célard turn left onto D328A. Site is up hill on the left, well signed.

## Gervanne Camping

**2612** Bellevue, 26400 Mirabel et Blacons

This spacious, riverside family run site with 177 pitches is divided into two sections. The newer section is adjacent to a superb swimming pool, jacuzzi and the sunbathing terrace from which there are mountain views. The pitches are of average size with some shade and are separated by small shrubs. The older section is close to the river and on the other side of the road, but is connected to the newer section by an underpass. The older section is less formally laid out and mature trees offer plenty of shade. All pitches, in both sections, have easy access to electricity (4 or 6A) and there are water points around the site. This interesting historic area on the edge of the Vercours National Park offers opportunities for walking, cycling and other outdoor activities. The pretty hillside villages sit amongst vineyards and fields of lavender and sunflowers.

**Facilities:** Each section has a well appointed toilet block with the majority of washbasins in cabins, and a baby room in each with bath, shower and changing facilities. Washing machine, tumble dryer, sinks for laundry and dishwashing. Large en-suite unit for disabled people. Bar/restaurant (1/6-15/9) with simple menu, takeaway service and internet terminal. Swimming pool. Small children's play area, table tennis and boules. Bicycle hire. Charcoal barbecues are not allowed. **Off site:** Supermarket next door. Fishing, canoeing and bathing in river Drome.

**Charges** 2002

| | |
|---|---|
| Per unit incl. 2 adults | € 11.90 - € 14.90 |
| extra person | € 3.40 - € 4.20 |
| child (up to 7 yrs) | € 1.70 - € 2.10 |
| dog | € 1.40 - € 1.60 |
| electricity (4/6A) | € 2.50 - € 3.10 |

**Tel:** (0)4 75 40 00 20. Fax: (0)4 75 40 03 97. E-mail: info@gervanne-camping.com. **Reservations:** Required mid July - end August; write with deposit. **Open** 1 April - 2 November.

**Directions:** Site is 22 km. east of exit 16 (D104 to Crest) on the A7 autoroute. After Crest follow signs to Die for about 6 km. and then turn left and cross the river into Mirabel et Blacons and follow signs to campsite.

## Camping Les Truffières

2609 lieu-dit Nachony, 26230 Grignan

This is a delightful small site in a rural setting within walking distance of the picturesque ancient village of Grignan with wonderful views and providing peace and tranquillity. The 85 good sized pitches are level and fairly stony with 79 for touring units. Shaded by oak trees and separated by rosemary or laurel hedging, water, waste water and refuse disposal are close at hand and each pitch has electricity (10A). The Croze family are most welcoming and achieve high standards of cleanliness and order while maintaining a friendly and relaxed atmosphere. The Drôme is one of the most beautiful regions of France, vineyards, olive orchards, lavender, sunflowers, wild flowers and fruit orchards abound. Many old towns and villages, reading like a wine list, are close at hand.

**Facilities:** The good, main toilet block provides all the necessary facilities. Extra facilities by the pool are opened when needed. Dishwashing and laundry facilities under cover. Washing machine and ironing board. Snack bar and takeaway with limited menu at mid-day and evening in congenial atmosphere (June - Sept). Swimming pool and smaller pool for children (no Bermuda shorts). Volleyball, table tennis and boules. Little in the way of on site entertainment but many off site activities can be booked. Dogs are not accepted.

**Charges** 2002

| | |
|---|---|
| Per unit incl. 2 adults | € 12.20 - € 14.30 |
| extra person | € 4.20 |
| child (under 7 yrs) | € 2.80 |
| electricity (10A) | € 3.70 |

**Tel:** 04 75 46 93 62. Fax: 04 75 46 93 62. E-mail: info@lestruffieres.com. **Reservations:** Contact site. **Open** 1 April - 30 September.

**Directions:** From N7 (or A7 autoroute exit 18) south of Montélimar, take D133 (changes to D541) signed Grignan. After 9 km, just before entering Grignan, take D71 towards Charamet and site is shortly on the left.

## Les 4 Saisons Camping de Grâne

2611 route de Roche-sur-Grâne, 26400 Grâne

Opened just a few years ago, this small, terraced site nestles in the hillsides of the lower Drôme valley. With its 80 pitches, it provides mainly overnight accommodation but it is worth a longer stay. The modern main building houses reception on the top floor, with other facilities below, and provides commanding views across the valley towards Crest and the Vercors. The pitches are level, cut out of the hillside and reached by a one-way system on tarmac roads. All pitches have electricity (6/16A), water and waste water drain. This is an excellent base for exploring the Drôme valley.

**Facilities:** A short flight of steps to a lower level leads to very adequate sanitary facilities that include roomy showers, washbasins in cabins, dishwashing and laundry facilities, two washing machines and a baby-room. There are en-suite facilities for disabled visitors but the site is very sloping and not suitable for wheelchairs. Bicycle hire. Bar and snacks. **Off site:** Village shops nearby. Riding 3 km.

**Charges** 2002

| | |
|---|---|
| Per unit incl. 2 persons | € 11.00 |
| extra person | € 3.00 - € 5.00 |
| electricity (6/16A) | € 4.00 |

**Tel:** 04 75 62 64 17. Fax: 04 75 62 69 06. E-mail: camping.4saisons@wanadoo.fr. **Reservations:** Advised for July/ Aug; contact site. **Open** 15 April - 15 October.

**Directions:** From A7 take exit 17, or N7 Loriol, on D104 Crest road. After 8 km. take D113 south from Grâne. Go through village for 600 m. to site on left.

## Camping Municipal de St Nazaire-en-Royans

2606M 26190 St Nazaire-en-Royans

The pretty village of St Nazaire-en-Royans is to be found on the western perimeter of the Parc Régional du Vercors, on the route between Romans and Grenoble, and is distinguished by its impressive bridge which straddles the Isère river. The municipal site here is 500 m. from the village and is fronted by the municipal tennis courts and boules area. With a well laid out, tidy and organised appearance, the site's 75 grass pitches are of a good size, numbered and separated by hedges. A few towards the bottom left overlook the river and trees give some shade. Most pitches have access to electricity (3/6A). This is a convenient base for exploring this not so well known, but scenic area.

**Facilities:** The sanitary block, although basic, is in good condition and clean. It provides British and Turkish style WCs, some curtained washbasin cabins, facilities for disabled visitors, dishwashing and laundry sinks, plus a washing machine. Very small children's play area with grass base. Security gate (locked 10 pm.-7 am).

**Charges** 2002

| | |
|---|---|
| Per unit incl. 2 persons | € 7.32 |
| extra person | € 3.05 |
| child (under 7 yrs) | € 1.52 |
| electricity (3/6A) | € 2.44 - € 3.20 |

**Tel:** 04 75 48 41 18. **Reservations:** Contact site. **Open** 1 May - 30 September.

**Directions:** From Romans-sur-Isère take N532 for 18 km. to St Nazaire-en-Royans. Site is clearly signed east of the village on the D76. The turn to the site off the road leading from St Nazaire is a left turn on the brow of a hill on a corner - take care.

## Camping Le Gallo Romain

**2608** route du Col de Tourniol, 26300 Barbières

Surrounded by wooded hills and mountains, this small simple site makes a good base from which to explore the spectacular Vercors plateau. It is quiet and peaceful, in an attractive location with pitches set on terraces that descend to a small stream. There are 80 pitches, some with a little grass, all with electricity (6A) and most with some shade at some part of the day. The area is ideal for walking or mountain biking with many special cycle tracks in the hills, or for wild flower or butterfly enthusiasts. English is spoken.

**Facilities:** Two sanitary blocks including washbasins in cubicles, are kept reasonably clean but could be stretched in peak season. Small shop high season only but fresh bread available all season. Small bar/restaurant (booking essential), plus takeaway. Swimming pool (17 x 8 m) and paddling pool. Games room, pool table, table tennis and volleyball. Small play area. **Off site:** Bicycle hire in the village 1 km, riding or golf 6 km. Shops at Barbières 1 km.

**Charges** 2002

| | |
|---|---|
| Per adult | € 2.80 - € 3.50 |
| child (under 7 yrs) | € 1.60 - € 2.00 |
| pitch | € 9.60 - € 12.00 |
| electricity (6A) | € 2.00 - € 2.50 |

**Tel:** 04 75 47 44 07. Fax: 04 75 47 44 07. E-mail: info@legalloromain.net. **Reservations:** Advised for high season; made for exact dates with deposit and fee. **Open** 1 May - 15 September.

**Directions:** Leave A49/E713 autoroute at exit 7 (Romans-sur-Isère) and turn south on D149, following signs to Col de Tourniol. Barbières is approx. 12 km. along this road. Drive carefully through narrow village streets; the site is a little way past on right.

---

## Camping L'Hirondelle

**2613** Bois de St Ferreol, 26410 Menglon

This natural, spacious and peaceful site is run by a very friendly family. It lies in a beautiful valley, south of the Vercors mountains and National Park, beside the River Bez, a tributary of the River Drôme. It is close to the interesting and ancient small town of Die. In natural openings in woodland, the 100 large to very large pitches all have electricity (3-6A) and are stony and slightly bumpy (rock pegs advised). There are 80 for touring units. If you are lucky you may see red squirrels and beavers and, in June there is a wide variety of flowers including several types of orchids. Although this site is not manicured like some others, the large pitches, separated from others by a wide variety of trees, the 1.5 km of river bank on one side and the large open field on the other give both privacy and plenty of space. It is a very good site for couples and young families.

**Facilities:** Two large and one small toilet block offer all the necessary facilities at a high standard. Very good bar/restaurant with good menus and takeaway (19/4-7/9). Small range of supplies, including bread, on sale from the bar. Traditional rectangular swimming pool, plus excellent complex with small slide, paddling pool, jacuzzi and a section that flows like a river (19/4-7/9). Playground. Club/TV room. Internet access. Fishing. Football, boules, volleyball, archery. Organised events for young children and adults. Advice on sporting activities, etc. Occasional evening events. **Off site:** Riding and bicycle hire 3 km.

**Charges** 2002

| | |
|---|---|
| Per pitch incl. 2 persons | € 14.50 - € 17.50 |
| extra adult | € 4.50 |
| child (2-10 yrs) | € 3.50 |
| electricity (3-6A) | € 2.50 - € 3.50 |
| local tax (1/7-31/8) | € 0.15 |

**Tel:** (0)4 75 21 82 08. Fax: (0)4 75 21 82 85. E-mail: contact@campinghirondelle.com. **Reservations:** Made with 30% deposit and fee (€ 18.50). **Open** 1 April - 13 September.

**Directions:** From Die follow D93 southward and in 5 km, at Pont de Quart, turn left on D539 signed Chatillon. After 4 km. turn right on D140, signed Menglon. Entrance on right after small river.

---

## Camping Municipal de Charlieu

**4201M** rue Riottier, 42190 Charlieu

Charlieu is a very attractive little town, well worth a visit, and the well cared for municipal site here is a good base for exploring the area. The 100 pitches (30 occupied by seasonal units), all have electricity, are reasonably large and well spaced, on level grass. Most are separated by trim hedges with some shade. There are few facilities as the small town is within about five minutes walk. A card from reception gives free entry to the municipal swimming pool adjacent to the site, plus discounts for attractions and activities in the town.

**Facilities:** The clean toilet block should be adequate, except perhaps in high season. It has British and Turkish style WCs, facilities for disabled visitors, dishwashing and laundry facilities. Bicycle hire. Volleyball, boules. Playground. Fishing.

**Charges** guide

| | |
|---|---|
| Per person | € 1.80 - € 2.10 |
| pitch and vehicle | € 2.30 |
| twin axle caravan | € 44.80 |
| electricity | € 1.40 - € 3.40 |

**Tel:** 04 77 69 01 70. **Reservations:** Made without fee; contact site. **Open** 1 May - 30 September.

**Directions:** Charlieu is 20 km. northeast of Roanne. Site is signed from the town centre. From Pouilly, on the D482, take D487 to Charlieu (5.5 km).

# Camping International Porte de Lyon

Porte de Lyon, 69570 Dardilly

6901M

Camping International is a modern overnight site just off the A6 autoroute. Kept busy with overnight trade, reception and the café (in main season) open until quite late. There are 175 separate numbered plots with electricity (10A). Those for caravans are mostly on hard-standings on a slight slope, with another small grassy part, while those for tents are on a flatter area of grass. A very large commercial centre has been developed just outside the site, with 8 hotels, restaurants, supermarket, petrol station, etc. Some road noise. Bus for Lyon nearby, timetables in reception.

**Facilities:** Three heated sanitary blocks, with free hot water (solar heated), washbasins in cabins. Washing up and laundry sinks. Baby changing facilities and washing machines. Unheated swimming and paddling pools (charged for). Children's playground. TV room, table tennis. Bar/snacks high season evenings.

**Charges** 2002

| | |
|---|---|
| Per person | € 2.90 |
| child (7-15 yrs) | € 2.20 |
| tent | € 6.10 |
| motorcaravan, caravan, 1 axle | € 7.60 |
| caravan, 2 axle | € 15.30 |
| electricity (higher in winter) | € 3.00 - € 4.60 |
| local tax | € 0.15 |

**Tel:** 04 78 35 64 55. Fax: 04 72 17 04 26. E-mail: camping.lyon@mairie-lyon.fr. **Reservations:** Made if you write, but there is usually space. **Open** all year.

**Directions:** Travelling south, do not take new A46 motorway around Lyon, but continue on A6 autoroute and take exit marked 'Limonest, Dardilly, Porte de Lyon' about 8 km. north of the Lyon tunnel; at once turn left for Porte de Lyon. Porte de Lyon is well signed from most directions.

# Camping Municipal La Grappe Fleurie

La Lie, 69820 Fleurie

6902M

With easy access from both the A6 autoroute and the N6, this site is ideally situated for night stops or indeed for longer stays to explore the vineyards and historic attractions of the Beaujolais region. Virtually surrounded by vineyards, but within walking distance (less than 1 km) of the pretty village of Fleurie, this is an immaculate small site, with 96 separated touring pitches. All are grassed and fairly level with the benefit of individual access to water, drainage and electrical connections (10A). Restaurant and shopping facilities are available in the village.

**Facilities:** Sanitary facilities in two blocks have British and Turkish style toilets and very satisfactory shower and washing facilities (showers closed 22.00-07.00 hrs). Two cold showers are provided for those wishing to cool down in summer. Small children's playground. Table tennis, tennis and volleyball. **Off site:** Swimming pool 8 km.

**Charges** 2002

| | |
|---|---|
| Per unit incl. 1 or 2 adults and electricity | € 12.00 |
| tent (1 or 2 persons) | € 10.00 |
| extra adult | € 3.30 |
| child (5-10 yrs) | € 2.50 |

**Tel:** 04 74 04 10 44. Fax: 04 74 69 85 71. E-mail: info@fleurie.org. **Reservations:** Advised in high season. **Open** 15 March - 26 October.

**Directions:** From N6 at Le Maison Blanche/Romanech-Thorins, take D32 to village of Fleurie from where site is signed.

# Provence

Map 14

Perhaps we should have called this tourist region the Provence Alpes because we have only included the départements from the mountainous hinterland of the official French region of Provence. The capital city of Provence is Marseille, but this now falls into our Mediterranean region.

Départements: 04 Alpes-de-Haute-Provence, 05 Hautes-Alpes, 84 Vaucluse

The river valleys provide natural routes through the mountain barrier, as the Romans recognised. Their influence is strong through the region, reminding one that the area was the first Province of Rome, which is why it is now called Provence. Roman monuments can be seen at Orange, and Vaison-la -Romaine, where a 2,000 year old bridge is still in use. Avignon was the site of the papal court and the Palais des Papes at Avignon is a spectacular construction.

The Hautes-Alpes will reward with scenic pleasures, peace and quiet. Briançon is the highest town in Europe and many of the high passes are not for the faint-hearted  – Hannibal used one of the routes!

The Vaucluse, the area made famous by Peter Mayle's book on the Luberon, where in the late spring the southern slopes of the Montagne du Luberon are a mass of colour from the glades of wild flowers. The extinct volcanic cone of Mont Ventoux, of Tour de France fame provides dramatic views. The scents and colours with an amazing intensity of light, have encour-aged artists and writers to settle amidst the sleepy villages, with narrow streets and ancient dwellings topped with sun-baked terracotta tiles, where the air is fragrant with the smell of wild herbs and lavender.

Note: Site reports are laid out by départe-ment in numerical order.

## Cuisine of the region

Influenced by the Savoie area to the north and the Côte d'Azur to the south, the cuisine emphasizes seasonings, such as herbs and garlic, and fish

*Aigo Bouido* –garlic and sage soup with bread (or eggs and cheese)

*Farcement (Farçon Savoyard)* –potatoes baked with cream, eggs, bacon, dried pears and prunes; a hearty stomach filler

*Plat Gratinée* –applies to a wide range of dishes; here this means cooked in bread-crumbs; gratins of all sorts show how well milk, cream and cheee combine together

*Pissaladière* – Provencal bread dough with onions, anchovies, olives, etc.

*Ratatouille* – aubergines, courgettes, onions, garlic, red peppers and tomatoes in olive oil

*Tartiflette* –potato, bacon, onions and Reblochon cheese

## Wine

The Côtes de Provence wine region is mainly known for its dry, fruity rosé wines: Bandol, Bellet, Palette, Cassis. Red wines include Côtes du Rhône and Châteauneuf-du-Pape.

## Places of interest

*Avignon* – ramparts, old city, Papal Palace, old palace, Calvet museum

*Mont Ventoux* – near Carpentras, one of the best known stages of the classic Tour de France annual cycle race

*Orange* – Roman city, gateway to the Midi, Colline St Europe

*Vaison la Romaine* – Roman city, the French Pompei

# Hotel de Plein Air L'Hippocampe

route de Napoléon, 04290 Volonne

Hippocampe is a friendly, lakeside site situated in a beautiful area of France. The perfumes of thyme, lavender and wild herbs are everywhere and the higher hills of Haute Provence are not too far away. There are 447 level, numbered pitches (271 for touring units), medium to very large (140 sq.m.) in size. All have electricity (10A) and 206 have water and a drain, most separated by bushes and cherry trees (June is the time for the cherries and you may help yourself). Some of the best pitches border the lake. This is a family run site with families in mind, with games, aerobics, competitions, entertainment and shows, plus a daily club for younger family members in July/August. A soundproof underground disco is set well away from the pitches and is very popular with teenage customers. Staff tour the site at night ensuring a good night's sleep. The site is, however, much quieter in low season and, with its good discounts, is the time for those who do not want or need entertaining. The Gorges du Verdon is a sight not to be missed and rafting, paragliding or canoe trips can be booked from the site. Being on the lower slopes of the hills of Haute-Provence, the surrounding area is good for both walking and mountain biking. Used by tour operators (20 pitches). English is spoken.

**Facilities:** Toilet blocks vary from old to modern, all with good facilities that include washbasins in cabins. They were very clean when we visited in June. Washing machines. Motorcaravan service point. Fridge rental. Bread available from reception (from 28/4), small shop (29/6-1/9). Bar (27/4-30/9). Restaurant, pizzeria and barbecue chicken shop (all 12/5-15/9). Large, attractive pool complex (from 27/4-30/9) with various pools of differing sizes and depths, heated in early and late seasons. Tennis (free outside 3/7- 21/8). Fishing, canoeing, boules. Bicycle and pedalo hire (high season). Large selection of sports facilities to choose from, some with free instruction, including archery (high season). Charcoal barbecues are not permitted. **Off site:** Village of Volonne 600 m. Riding 500 m. Monuments, ancient churches, museums, markets, festivals and vineyards. Rafting, canoeing, canyoning, torrent walking, mountain biking, paragliding and hang gliding.

**Charges** 2002

| | |
|---|---|
| Per unit with 2 persons | € 12.00 - € 20.00 |
| with electricity | € 15.00 - € 24.50 |
| with water/drainage 100 sq.m. | € 15.00 - € 26.70 |
| with water/drainage 140 sq.m. | € 15.00 - € 30.50 |
| extra person (over 4 yrs) | € 2.50 - € 5.50 |
| dog | free - € 3.00 |
| local tax (June-Sept) | € 0.15 - € 0.38 |

**Tel:** 04 92 33 50 00. Fax: 04 92 33 50 49. E-mail: camping@l-hippocampe.com. **Reservations:** Made with deposit (varies with size of pitch from € 50 - € 95) and booking fee (€ 25). **Open** 1 April - 30 September.

**Directions:** Approaching from the north turn off N85 across river bridge to Volonne, then right to site. From the south right on D4, 1 km. before Château Arnoux.

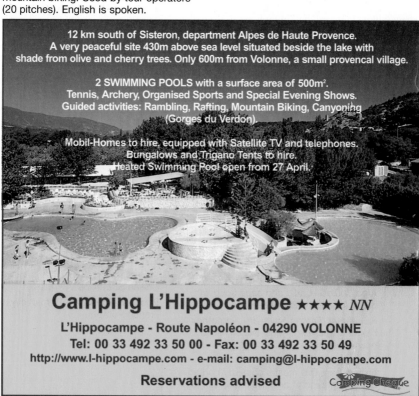

## Camping-Caravaning Le Haut-Verdon

RD 908, 04370 Villars-Colmars

**0406**

On the banks of the Verdon, a good trout river, which then flows through the spectacular gorge, Camping Le Haut-Verdon is a family site. Surrounded by the majestic peaks of the Alpes-de-Haute-Provence, it is on the doorstep of the Mercantour National Park. It is however only open for a short season. Set amongst the pines, the 106 pitches are mostly on the large size but are rather stony. With 93 for touring units, all have electricity (6/10A; but some will require long leads). There is a small village near, and the town of St André is 23 km. English is spoken. A `Sites et Paysages' member.

**Facilities:** The main toilet block is heated and includes bidets and washbasins in cabins. Most WCs are British style. Washing machines and irons, dishwashing and laundry sinks. Freezer for ice packs and room for tenters when inclement weather strikes. Motorcaravan service point. Small shop. Bar/restaurant and takeaway. Barbecue areas (portable ones banned). Swimming and paddling pools. Small play area. Volleyball, basketball, giant chess, bowling alley, table tennis, tennis and TV. Entertainers organise games and competitions. Fishing. **Off site:** Bicycle hire and riding 10 km.

**Charges** 2003

| | |
|---|---|
| Per person over 4 yrs | € 4.00 |
| child (2-6 yrs) | € 2.50 |
| pitch | € 6.00 - € 10.00 |
| electricity | € 2.50 - € 3.00 |
| local tax | € 0.15 |

**Tel:** 04 92 83 40 09. Fax: 04 92 83 56 61. E-mail: campinglahautverden@wanadoo.fr. **Reservations:** Made with deposit (30%) and fee (€ 15,24). **Open** 1 May - 30 September.

**Directions:** Follow D955 north from St André les Alpes towards Colmar. After about 11 km. the road number changes to D908. Site is on right at the southern edge of Villars-Colmars. Caravans are not advised to use the D908 from Annot or the Col d'Allos from Barcelonnette.

## Camping-Caravaning L'Etoile des Neiges

04140 Montclar

**0408**

This attractive, family run site near the mountain village and ski resort of St Jean Montclar is open all year so is suitable for both summer and winter holidays. The shady pitches are laid out in terraces and separated by small shrubs. All pitches are close to electricity and water points. An attractive bar and restaurant overlook the swimming pool, with a new pool complex with slides, etc. planned. The site has no shop as the local shops are only a few minutes walk away. Although situated in the southern high Alps, the site can be reached without climbing any stiff gradients. A 'Sites et Paysages' member.

**Facilities:** The central toilet block, heated in winter, includes washbasins in cabins. Separate room containing facilities for disabled visitors. Washing machines. Motorcaravan service point. Bar/restaurant (1/6-7/9). Swimming pool (1/6-7/9). Tennis, table tennis and boules. Two play areas. New multi-sport area. Rafting and walking organised in July/Aug. **Off site:** Shops in village a few minutes walk. Bicycle hire and riding 200 m. in village. Watersports at Lac Serre Ponçon. Fishing 1.5 km.

**Charges** 2003

| | |
|---|---|
| Per unit incl. 2 persons | € 11.00 - € 21.00 |
| extra adult | € 4.00 - € 5.00 |
| child (2-7 yrs) | € 2.50 - € 3.00 |
| electricity (6A) and water | € 3.00 |

**Tel:** (0)4 92 35 01 29. Fax: (0)4 92 35 12 55. E-mail: contact@etoile-des-neiges.com. **Reservations:** Advised for July/Aug. **Open** 1 January - 30 September, and 22 - 31 December.

**Directions:** From Gap take D900B beyond Serre Ponçon. Turn right onto D900 signed St Jean Montclar and follow signs to site on the left.

# Camping International

Route Napoleon, 04120 Castellane

Camping International has very friendly, English speaking owners and is a reasonably priced, less commercialised site situated in some of the most dramatic scenery in France with good views. The 250 pitches, 130 good sized ones for touring, are clearly marked, separated by trees and small hedges, and all have electricity and water. The bar/restaurant overlooks the swimming pool with its sunbathing area set in a sunny location, and all have fantastic views. In high season English speaking young people entertain children (3-8 years) and teenagers. On some evenings the teenagers are taken to the woods for campfire 'sing-alongs' which can go on till the early hours without disturbing the rest of the site. There are twice weekly guided walks into the surrounding hills in the nearby Gorges du Verdon - a very popular excursion. The weather in the hills here is very pleasant without the excessive heat of the coast. Access is good for larger units.

**Facilities:** Several small toilet blocks are of an older design with small cubicles and, although they are quite basic, the showers are fully controllable. One newer block has modern facilities, including those for disabled visitors, but this is not open early and late in the season. Washing machines, dryer and irons and a baby room. Chemical disposal at motorcaravan service point. Fridge hire. Shop. Restaurant/takeaway. Swimming pool (all 1/5-30/9). Club/TV room. Children's animation and occasional evening entertainment in July/Aug. Play area. Volleyball, football and boules pitches. Internet access. **Off site:** Castellane (1.5 km) is an very attractive little town with a superb river, canyon and rapids, ideal for canoeing, rafting and canyoning etc. Ideal country for walking and biking. Riding 800 m. Boat launching 5 km.

**Charges** 2002

| | |
|---|---|
| Per unit incl. 2 persons | € 12.00 - € 17.00 |
| extra person over 10 yrs | € 3.00 - € 4.50 |
| child 4-10 yrs | € 1.80 - € 3.50 |
| child under 4 yrs | € 1.65 - € 3.35 |
| dog | € 2.50 |
| local tax | € 0.15 - € 0.30 |

**Tel:** (0)4 92 83 66 67. Fax: (0)4 92 83 77 67. E-mail: info@campinginternational.fr. **Reservations:** Necessary for July/Aug. and made with deposit (€ 45), no booking fee. **Open** 1 April - 30 September.

**Directions:** Site is 1 km. north of Castellane on the N85 'Route Napoleon'.

# Camping du Plan

04400 Barcelonnette

The area around Barcelonnette is not high in the holiday popularity table, but it is appealing to those who like dramatic mountain scenery and the more rugged pursuits of mountaineering, mountain cycling and white water canoeing. Few caravanners and motor caravanners find their way in to this mountainous region, but it is popular amongst campers with cycles or motorcycles. In an area where most of the sites are rather crowded and basic, Camping du Plan, a compact site, has fair sized pitches defined by mature trees which provide welcome shade in high summer. Pitches near the road can be fairly noisy during the day, mostly because of motorcycles passing on their way to tackle Col D'Allos. Eight kilometres from Barcelonnette is the other infamous mountain pass, the Col de la Bonette which is the highest paved road in Europe. This pass is really only suitable for two wheeled vehicles. There is a motorcaravan service point at Barcelonnette airport, and from there the brave can take a brief powered or gliding tour of the surrounding mountains.

**Facilities:** The toilet block is old fashioned with mostly Turkish style toilets, but it is kept very clean. The bar, which doubles as reception, serves breakfasts and fairly basic but filling evening menu. Site is not suitable for large motorcaravans and twin axle caravans. **Off site:** Town is within walking distance.

**Charges** guide

| | |
|---|---|
| Per unit incl. 2 persons | € 10.60 |
| extra person | € 3.43 |
| child (under 5 yrs) | € 2.06 |
| electricity (3-6A) | € 2.67 - € 3.50 |

**Tel:** 04 92 81 08 11. **Reservations:** Contact site. **Open** May - end September.

**Directions:** From Barcelonnette bypass turn right (if coming from Gap) over the bridge and right again at T-junction on D902 signed Allos. Camping du Plan is the first site on the right after 300 yards.

## Provence
# Camping Lac du Moulin de Ventre
0403 Niozelles, 04300 Forcalquier

This is a friendly, English speaking, family run site in the heart of Haute-Provence, near Forcalquier, a bustling small French market town. Attractive located beside a small lake and 28 acres of wooded, hilly land is available for walking. Herbs of Provence can be found growing wild and flowers, birds and butterflies abound - a nature lovers delight. The 124 level, grassy pitches for tourists are separated by a variety of trees and small shrubs, 114 of them having electricity (6A; long leads may be necessary). Some pitches are particularly attractive, bordering a small stream. The site is well situated to visit Mont Ventoux, the Luberon National Park, the Gorges du Verdon and a wide range of ancient hill villages with their markets and museums.

**Facilities:** The toilet block, recently refurbished, provides very good, clean facilities including wash-basins in cabins and facilities for disabled people. Baby bath. Washing machines. Fridge hire. Bread and a few essentials on sale. Bar/restaurant and takeaway (all season). Pizzeria. Large and small swimming pools (15/5-15/9). Playground. Fishing and boules. Library. Some activities organised in high season. No discos. Charcoal barbecues not permitted. **Off site:** Shops 2 km. Riding, bicycle hire 5 km.

**Charges** 2002

| | |
|---|---|
| Per unit incl. 2 persons, electricity | € 15.00 - € 22.00 |
| extra person | € 3.50 - € 5.50 |
| child (2-4 yrs) | € 2.00 - € 3.00 |

**Tel:** 04 92 78 63 31. Fax: 04 92 79 86 92. E-mail: moulindeventre@free.fr. **Reservations:** Advisable for July/Aug with 30% deposit and fee (€ 23). **Open** 1 April - 30 September.

**Directions:** From A51 motorway take exit 19 (Brillanne). Turn right on N96 then left on N100 (west signed Forcalquier) for 3 km. Site is signed on left, just after a bridge 3 km. southeast of Niozelles.

## Provence
# Camp du Verdon
0402 Domaine de la Salaou, 04120 Castellane

Close to 'Route des Alpes' and the Gorges du Verdon, this is a very popular holiday area, the gorge, canoeing and rafting being the main attractions, ideal for active families. Two heated pools and numerous on-site activities help to keep non-canoeists here. Du Verdon is a large level site, part meadow, part wooded, with 500 grassy, partly shaded pitches (350 for tourists). Numbered and separated, they vary in size, have 6A electricity, and 120 also have water and waste water. They are mostly separate from the mobile homes (45) and pitches used by tour operators (110). Some overlook the unfenced river Verdon, so watch the children. With the facilities open all season, the site is very popular.

**Facilities:** The toilet blocks are being refurbished, the finished ones having British style WCs and all the latest equipment. One block has facilities for disabled visitors. Washing machines. Motorcaravan service points. Restaurant with terrace and bar. Large well stocked shop. Pizzeria/crêperie. Takeaway. Two heated pools and paddling pool (all season). Games, competitions, dances, discos (July/Aug). Playgrounds. Minigolf, table tennis, archery, basketball and volleyball. Organised walks. Bicycle hire. Riding. Small fishing lake. **Off site:** Castellane (1 km). Riding 2 km.

**Charges** 2002

| | |
|---|---|
| Per unit with up to 3 persons | € 14.00 - € 24.00 |
| with 6A electricity | € 18.00 - € 28.00 |
| extra person over 4 yrs | € 6.00 - € 8.00 |

**Tel:** 04 92 83 61 29. Fax: 04 92 83 69 37. E-mail: contact@camp-du-verdon.com. **Reservations:** Made with deposit and fee. **Open** 15 May - 15 September.

**Directions:** From Castellane take D952 westwards towards Gorges du Verdon and Moustiers. Site is 1 km. on left. **See advert on page 261**

## Provence
# Camping Le Clavet
0409 04120 Castellane

In the hills, six kilometres south of Castellane and built into a fairly steep hillside, the level terraced pitches with a sunny aspect and glorious views at Le Clavet are very pleasant. Most have electricity (10A, long leads may be needed) and some are fully serviced. The attractive pool with a sunbathing area is located near the entrance to the site and is overlooked by the bar/restaurant. A quiet site, the area is a haven for walkers and both canoeing and canyoning are possible at Castellane. The site's owners are keen to attract British visitors and their policy of 'no unaccompanied teenage groups' should ensure that the site is kept peaceful. A 'Sites et Paysages' member.

**Facilities:** The toilet blocks are modern and well maintained with good facilities. One block has facilities for disabled people although the nature of the terrain could make it a little difficult for wheelchairs. Dishwashing and laundry sinks. Washing machines. Small shop open twice daily (15/5-15/9). Bar, restaurant/takeaway (lunchtime and evenings all season). Swimming pool. Computer room. Two play areas, boule and tennis court. Mini-club in July/Aug.

**Charges** 2002

| | |
|---|---|
| Per unit incl. 2 persons | € 11.89 - € 18.98 |
| with electricity | € 15.24 - € 21.65 |
| extra adult | € 3.81 - € 5.34 |
| child (3-10 yrs) | € 3.05 - € 4.75 |

**Tel:** (0)4 92 83 68 96. Fax: (0)4 92 83 75 40. E-mail: leclavet@wanadoo.fr. **Reservations:** Made for min. 7 nights with booking fee (€ 16,77). **Open** 15 May - 15 September.

**Directions:** Site is 9 km. south of Castellane on the N85 'Route Napoleon'.

Haute-Provence
## Camping Lac du Moulin de Ventre
04300 Niozelles
Tel: 0033 492 78 63 31
　　 0033 492 79 82 52
Fax: 0033 492 79 86 92
www.moulindeventre.com

## Camping des Princes L'Orange

05700 Orpierre

This attractive, terraced site, set on a hill-side above the village, has been gradually and thoughtfully developed by its owners over 20 years. Their genuine, friendly welcome means many families return year upon year, bringing in turn new generations. Divided into five terraces, all its 120 generously sized pitches (96 for tourists) enjoy good shade from trees and wicker canopies and have electricity connections (4A). Renowned as a serious rock climbing venue, Orpierre also has an enchanting maze of medieval streets and houses, a walk through is to be recommended - almost like a trip back through the centuries. Whether you choose to drive, climb, walk or cycle there is plenty of wonderful scenery to discover in the immediate vicinity, whilst not far away, some exhilarating hang gliding and parascending can be enjoyed. Whilst the steepness of the terrain and its somewhat remote location may not suit all, there can be no doubt that you will be made most welcome and will enjoy the quiet splendours the region has to offer.

**Facilities:** Six toilet blocks with mostly British style WCs and washbasins in cubicles are extremely clean and accessible from all levels. Baby bath. Dishwashing and laundry sinks. Laundry facilities near reception. Bread available from bar each morning (other basics from village). Reasonably priced takeaway service from the bar in high season. Swimming pool (20 x 10 m), paddling pool (15/6-15/9). Children's play area including small trampoline with safety net. Table tennis, boules and games room. Fridge hire. Only gas barbecues are permitted. **Off site:** Orpierre with a few shops and bicycle hire 500 m. Nearest shopping centre Laragne, 12 km. Fishing 7 km. Riding 19 km. Hang gliding, parascending. Gorges de Guil.

**Charges** 2002

| | |
|---|---|
| Per unit incl. 2 persons | € 16.50 |
| incl. 3 persons | € 18.00 |
| extra person | € 3.75 |
| child (under 7 yrs) | € 2.50 |
| electricity | € 2.50 |
| dog | € 1.00 |
| local tax (over 16 yrs) | € 0.15 |

**Tel:** 04 92 66 22 53. **Fax:** 04 92 66 31 08. **E-mail:** campingorpierre@wanadoo.fr. **Reservations:** Made with deposit (€ 84) and fee (€ 9). **Open** 1 April - 25 October.

**Directions:** Turn off N75 road at Eyguians onto D30 - site is signed on left at crossroads in centre Orpierre village.

0500

# Camping-Caravaning Les Grillons

roure de Madeleine, 05200 Embrun

05501

The town of Embrun, 'le petit Nice' of the Alps, lying in the Durance valley between Les Ecrins (the largest National Park in France) and the Queyras valley, is a pivotal point for exploring this area of outstanding natural beauty. Situated between Gap and Briançon, the roads are easily negotiated. The resorts in the area are well known for winter recreation. The summer season is particularly short - the possibility of quite cool nights contrasting sharply with hot days. Les Grillons, family owned, although lacking somewhat in sophistication, has a friendly and peaceful ambience (little English is spoken). It has 95 grassy pitches set in rounded alcoves with trees offering separation and some shade. The site is 850 m. high and a short ride gives access to alpine meadows of stunning beauty.

**Facilities:** Basic provision offers the usual facilities with warm water, British and Turkish style toilets and a baby bath, but no facilities for disabled people. Laundry and dishwashing areas. Washing machine and dryer. Very simple snacks (July/Aug). Bread to order. Two medium sized unheated swimming pools (1/7-15/9). Tennis court, skateboard ramps, table tennis, volleyball and boules. Play area. **Off site:** Embrun 3 km. Fishing 800 m. Bars and restaurants at De Bartier, 1 km. Lac Serre Ponçon, 2 km.

**Charges** 2002

| | |
|---|---|
| Per unit incl. 1 or 2 persons | € 12.82 |
| extra person | € 1.98 - € 3.66 |
| electricity 3-10A | € 2.44 - € 3.96 |

**Tel:** 04 92 43 32 75. **Fax:** 04 92 43 32 75. **E-mail:** info@lesgrillons.com. **Reservations:** Made with deposit (€ 92) and fee (€ 9,15). **Open** 15 May - 15 September.

**Directions:** From Gap take N94 towards Briançon. Approaching Embrun, at first roundabout, turn right on D40 signed Les Orres. After crossing a river bridge (1 km) turn left on D340. Shortly turn left (site signed) and the site is 400 m. on the right.

# Caravaneige de Serre-Chevalier

05330 Saint-Chaffrey

0502

Set at the crossroads of several mountain routes and not far from the old town of Briançon, this is an ideal centre for explor-ing the region. This attractive site is at the foot of the cable car taking you to the Serre Chevalier mountains. In winter it is close to several ski runs and chairlifts. In summer it is surrounded by mountain tracks and passes waiting to be explored. There is a variety of pitches, most with good mountains views. Some are regularly laid out, others are scattered amongst the trees, the latter having more shade. Of the 198 level grassy, pitches, 170 are used for touring. The site is divided into two sections, each with a toilet block, with the section furthest from the entrance only open in high season.

**Facilities:** Two modern toilet blocks with all the necessary facilities are both heated in cold weather. One may be closed in the low season, Room for drying clothes and equipment. Bar and restaurant with good range of menus and takeaway food. Small heated swimming pool and attractive sunbathing area. Fishing. Volleyball. Bicycle hire. **Off site:** Shops 300 m. Briançon 6 km. Tennis 100 m. Cable car to Serre Chevalier 200 m.

**Charges** 2002

| | |
|---|---|
| Per unit incl. 2 persons | € 20.00 |
| extra person | € 4.00 - € 5.00 |
| electricity | € 2.75 - € 4.30 |

**Tel:** (0)4 92 24 01 14. **Fax:** (0)4 92 24 18 62. **Reservations:** Contact site. **Open** 20 Dec - 20 April and 12 June - 9 Sept.

**Directions:** From Briançon take the N91 toward Grenoble. Site is approx. 5 km northwest of Briançon and just past the village of Chantemerle, signed 'Caravaneige'.

# Camping Municipal Le Brégoux en Provence

chemin du Vas, 84810 Aubignan

8403M

Generally speaking, reasonably priced sites of a good standard in this area are few and far between. This attractive municipal site is an exception and well worth considering as a base for exploring the region, being conveniently situated for visiting Mont Ventoux and the Dentelles de Montmirail, Orange, Carpentras, Vaison la Romaine, Avignon and even Aix-en-Provence. The site itself is about 10 minutes walk from the village, is on level grass and fairly well shaded. The 170 or so pitches, all for tourists, are of a reasonable size and are partially separated with trees and shrubs, most with electricity.

**Facilities:** Three fully equipped sanitary blocks include some washbasins in cabins, covered wash-ing up areas, facilities for disabled people and two washing machines, all very clean when inspected. Machine for drinks and ice creams all season. Table tennis and tennis. **Off site:** Shops. restaurants and gas in the village.

**Charges** 2002

| | |
|---|---|
| Per person | € 2.60 |
| child (under 10 yrs) | € 1.40 |
| pitch | € 2.60 |
| electricity | € 2.50 |

**Tel:** 04 90 62 62 50. **Fax:** 04 90 62 65 21. **E-mail:** camping-lebregoux@wanadoo.fr. **Reservations:** Contact site. **Open** 1 March - 31 October.

**Directions:** Take the D7 north from Carpentras for abut 6 km. On entering Aubignan turn right on D55 and follow signs to the site.

## Provence

# Camping Club International Carpe Diem

route de St Marcellin, BP 68, 84110 Vaison-la-Romaine

Perhaps Carpe Diem is a shade preten-tious with its Greek statues and amphithe-atre surround to its main pool. A develop-ing site, it is only a few years old and will no doubt mellow as the trees and shrubs grow and old and new blend together. It is a good site for active families seeking all day entertainment and the situation is quite impressive with magnificent views over one of the most beautiful parts of France, yet only 800 m. from the village of Vaison la Romaine. There are 210 pitches with 100 small to medium, grass touring pitches all with electricity (6/10A) and many with some degree of shade. A new terraced area has mobile homes, chalets and unshaded touring pitches. The main pool is impressive with its tiered seating, plants, etc. It is used as a theatre for evening entertainment. A simpler square pool is near the play area with grass surrounds.

**Facilities:** The central toilet block - with fountain - provides mainly British and a few Turkish style toilets, washbasins in cabins and showers with an unusual cupboard for your clothes. Dishwashing and laundry sinks. Small editions of everything are provided for children. Washing machine. Extra facili-ties are behind the main pool. Motorcaravan service point. Reception provides a small shop (30/3-3/11). Bar near the main pool and pizzeria (both 15/6-31/8). TV room. Swimming pools (30/3-3/11). Play area. Minigolf, archery (cross-bow type), volleyball, football and basketball. Mountain bike hire. Mini-club. Extensive entertainment programme, including Roman extravagansas (which can be noisy) and off site activities in high season. There is a charge for participation in sports and entertainment. **Off site:** Fishing 1 km. Riding 2 km. Golf 20 km. Organised canoeing, riding, climbing, walking, mountain biking. Vaison la Romaine (800 m) with its magnificent Roman ruins, shops, restaurants, market and excel-lent wine.

**Charges** 2002

| Per pitch incl. 1-3 persons | € 5.50 - € 25.00 |
|---|---|
| extra adult | € 4.00 - € 5.00 |
| child (2-10 yrs) | € 2.50 - € 4.00 |
| electricity (6A) | € 2.60 |
| dog | € 2.00 |

**Tel:** 04 90 36 02 02. Fax: 04 90 36 36 90. E-mail: contact@camping.carpe.diem.com. **Reservations:** Made with deposit and fee (€ 77). **Open** 1 March - 9 November.

**Directions:** Leave Vaison la Romaine on D938 heading south towards Carpentras. One km. beyond the Super U roundabout turn left on D151, signed St Marcellin. Site entrance is on the left immediately after the junction.

## Provence

# Camping Le Soleil de Provence

Route de Nyons, 84110 Saint-Romain en Viennois

The views from this spacious, family run site must take some beating. The 360 degree panorama includes Mont Ventoux, the surrounding hills and the vineyards of northern Provence. It offers an excellent base from which to explore this very inter-esting area. Within a few kilometres one can find old towns such as Nyons, the olive capital of France, Orange and Avignon. The countryside is full of vine-yards, lavender and sunflowers and the mountains offer a challenge to walkers and cyclists. The site has been developed to a high standard. The 140 pitches are of aver-age size, most having some shade. They are all supplied with 10A electricity and there are a good number of water points The swimming pool, surrounded by a sunbathing terrace, and overlooked by the bar, is an unusual shape with an island in the centre. Although there is no paddling pool one end of the pool is very shallow. A good quiet family site with very little organ-ised entertainment.

**Facilities:** Two toilet blocks, heated early and late season, are very well appointed and include wash-basins in cabins, facilities for disabled visitors and a baby changing room. Dishwashing and laundry sinks, washing machine, dryer and facilities for iron-ing. Motorcaravan service point. Small shop for bread,etc, open on demand. Bar and snack bar open most of the day. Swimming pool. Small play area. **Off site:** Tennis 1 km. Riding 10 km. Vaison la Romaine 4 km.

**Charges** 2003

| Per person | € 3.50 - € 4.90 |
|---|---|
| child (0-10 yrs) | € 1.75 - € 2.45 |
| pitch | € 2.10 - € 3.00 |
| electricity (10A) | € 2.50 |

**Tel:** (0)4 90 46 46 00. Fax: (0)4 90 46 40 37. **Reservations:** Advised for July/Aug. **Open** 1 April - 31 October.

**Directions:** Site is 4 km. from Vaison la Romaine on the D938 road to Nyon.

## Provence
# Camping Les Verguettes
Route de Carpentras, 84570 Villes sur Auzon

8411

Friendly and family run, this small campsite is surrounded by fields and vineyards and should appeal to those seeking a more relaxed holiday. It is probably not the ideal site for active youngsters. It lies on the outskirts of the village of Villes sur Auzon and at the foot of Mont Ventoux and the Nesque Gorge (1 km). Of the 89 pitches 81 are for touring. They are on the small side and are arranged in groups of 6 either side of the campsite road and are attractively laid out, separated by a variety of trees and shrubs. They all have electrical connections (5A but a few with 10A) but long leads may be necessary. Close to the attractive pool are the bar and small outside restaurant - a pleasant place to relax after a day sightseeing.

**Facilities:** There are two toilet blocks, one near the entrance and other at the far end of the site. The buildings are old but have been refurbished to a high standard. Motorcaravan service point. Bar (all season). Small outside restaurant (20/5-31/8) with simple menu and takeaway. Small swimming pool. Tennis. Minigolf. Boules. Table tennis and small games/TV room. **Off site:** Carpentras 10 km. Mont Ventoux, Nesque Gorge 1 km.

**Charges** 2002

| | |
|---|---|
| Per pitch | € 6.50 |
| person | € 4.50 |
| child (under 7 yrs) | € 2.30 |
| electricity | € 2.50 |

**Tel:** (0)4 90 61 88 18. Fax: (0)4 90 61 97 87. E-mail: info@provencecamping.com. **Reservations:** Made with deposit (€ 16) and booking fee (€ 23). **Open** 1 April - 30 September.

**Directions:** From A7 autoroute exit 22 just south of Orange take D950 to Carpentras. Then D942 east, signed Sault and Mazan. Site is 10 km. on right just after roundabout on entering Villes sur Auzon.

## Provence
# Camping des Sources
Route de Murs, 84220 Gordes

8412

This family run campsite is only 2 km. from the stunning ancient hill village of Gordes. Also close by are many other equally magnificent villages. The views from the campsite over the valley, with its vineyards, lavender fields and olive trees are fantastic. This site is ideal for 'lovers of the great outdoors'. The roads around the hillside campsite are stony and some slope significantly. The 100 terraced pitches (rock pegs essential) are placed naturally amongst a variety of ancient trees (mainly olives and oaks) and are irregular in shape and size. All pitches have access to electricity (5A) though some may need long leads and a few leads may cross the roads. Access to some pitches is not easy and this site is not recommended for large units.

**Facilities:** Two toilet blocks are of a high standard and clean. Facilities are provided for disabled people but the hilly terrain is not really suitable for the physically disabled. Motorcaravan service point. Bar. Restaurant with simple menu and takeaway. Bread available but no shop. Play room and simple playground. Volleyball, boules. Activities arranged in high season. Evening soirées etc. but no discos. Bicycle hire. Central barbecue (individual barbecues forbidden). **Off site:** Gordes 2 km.

**Charges** 2002

| | |
|---|---|
| Per person | € 2.70 - € 4.30 |
| pitch | € 4.00 - € 6.30 |
| electricity | € 2.90 |

**Tel:** (0)4 90 72 12 48. Fax: (0)4 90 72 09 43. E-mail: julio.moreina@wanadoo.fr. **Reservations:** Contact site. **Open** 15 March - 15 October.

**Directions:** From A7 autoroute exit 25 (Cavaillon) take D2 northeast. Cross N100 and continue to Gordes. In the centre turn left on D15, signed Murs. Continue up hill for 2 km. and turn left at site sign. The entrance is a further 400 m. up a narrow lane.

## Provence
# Camping-Caravaning La Simioune
84500 Bollène

8408

This unsophisticated, rural site is a paradise for horse lovers, set amongst tall pines on sandy, undulating ground. However, don't go to La Simioune if you prefer neat lawns and flower beds or lots of entertainment. In fact, first impressions here are of it being untidy. It will appeal to lovers the countryside, with half tame rabbits and well cared for horses in the nearby yards. This is actually a riding school with local children coming for lessons. Campers can also hire horses by the hour, although the favourite seems to be the day-long trek with a river crossing and picnic lunch. The 80 unmarked pitches are of varying size and shape, most with electricity (6A).

**Facilities:** The toilet block is basic and adequately cleaned. Small room for babies. Room for disabled people although the site itself may be difficult for wheelchairs due to the terrain. Laundry and dishwashing sinks with two hot taps to draw from and an old washing machine. Small bar serves simple meals in July and Aug. Small swimming and paddling pool (Jun to Sept). Riding. Table tennis, boules, volleyball. Barbecues are not permitted.

**Charges** 2002

| | |
|---|---|
| Per unit incl. 2 persons | € 14.00 - € 24.10 |
| extra person | € 2.80 - € 4.05 |
| electricity | € 2.50 - € 2.80 |

**Tel:** 04 90 30 44 62. **Reservations:** Contact site for details. **Open** all year.

**Directions:** From A7 take exit 19 (Bollène). At first roundabout take third exit signed Carpentras (site signed). Shortly take third road on left, signed Lambisque (Rue Alphonse Daudet) and follow site signs for approx. 5 km.

# Camping-Caravaning La Sorguette

route d'Apt, 84800 L'Isle sur la Sorgue

**8405**

The entrance and access roads at La Sorguette, a former municipal site, are wide giving the site a spacious feel. Arranged in fours, the 164 level pitches are of a good size, all with electricity connections. Hedged with various types of shrubs and trees, most have a little shade at some part of the day. In high season a few competitions are organised (boule or volleyball), plus some children's entertainment, but this is quite low key and the general feel of the site even in high season is calm and peaceful. Running alongside a part of the site (fenced with a gate), the river Sorgue is only 6 km. from its source in the mountains at Fontaine de Vaucluse (a big tourist attraction) and consequently is still very clear and can be used for canoeing, swimming or fishing. Isle sur la Sorgue (1.5 km.) is a very attractive small town, dominated by the river which forms small canals and waterways, interspersed with a number of water wheels. There are many bars and restaurants, some with seating overlooking the water which has a cooling effect in the height of summer. Its two well attended market days provide even more colour and virtually fill the old streets of the town, and brightly coloured pottery, table covers, fruit and vegetable make it a photographer's paradise. Site staff are very friendly and English is spoken.

**Facilities:** Three strategically placed, clean and well maintained toilet blocks include some washbasins in cubicles for ladies, mainly British style WCs and dishwashing and laundry sinks. Two blocks have washing machines, dryer, ironing boards and clothes lines. Units for disabled people at all three. Baby room. Motorcaravan service point. Fridge hire. Shop and bar with snacks (1/7-25/8) set well away from the pitches, outside the entrance which ensures that the occasional entertainment in July/Aug. does not disturb campers. Children's play area, volleyball, half-court tennis and basketball. Canoe and bicycle hire. **Off site:** Many quiet D-class roads ideal for cycling.

**Charges** 2003

| | |
|---|---|
| Per unit incl. 2 persons | € 14.50 - € 18.00 |
| extra person (over 7 yrs) | € 4.80 - € 6.20 |
| child (1-6 yrs) | € 2.50 - € 3.00 |
| animal | € 2.00 - € 2.50 |
| electricity (4/10A) | € 3.50 - € 6.00 |
| local tax (over 12 yrs) | € 0.35 |

**Tel:** 04 90 38 05 71. **Fax:** 04 90 20 84 61. **E-mail:** sorguette@wanadoo.fr. **Reservations:** Made with deposit (€ 61) and fee (€ 12,20). **Open** 15 March - 15 October.

**Directions:** Site is on the N100 to Apt, 1.5 km. east of L'Isle sur la Sorgue and is well signed.

# Camping du Pont d'Avignon

Ile dela Barthelasse, 84000 Avignon

**8409**

Camping du Pont d'Avignon is a city site, yet it is in a quiet location and only a short walk from the town. With its island situation, some of the pitches are only yards away from the famous bridge, only the mighty Rhône separating them. These pitches have wonderful views of the 'Pont' and also of the Pope's palace which is floodlit at night. All the pitches are level with some shade and out of 300 pitches, 118 have electricity. A small play area, tennis courts and volleyball pitch are in the centre of the site separating the tent pitches on one side and the electric pitches on the other, all separated by small hedges. English is spoken at reception and internet access is available. The amenities are grouped around the new pool. The site, although within a 15-20 minute walk from the historic centre of Avignon, has a very rural feel, due no doubt to the many flowering trees and shrubs and the fact it is on an island.

**Facilities:** Well positioned toilet blocks are of an older design but are kept very clean and well maintained. Mainly British style toilets, roomy showers and all washbasins in cubicles. Dishwashing and laundry sinks. Three washing machines and a dryer. One block has full facilities for disabled visitors. Motorcaravan service point. Well stocked shop (1 April - end Sept.). Bar/restaurant and takeaway (1 May - end Sept). Swimming pool and paddling pool (1 June - end Sept). Children's play area. Tennis (free). Volleyball.

**Charges** 2003

| | |
|---|---|
| Per unit incl. 2 persons | € 14.00 - € 24.10 |
| extra adult | € 2.80 - € 4.05 |
| child 3-12 yrs | free - € 4.05 |
| electricity | € 2.50 - € 2.80 |
| dog | € 0.80 - € 2.05 |
| local tax (over 18 yrs) | € 0.34 |

**Tel:** (0)4 90 80 63 50. **Fax:** (0)4 90 85 22 12. **E-mail:** info@camping-avignon.com. **Reservations:** Necessary for July/Aug. **Open** 24 March - 26 October.

**Directions:** Site is on the Ile de la Barthelasse in the middle of the river Rhône. It is well signed from the many roads into Avignon and accessed from one of the bridges crossing to Villeneuve les Avignon on the west bank of the river.

# Midi-Pyrénées

Map 15

Major city: Toulouse

Départements: 09 Ariège, 31 Haute-Garonne, 32 Gers,
65 Hautes-Pyrénées, 81 Tarn, 82 Tarn-et Garonne

We have left the official region of the Midi-Pyrénées almost intact except for départements of Aveyron (12) and Lot (46) which we believe sit better in our Tourist region of the Dordogne/Aveyron.

Home of Armagnac, Rugby and the Three Musketeers, the Midi-Pyrénées is the largest region of France, extending from the Dordogne in the north to the Spanish border. It is blessed by bright sunlight and a fascinating range of scenery. High chalk plateaux, majestic peaks, tiny hidden valleys and small fortified sleepy villages, which seem to have changed little since the Middle Ages, contrast with the high-tech, industrial and vibrant university city of Toulouse; also rich in art and architecture. Lourdes is one of the most visited pilgrimage sites in the world. Toulouse-Lautrec, the artist, was born at Albi the capital of the département of Tarn. Much of the town is built of pink brick which seems to glow when seen from the distance. In the east, the little town of Foix, with its maze of steep, winding streets, is a convenient centre from which to explore the prehistoric caves at Niaux and the Aladdin's Cave of duty-free gift shops in the independent state of Andorra. The Canal du Midi that links Bordeaux to the Mediterranean was commissioned by Louis XIV in 1666 and is still in working order to day.
Note: Site reports are laid out by département in numerical order.

### Cuisine of the region

The cuisine of the Midi-Pyrénées is rich and strongly seasoned, making generous use of garlic and goose fat
*Foie Gras* – specially preserved livers of goose and duck
*Cassoulet* – a hearty stew of duck, sausages and beans
*Confit de Canard (d'oie)* – preserved duck meat (goose)
*Magret de canard* – duck breast fillets
*Poule au pot* – chicken simmered with vegetables
Seafood such as oysters, salt-water fish, or piballes from the Adour river
*Ouillat (Ouliat)* – Pyrénées soup: onions, tomatoes, goose fat, garlic
*Tourtière Landaise* – a sweet of Agen

prunes, apples and Armagnac
*Grattons (Graisserons)* – a mélange of small pieces of rendered down duck, goose,and pork fat; served as an appetiser – very filling

### Wine

There are some excellent regional wines, such as full-bodied red Cahors and, of course, Armagnac to follow the meal. Try 'Floc', a mixture of Armagnac and grape juice

### Places of Interest

*Albi* – birthplace and Museum of Toulouse-Lautrec, imposing Ste Cécile cathedral with 15C fresco of 'The Last Judgement'
*Collonges-la-Rouge* – picturesque village of Medieval and Renaissance style mansions and manors in red sandstone
*Conques* – 11th century Ste Foy Romanesque church
*Cordes* – medieval walled hilltop village
*Foix* – 11th/12th century towers on rocky peak above town; 14th century cathedral.
*Lourdes* – famous pilgrimage site where Ste Bernadette is said to have spoken to the Virgin Mary in a grotto and known for the miracles said to have been performed there
*Auch* – capital of ancient Gascony, boasts a fine statue of d'Artágnan

## Camping L'Arize

Lieu-dit Bourtol, 09240 La Bastide-de-Sérou

0902

You will receive a warm welcome from Dominique and Brigitte at this friendly little family site and Brigitte speaks excellent English. The site sits in a delightful, tranquil valley among the foothills of the Pyrénées and is just east of the interesting village of La Bastide de Sérou beside the River Arize (good trout fishing). The river is fenced for the safety of children on the site, but may be accessed just outside the gate. Deer and wild boar are common in this area and may be sighted in quieter periods. The owners have built this site from ground level over the last few years and have put much love and care into its development. The 70 large pitches are neatly laid out on level grass within the spacious site. All have 3/6A electricity (French type sockets) and are separated into bays by hedges and young trees. Discounts have been negotiated for several of the local attractions (details are provided in the comprehensive pack provided on arrival - in your own language). This is a comfortable and relaxing base for touring this beautiful part of the Pyrénées with easy access to the medieval town of Foix and even Andorra for duty-free shopping.

**Facilities:** The central sanitary block (unheated) includes washbasins in cabins and good facilities for babies and disabled people. Laundry room with dryer. Dishwashing under cover. The only omission is a chemical disposal point - the organic sewage system is incompatible with chemicals. Entertainment in high season, weekly barbecues and welcome drinks on Sundays. Fishing, riding and bicycle hire on site. **Off site:** Golf 5 km. Several restaurants and shops are within a few minute's drive and the nearest restaurant, which is located at the national stud for the famous Merens horses just 200 m. away, will deliver takeaway meals to your pitch.

**Charges** 2002

Per pitch incl. 2 persons, electricity € 12.50 - € 18.00
extra adult                          € 3.50 - € 4.50
child (0-7 yrs)                      € 2.50 - € 3.00
dog                                         € 1.00

**Tel:** 05 61 65 81 51. Fax: 05 61 65 83 34. E-mail: camparize@aol.com. **Reservations:** Made with 25% deposit and fee (€ 10). **Open** 28 March - 4 November.

**Directions:** Site is southeast of the village La Bastide-de-Sérou. Take the D15 towards Nescus and site is on right after approx. 1 km.

## Camping Le Montagnou

route de Guzet, 09140 Le Trein d'Ustou

0903

The road going south out of St Girons appears to lead to nowhere other than Guzet, but it is well worth the short detour over easy roads to the little village of Le Trein d'Ustou, which is no more than 10 or 15 minutes short of the up and coming winter sports resort of Guzet. Just before Le Trein d'Ustou you will find Le Montagnou, a delightful small campsite nestling among the lush lower slopes of the mountains. Robert and Daniele are a jolly couple who created this charming site from the forest. It is an attractive proposition either as a base for winter sports activities or for touring this lovely area, with 60 level pitches on grass, 30 with electricity (6, 10 or 16A). At a lower level there is an area of the river running alongside the site which the locals use for swimming, but really the attraction here is the surrounding mountains which offer excellent winter sports facilities which include a ski-lift (10 minutes drive) and no less than 24 pistes! There are also many places of interest which Robert, who doubles as the local Director of Tourism, will be pleased to tell you about and brief you on the local wildlife. The walks in this area are renowned - watch out for marmots and, yes, even bears!

**Facilities:** Two toilet blocks (one open in low season) can be heated and are kept clean. They include washbasins in cabins, covered dishwashing and laundry sinks, washing machine and dryers, and good facilities for disabled visitors. Snack bar with takeaway. Gas supplies. Library (some English books) and TV. Fishing. **Off site:** Riding 15 km. Restaurant 50 m. in the village.

**Charges** 2002

Per unit incl. 2 persons
and 6A electricity                 € 3.75 - € 5.00
extra person                               € 4.00
child (2-7 yrs)                           € 2.50
dog                                           € 1.10

**Tel:** 05 61 66 94 97. Fax: 05 61 66 91 20. E-mail: campinglemontagnon@wanadoo.fr. **Reservations:** Contact site by letter. **Open** all year.

**Directions:** From St Girons follow signs for Guzet; take first right at roundabout (Guzet), second right at next roundabout (Guzet, Seix) and second right at third roundabout to Seix. Go through Seix (the river is on your right) and at Pont de la Taule turn left towards Trein d'Ustou. Site is on left before village.

# Camping Le Pré Lombard

09400 Tarascon sur Ariege

Didier Mioni, the manager here follows the town motto S'y passos, y demoros - if you wish to come here, you will stay here' in his aim to ensure your satisfaction on his site. This busy, good value site is located beside the attractive river Ariége on the outskirts of the town. There are around 180 level, grassy, numbered pitches with shade provided by a variety of trees. At the rear of the site are 60 site-owned chalets and mobile homes. Electricity is available to all. A gate in the fence provides access to the river bank for fishing (licences required). The ducks here will be uninvited guests at your table if you are parked close to the river and provide an amusing diversion. As this is a town site there is some town and traffic noise during the day and evening. Open all year, it is an excellent choice for early or late breaks, or as a stop-over en-route to your winter sun destinations in Spain. This region of Ariége is in the foothills of the Pyrénées and 45 km. from Andorra. At Tarascon itself you can go underground at the Parc Pyrénéen de l'Art Préhistorique to view prehistoric rock paintings, or the really adventurous can take to the air for paragliding, hangliding, or microlighting. The Vallées Ax famous for cross-country ski-ing are within reasonably easy reach for winter sports enthusiasts.

**Facilities:** The site is well served by five sanitary units of varying age, design and size (not all opened in low season). Mostly British WCs, open and cubicled washbasins. Facilities for disabled people. Dishwashing and laundry sinks. Laundry. Excellent motorcaravan service point. Bar and takeaway (open according to demand). Bread, gas, papers and daily requirements sold in the bar. Good restaurant with entertainment and dancing, creating a very enjoyable French ambience. The associated covered riverside terrace is very smart (1/5-30/9). Fenced, unsupervised swimming pool (1/5-30/9, a new covered pool is planned). Separate playgrounds for toddlers and older children. Video games machines, table tennis, table football, boules and volleyball. Fishing. Full programme of entertainment for families in main season. kayaking and fishing nearby. **Off site:** Large supermarket 300 m. Town 800 m. Archery, kayaking and fishing nearby.

**Charges 2002**

| | |
|---|---|
| Per unit incl. 2 adults, electricity | € 14.00 - € 22.00 |
| extra person | € 4.00 - € 7.00 |
| child under 4 yrs | free |
| animal | € 1.00 - € 2.00 |
| local tax | € 0.15 - € 0.30 |

**Tel:** 05 61 05 61 94. Fax: 05 61 05 78 93. E-mail: contact@camping.leprelombard.com. **Reservations:** Advised for high season and made with 25% deposit and € 15,24 booking fee. **Open** 1 February - 1 November.

**Directions:** Site is 800 m. south of the town centre adjacent to the river. Turn off main N20 into the town centre and there are prominent camp signs.

# Camping du Lac

RN 20, 09000 Foix

Du Lac is a new, large and sprawling lakeside site with many facilities. It is just 3 km. north of the very pretty town of Foix. There is some road noise as the site is alongside the old N20 but there is lots of room to manoeuvre at the entrance and a smart, air conditioned reception building. The site is informally divided into four areas, one for parking vehicles. The other areas are generally flat and some shade can be found under mature trees. There are 135 pitches, most with electricity, but the site is so big there appear to be more - there is lots of room. Access to the lake is through a gate which is locked at night and the fence is secure. Children will need supervision in this area. The lake is owned by a separate company but campers have free use of the attractive area. Here you will find canoeing and pedaloes, along with fishing, or just picnics and barbecues with a small bar operating. The lake is not for swimming as there is a fair amount of forbidding green weed but there is a clear area for canoes. The site is ideal for visiting Foix and exploring the local area.

**Facilities:** Four unisex sanitary blocks of different designs are all new, some of brick and others resembling pretty 'wendy houses' made of wood. The facilities are modern, clean and well equipped. One of the little blocks contains a washing machine, excellent facilities for disabled campers and a well equipped baby room. Reception sells basic goods but no fresh food. Pizza hut and bar/drinks stall close to the pool (a restaurant is planned). Swimming pool and separate paddling pool. Children's play areas round the site and another by the lake. Watersports, fishing and canoe instruction (hire charges apply). TV room, electronic games. Tennis court and boules pitch. Some animation in high season. Torches are necessary. **Off site:** Cycling and walking tours, riding, golf or even white water rafting.

**Charges 2002**

| | |
|---|---|
| Per unit incl. 2 persons and | |
| 4A electricity | € 10.00 - € 15.00 |
| 13A electricity | € 20.00 - € 35.00 |
| extra person | € 1.50 - € 4.00 |
| dog | € 0.50 - € 1.50 |

**Tel:** 05 61 65 11 58. Fax: 05 61 65 19 98. E-mail: camping-du-lac@wanadoo.fr. **Reservations:** Advised for July/Aug. **Open** all year.

**Directions:** From Foix stay on the old N20 north for 3 km. (avoid the new bypass and tunnel). Site is well signed on the left.

## Camping Municipal La Prade

09110 Sorgeat

**0905M**

Superbly situated high up on the mountainside overlooking the valley this site has magnificent views, with the river 300 m distant and a lake at 2 km. A small site, it provides just 38 pitches on terraces. About half are occupied by long stay units. Well supervised, with the warden present all evening, the site is kept very clean. Electrical connections (5/10A) are available. A small stream tinkles through the centre of the site and the attractive hills towering above it reverberate with the pleasant sounds of goat bells. A separate area has permanent brick barbecues for use by campers. A most reasonably priced campsite.

**Facilities:** The rather small sanitary block has only two showers and two WCs (one British, one Turkish) in each half. However, standards are very high - there are even clean foot towels in the showers. Hot water is provided for dishwashing. Facilities for the disabled are also very good with special washbasin and a very large shower suite. No chemical disposal or waste water point (the Turkish toilet is used). Small children's play area.

**Charges** guide

| | |
|---|---|
| Per pitch | € 1.37 |
| person | € 1,52 - € 2.67 |
| electricity (5/10A) | € 2.29 - € 3.81 |

**Tel:** 05 61 64 36 34. **Reservations:** Advised for high season - contact site. **Open** all year.

**Directions:** From N20 Foix - Andorra road through Ax-les-Thermes, in the centre of the village take the D613 to the left, signed to Quillen (hairpin bends) for 5 km. Site is signed on the right. The last kilometre is a narrow two way winding road. There are several other sites as you climb the hillside so a sharp eye is required to pick this out - it is worth the effort!

## Camping Municipal de Lavelanet

rue Jacquard, 09300 Lavelanet

**0907M**

This quiet, neat site is adjacent to the municipal swimming pool and sports complex. It has a very nice modern sanitary unit with an open central atrium containing a well tended flowerbed. There are 100 neatly numbered grassy level pitches, about half separated by hedges, some very private, and most have electricity (15A). A notice board at reception gives details of entertainment and local activities and there is a small library. Torches are necessary here and unusually dogs are allowed to run free. We see this as a stop over site or somewhere to relax in peace with no frills.

**Facilities:** The toilet unit provides mostly British style toilets, washbasins (a few in cubicles), push-button showers (no divider) and a toilet /washbasin cubicle for disabled people. Dishwashing and laundry sinks. Washing machine plus iron in laundry room. Minigolf (free), table tennis, barbecue areas, archery and volleyball. **Off site:** Municipal swimming pool open July/Aug. Activities arranged (with a guide) including walking, canoeing, canyoning and caving. Shops and other services close by in the town.

**Charges** 2002

| | |
|---|---|
| Per pitch | € 3.50 |
| adult | € 3.50 |
| child (under 7 yrs) | € 1.50 |
| electricity | € 1.50 |

**Tel:** 05 61 01 22 20. Fax: 05 61 03 06 39. E-mail: lavelanet.tourisme@wanadoo.fr. **Reservations:** Not normally necessary but will be made. Contact: Service Tourisme, Maison de Lavelanet, BP 89, 09300 Lavelanet. **Open** 15 June - 31 August.

**Directions:** Lavelanet is 27 km. east of Foix. The site is just off the D117 at the western end of the town, signed at the entrance to town.

## Camping Le Talouch

32810 Roquelaure

**3208**

Although enjoying an `away-from-it-all` location, Auch the region`s capital is within a 10 km. drive from this family run site, which takes its name from the small Talouch river. The entrance, off the D148 road, is fronted by a parking area with reception to the right and the bar and restaurant facing. Beyond this point lies the top half of the touring area with generous pitches of at least 120 sq.m. located between mature trees and divided by hedges, some with chalets. There are 105 pitches, with electricity (4A), 10 of which are serviced with water and drainage. The rear half of the site has unshaded pitches in a more open aspect.

**Facilities:** There are two immaculate toilet blocks, the larger refurbished building offering modern units with a clean appearance. The smaller block is of a more modern and unusual style. Baby bathroom/ shower which can be used by people with disabilities. Small shop (1/5-30/9). Two swimming pools. Bicycle hire. Play areas, volleyball, tennis and 9 hole swing golf course. Entertainment in high season.

**Charges** 2003

| | |
|---|---|
| Per unit incl. 2 adults | € 18.87 |
| with electricity | € 22.22 |
| extra adult | € 5.89 |
| child (3-7 yrs) | € 4.73 |

**Tel:** 05 62 65 52 43. Fax: 05 62 65 53 68. E-mail: info@camping-talouch.com. **Reservations:** Advisable for July/Aug. **Open** 1 April - 30 September.

**Directions:** From Auch take N21 for 8.5 km. north and turn west on D272 to village of Roquelaure. Follow signs to site 2 km. south of village on D148.

# Le Camp de Florence

route Astaffort, 32480 La Romieu

**the travel service**
TO BOOK
Ferry ✓
Pitch ✓
Accommodation ✓
01892 55 98 98

Camp de Florence is an attractive site on the edge of an historic village in pleasantly undulating Gers countryside. It is run by the Mynsbergen family who are Dutch (although Susan is English) and they have sympathetically converted the old farmhouse buildings to provide facilities for the site. The 201 pitches (95 for tourers) are all over 100 sq.m. plus, all with electricity, 10 with hardstanding and terraced where necessary. They are arranged around a large field (full of sunflowers when we visited) with rural views, giving a feeling of spaciousness. The older pitches near the main buildings have good shade but it gets progressively less the newer the pitch. However, 25 of these are fully serviced and shade will develop. The 13th century village of La Romieu is on the Santiago de Compostela pilgrim route and the collegiate church, visible from the site, is well worth a visit (the views are magnificent from the top of the tower), as is the local arboretum, the biggest collection of trees in the Midi-Pyrénées. The Pyrénées are a two hour drive, the Atlantic coast a similar distance. There are 20 tour operator pitches.

**Facilities:** Two unisex toilet blocks include some washbasins in cabins. These facilities may be under pressure at peak times and are a long walk from certain corners of the site. Washing machine and dryer. Motorcaravan services. Water points are limited. A good upstairs, air-conditioned restaurant, open to the public as well as campers, serves a range of food, including local specialities and an à la carte menu (15/5-30/9, closed Weds, with a barbecue instead). Takeaway. Bread on site in season. Swimming pool area (rebuilt by experts and an attractive feature) with jacuzzi, central island and protected children's pool (all open to the public in the afternoons). Children's adventure play area, games area and pets area. Games room, tennis, table tennis, volleyball and petanque. Bicycle hire. Video shows, discos, picnics, animation and musical evenings and excursions organised. **Off site:** Shop 500 m. in village. Fishing 5 km, riding 10 km. Walking tours, excursions and wine tasting arranged.

**Charges** 2002

| | |
|---|---|
| Per unit incl. 2 persons | € 10.40 - € 20.20 |
| extra person | € 3.50 - € 6.00 |
| child (4-9 yrs) | € 2.60 - € 4.30 |
| electricity (6A) | € 3.10 |
| water and drainage | free - € 2.50 |
| dog (max 2) | € 1.60 |
| local tax | € 0.15 |

**Tel:** 05 62 28 15 58. Fax: 05 62 28 20 04. E-mail: info@campdeflorence.com. **Reservations:** Write or phone for information (English spoken). **Open** 1 April - 31 October.

**Directions:** Site is signed from D931 Agen - Condom road. Small units can turn left at Ligardes (signed) and follow D36 for 1 km. and take right turn for La Romieu (signed). Otherwise continue until outskirts of Condom and take D41 left to La Romieu and pass through village to site.

Le Camp de Florence - 32480 La Romieu

## Sun * Comfort * Nature * Water

The Gers - A region waiting to be discovered, an unspoilt landscape of rolling hills, sunflowers and historic fortified villages and castles. Peace, tranquillity, the home of Armagnac, Fois Gras and Magret de Canard. A four star camping / caravanning site with bungalows, mobil-homes and Trigano tents for hire.

Tel: 0033 562 28 15 58 - Fax: 0033 562 28 20 04
E-mail: info@campdeflorence.com - www.campdeflorence.com

## Camping Lac des Trois Vallées

32700 Lectoure

**3206**

Lac des Trois Vallées is a large 40 hectare lively, busy site site with many facilities. It is set in the heart of Gascony, a land of fortified villages wine and 'foie gras', near the town of Lectoure. The site with its attractive ivy covered reception complete with water features, is popular with those who like activities and entertainment. It is, in fact, a large holiday complex and good for families with teenagers. The emphasis is on water sports and you can choose between the activities on the lakes or the excellent pool complex. The impressive complex has pleasant paved areas for sunbathing. There are two restaurants, one under bright white canvas beside the pool and one by the lake, and three bars including `The Pub'. There are some steep inclines from the lakeside to the pitches. Of the 500 pitches, over 300 are for touring units on shaded or open ground, all with electricity (10A). Used by tour operators (100 pitches). A Yelloh Village member.

**Facilities:** Eight sanitary blocks, one of ultra-modern design, the rest refurbished, and open air baby baths. As this is a busy site they receive heavy use but when we visited all was in order. Launderette. Motorcaravan service point. Mini-market. Two restaurants and three bars (hours vary according to season). Snack bar by the lake plus a drinks kiosk. Swimming pool complex with paddling pools and jacuzzis (from 20/5). Lake complex with slides and diving platforms (open to the public, from 15/5). Lifeguards supervise both areas in season. Watersports and fishing. Tennis and mountain biking (bicycles hire), with cabaret, shows at the large lakeside amphitheatre and craft activities for all ages. Disco and cinema and children's 'Tepee Club'. Woods and fields for walking. Light aircraft flights. Caravan storage. **Off site:** Riding 4 km, golf 10 km.

**Charges** 2002

| | |
|---|---|
| Per unit incl. 2 persons, electricity | € 15.00 - € 32.00 |
| plus water | € 17.00 - € 34.00 |
| extra person | € 4.00 - € 7.00 |
| dog | free - € 2.50 |

**Tel:** 05 62 68 82 33. Fax: 05 62 68 88 82. E-mail: lac.des.trois.vallees@wanadoo.fr. **Reservations:** Made with deposit (€ 81) and non-refundable fee (€ 22,87). **Open** 1 May - 14 September.

**Directions:** Site well signed 2 km. outside Lectoure to the south, off the N21.

---

## Camping-Caravaning Le Rioumajou

Bousrisp, 65170 Saint-Lary Soulan

**6507**

Located in the heart of the Aure valley, adjacent to a fast flowing unfenced river, and with views to the surrounding mountains and countryside, Le Rioumajou is a good base from which to explore this part of the Hautes-Pyrénées. There are 240 pitches, with 48 mobile homes, leaving around 190 pitches for tourists. They are generally separated, varying in size, some shady and some more open, and all with electricity hook-ups (2-10A), and 10 are all weather pitches. A good cycle track runs alongside the main road in both directions from the site. Nearby is the Réserve Naturel du Néouvielle National Park, and the Spanish border via the Aragnouet - Bielsa tunnel, and the tourist village of Saint-Lary Soulan is 2 km.

**Facilities:** Three modern toilet blocks (one heated) have some washbasins in cabins, controllable hot showers including some spacious twin units, a laundry with a large drying room. One block has a dedicated baby room. Facilities for disabled visitors (access by key). Small shop for essentials (July/Aug). Well fenced, outdoor heated swimming pool (10 x 25m; June-Sept). Sauna and jacuzzi. Good adventure style playground.

**Charges** guide

| | |
|---|---|
| Per adult | € 4.42 - € 5.64 |
| child (under 10 yrs) | € 1.99 - € 2.44 |
| electricity 2/10A | € 2.59 - € 5.80 |
| local tax | € 0.34 |

**Tel:** (0)5 62 39 48 32. **Reservations:** Advised for high season. **Open** all year.

**Directions:** From Lannemezan take the D929 south, pass through Arreau, and continue for about 12 km. to Bourisp. Site is on northern side of village on right hand side.

# Sunêlia Les Trois Vallées

6502 Ave des Pyrenees, 65400 Argelès-Gazost

the **travel service**
TO BOOK
Ferry ✔
Pitch ✔
Accommodation ✔
**01892 55 98 98**

We felt this was the most promising site along the valley road from Lourdes into the Pyrénées, and one of few with room and plans for development. It has a rather unprepossessing entrance and pitches near the road suffer from noise, but at the back, open fields allow views of surrounding mountains on all sides. Recent additions include an indoor pool and two jacuzzis. Recently extended, the site now has 400 flat, grassy, marked out pitches of reasonable size, all with electricity. Water points were scarce, but the owner hoped to remedy this, given the go-ahead by local officialdom. The proximity to the road is at least advantageous for touring the area, being by a roundabout with Lourdes one way, Luz-St-Sauveur and mountains another way, and the dramatic Pyrénées Corniche Col d'Aubisque going off to the west. Argelès-Gazost is an attractive town with excellent restaurants and cultural interests. The site is popular with young people and could be quite lively at times.

**Facilities:** The two unisex toilet blocks are fairly modern and include facilities for disabled people and a laundry room. Cleaning can be variable and facilities could be under pressure at peak times. Bread available on site. Bar/disco. Café and takeaway. Swimming pool complex (from 1/6) with paddling pool and two water slides. TV room. Good children's playground. Volleyball, football, boules and archery. **Off site:** Supermarket across the road. Fishing 500 m, bicycle hire 50 m, riding 3 km.

**Charges** 2002

| | |
|---|---|
| Per pitch incl. 2 persons | € 10.00 - € 20.00 |
| with electricity (3A) | € 13.00 - € 23.00 |
| extra person | € 3.40 - € 6.00 |
| child (under 7 yrs) | € 1.80 - € 5.00 |
| electricity 6A | € 2.50 |

**Tel:** 05 62 90 35 47. **Fax:** 05 62 90 35 48. **E-mail:** 3_valees@wanadoo.fr. **Reservations:** Advised for July/Aug. and made with deposit (€ 77 ) and fee (€ 15,24). **Open** 1 April - 30 September.

**Directions:** Take N21 from Lourdes to Argelès-Gazost. As you approach Argelès, pass a Champion supermarket on your right, and then a roundabout - take the furthest left exit and the site entrance is 100 m. or so on the left.

300m from the street center and spa

Sunêlia open style

# Les Trois Vallées

Avenue des Pyrénées
65400 Argelès-Gazost
Tél: 0033 562 90 35 47
Fax: 0033 562 90 35 48
Website: camping-les-3-vallees.fr

# Camping Le Lavedan

6508 Lau-Balagnas, 65400 Argelès-Gazost

Reasonably priced, Camping du Lavedan is an old established site set in the Argelès Gazost valley south of the Lourdes. It is beside the road so there is some daytime road noise. The 105 touring pitches are set on grass with some shade. All have electricity (2-10A), water and waste water point. The area is fine for walking, biking, rafting and of course in winter skiing. There is a swimming pool which can be covered in inclement weather. A twice weekly event is organised in July/Aug and weekly in June. Not a pristine site when we visited but the price reflects this.

**Facilities:** The toilet block is quite old with dark tiles, some Turkish style toilets, bidets and small showers, but some washbasins are in cabins. Baby shower and bath. Facilities for disabled people. Washing machines and dryer in separate small block. Restaurant/takeaway (1/5-15/9). Bar (all year). No shop but supermarket 2 km. and bread delivery daily (1/5-15/9). Swimming pool (can be covered) and paddling pool. Good play area with table tennis. **Off site:** Fishing 1 km. Rafting 2 km. Riding 5 km. Bicycle hire 1 km. Golf 15 km.

**Charges** 2002

| | |
|---|---|
| Per unit incl. 2 persons | € 11.50 - € 15.00 |
| extra person | € 2.50 - € 4.50 |
| electricity (2-6A) | € 2.00 - € 6.00 |

**Tel:** 05 62 97 18 84. **Fax:** 05 62 97 55 56. **E-mail:** MICHEL.DUBIE@wanadoo.com. **Reservations:** Contact site. **Open** all year.

**Directions:** Site is on the right side of the N12 (Lourdes - Spain), just past the village of Lau Balagnas, which is 15 km. south of Lourdes.

## Camping Soleil du Pibeste

16 rue du Lavedan, 65400 Agos Vidalos

**6509**

Soleil du Pibeste is a quiet rural site with well tended grass and flower beds. It has 23 mobile homes to rent and 67 pitches for tourers. All pitches have electricity (3-15A) and there is some shade. It is a perfect site for the active as many activities are organised from the site - from gentle ones like painting, sculpture and Chinese dancing to walking, rafting, parasailing, climbing, horse riding and of course in the winter skiing. There is no shop as the supermarket is only 5 km. and ordered bread is delivered to your door daily. The swimming pool is on a terrace above the pitches with sunbeds, a paddling pool and waterfall and the most magnificent view of the mountains. The same wonderful view can be enjoyed whilst doing the washing up. There could be some daytime road noise.

**Facilities:** Two heated toilet blocks have washbasins in cabins, large showers, baby room, washing machine and dryer and facilities for disabled visitors (key). Motorcaravan service point. Bar with piano and internet access, which also servers snacks. Adjoining room for playing cards or reading. Swimming pool and paddling pool. Small play area. Boule, archery, basketball and volleyball. Table tennis. Bicycle hire. **Off site:** Fishing 800 m. Golf 10 km. Rafting 2 km. Skiing 2 km.

**Charges** 2002

| Per unit incl. 2 persons | |
| --- | --- |
| and 3A electricity | € 14.00 - € 16.00 |
| extra person | € 3.00 - € 4.00 |
| extra 3A electricity | € 3.00 |
| animal | € 2.00 |

**Tel:** 05 62 97 53 23. Fax: 05 62 97 53 23. E-mail: campingpibeste@wanadoo.fr. **Reservations:** Made with 25% deposit and € 22 fee. **Open** all year.

**Directions:** Agos Vidalos is on the N21, 5 km. south of Lourdes. Site is well signed on the right just after end of dual-carriageway (in village).

## Castel Camping Pyrénées Natura

route du Lac, 65400 Estaing

**6506**

the travel service
TO BOOK

| Ferry | ✔ |
| --- | --- |
| Pitch | ✔ |
| Accommodation | ✔ |

01892 55 98 98

Pyrénées Natura, at an altitude of 1,000 metres, on the edge of the National Park. is the perfect site for lovers of nature. Eagles and vultures soar above the site and a small open air observatory with seats and binoculars is provided. The Ruysschaert family's aim is that you go home from a holiday here feeling at peace with the world, having hopefully learned something about the flora and fauna of the High Pyrénées. Tristan, their son, is qualified to take groups walking in the mountains to see chamois, marmots and the varied flora and fauna (there are even a few bears but they are seen very rarely). The 60 pitches, all with electricity, are in a large, level, open and sunny field. Around 75 varieties of trees and shrubs have been planted - not too many to spoil the view though, which can only be described as fantastic. Reception is in a traditional style stone building with timber floors and an open staircase. The small shop is quite unique. Housed in the old water mill, it stocks a variety of produce, including wine. This is left unmanned and open all day and, after you have chosen your goods, you pay at reception - very trusting, but they have not been let down yet. The last weekend in May is a special time when the local shepherds take their flocks up to the high pastures. Campers help by walking up with them and then helping to separate the different flocks. Returning to the site by bus, with a good old sing-song with the shepherds, the site provides food for everyone. That sounds like a trip worth making.

**Facilities:** First class toilet facilities with high quality fittings include a cubicle for children with shower, WC and washbasin, full facilities for disabled visitors and, in the same large room, baby bath, shower and changing mat. WCs have individual paper seat covers. Dishwashing and laundry sinks. Washing machine and airers are provided to avoid unsightly washing lines. Motorcaravan service point. Dog shower. Small shop. Small bar (15/5-15/9) and lounge area, extra upstairs lounge, library and TV (mainly used for videos of the National Park). Small play area for the very young. Table tennis, boule and giant chess. Weekly evening meal in May, June and Sept. **Off site:** Village has two restaurants.

**Charges** 2003

| Per unit incl. 2 persons and electricity (3A) | € 19.50 |
| --- | --- |
| extra person | € 3.50 |
| child (under 8 yrs) | € 2.00 |
| electricity (6/10A) | € 1.50 - € 3.00 |
| animal | € 1.50 |
| local tax | € 0.45 |

**Tel:** 05 62 97 45 44. Fax: 05 62 97 45 81. E-mail: info@campping-pyrenes-natura.com. **Reservations:** Made with deposit (€ 55). **Open** 1 May - 20 September.

**Directions:** From Lourdes take N21 to Argelès-Gazost. At the roundabout at Argelès, take D918 signed Aucun, turning left after 5.5 km. onto D13 to Bun. After Bun cross the river and right onto D103 to site (5.5 km). Some parts are narrow but with passing places.

## Airotel Pyrénées

65120 Esquieze-Sere

6503

Airotel Pyrénées is a small site in the heart of the Pyrénées. It is located on the main road into the mountains, south from Argelès-Gazost and surrounded by the high peaks (some pitches will have daytime road noise). There are 165 level pitches, all with electricity and 35 fully serviced, with 100 available for touring units. They are on terraced ground and separated by bushes. Some up and down walking is required between the pitches and the services. In high season a programme of activities and tournaments is arranged, from walking and mountain bike trips to rafting. There are tour operator pitches.

**Facilities:** The two toilet blocks, both fairly modern and well appointed, include washbasins in cubicles, mixed British and Turkish style WCs and can be heated. Facilities for disabled people, also doubling as a baby room. Indoor dishwashing and laundry sinks. When we visited we were told that bottled water is advised for drinking and cooking. Motorcaravan service point. Small shop (1/7-31/8) but bread available 15/5-15/9. Outdoor pool (15/6-15/9). Indoor pool, sauna and fitness room. Practice climbing wall, half court tennis, boule and table tennis. **Off site:** Skiing 10 km.

**Charges** 2003

| | |
|---|---|
| Per unit incl. 2 persons | € 14.50 - € 16.50 |
| extra person | € 4.00 |
| electricity (3/10A) | € 2.80 - € 6.20 |

**Tel:** 05 62 92 89 18. **Fax:** 05 62 92 96 50. **E-mail:** airotel.pyrenees@wanadoo.fr. **Reservations:** Advised for most periods and made with deposit (€ 46) and fee (€ 2,29). **Open** all year, except 1 Oct - 1 Dec.

**Directions:** Take N21 from Lourdes through Argelès-Gazost towards Luz-St-Sauveur. Site is on left at Esquièze-Sere, just outside Luz-St-Sauveur, immediately after Camping International.

## Camping Relais de L'Entre Deux Lacs

81120 Teillet

8101

This is a small, quiet site between the Rassisse and Bancalié lakes, open all year. The site is under new ownership. Situated in part meadow, part semi-cleared woodland, a small farm is alongside. The 65 pitches, all with electricity (6/10A, long leads may be required), are on level terraces and of varying size (up to 100 sq.m), most with ample shade from mature trees. Those near the bar/restaurant could experience some noise. Late arrivals or those wishing to leave before 8 am. are sited in an adjacent small meadow (although there may be some village traffic noise). This site is well situated for a variety of interesting excursions in an area not that well known to British visitors.

**Facilities:** There are two toilet blocks, with extra toilets on lower part of the site. The larger modern block is only opened in the main season and is closed at 22.00 hrs each night. It includes washbasins in cabins and dishwashing sinks under cover. An older, smaller block, in the converted pigeon house, has similar but older style facilities and should be heated in winter. Facilities for disabled people. Washing machines. Bar/restaurant (all 1/5-30/9). Small library with some English books and board games. Playground and children's farm. Volleyball, table tennis, boules. Bicycle hire. Charcoal barbecues are not permitted. **Off site:** Fishing 2 km. Canoes and kayaks for hire on the Rassisse lake. Shop (for bread) 250 m. in the village.

**Charges** guide

| | |
|---|---|
| Per unit incl. 2 adults | € 12.20 |
| with electricity | € 16.01 |
| extra person | € 3.81 |

**Tel:** 05 63 55 74 45. **Fax:** 05 63 55 75 65. **E-mail:** contact@camping-entredeuxlacs.com. **Reservations:** Contact site. **Open** all year.

**Directions:** From Albi ring-road, take D81 southeast to Teillet (20 km). Go through village to site on right.

## Camping Le Moulin de Julien

81170 Cordes-sur-Ciel

8102

Close to picturesque fortified old town in a secluded valley location in the heart of the Tarn region, this traditional style site has 130 spacious pitches. The pitches are mostly on grass, with good shade in parts, and are arranged around a fishing lake. All have electricity hook-ups (5A). The area has magnificent scenery to enjoy and picturesque fortified towns to discover, including medieval Cordes (1 km). This site is very quiet outside the main season and no English is spoken.

**Facilities:** Two rather elegant, well maintained sanitary buildings provide open and curtained washbasins, dishwashing and laundry sinks, a washing machine, plus facilities for disabled people. Well fenced swimming pool (June - Sept) and splash pool with slide (July/Aug). Minigolf, table tennis, TV room and boules. Fishing. Gates locked 22.00-08.00 hrs.

**Charges** 2002

| | |
|---|---|
| Per unit incl. 2 persons | € 18.00 |

**Tel:** (0)5 63 56 11 10. **Fax:** (0)5 63 56 11 10. **Reservations:** Contact site. **Open** 1 April - 30 September.

**Directions:** Cordes is 25 km. northwest of Albi. From D600 just east of Cordes take D922 south, and within 0.5 km. the site is signed at a minor road junction to your left.

## Camping Municipal de Gourjade

route de Roquecourbe, 81100 Castres

**8103M**

Camping de Gourjade is set in a country park belonging to the town of Castres. It has the river running along one side and the country park on the other. There are 100 level pitches, all with electricity (6A) and separated by well trimmed hedges, and some with shade. There is a barrier at the entrance and a night watchman for security. A small play area caters for children of 3-12 yrs but the adjoining country park has everything - large indoor and outdoor pools with slides etc, minigolf, table tennis, a miniature railway and a 9-hole golf course. In July/Aug competitions are organised. A boat makes regular trips for the 2 km. journey into the centre of Castres for markets and museums.

**Facilities:** The unisex toilet blocks are very clean with good adjustable showers, facilities for disabled visitors and baby changing. Washing machine and dryer. Drive over motorcaravan emptying point. Very limited shop, with bread daily. Attractive restaurant (all season). Bicycles kept at reception (in good condition) for the free use of campers. Country park with reduced charges for campers. **Off site:** Supermarket 1 km.

**Charges** guide
| | |
|---|---|
| Per pitch and vehicle | € 6.18 |
| extra person | € 1.60 |
| electricity | € 2.21 |

**Tel:** 05 63 59 72 30. **Fax:** 05 63 50 88 91. **E-mail:** gourjade@ville-castres.fr. **Reservations:** Made with 20% deposit. **Open** 1 April - 30 September.

**Directions:** From Castres follow signs to Roquecourbe until roundabout with supermarket, then signs to 'Rive droite', Castres and camping. Site is 1 km. on left.

## Camp Municipal des Auzerals

81800 Rabastens

**8104M**

Camping Municipal des Auzerals is a small, reasonably priced site. The 44 pitches are near the lake where fishing is possible and there are walks from the site (leaflets from the tourist information office in the town). This is a perfect site for couples seeking peace and quiet, especially in May, June and Sept. All the pitches are on grass, hedged with neat bushes and all with water, drainage and electricity (10A). The local swimming pool is adjacent and the village is only 2.5 km. away. There is no shop (ices from the reception) but a baker calls in July/Aug. All provisions can be found in the village - gas, food and restaurants. This is an unspoilt region of the Tarn within easy reach of Albi and Montauben.

**Facilities:** The sanitary block is basic but very clean, with mainly Turkish style WCs, good adjustable showers and some washbasins in cubicles. The dishwashing and laundry sinks have hot water and there is a washing machine and a freezer available in the telephone room. Baker calls. **Off site:** Village 2.5 km.

**Charges** guide
| | |
|---|---|
| Per pitch | € 1.52 |
| adult | € 2.13 |
| child (under 7 yrs) | € 1.07 |
| electricity (10/12A) | € 1.37 |

**Tel:** 05 63 33 70 36. **Fax:** 05 63 33 70 36. **E-mail:** mairie.rabastens@libertysurf.fr. **Reservations:** Contact site. **Open** 1 May - 15 September.

**Directions:** Site is northeast of Toulouse. Heading south leave A20 at exit 66 and take D930 south. This road changes to the D630 in 23 km.. Follow until sign for Albi on D988. Rabastens is 8 km. and site is signed to left on entry to village.

## Camping Les Trois Cantons

82140 St Antonin-Noble-Val

**8201**

With only 100 pitches, Les Trois Cantons is a very friendly site with level pitches, some set among trees, others open and sunny. All have electricity connections (2-10A). The swimming pool is covered and heated in early and late season, with activities organised there in July and August.. There are also walks, archery and boules, plus wine tastings and a weekly dance. It is though, primarily a site for nature lovers with peaceful evenings and nights. There are walks and mountain bike rides from the site.

**Facilities:** There are two toilet blocks, one quite basic but the other one refurbished. Both British and Turkish style WCs, quite large showers, and facilities for the disabled. Very limited shop (bread daily). Bar serving snacks and takeaways (all season). Games room. Play area. Tennis court. Volleyball. Boules. Bicycle hire. **Off site:** Riding 4 km, fishing 7 km. The area has many pretty medieval villages to visit.

**Charges** 2002
| | |
|---|---|
| Per pitch | € 6.30 |
| adult | € 5.00 |
| child (under 7 yrs) | € 3.30 |
| electricity (2/5A) | € 1.90 - € 3.45 |

Less in low seasons. **Tel:** 05 63 31 98 57. **Fax:** 05 63 31 25 93. **E-mail:** info@3cantons.fr. **Reservations:** Contact site. **Open** 15 April - 30 September.

**Directions:** From N20 at Caussade, take D296 signed Caylus and Septfonds. In about 13 km. site is signed to right (7 km. after Septfonds).

# Mediterranean - part 1

Map 16

Our 'Mediterranean' Tourist region includes all the areas which border the Mediterranean, divided into Parts 1 and 2 (our map covers all the Mediterranean region). Part 1 covers the south west coastal region.

## LANGUEDOC-ROUSSILLON

Major cities: Montpellier, Perpignan, Nîmes, Carcassonne
Départements: 11 Aude, 30 Gard, 34 Hérault, 66 Pyrénées-Orientales

Once an independent duchy, the ancient land of Languedoc combines two distinct regions: the vineyards of the Corbières and Minervois and the coastal plain stretching from the Rhône to the Spanish border. Much of the region is rugged and unspoilt and there is ample evidence of the dramatic past. Ruins of the former Cathar castles can be seen throughout the region. The walled city of Carcassonne with its towers, dungeons, moats and drawbridges is one of the most impressive examples of medieval France. Today, Languedoc and Roussillon (the area between Narbonne and the Pyrénées) are wine and agricultural regions. Languedoc, with considerable success, is a producer of much of the nation's cheap table wine.

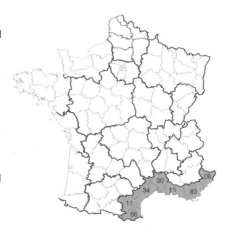

On the coast the vast sandy beaches/resorts, for example La Grande Motte, Cap d'Agde and Canet, are being promoted as an alternative to the more famous Mediterranean stretches of the Côte d'Azur. It is interesting to note that this far south there is a strong Spanish influence – in the look of the people, their culture, accent and in their language too. The local tongue, the ancient 'Occitan' is still spoken in rural areas, while down the coast in the Roussillon area, Catalan is spoken almost as much as French.

Note: site reports are laid out by département in numerical order.

### Cuisine of the region

Cooking is Provençal, characterised by garlic and olive oil with sausages and smoked hams
Fish is popular along the coast – fish soup bourride in Sète
*Aïgo Bouido* – garlic soup; the garlic is boiled so its impact is lessened; served with bread
*Boles de picoulat* – small balls of chopped-up beef and pork, garlic and eggs, served with tomatoes and parsley
*Bouillinade* – a type of 'bouillabaisse' with potatoes, oil, garlic and onions
*Boutifare* – a sausage-shaped pudding of bacon and herbs
*Cargolade* – snails, stewed in wine
*Ouillade* – heavy soup of bacon, 'boutifare' (see above), leeks, carrots, and potatoes

*Touron* – a pastry of almonds, pistachio nuts and fruit

### Wine

Wines include the reds of Corbières, Minervois, and the sweet Banyuls and Muscat

### Places of interest

*Aigues-Mortes* – medieval city
*Béziers* – wine capital of the region, St Nazaire cathedral, Canal du Midi
*Carcassonne* – largest medieval walled city in Europe
*Limoux* – medieval town, Notre Dame de Marseilla Basilica, St Martin church
*Montpellier* – famous for universities, Roman sites; Gothic cathedral
*Narbonne* – unfinished Gothic cathedral dominates the town. Excellent archeological museum near the cathedral which shows how Rome and North Africa have influenced the area.
*Nîmes* – Roman remains and amphitheatre, Pont du Gard
*Perpignan* – Kings Palace; Catalan characteristics; the old fortress dominates the centre of the city and many of the side streets are more Spanish than French
*Pézenas* – Molière's home
*Villeneuve-lès-Avignon* – Royal City and residence of popes in 14th century

# Domaine d'Arnauteille

11250 Montclar

Enjoying some beautiful and varied views, this rather unusual site is ideally situated for exploring, by foot or car, the little known Aude Département, the area of the Cathars and for visiting the walled city of Carcassonne (10 minutes drive). However, access could be difficult for large, twin axle vans. The site itself is set in 115 hectares of farmland and is on hilly ground with the original pitches on gently sloping, lightly wooded land and newer ones with water, drainage and electricity (5/10A), semi-terraced and partly hedged. The facilities are quite spread out with the swimming pool set in a hollow basin surrounded by green fields and some newly developed pitches. The reception building is vast; originally a farm building, with a newer top floor being converted to apartments. Although architecturally rather strange, from some angles it is quite attractive and mature trees soften the outlines. This is a developing site with enthusiastic owners for whom riding is the principle theme with stables on site (remember that the French are more relaxed about hard hats, etc). Some up and down walking between the pitches and facilities is unavoidable. A 'Sites et Paysages' member.

**Facilities:** The main, heated sanitary block is now a distinctive feature, rebuilt to a very high specification with a Roman theme. Three other smaller blocks are located at various points. They include washbasins in cabins, dishwashing under cover (hot water), washing machines, facilities for disabled people and a baby bath. Facilities can be stretched at peak times. Motorcaravan service point and gas. Small shop (15/5-30/9 - the site is a little out of the way). Restaurant in converted stable block offers plat du jour, grills, takeaway (15/5-15/9). Swimming pool (25 x 10 m.) with children's pool. Play area. Table tennis and volleyball. Riding (stables open 15/6-15/9). **Off site:** Bicycle hire 8 km, fishing 3 km, golf 10 km, rafting and canoeing near, plus many walks with marked paths.

**Charges** 2003

| | |
|---|---|
| Per pitch incl. 2 persons | € 13.50 - € 20.00 |
| with 5A electricity | € 17.00 - € 23.50 |
| with electricity, water, drainage | € 20.00 - € 27.50 |
| extra person | € 4.00 - € 5.50 |
| child (under 7 yrs) | € 2.50 - € 3.60 |
| dog | € 1.50 - € 2.20 |
| electricity 10A, plus | € 1.60 |

**Tel:** 04 68 26 84 53. Fax: 04 68 26 91 10. E-mail: arnauteille@mnet.fr. **Reservations:** Made with deposit (25%) and fee (€ 23). **Open** 1 April - 30 September.

**Directions:** Using D118 from Carcassonne, after bypassing the small village of Rouffiac d'Aude, there is a small section of dual carriageway. Before the end of this, turn right to Montclar up a rather narrow road for 2.5 km. Site is signed sharp left and up hill before the village.

## Camping Val d'Aleth

11580 Alet les Bains

**1111**

In the gateway to the upper Aude valley and open all year round, this popular small site is run by Christopher and Christine Cranmer who offer a warm welcome and personal service. The mellow medieval walls of Alet les Bains form one boundary of the site, while on the other and popular with anglers, is the River Aude (fenced for safety). Beyond this is the D118 and a railway which can produce some noise at times. The 37 numbered pitches with electricity hook-ups (4A or more) vary in size and are separated by hedges and mature trees which give shade. Recent works include improvements to the pitches and some hardstandings for winter use. Medieval Alet is a spa town with the thermal pool where the French take 'the cure'. The past life of the old city can be traced through its narrow streets, interesting buildings and the remains of an abbey and cathedral. The town has all services, including three restaurants and a Casino (a remnant of old aristocratic days). The site owners are keen to assist, with books, guides and walking maps available on loan along with brochures (in English) of attractions in the area. Bed and breakfast is also available.

**Facilities:** There are plans to replace the unsophisticated toilet block which is adequate, with mostly British type WCs and high pressure hot showers. Laundry sinks and washing machine under cover, basic dishwashing in the open. Reception stocks essential goods, drinks, wine and beer, and the use of a freezer. Small children's play area. Mountain bike hire. **Off site:** White water sports nearby. The area is a Mecca for walkers and mountain-bikers. Bus and train services to Carcassonne and Quillan. Shops and restaurants in town.

**Charges** 2002

| | |
|---|---|
| Per unit incl. 2 persons | € 9.10 |
| extra person | € 2.50 |
| child (under 8 yrs) | € 1.40 |
| dog | € 0.95 |
| electricity (4A) | € 2.30 |

**Tel:** 04 68 69 90 40. Fax: 04 68 69 94 60. E-mail: camping.valdaleth@wanadoo.fr. **Reservations:** Contact site. **Open** all year.

**Directions:** From Carcassonne take D118 south for 32 km. Ignore first sign to Alet (to avoid narrow stone bridge) and after crossing the river, turn into town. Site is 800 m. on the left (signed).

## Camping Le Martinet Rouge

11390 Brousses et Villaret

**1104**

Le Martinet Rouge provides a rather quaint retreat in the Aude countryside to the north of Carcassonne. It is a small site where the owners have been working hard to improve the facilities and evidence of their continued efforts can make the site less than tidy. The most striking features of the site are the massive granite boulders (outcrops of smooth rock) throughout the area used for sunbathing and for children's games. The site offers only 50 pitches, all with electricity (6A), in two contrasting areas - one is well secluded with irregularly shaped, fairly level, large pitches amongst a variety of trees and shrubs, while the other is on open meadow with mature oaks more typical of English rather than French sites with the pool attractively landscaped using the original boulders. This is a useful situation from which to visit Carcassonne and to follow the Cathare trail.

**Facilities:** Four sanitary blocks, including a good new one, have washbasins in cabins, facilities for disabled visitors, baby bathroom and dishwashing and laundry facilities. Swimming pool (15/6-15/9, no bermuda style shorts). Small shop (no others locally). Small `pub` bar with terrace serving snacks (both 15/6-15/9). Barbecue area. New fitness room. Croquet, volleyball, half court tennis, table tennis and a small play area. **Off site:** Restaurants 50 m. Tennis, riding and fishing quite close.

**Charges** 2003

| | |
|---|---|
| Per standard pitch incl. 2 persons and car | € 11.50 |
| with electricity | € 14.00 |
| extra person | € 3.50 |
| child (under 7 yrs) | € 2.00 |
| animal | € 1.00 |

**Tel:** 04 68 26 51 98. Fax: 04 68 26 51 98. **Reservations:** Made with deposit of 20%. **Open** 1 April - 31 October.

**Directions:** Site is just south of Brousses-et-Villaret, approx. 20 km. northwest of Carcassonne. It is best approached from the D118 Carcassonne - Mazamet road. Turn onto D103 15 km. north of Carcassonne to Brousses-et-Villaret. On western outskirts of village turn south on D48 to site.

## Mediterranean
### Camping L'Eden II
Domaine de Carbonas, 11230 Villefort

**1101**

Set in beautiful surroundings, this well equipped, modern site is in the foothills of the Pyrénées and provides an ideal location to explore this area. Growing trees provide some shade on a number of the terraced pitches, with the other large, marked pitches on the lower, level part mostly provided with good natural shade (75 pitches in total). All have electricity (6/10A) and the majority have drainage. Eight are very large 'super-pitches' with their own sanitary facilities. Reception and facilities, the pool area and tennis courts are at the top of the site up a fairly steep slope. Comprehensive literature and ideas about activities in the area are provided.

**Facilities:** The large main toilet block includes a small unit for disabled people, free washing machine and ironing facilities. Motorcaravan service point. Small bar, mini-shop, restaurant, snacks and takeaway (all 15/5-15/9). Refrigerator for ice packs. Attractive, partly shaded swimming pool (25/5-15/9, depending on the weather). Children's playground. Tennis courts, archery, table tennis, volleyball, tennis and golf practice. Fishing. Bicycle hire. **Off site:** Watersports near. Ski station 30 km.

**Charges** 2002

| | |
|---|---|
| Per unit incl. 2 persons | € 9.20 - €12.80 |
| pitch incl. electricity and water | €16.40 - €23.50 |
| with individual sanitary unit | €19.60 - €29.30 |
| extra person (max. 5) | € 3.10 - € 3.30 |

**Tel:** (0)4 68 69 26 33. Fax: (0)4 68 69 29 95. E-mail: eden2.villefort@libertysurf.fr. **Reservations:** Advised for July/Aug. with min. € 31 deposit and fee ( € 23); contact site for details. **Open** 1 April - 30 September.

**Directions:** Site is between Quillan and Lavelanet, off the D117. Take the D16 north at Puivert towards Chalabre; site is on left before village of Villefort.

## Mediterranean
### Camping de la Cité
11000 Carcassonne

**1110**

Carcassonne has had a turbulent history and the old city was saved from demolition in 1850 by three far-sighted Carcassonne residents. It can now be admired as one of Europe's most complete examples of a fortified medieval city. Camping de la Cité is extremely well placed for such visits, being within one kilometre of the town along a shaded footpath beside a stream. Being a city site there is much movement and places can usually be found in mid afternoon. Most pitches are very large, separated by bushes and with a little shade. There are also undefined places in deep shade under trees for small tents. Electricity (10A) is available on 100 pitches.

**Facilities:** Toilet blocks are basic and functional, but are kept clean and well maintained. They provide mainly British style toilets, washbasins in cabins and rather small and basic showers. Well equipped laundry room. Large fridges for hire. Very limited shop with bread, wine and a few basic camping supplies. Bar open all day for bread and snacks, but no alcohol unless food is bought and eaten there. Swimming pool (May - end Sept). Small children's play area, table tennis, petanque, volleyball and a field for football. **Off site:** Fitness track and fishing within 100 m.

**Charges** 2002

| | |
|---|---|
| Per unit incl. 2 persons | €12.20 - €16.80 |
| extra adult (over 7 yrs) | € 3.70 - € 4.60 |
| electricity | € 3.10 |

**Tel:** 04 68 25 11 77. Fax: 04 68 47 33 13. **Reservations:** Not normally necessary. **Open** 15 March - 10 October.

**Directions:** From A61 autoroute take exit 24 onto N113 following signs for city centre. Site is well signed (look carefully) from all roads into the city.

## Mediterranean
### Camping Municipal La Pinède
avenue Gaston Bonheur, 11200 Lézignan-Corbières

**1103M**

Within walking distance of the little town and only 35 km. from Narbonne Plage, La Pinède is laid out in terraces on a hillside, with good internal access on made-up roads. The 90 individual, level pitches vary in size and are divided up mainly by various trees and shrubs with 6A electricity (some 20 for mobile homes and chalets). The guardian sometimes organises local wine tasting and he also has a vegetable patch in one corner of the site where you can sample really fresh vegetable (charged). Outside the gates are a municipal swimming pool (July/Aug), a disco, a restaurant and tennis courts. Generally better than many municipal sites in season - it is uncomplicated and peaceful.

**Facilities:** Three sanitary blocks of good quality are fully equipped and recently refurbished. Not all blocks are opened outside high season. Washing machine. Small shop with gas. Pleasant bar also providing decently priced hot food that can be eaten on the terrace (all July/Aug). A barbecue functions here in season (private barbecues are not permitted). Torches are necessary. Caravan storage. **Off site:** Fishing 4 km, bicycle hire or riding 2 km.

**Charges** 2002

| | |
|---|---|
| Per adult | € 3.00 - € 4.00 |
| child | € 1.90 - € 3.00 |
| pitch | € 5.50 - € 7.00 |
| animal | € 1.00 |

**Tel:** 04 68 27 05 08. Fax: 04 68 27 05 08. **Reservations:** Advisable in season. **Open** 1 March - 30 October.

**Directions:** Access is directly off the main N113 on west side of Lézignan-Corbières.

## Mediterranean
# Camping Les Mimosas
chaussée de Mandirac, 11100 Narbonne

Being some six kilometres inland from the beaches of Narbonne and Gruissan, this site benefits from a somewhat less hectic situation than others in the popular seaside environs of Narbonne. The site itself is, however, quite lively with plenty to amuse and entertain the younger generation while, at the same time, offering facilities for the whole family. The 250 pitches are mainly of good size, most with electricity (6A), including a few 'grand confort', and they benefit from a reasonable amount of shade. This could be a very useful site offering many possibilities to meet a variety of needs, on-site entertainment (including an evening on Cathare history), and easy access to popular beaches, interesting towns such as Narbonne itself, Béziers or the 'Cité de Carcassonne', the Canal du Midi and Cathare castles.

**Facilities:** Four sanitary buildings, all refurbished to high standards, include washbasins in cabins, some British WCs, baby baths, laundry and dishwashing sinks, and washing machines. Shop (1/4-15/10). Bar. Small lounge, amusements. Restaurant (1/4-15/10). Heated swimming pool complex including new, land-scaped pool with slides and islands, the original pool and a children's pool (1/5-30/9). New adventure play area. Minigolf planned. **Off site:** Riding near. Lagoon for boating and fishing can be reached via footpath (about 200 m).

**Charges** 2002

| | |
|---|---|
| Per pitch incl. 1 or 2 persons | € 11.70 - € 17.20 |
| pitch with electricity | € 14.30 - € 21.30 |
| extra person | € 3.40 - € 4.60 |
| child (2-7 yrs) | € 2.00 - € 3.00 |
| animal | € 1.30 - € 2.20 |

**Tel:** 04 68 49 03 72. Fax: 04 68 49 39 45. E-mail: info@lesmimosas.com. **Reservations:** Made with deposit ( € 91,47) and fee ( € 19,82). **Open** 24 March - 31 October.

**Directions:** From A9 take exit 38 (Narbonne Sud) and go round roundabout to last exit taking you back over the autoroute (site signed from here). Follow signs to La Nautique and then Mandirac and site (total 6 km. from autoroute).

Camping Club ☆☆☆
1 heated swimming-pool

Camping Club LES MIMOSAS
Chaussée de Mandirac · 11100 NARBONNE
℃ + 33 4 68 49 03 72 · Fax +33 4 68 49 39 45
www.lesmimosas.com
e-mail : info@lesmimosas.com

CHALETS AND MOBILE HOMES TO RENT

• Tennis • Sauna
• Mini golf
• Restaurant - Bar
• Shop
• Riding 50 m
• Windsurfing
  and fishing 300 m
• 6 km to beach
  at Gruissan

*THE REGION OF CATHAR CASTLES AND PINK FLAMINGOS*

## Mediterranean
# Camping La Nautique
La Nautique, 11100 Narbonne

This extremely spacious site is situated on the Etang de Bages, where flat water combined with strong winds make it one of the best windsurfing areas in France and is owned and run by a very welcoming Dutch family. The site is fenced off from the water for the protection of children and wind-surfers can have a key for the gate (with deposit) that leads to launching points on the lake. La Nautique has 390 huge, level pitches (a small one is 130 sq.m), with many used for site owned mobile homes and chalets and 30 tour operator pitches. There are also 6 or 7 overnight pitches with electricity in a separate area. The wide range of evergreens, flowering shrubs and trees on site give a pleasant feel and each pitch is separated by hedges making some quite private. All have electricity (10A) and water. The difference between this and other sites is that each pitch has an indi-vidual toilet cabin. Tent campers may find the ground rather rocky. A variety of enter-tainment is organised in July/Aug, plus a sports club for supervised surfing, sailing, rafting, walking and canoeing (some activi-ties are charged for). English is spoken by the welcoming Schutjes family. This site caters for families with children including teenagers (in fact they say 8 months to 86 years!)

**Facilities:** Each individual cabin has a toilet, shower and washbasin (key deposit) and, as each pitch empties, the facilities are cleaned in readiness for the next. Special pitches for disabled people with facili-ties fitted out to cater for their needs. Two fully equipped laundry areas. Additional dishwashing sinks strategically placed. Shop at entrance (1/6-15/9) with reasonable stock. Bar/restaurant (evenings only May and Sept) plus large TV. Snack bar 1/7 - 31/8. Takeaway. Swimming pools (solar heated), water slide and paddling pool with fountain and slide, and poolside bar (1/7-31/8). New children's play areas and active children's club. Tennis, table tennis, basketball, volleyball, football, minigolf and boules. Teenagers' disco organised in high season. Recreation area with TV for youngsters. Internet connection. Only electric barbecues are permitted. Torch useful. **Off site:** Large sandy beaches at Gruissan (10 km) and Narbonne Plage (15 km). Narbonne is only 4 km. Walking and cycling. Riding. Canoeing, sailing and windsurfing on the Etang.

**Charges** 2002

| | |
|---|---|
| Per unit incl. 1 or 2 persons, electricity, water and sanitary unit | € 14.15 - € 24.50 |
| extra person | € 3.65 - € 4.75 |
| child (1-7 yrs) | € 1.55 - € 2.74 |
| dog or cat | € 1.25 - € 1.90 |
| local tax | € 3.00 |

**Tel:** 04 68 90 48 19. Fax: 04 68 90 73 39. E-mail: info@campinglanautique.com. **Reservations:** Made with deposit ( € 104) and fee ( € 16). **Open** 1 March - 17 November.

**Directions:** From A9 take exit 38 (Narbonne Sud). Go round roundabout to last exit and follow signs for La Nautique and site, then further site signs to site on right in 3 km.

## Mediterranean
# Camping Domaine de Gaujac
Boisset et Gaujac, 30140 Anduze

This large, woodland holiday site is enthusiastically run by the energetic and friendly Holley family. The 293 level pitches are well shaded and access to some areas, particularly those with hedged pitches, can be difficult for larger units due to narrow access roads, trees and hedges. Larger units should ask for lower numbered pitches (1-148) where access is a little easier. In high season this region is dry and hot, thus grass quickly wears off many pitches leaving just a sandy base. There are 12 special hardstanding pitches for motorcaravans. With tour operators occupying 40 pitches, the remainder are for tourists, most with electricity (4/6A). The site has a new covered animation area and courtyard terrace. Organised activities in main season include a children's club, plus cabaret, karaoke, disco, buffet parties and even cinema shows. Just across the lane is the river with a small beach where one can swim, boat or fish. Tourist attractions in the region include the mining museum at Alès, steam trains run between Anduze and St Jean-du-Gard, a music museum at Anduze, and a number of spectacular caverns and grottoes.

**Facilities:** Four sanitary units of varying ages and design are opened one by one as the season progresses. They include some washbasins in cubicles and a children's unit with special low level equipment. Dishwashing and laundry sinks, washing machines, dryer and ironing facilities. Units for disabled visitors. Clean and practical rather than luxurious, one small block can be heated in cool weather. Motorcaravan service point. Well stocked shop, newsagent. Takeaway/crêperie. Bar and restaurant open in main season (on demand other times, 15/5-15/9). Fenced swimming pool and children's pool complex (lifeguard 5/7-15/8), open during low season, weather permitting. Children's playground plus sports field for football, volleyball etc. Two tennis courts (free off season). Minigolf. **Off site:** Riding 500 m. Bicycle hire 5 km. Golf 10 km.

**Charges** 2002

| | |
|---|---|
| Per unit incl. 2 adults | € 15.00 |
| extra adult | € 3.50 |
| child (2-7 yrs) | € 2.70 |
| dog | free - € 2.30 |
| electricity (4A) | € 2.50 |

**Tel:** 04 66 61 80 65. Fax: 04 66 60 53 90.
**Reservations:** Necessary in high season and made with deposit ( € 107) and fee ( € 12,20). **Open** 1 April - 30 September.

**Directions:** From Alès take N110 towards Montpellier. At St Christol-lès-Alès fork right on D910 towards Anduze, and in Bagard turn left on D246 to Boisset et Gaujac. Site is signed from village.

## Mediterranean
# Camping Domaine des Fumades
Les Fumades, 30500 Allègre

Domaine des Fumades is a pleasant, busy site with a friendly atmosphere near the thermal springs at Allègre. Reception at the site is a joy to behold. Set in an attractive courtyard, within the farmhouse, it has a central fountain and masses of tubs and baskets of colourful flowers. The entrance as a whole has a very tropical feel with its banana plants and palm trees. The 230 pitches are large and level, all with 4A electricity. A variety of trees add privacy and welcome shade. Three pleasantly landscaped swimming pools have ample sunbathing space, bridges and new jacuzzis. This is a good area for walking, cycling, riding, climbing and fishing. Used by tour operators (80 pitches). A `Sites et Paysages` member.

**Facilities:** Two well appointed sanitary blocks and one new one seem to cope well in high season. Some washbasins in cabins, baby baths and facilities for disabled people. Laundry and dishwashing sinks. These facilities are both clean and well maintained. Well stocked shop. Bar, enlarged restaurant, snack bar and takeaway (all with reasonable prices). Two designated barbecue areas. Swimming pools with ample sunbathing space. Large, well equipped and fenced playground. Games room, tennis, volleyball, table tennis and boules. Well planned animation and entertainment programme, designed to appeal to families. Barbecues are not permitted. **Off site:** Riding 2 km.

**Charges** 2002

| | |
|---|---|
| Per standard pitch incl. 2 persons | € 2.20 - € 18.50 |
| extra adult | € 3.10 - € 5.10 |
| child (2-7 yrs) | € 1.50 - € 2.50 |
| electricity (6/10A) | € 3.10 - € 3.80 |
| pet | € 1.20 - € 2.30 |
| local tax | € 0.15 |

**Tel:** 04 66 24 80 78. Fax: 04 66 24 82 42. E-mail: domaine.des.fumades@wanadoo.fr. **Reservations:** Made with deposit ( € 121) and fee € 22,87). **Open** 1 May - 14 September.

**Directions:** From Alès take D16 through Salindres, continue towards Allègre, until signs for Fumades (and thermal springs) on the right.

## Mediterranean
# Camping Château de Boisson
**3007** Boisson, 30500 Allegre-Les Fumades

Château de Boisson is a quiet family site within easy reach of the Cévennes, Ardèche or Provence. Under new management, it is set in the grounds of the château, beside the small medieval village of Boisson. Reception at the entrance is new, light and cool, built from the local stone in the local style so it blends beautifully with the rest of the buildings. The site is hilly so the pitches are on three levels, but they are level and have 5A electricity connections. A few have personal cabins that provide a WC, washbasin and shower. Trees provide some shade. The large swimming pool with a toboggan and paddling pool is at the castle in a sunny location (1/4-30/9) and there is also an indoor pool (all season) of excellent quality. The restaurant in the castle is cool and elegant with tables also available outside.

**Facilities:** The two toilet blocks are quite old, but very clean and well maintained with washbasins in cabins - refurbishment is planned for 2003. Washing machines at both blocks, baby bath and shower, facilities for disabled visitors. Small shop. Restaurant, bar and snacks. Internet point. Play area. Indoor pool (all season). Outdoor pool (1/4-30/9). Bridge tournaments in low season. Painting classes. Tennis, boule, volleyball and basketball. Animation in July and Aug for 4-12 yr olds and outdoor competitions for adults. Dogs are not accepted. Barbecues are not allowed. Apartments to rent in the castle.

**Charges** 2002

| | |
|---|---|
| Per pitch incl. 2 persons, electricity | € 16.50 - € 30.00 |
| with water and drainage | € 18.00 - € 33.00 |
| with private facilities | € 21.00 - € 36.00 |
| extra person | € 5.00 - € 6.00 |
| child (under 5 yrs) | € 2.00 - € 3.00 |
| local tax | € 0.15 |

**Tel:** 04 66 24 82 21. **Fax:** 04 66 24 80 14. **E-mail:** reception@chateau-boisson.com. **Reservations:** Made with deposit and 15 fee; contact site. **Open** 30 March - 3 November.

**Directions:** From Alès take D16 northeast towards Salindres and Auzon. Just after Auzon turn right on D37 signed Boisson and site is signed from there.

## Mediterranean
# Camping Le Mas de Reilhe
**3008** Crespian, 30260 Quissac

Set under tall, 200 year old pine trees, this small family site has only 90 pitches (16 for site hire, the rest for tourers). Mas de Reilhe will probably appeal to couples and young families. The organised entertainment is for the children with just the occasional competition for adults. There will be road noise on some of the pitches. The lower ones are all level, separated by small bushes and most with 6A electricity and these are mainly reserved for caravans. Tents and trailer tents use the terraced hillside, with level pitches and some views. A newly tiled pool is in a sunny position with sunbeds and a paddling pool. There are no shops in the village, the nearest being at the medieval city of Sommières 10 km. away (and well worth a visit).

**Facilities:** The toilet blocks, one new, are clean and functional. They provide washbasins in cabins, British style WCs and pre-set showers. Dishwashing and laundry sinks. Washing machine. Reception doubles as a bar. Limited shop (from 1/6). Takeaway and restaurant (1/7-31/8). Swimming pool. Small play area on grass. Table tennis. **Off site:** Riding 5 km. Fishing 3 km. Tennis 1 km. The sea, the gorges and Nimes are all approx 30 km.

**Charges** 2002

| | |
|---|---|
| Per unit incl. 2 persons | € 12.20 - € 18.50 |
| extra adult | € 3.10 - € 5.10 |
| child (2-7 yrs) | € 1.50 - € 2.50 |
| electricity 6A/10A | € 3.10 - € 3.80 |
| animal | € 1.20 - € 2.30 |

**Tel:** 04 66 77 82 12. **Fax:** 04 66 20 26 50. **E-mail:** info@camping-mas-de-reilhe.fr. **Reservations:** Made with deposit ( € 45,73 per week booked) and booking fee ( € 12,20). **Open** 1 May - 24 September.

**Directions:** Site is on the N110 road (Ales - Montpellier) at the southern end of village, not far from where the D999 road (Nimes - Quissac) crosses the N110.

## Mediterranean
# Camping du Mas de Rey
Arpaillargues, 30700 Uzès

**3011**

A warm welcome from the English speaking Maire family is guaranted at this small, unsophisticated 70 pitch site. Most of the large (150 sq.m) pitches are separated by bushes, many are shaded and all have 10A electricity. Due to the wonderful climate, grass can at times be hard to find. The reception, bar, restaurant and shop are in the same large airy building. Reception has a wealth of tourist information and they are always willing to give advice on the numerous things to see and do in the area. The owners say the wine festivals in early August at Châteauneuf du Pape and at Uzès in mid Aug. are festivals not to be missed.

**Facilities:** Two well maintained unisex toilet blocks, one quite new with facilities for disabled visitors, baby room and en-suite family cubicles. Dishwashing and laundry sinks. Washing machine and iron. Shop (high season only but bread to order all season). Bar serves a simple 'menu of the day' most evenings (1/7-31/8). Small circular swimming and paddling pools (1/5-15/10, closed lunch-times). **Off site:** Riding 5 km, golf or fishing 3 km. and canoeing 10 km. Nîmes, Avignon and the Pont du Gard all near

**Charges** 2002

| | |
|---|---|
| Per unit incl. 2 persons | € 15.50 |
| extra person | € 4.10 |
| child (under 7yrs) | € 2.50 |
| electricity | € 2.90 |

**Tel:** 04 66 22 18 27. Fax: 04 66 22 18 27. E-mail: masderey@hvtour.fr. **Reservations:** Made with deposit (€ 46) and fee (€ 7,62). **Open** 10 April - 15 October.

**Directions:** From D981 in Uzès take D982 westwards signed Arpaillargues, Anduze, Sommieres, Moussac. Site is 3 km. on the left, well signed.

## Mediterranean
# Camping Campeole-TCS Ile des Papes
Barrage de Villeneuve, 30400 Villeneuve les Avignon

**3012**

Ile des Papes, new in '94, is a large, open and very well equipped site near Avignon with an extensive swimming pool area and a fishing lake. The railway is quite near but noise is not too intrusive. The 342 pitches are of a good size on level grass and all have electricity (10A), some taken by mobile homes or chalets. Avignon and its Palace and museums is 8 km. away.

**Facilities:** The toilet blocks are of very good quality. Baby rooms. Dishwashing and laundry sinks. Washing machines. Motorcaravan service point. Well stocked shop (limited hours in low seasons). Bar and restaurant. Swimming pools. Play area. Lake for fishing. Archery, tennis, table tennis, volleyball, minigolf and basketball (all free). Bicycle hire. Games and competitions in high season. **Off site:** Riding 3 km.

**Charges** 2002

| | |
|---|---|
| Per unit incl. 2 persons | € 12.96 - € 20.58 |
| extra person | € 2.29 - € 4.57 |
| electricity (6A) | € 3.05 |

**Tel:** 04 90 15 15 90. Fax: 04 90 15 15 91. E-mail: ile.papes@wanadoo.fr. **Reservations:** Made with deposit (25%) and fee (€ 15,21). **Open** 25 March - 20 October.

**Directions:** Take N100 Nîmes road out of Avignon towards Bagnoles-sur-Cèze and turn right after crossing the Rhône. Turn left along the river bank and follow signs for Roquemaure (D980). In about 6 km. turn right onto D228 signed Barrage de Villeneuve and site is 1 km.

## Mediterranean
# Camping La Soubeyranne
route de Beaucaire, 30210 Remoulins

**3014**

the travel service
TO BOOK
Ferry ✔
Pitch ✔
Accommodation ✗
01892 55 98 98

This site is well positioned for visiting the Pont du Gard, Nîmes and Uzès, famed for their Roman connections. It is approached by a short tree-lined avenue which leads to reception. The 200 pitches offer extremely generous amounts of shade and keeping the 4.5 hectares watered involves over 5 km. of hose pipe. Pitches are large, level, numbered and separated, with 170 having 6A electricity connections. An animation programme (July/Aug) is mainly for young children (teenagers may find the site rather quiet). Whilst quiet in some respects, train noise both by day and night can be an irritant.

**Facilities:** Two well appointed, unisex toilet blocks are basic but clean and include washbasins in cubicles. Dishwashing and laundry facilities. Fridge hire. Motorcaravan service point. Small shop selling basics. Restaurant, bar and takeaway (all from 1/5) - menu not extensive but adequate and moderately priced. Swimming pools (unsupervised). Play area, table tennis, boules, tennis and volleyball. Bicycle hire. **Off site:** Fishing 1 km. Remoulins 1.5 km.

**Charges** guide

| | |
|---|---|
| Per unit incl. 2 persons | € 12.00 - € 15.00 |
| with electricity | € 14.00 - € 18.00 |
| extra person | € 3.00 - € 4.00 |

**Tel:** 04 66 37 03 21. Fax: 04 4 66 37 14 65. E-mail: soubeyranne@wanadoo.fr. **Reservations:** Contact site for details. **Open** 6 April - 16 September.

**Directions:** From Uzès take D981 to Remoulins, turn right at lights over river bridge, left at roundabout, then left (D986 Beaucaire). Site is 1.5 km. further on left.

## Camping Abri de Camargue

**3003** 320 rte du Phare de l'Espiguette, Port Camargue, 30240 Le Grau-du-Roi

This pleasant site has an attractive pool area overlooked by the bar and its outdoor tables on a pleasant sheltered terrace. The larger outdoor pool has surrounds for sunbathing and the smaller indoor one is heated. With 470 level pitches, there are 139 for touring units, mainly of 100 sq.m. (there are also smaller ones). Electricity and water are available on most, and the pitches are well shaded, with trees and flowering shrubs quite luxuriant in parts. A summer fair is within walking distance which can be noisy until quite late. English is spoken.

**Facilities:** Three well appointed toilet blocks, include washbasins in cubicles, dishwashing and laundry sinks. Convenient motorcaravan service point. Shop. Bar with TV, restaurant and takeaway (all open when site is open). New cinema room. Children's play area of the highest quality (one of few with a rubberised EU standard safety base). Petanque. **Off site:** Tennis 800 m. Fishing, riding, golf and bicycle hire within 2 km. The nearest beach at Port Camargue is 900 m. and the one at L'Espiguette is 4 km. (in July/Aug. a free bus passes the gate to L'Espiguette).

**Charges** 2002

| Per unit incl. 1 or 2 persons | |
|---|---|
| and electricity | € 21.00 - € 43.00 |
| 3-5 persons | € 25.00 - € 45.00 |
| extra person | € 5.00 - € 9.00 |
| pet | € 5.00 |

**Tel:** 04 66 51 54 83. Fax: 04 66 51 76 42. E-mail: abridecamargue@hotmail.com. **Reservations:** Advised for high season (1/7-31/8) when made for min. 1 week with    33 fee. **Open** 1 April - 30 September.

**Directions:** A road now bypasses Le Grau-du-Roi from the west as well as the approach from Aigues-Mortes. Turn left at sign to 'Port Camargue' and 'Campings' just northeast of Grau-du-Roi. At next crossroads go left again towards l'Espiguette and site is on right after 200 m. If approaching via D979 from north, turn onto D62 and D62A towards La Grande Motte at junction north of Aigues-Mortes.

## Camping L'Eden

**3005** route de l'Espiguette, Port Camargue, 30240 Le Grau-du-Roi

L'Eden is a well run, good example of a modern, purpose built 4-star site. It is on flat ground about 500 m. from a sandy beach, with 369 individual hedged pitches. Flowering shrubs and trees make it cool and very pretty. Good shade is available on many of the pitches, electricity on most and some are fully serviced. Access to some pitches is rather narrow. Suitable for all the family with a wide range of facilities and activities, reservation is advisable for the main season. An attractive swimming pool has a bridge, water toboggan and children's pool. A free bus service is provided to the beach in the main season. Tour operators take some pitches.

**Facilities:** Four modern, unusually designed toilet blocks include some each of British style toilets, washbasins in cabins, and en-suite showers with washbasins. Unit with baby bath. Full facilities for disabled people. Laundry facilities. Supermarket, boutique, bar and restaurant with takeaway (all open all season). TV room and meeting room. Swimming pool from mid April). Fitness centre. Half court tennis, minigolf, table tennis and a sports area with volleyball and basketball. Bicycle hire and archery (July/Aug). Play area for 1-8 year olds. Organised sports, excursions and entertainment, and mini club for children (1/7-31/8). Only one dog per unit is accepted. **Off site:** Marina with sailing lessons, fishing, riding and tennis nearby.

**Charges** 2003

| Per pitch incl. 2 persons | € 16.00 - € 33.00 |
|---|---|
| extra person | € 2.13 - € 4.57 |
| dog (max 1) | free - € 2.30 |
| local tax | € 1.20 |

**Tel:** 04 66 51 49 81. Fax: 04 66 53 13 20. E-mail: camping-eden@wanadoo.fr. **Reservations:** Made with deposit and fee (Sat.-Sat. in high season). Write between 1/1 and 15/5. **Open** 7 April - 4 October.

**Directions:** A road now bypasses Le Grau-du-Roi from the west, which is easier if towing a caravan, as well as the approach from Aigues-Mortes. Turn left at sign to `Port Camargue' and `Campings' just northeast of Grau-du-Roi and follow signs for l'Espiguette and after 200 m. right at second sign for l'Eden. It is not the site with entrance where you turn; for l'Eden go hard right onto access road and a further 200 m. around corner to site on left (it is a busy access).

# Camping-Caravaning Le Boucanet

30240 Le Grau du Roi

**3016**

On the beach between Grande Motte and Le Grau-du-Roi, this is a sunny site with only a little shade. Many trees have been planted but as yet most are not tall enough to give much shade. As to be expected, the 462 pitches are sandy and level. The 357 for touring units are separated by small bushes, most with electricity (6A). The pleasant restaurant overlooks the large pool and is open lunchtimes and evenings. An excellent shopping arcade provides groceries, fruit, newspapers, a butcher and cooked meats, rotisserie and pizzas. In July and August organised activities include games, competitions, gymnastics, water polo, jogging and volleyball for adults. Horse riding on the white horses of the Camargue is to be found within a few kilometres.

**Facilities:** The toilet blocks are convenient for the pitches providing washbasins in cubicles and some British style toilets in two blocks, the remainder Turkish style (about 70%). Facilities for disabled people at two blocks. Baby rooms. Dishwashing and laundry sinks have warm water. Washing machines, dryers, irons and fridge hire. Motorcaravan service point. Range of shops. Restaurant. Bar with snacks (all these facilities open all season). Large swimming pool and paddling pool. Play area on sand and mini-club in July/Aug. Table tennis, tennis. Bicycle hire. Dogs are not accepted. **Off site:** Golf 1.5 km. Riding 500 m.

**Charges** 2002

| | |
|---|---|
| Per unit incl. 2 persons | € 18.50 - € 25.00 |
| with electricity | € 21.50 - € 28.00 |
| supplement for pitch on first row of beach | € 4.65 - € 8.40 |
| extra adult | € 6.80 - € 8.20 |
| child (under 7 yrs) | € 5.40 - € 6.60 |
| local tax | € 0.10 - € 0.20 |

**Tel:** (0)4 66 51 41 48. Fax: (0)4 66 51 41 87. E-mail: campingboucanet@wanadoo.fr. **Reservations:** Necessary for July/Aug. and made with 25% deposit and booking fee ( € 23); by money order or cheque only. **Open** 4 May - 28 September.

**Directions:** Site is between La Grand Motte and Le Grau-du-Roi on the D255 coastal road, on the seaward side of the road.

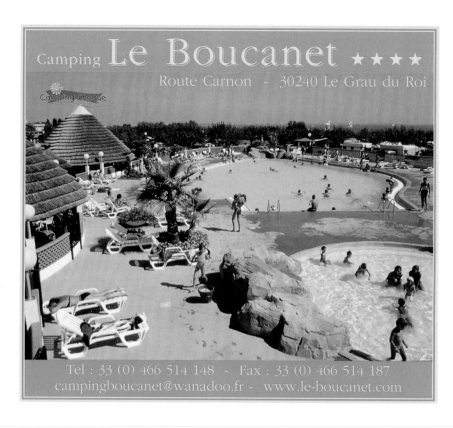

Camping Le Boucanet ★★★★

Route Carnon - 30240 Le Grau du Roi

Tel : 33 (0) 466 514 148 - Fax : 33 (0) 466 514 187
campingboucanet@wanadoo.fr - www.le-boucanet.com

# Camping-Caravaning La Petite Camargue

BP 21, 30220 Aigues-Mortes

This is a large, impressive site (554 pitches) with a huge swimming pool complex and other amenities to match, conveniently situated beside one of the main routes across the famous Camargue. Its position alongside this busy road is an advantage for access but could perhaps be a drawback in terms of traffic, although when we stayed overnight in season it was virtually silent. It offers a variety of good sized pitches, regularly laid out and with varying amounts of shade. There are 106 touring pitches (with 10A electricity) interspersed amongst more than 300 mobile homes and 145 tour operator pitches. The main activity area, situated between the pitches and the road, is attractively designed and provides a wide range of facilities, including the pool area and shops, almost like a village centre. The site is conveniently situated for visiting the Camargue and not far from the sea, beaches and other sport facilities and activities. It also provides a range of on site entertainment with a good activity programme. English is spoken at this well run, busy site. A Yelloh Village member.

**Facilities:** Four toilet blocks provide modern facilities including many combined showers and washbasins. Laundry facilities. Motorcaravan service point. Range of shops, bar/restaurant with pizzeria and takeaway (27/04 22/09) Hairdresser and beauty centre. L-shaped swimming pool complex. Children's play area, and children's club (July/Aug. 4-12 yrs). Riding at adjoining large stables. Football, volleyball, basketball, tennis (charged July/Aug) and table tennis. Bicycle hire. Quad bikes. Disco. Winter caravan storage. **Off site:** Fishing 3 km, golf 8 km. Nearest beach 3.5 km, with free bus service July/Aug.

**Charges** 2002

| Per unit incl. 1 or 2 persons | |
|---|---|
| and electricity | € 15.00 - € 33.00 |
| extra person | € 4.00 - € 6.00 |
| dog | € 3.00 |
| local tax | € 0.15 |

**Tel:** 04 66 53 98 98. Fax: 04 66 53 98 80. E-mail: petite.camargue@wanadoo.fr. **Reservations:** Made with 25% deposit and € 30 fee. **Open** 27 April - 22 September.

**Directions:** From autoroute A9 take exit 26 (Gallargues) towards Le Grau-du-Roi. Continue past Aigues-Mortes on the D62 and site is 2 km. on the right, just before large roundabout for La Grand-Motte and Le Grau-du-Roi junction. Site is approx. 18 km. from exit 26.

---

# Camping Le Mas du Padre

4 chemin du Mas du Padre, 34540 Balaruc les Bains

The Durant family took over this site a few years ago and have made many alterations and improvements. It is a small site, just 2.5 km. from Balaruc-Les-Bains, near the Lake of Thau and unusually is part of an estate that has obviously been built around it over the years. Its 116 secluded pitches of varying sizes are enclosed by hedges and mature trees, some on a very gentle slope and 98 have electricity (6/10A). The site is peaceful and popular with the French who love its simplicity, although a large commercial centre is just 500 m. Beaches and many local attractions are close, but if you decide to stay here it would be advisable to have transport. The road to Agde passes some rather unsightly factory works - don't be put off.

**Facilities:** Two neat, fully equipped toilet blocks include baby changing area, facilities for disabled campers, dishwashing and laundry sinks, and washing machines. Reception sells basic provisions, gas and bread (to order in low season). Two small circular pools including one for children (20/5-16/9).Tennis half-court, table tennis, four flood-lit boules courts, mini-adventure playground. Sports programme including tournaments, aquarobics, animation for children, along with a weekly dance when a temporary bar is organised (all in high season). Torch useful. **Off site:** Fishing or riding 2 km, golf 20 km. Bus service to the historic city of Balaruc-Les-Bains from just outside the site.

**Charges** 2002

| Per unit incl. 2 persons, electricity, | | |
|---|---|---|
| 80 sq.m. | € 12.65 - | € 19.40 |
| 100 sq.m. | € 14.30 - | € 28.40 |
| 4 persons | € 19.30 - | € 28.40 |
| extra adult | € 2.50 - | € 3.60 |
| child acc. to age and season | € 0.95 - | € 3.00 |
| dog | € 0.80 - | € 1.75 |
| electricity (6A) | € 2.30 - | € 2.85 |

**Tel:** 04 67 48 53 41. Fax: 04 67 48 08 94. E-mail: mas-du-padre@wanadoo.fr. **Reservations:** Advised for high season only. **Open** 29 March - 12 October.

**Directions:** From A9 take exit for Sete and follow N800 to Balaruc le Vieux, then D2e to Sete. Don't take turn for Balaruc Les Bains but continue following ing road to Sete where site is signed just after the turn.

## Mediterranean
# Camping Le Garden

**3402** 44, Place des Tamaris, 34280 La Grande Motte

Le Garden is a mature site, situated 300 m. back from a fine sandy beach and with all the choice of sports, entertainment and other facilities of the popular holiday resort of La Grand Motte. With space for 117 caravans and 85 mobile homes, the 100 sq.m. pitches are hedged with good shade. All have electricity (6A), water and waste water. Amenities nearby include tennis courts, a riding club, a casino and a night club.

**Facilities:** Three well situated toilet blocks include washbasins in cabins and baby bath. Dishwashing and laundry sinks. Washing machines. Unit for disabled people. Shopping complex to one side of the site with groceries, cigarettes, newspapers, boutique, etc. alongside restaurant, bar and take-away service. Swimming pool and children's paddling pool.

**Charges** 2002

| | |
|---|---|
| Per unit with 1-3 persons | € 23.00 |
| with electricity, water and drainage | € 30.00 |
| extra person | € 6.00 |
| local tax | € 0.25 - € 0.50 |

**Tel:** 04 67 56 50 09. Fax: 04 67 56 25 69.
**Reservations:** Not made. **Open** 1 March - 31 October.

**Directions:** Entering La Grand Motte from D62 dual-carriageway, keep right following signs for `campings`. Turn right at Centre Commercial on Ave de la Petite Motte and site is first on the right.

## Mediterranean
# Camping Le Neptune

**3413** Route du Grau, 34300 Agde

Camping Neptune is a rare find in this area of `all singing, all dancing` campsites. This small, family run site with only 165 pitches makes a delightful change. The Fray family are very welcoming and, even though it is in a busy area, it is a little oasis of calm, very suited to couples and young families. Placed along the D32 to Grau d`Agde which is beside the river Herault, there will be a little daytime road noise. The pitches are mostly separated by flowering bushes, with some shade and most have 6A electricity. The swimming pool is in a sunny position with sunbeds and overlooked by the bar. The only entertainment is in high season and is a twice weekly mini-club for children. The beach and the small resort of Grau d`Agde are 1.5 km.

**Facilities:** The single toilet block has been refurbished to give washbasins in cabins and mainly British style WCs. Laundry and dishwashing sinks. Two washing machines and dryer. Small shop. Bar (both 15/5-30/9). Fridge hire. Swimming pool heated in cool weather, bracelets required ( € 7,62 p/person). Table tennis and field for sports. Bicycle hire. Boat mooring facility on the River Herault across the road. Not all breeds of dog are accepted.

**Charges** 2002

| | |
|---|---|
| Per unit incl. 2 persons | € 15.00 - € 22.00 |
| with electricity | € 16.00 - € 24.50 |
| extra person | € 2.00 - € 5.00 |

**Tel:** (0)4 67 94 23 94. Fax: (0)4 67 94 48 77. E-mail: info@campingleneptune.com. **Reservations:** Necessary for July and August. **Open** 1 April - 30 September.

**Directions:** From A9 autoroute exit 34, follow N312 for Agde which joins the N112. After crossing bridge follow signs for Grau d`Agde then at triangle turn left at Grau d`Agde, Les Berges de l`Herault, site signed and situated alongside the D32 which runs parallel to the River Herault.

## Mediterranean
# Camping-Caravaning Les Champs Blancs

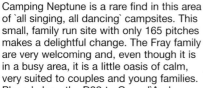

**3419** route de Rochelongue, 34300 Agde

Les Champs Blancs is set in high trees, two kilometres from Agde and two from the sea. The 169 touring pitches, on level, sandy grass, are bordered with bushes with plenty of shade and greenery. All have 10A electricity and 58 have private sanitary cabins. The pool is in a sunny position with sunbeds provided, a paddling pool and several slides. Games, shows and competitions are arranged in July and August. There are mobile homes on the site. There are tennis courts and other leisure facilities in the area nearest the road, bordered by trees to deaden possible road noise.

**Facilities:** Two toilet blocks have been refurbished to provide showers and washbasins together, plus British style WCs. Unit for disabled visitors. Washing machines and dryers. Also 58 private cabins containing WC, shower and washbasin. Well stocked shop in July/Aug; only bread available in low season. Bar (all season). Restaurant and bakery at busy times. Swimming pool. Good play area, minigolf, table tennis, tennis, basketball and volleyball. Bicycle hire.

**Charges** 2002

| | |
|---|---|
| Per pitch incl. 2 persons | € 12.96 - € 27.44 |
| with individual sanitary facilities | € 15.24 - € 32.06 |
| extra person | € 4.75 - € 7.62 |

**Tel:** 04 67 94 23 42. Fax: 04 67 21 36 75. **Reservations:** Necessary for July and August. **Open** 1 April - 30 September.

**Directions:** From N112 Beziers - Sete road, after crossing high river bridge take first turn signed Rochelongue, Grau d'Agde. At first crossroads (1 km.) take left signed Agde. Site on left in 1 km.

## Mediterranean
# Camping-Caravaning Les Mimosas
Port Cassafières, 34420 Portiragnes Plage

Les Mimosas is quite a large site with 400 pitches - 200 for touring units, the remainder for mobile homes - set back from the village and beach. The level, grassy pitches are of average size, separated and numbered and all with 6A electricity (long leads may be required). Some are in the shade, the choice is yours. The pool area is very large with lots of free sun beds, two toboggan pools, a paddling pool and a large swimming pool. Many day trips and excursions are arranged, from canoeing to visiting castles, all season. Portiragnes Plage is about 1 km. and it can be reached by cycle tracks. The Canal du Midi is also close, another easy cycle ride. A friendly family run site with families in mind.

**Facilities:** One large new toilet block has family sized, en-suite facilities, washbasins in cabins, baby rooms, and good facilities for disabled people. The other two blocks are older with some Turkish style toilets and to be re-furbished in the future. Dishwashing and laundry sinks. Washing machines and dryers. Fridge hire. Large well-stocked shop. Bar with snacks all season, restaurant in high season only. Swimming pool complex all season with lifeguards in July/Aug. Play area. Boules. Gym (free) and sauna (charged).

**Charges** 2002

| Per unit incl. 2 persons | € 20.00 - € 27.00 |
| with electricity | € 23.00 - € 31.00 |
| extra person | € 4.00 - € 6.50 |
| private sanitary unit | € 7.00 - € 8.00 |

**Tel:** (0)4 67 90 92 92. Fax: (0)4 67 90 85 39. E-mail: les.mimosas.portiragnes@wanadoo.fr. **Reservations:** Needed for July/Aug. **Open** 1 May - 15 September.

**Directions:** From A9 autoroute exit 35 (Bezieres Est) take N112 south towards Serignan (1 km). At roundabout follow signs for Cap d'Agde but watch carefully for D37 Portiragnes (1-2 km) and follow signs for Portiragnes Plage. Site is well signed.

## Mediterranean
# Camping La Creole
74 av des Campings, 34340 Marseillan-Plage

This is a surprisingly tranquil, well cared for small campsite almost in the middle of this bustling resort that will appeal especially to those seeking a rather less frenetic ambience than that which typifies many sites in this area. Family orientated, it offers around 100 good-sized, level grass pitches, all with 6A electricity and mostly with shade. It has direct access to an extensive sandy beach and the fact that there is no pool or bar actually contributes to the tranquillity and may even be seen as an advantage for families with younger children. The beach will be the main attraction here no doubt, and the town's amenities are within a couple of minutes walk

**Facilities:** Toilet facilities are in a traditional building, modernised inside to provide perfectly adequate, if not particularly luxurious, facilities including some washbasins in cabins and a baby room. Small play area. Table tennis. In high season beach games, dances, sangria evenings etc, are organised, all aimed towards families. Barbecue area.

**Charges** 2002

| Per unit incl. 2 persons | € 12.00 - € 18.00 |
| extra person | € 2.50 - € 3.50 |
| electricity | € 2.50 |

**Tel:** (0)4.67.21.92.69. Fax: (0)4.67.28.58.16. E-mail: campinglecreole@wanadoo.fr. **Reservations:** Made with deposit ( € 84) and fee ( € 16). **Open** 6 April - 8 October.

**Directions:** From autoroute A9 take exit 34 on N312 towards Agde, then N112 towards Sete keeping a look-out for signs to Marseillan Plage off this road. Site is well signed in Marseillan Plage.

## Mediterranean
# Camping-Club Charlemagne
34340 Marseillan Plage

Charlemagne is under the same family ownership as Nouvelle Floride and situated across the road from it, 200 metres from the beach. It boasts a large range of amenities including a large supermarket, takeaway, bar, restaurant and disco. Facing the main street, these are open to the public and are consequently well stocked and open for the whole season. The site is traditionally laid out under the shade of tall trees providing 480 level pitches. Of these 270 are for touring units, neatly hedged and all with electricity (6A) and water. Access to the beach is by a footpath past Nouvelle Floride. This is a site which caters for all ages with a wide range of activities.

**Facilities:** Four toilet blocks, two modern providing washbasins in cabins, dishwashing, laundry sinks and washing machine. The more traditional blocks have some Turkish toilets. Motorcaravan service point. Fridge hire. Shops, bar/cafe, restaurant, takeaway and disco, all open all season. Swimming pool. Good fenced play area. Mini-club (May-Sept). Evening entertainment with concerts, cabarets, dances and discos. **Off site:** Nearby tennis, golf, karting, riding, bicycle hire and water sports.

**Charges** 2003

| Per unit incl. up to 2 persons, | |
| water and electricity | € 15.00 - € 38.00 |
| extra person | € 5.00 - € 8.00 |

**Tel:** (0)4 67 21 92 49. Fax: (0)4 67 21 86 11. E-mail: info@charlemagne-camping.com. **Reservations:** Needed for July/Aug. **Open** 5 April - 27 September.

**Directions:** From A9 exit 34, follow N314 to Agde then N112 towards Sete and watch for signs to Marseillan Plage from where site is well signed.

# Camping-Club Nouvelle Floride

34340 Marseillan Plage

**3415**

Marseillan Plage is a small, busy resort just east of Cap d'Adge and La Nouvelle Floride enjoys a super position immediately beside a long gently shelving sandy beach. It is a good quality site, very traditional in style and set under tall trees with neat hedges to separate the 520 pitches (370 for tourers). These are on sandy soil and all have water and electricity (6A). Some of the pitches in the newer area (across a small lane) and the hardstanding pitches near the beach have little shade as yet. There are a number of mobile homes but the site is mainly for tourers. Amenities and facilities are generally of excellent quality and include a strikingly attractive bar area overlooking the beach with a raised stage for entertainment. Alongside the play area is a multi-purpose ball court and fitness centre, also on sand with robust machines with the idea of keeping Mum and Dad fit whilst still keeping an eye on the children. Essentially a `holiday site`, there is an extensive programme of entertainment and activities catering for all ages, and a new, 'state of the art' pool complex. However, the main attraction for most will almost certainly be the direct access to a fine beach. The gates on the beach entrance are locked at 9 pm. for security. This is a well run, family run site aimed at families.

**Facilities:** The four toilet blocks are impressive, including two with a number of en-suite showers and washbasins, otherwise washbasins all in cabins. Baby rooms, excellent facilities for disabled visitors and even a dog shower. The showers and washing up areas are closed between 23.00-07.00 hrs. Motorcaravan service point. Bar and restaurant. Shop all season, plus a range of shops at Charlemagne across the road. Pool complex with slides, jacuzzi, paddling pools, etc (all season). Play area, fitness centre and multi-purpose ball court. Table tennis. Weekly films (DVD) and variety of organised games, competitions, dances and discos. Mini-club in school holidays. Bicycle hire. **Off site:** Riding and bicycle hire 500 m. Golf 5 km.

**Charges** 2003

| | |
|---|---|
| Per unit incl. 1 or 2 persons, water and electricity | € 19.00 - € 38.00 |
| extra person | € 5.00 - € 8.00 |
| child under 1 yr | free |
| pet | € 3.00 - € 3.50 |
| local tax | € 0.30 |

**Tel:** (0)4 67 21 94 49. Fax: (0)4 67 21 81 05. E-mail: info@nouvelle-floride.com. **Reservations:** Contact site. **Open** 12 April - 28 September.

**Directions:** From A9 autoroute exit 34, follow N312 to Agde then take N112 towards Sete. Watch for signs to Marseillan Plage from where site is well signed.

## Camping Le Club Farret
34450 Vias-Plage

**3411**

This superb site of excellent quality has been developed by the Giner family with love and care over the last 40 years. Well maintained and with welcoming, helpful staff (English spoken), everywhere is neat and tidy - quite outstanding and impressive. It is a large site but even though it was very busy when we visited, the atmosphere seemed very relaxed and not too frantic. There are 782 pitches, with 452 for touring units and only 14% for tour operators, which do not overwhelm at all. The good-sized, level pitches are on grass and sand, with 6A electricity. There is some shade and many trees and shrubs provide a green environment. The mobile home area is smart, landscaped and has an African theme. The large heated pool has lots of sunbathing room. The safe beach is alongside the site so some pitches have sea views. There is a wide range of evening entertainment and the list of activities includes an unusual art programme offering pottery, silk painting, mosaics and water colours. The restaurant is high above the pool with views of the sea. Everything is open all season, so a visit in the quiet months of May, June or September doesn't mean less facilities. Advance bookings are not taken for the touring pitches - they say that they rarely turn anyone away and will accept a phone call the day before arrival to give details of availability. A Yelloh Village member.

**Facilities:** Very clean toilet blocks provide excellent facilities, especially the new blocks, with British style toilets (one or two Turkish in the older blocks). Large showers, many with washbasin. Children's toilets, baby rooms and children's showers in the guise of a clown. Full facilities in large rooms for disabled customers. Washing machines. Dog shower at the block nearest the beach. The toilets are open all night but the showers are closed. Well stocked supermarket. Hairdresser. Bars with pizzas and snacks to takeaway. Restaurant. Swimming pool complex with lifeguard all season. Children's play areas. Mini-club (5-10 yrs). Teenagers' club (11-15 yrs). Tennis, table tennis, archery, volleyball, football and a full programme of games. Windsurfing. Bicycle hire. **Off site:** Golf 5 km. Riding 1 km.

**Charges** 2002

| | |
|---|---|
| Per unit incl. 1 or 2 persons | € 22.00 - € 35.00 |
| extra person | € 5.00 - € 6.00 |
| pet | € 3.00 |
| local tax (15/6-15/9) | € 0.40 |

**Tel:** (0)4 67 21 64 45. Fax: (0)4 67 21 70 49. E-mail: farret@wanadoo.fr. **Reservations:** Not accepted. **Open** Easter - 28 September.

**Directions:** Site is south of Vias at Vias Plage. From N112 (Beziers - Agde) take D137 signed Vias Plage. Site is on left.

---

## Camping International Le Napoléon
avenue de la Méditérranée, 34450 Vias-Plage

**3403**

the travel service
TO BOOK

| | |
|---|---|
| Ferry | ✔ |
| Pitch | ✔ |
| Accommodation | ✗ |

01892 55 98 98

Le Napoléon is a smaller, family run site situated in the centre of the village of Vias Plage bordering the Mediterranean. The town of Vias itself is set further back from the sea, in the wine-growing area of the Midi, an area which includes the Camargue, Béziers and popular modern resorts such as Cap d'Agde. The single street that leads to Vias Plage is hectic to say the least in season, but once through the security barrier and entrance to Le Napoléon, the contrast is marked - tranquillity, yet still only a few yards from the beach and other attractions. Not that the site itself lacks vibrancy, with its Californian style pool, amphitheatre for entertainment and other new facilities, but thoughtful planning and design ensure that the camping area is quiet. With good shade from many tall trees, the 250 mainly hedged pitches (105 with hire units) vary in size from 80-100 sq.m. and most have electricity connections. No British tour operators.

**Facilities:** Three sanitary blocks are of a reasonable standard and were well maintained when seen in peak season. They include washbasins in cabins, baby bath, laundry and facilities for disabled people. Motorcaravan services. Fridges for hire. Well stocked supermarket. Bar. Restaurant/pizzeria. Heated swimming pool with lively piped music. Excellent new sauna, sun room and gym. Bicycle hire. Tennis, archery, volleyball, boules. New TV and young people rooms. Children's club. New amphitheatre and wide range of free entertainment. **Off site:** Shops, restaurants, and laundry etc. immediately adjacent. Fishing nearby.

**Charges** 2002

| | |
|---|---|
| Per unit incl. 1 or 2 persons and electricity | € 18.00 - € 38.00 |
| extra person | € 3.50 - € 5.00 |
| dog | € 2.30 - € 3.10 |
| local tax | € 0.20 - € 0.40 |

**Tel:** 04 67 01 07 80. Fax: 04 67 01 07 85. E-mail: reception@camping-napoleon.fr. **Reservations:** Taken from 1 Jan. with 30% deposit and fee incl. cancellation insurance. **Open** 25 March - 1 October.

**Directions:** From autoroute take exit for Vias. From town, take D137 towards Vias Plage. Site is on the right near the beach; watch carefully for turning between restaurant and shops.

## Mediterranean
# Haven Camping La Carabasse
3414 Vias-Plage, 34450 Vias-sur-Mer

La Carabasse, a Haven Europe holiday park, is on the outskirts of Vias Plage, a popular place with lots of shops and restaurants. The site has everything you could need with two good pools, and its own bars and a restaurant L'Atoll. There are lots of activities for young families and teenagers. The bars and restaurant provide live music in the evenings and entertainment. There are 950 pitches, 400 for touring, with many mobile homes and a good number of tour operator pitches. The touring pitches are set amongst tall poplar and birch trees. Level and spacious, all have electricity and partial shade. Some have private sanitary facilities. The beaches are close and La Carabasse has its own beach club. It is a lively busy site in high season, and Vias Plage itself can also be quite hectic. Haven Europe are continuing to improve the site with a wide range of facilities for children and teenagers.

**Facilities:** Two of the toilet blocks are modern and fully equipped, with an older block used in high season. Maintenance can be variable. Some pitches have their own private sanitary cabin providing a WC and shower (extra charge). Bars, restaurant and swimming pools. Beach club for windsurfing and pedaloes. Wealth of daytime activities (some charged for) from golf lessons to aqua-aerobics and tennis tournaments. Children's clubs and multi-sports unit. Evening entertainment in the Haven Europe style. **Off site:** Trips on the Canal du Midi. Vias town with twice weekly market. Modern resort of Cap d'Adge nearby with Aqualand and golf course (18 holes).

**Charges** 2002
| | |
|---|---|
| Per pitch incl. up to 2 persons and electricity | € 13.72 - € 31.86 |
| with private sanitary cabin | € 18.29 - € 38.11 |
| extra person | € 3.05 - € 5.34 |

**Tel:** (0)4 67 21 56 05. **Reservations:** Accepted at any time for min. 4 days; no booking fee. Contact site or Haven Europe in the UK on 0870 242 7777 for information or reservation. **Open** 15 April - 15 September.

**Directions:** Site is south of Vias. From N112 (Agde - Beziers) road turn right at signs for Vias-Plage (D137) and site (on the left).

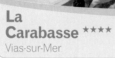

An excellently positioned parc on the sunny Mediterranean with two excellent pool complexes and its very own Beach Club.

- Groupings of touring areas, some pitches have their own shower & WC
- Two outdoor pools with 4-lane waterslide
- Wide range of sports & leisure activities
- 3 children's clubs for all ages
- Restaurant, bar, pizzeria (14 June - 14 Sept) & takeaway
- Superb low season prices
- Bilingual staff on parc
- Site open from: 15 April - 15 September

La Carabasse ★★★★
Vias-sur-Mer

La Carabasse, Route de Farinette, 34450 Vias-sur-Mer, France
Tel:00 33 467 21 64 01 Fax:00 33 467 21 76 87
To book please call the number above, quoting code FAR03

A B T A
V2819

## Mediterranean
# Camping Club Californie Plage
3420 Côte Ouest, 34450 Vias-Plage

the travel service
TO BOOK
| Ferry | ✓ |
|---|---|
| Pitch | ✗ |
| Accommodation | ✓ |

01892 55 98 98

With the benefit of direct access to a sandy cove, with a few, much sought-after pitches overlooking the sea, this is a fairly typical holiday-style campsite with a range of good quality facilities. These include a covered pool on the site and a superb pool complex with the inevitable toboggans, etc., and even a naturist swimming pool across the road from the Californie Plage site in the grounds of its sister site. Both sites are located away from Vias Plage, on the Côte Ouest and thereby enjoy a degree of tranquillity in this bustling resort area. The site is traditionally laid out, with mobile homes to one side of the central road and touring pitches to the other. Pitches are mostly of 100 sq.m, although those close to the beach are slightly smaller, and mainly on level sandy ground. Nearly all have electricity and some shade.

**Facilities:** Sanitary facilities are of a generally good standard, in three traditional blocks which have been fully refurbished in recent years. Washbasins in cabins, baby rooms, facilities for disabled visitors. Laundry with washing machines and dryer. Shop. Comfortable restaurant. Bars. Covered pool on site (1/4-30/10). Range of pools on sister site across the road (1/7-31/8; code supplied). Tennis court. Bicycle hire. Games room. Extensive entertainment programme and children's activities in July/Aug.

**Charges** 2002
| | |
|---|---|
| Per unit incl. 1 or 2 persons and 6A electricity | € 15.25 - € 29.00 |
| extra person (4 yrs and over) | € 2.80 - € 4.60 |
| 10A electricity | € 1.60 |
| local tax | € 0.20 - € 0.40 |
| special family price on booking | € 20.85 - € 41.60 |

**Tel:** (0)4 67 21 64 69. Fax: (0)4 67 21 54 62. **Reservations:** Made with deposit ( € 102) and fee ( € 23). **Open** Easter - 15 October.

**Directions:** From N112 Béziers-Agde road take D137 Vias Plage turn. Watch for signs to 'Cote Ouest' and follow campsite signs thereafter.

## Mediterranean
# Camping Lou Village
BP 30, chemin des Montilles, 34350 Valras-Plage

**3404**

Valras is perhaps smarter and is certainly larger than nearby Vias and it has a good number of campsites. Lou Village is a family owned site with direct access to a sandy beach. A busy site with lots of facilities and quite competitive prices, it does becomes crowded in high season as this is a popular area. The central `village` area is a veritable hive of holiday activity, with several attractively designed pools and water slides, bars, pizzeria, restaurant and a purpose built stage for the site`s extensive entertainment programme. With straw parasols and palm trees, it is an attractive, clean area with a pleasant ambience. There are 600 pitches (200 with mobile homes), all with electricity (10A) and 100 also with water and waste water facilities. Pitches further inland are of grass, partly separated by tall trees that provide good shade; nearer the beach the pitches are smaller, sandy and separated by bushes and bamboo hedges. English is spoken.

**Facilities:** Four modern, well sited toilet blocks, all recently refurbished, have reasonable facilities. Mixture of Turkish and British style WCs, showers with no separator and half the washbasins in cabins. Facilities for disabled visitors and babies. Dishwashing and laundry sinks at each block. For a beach site, maintenance seems quite satisfactory. Supermarket, bakery, bazaar and, in high season, a hairdressing salon. Bar and restaurant with ample seating. Takeaway. Swimming pools. Playground, children`s club and football field. Tennis. Volleyball. Minigolf. Bicycle hire. **Off site:** Riding 500 m. Canoe kayaking, river fishing 1 km. Golf 12 km.

**Charges** 2002

| | |
|---|---|
| Per unit incl. 2 persons, electricity | € 18.00 - € 28.00 |
| extra person | € 4.00 - € 5.00 |
| child (under 7 yrs) | free - € 3.00 |
| local tax | € 0.40 |

**Tel:** 04 67 37 33 79. Fax: 04 67 37 53 56. E-mail: info@louvillage.com. **Reservations:** Made with deposit ( 183) and fee ( 30). **Open** 26 April - 14 September.

**Directions:** Site is south of Béziers. From autoroute, take Béziers-Ouest exit for Valras Plage and continue for about 14 km. Follow `Casino` signs and site is 1 km south of centre of Valras Plage in the direction of Vendres. Site signed to left at end of Valras Plage and the start of Vendres Plage.

## Mediterranean
# Camping-Club Les Vagues
34350 Vendres

**3412**

Les Vagues is a large site divided into three areas, two catering mainly for mobile homes with only a few touring units. The third area with the most tourers also contains the magnificent pool complex. This comprises a paddling pool, water slide, swimming pool and a wave pool - all surrounded by sunbathing areas. This is a very popular attraction, even though the sea and beach are only 300 m. The long, sandy beach is safe, being shallow for some distance and has lifeguards in July/Aug. The site's level pitches are shaded by tall trees and on sandy soil, the majority with electricity. A full entertainment programme in July/Aug. should keep most people happy. The low season is a quiet time, although everything remains open, ideal for couples and families.

**Facilities:** Modern toilet blocks provide mainly British style toilets, large forceful pre-set showers, washbasins mainly in cabins, baby baths and provision for disabled visitors. Dishwashing and laundry sinks, washing machines, all with ample hot water. Shop, bar and restaurant open all season. Swimming pool complex. Play areas on sand. Minigolf, table tennis and games room.

**Charges** 2002

| | |
|---|---|
| Per unit incl. 2 persons, electricity | € 14.00 - € 30.00 |
| extra adult | € 3.00 - € 5.00 |
| child | € 2.00 - € 3.00 |
| animal | € 6.00 |
| local tax | € 0.34 |

**Tel:** (0)4 67 37 33 12. Fax: (0)4 67 37 50 36. **Reservations:** Advised and made with booking fee ( 28). **Open** 1 April - 30 September.

**Directions:** From A9 autoroute take exit 36 on D64 and follow signs for Valras Plage and Vendres Plage. Pick up the signs for Vendres Plage Ouest. Follow small blue signs at all roundabouts then at sign for Vendres town, turn left at blue signboard.

This is the sister site to Sérignan Plage Naturist (no. 3408N), owned by Jean Paul Amat and his family who you will see around the site. Have a chat - his English is excellent and he likes to practise. It is a large, but very comfortable site, built in a genuinely unique style with direct access to a beautiful sandy beach. You will normally find room even in the high season, with 450 touring pitches in several different areas and three different styles to choose from, with the benefit of some of the most comprehensive amenities we have encountered. The touring pitches by the beach have little shade, are sandy and a little smaller. The others are mostly of a very good size on level grass with plenty of shade. All pitches have electricity (5A) and are mostly separate from a similar number of seasonal pitches and rented accommodation in the centre section of the site. Perhaps the most remarkable aspect of this site is the cluster of attractive buildings which form the central 'village' area with shops, pretty bars and a smart restaurant, amongst which is a small indoor heated swimming pool of unusual design mainly for out of season use. To complement this an amazing outdoor pool complex has now been added near the touring area. With interlinked pool areas, deep parts for swimmers, exciting children's areas with slides, bridges and islands, it is attractively landscaped and surrounded by a very large grass sunbathing area complete with sun loungers. The village area with inner and outer courtyards, has a lively, international atmosphere (well used and perhaps showing some wear and tear). Entertainment is provided every evening in high season, including shows at the outdoor stage in the outer courtyard, discos most nights and daily sporting activities. Wine and food tastings with tourist information presentations each Monday at 5 pm. Giant screen for news and current affairs. There is something for everyone here and you will not need to leave the site if you do not wish to. Remember, this is a seaside site in a natural coastal environment, so do not expect it to be neat and manicured; in parts nature still predominates. The site has direct access to a superb, large sandy beach and to the adjoining naturist beach, both of which slope very gently and offer safe bathing at most times. Used by tour operators (99 pitches).

**Facilities:** Nine unisex toilet blocks. The older circular ones with a mixture of British and Turkish style WCs are nearest the sea and central 'village' area, seasonal units and mobile homes, etc. and thus take the brunt of the wear and tear. The touring area, furthest from the sea but near the pool complex has three modern toilet blocks of individual design. Well planned with good facilities, these include a number of large controllable hot showers with washbasin (non-slip floor) and WC en-suite, well equipped baby rooms, facilities for disabled people. Dishwashing and laundry facilities in all blocks and central launderette. At peak times maintenance can be a little variable. Well stocked supermarket, bakery, newsagent/tabac, ATM and range of market stalls. Poissonnerie and boucherie (7/6-8/9). Hairdresser. Bars, restaurant serving local specialities plus take-away choices (all 7/4-10/9). Much animation for children, amusement machines and a range of evening entertainment in the amphitheatre and even a separate, secluded roof-top bar (9 pm - 1 am) - ask for a 'Cucaracha'! Soundproof disco. Heated indoor pool and landscaped outdoor pool complex (also heated) with lifeguards in the main season and an ID card system to prevent abuse (April - Sept). Range of sporting activities organised by site staff. Bicycle hire. **Off site:** Riding 2 km, golf 10 km. Bicycle hire. Sailing and windsurfing school on beach (lifeguard in high season).

**Charges** 2002

| Per unit incl. 1 or 2 persons and 5A electricity | € 17.00 - € 29.00 |
| --- | --- |
| extra person | € 3.00 - € 5.00 |
| pet | € 3.00 |

**Tel:** 04 67 32 35 33. Fax: 04 67 32 26 36. E-mail: info@leserignanplage.com. **Reservations:** Made from 1 Feb. with deposit (25%) and fee (€ 30). **Open** 10 April - 22 September.

**Directions:** From A9 exit 35 (Béziers Est) follow signs for Sérignan on D64 (9 km). Don't go into Sérignan, but take sign for Sérignan Plage for 4 km. At small multi sign (blue) turn right on single carriageway. At T-junction turn left over small road bridge and after left hand bend, site is 100 m. after naturist site and also Sérignan Plage Nature.

# YOUR HOLIDAYS BY THE SEA

Sérignan-Plage can be likened to an open-air auberge with the Mediterranean on your doorstep

FROM APRIL TO SEPTEMBER: 850 m$^2$ heated lagoon pool • heated indoor pool • activities and shows • mini-club • restaurant • bar • shops...

## Sunshine Guarantee

For bookings made in April, May and September you only pay for the nights you stay, if exceptionally the sun should not shine. For further information, refer to the general conditions of sale.

Le Sérignan Plage
34410 Sérignan
Languedoc-Roussillon
tél. 00 33 467 32 35 33
fax. 00 33 467 32 26 36
info@leserignanplage.com
www.leserignanplage.com

DDB nouveau monde LE TOURISME

Le sérignan plage
BORD DE MER
CAMPING AUBERGE
MÉDITERRANÉE

CAMPING VILLAGES
yelloh!
VILLAGE

## Mediterranean
# Camping-Caravaning Domaine de la Yole
BP23, 34350 Valras-Plage

**3409**

the **travel service**
TO BOOK

| Ferry | ✓ |
| Pitch | ✓ |
| Accommodation | ✗ |

01892 55 98 98

We were pleasantly surprised when we visited de la Yole - the thought of over 1,100 pitches was a little daunting and we expected things to be very hectic when we arrived on a busy day in mid-August. However, the multi-lingual reception was calm and people were enjoying themselves. There are 590 pitches for touring units, the remainder taken by mobile homes and a few tour operator pitches. Most pitches are of a good size, all are level and have electricity, water and waste water points and, very importantly for this area, they all have shade. The extensive pool area is attractive with lots of sunbathing areas and the impressive activities are located in a central area. A shopping area provides a supermarket, outdoor vegetable stall, fish stall, butchers, wine shop (take your own bottles for really good wines on draught), boutique and a take-away, all set under low trees very much like a village market. The beach, a long stretch of beautiful sand, is 500 m. and here is trampolining, paragliding and jet-skis. This is a busy site with something for all the family. English is spoken.

**Facilities:** Fully equipped toilet blocks include some showers and washbasins en-suite, mostly British style WCs and many washbasins in cubicles. Extra large cubicles with everything including a baby bath can be used by families or disabled visitors. Seven blocks have been recently refurbished and the eighth one is new. Maintenance can be variable. All blocks have dishwashing and laundry sinks. Central laundry with washing machines and dryers. Motorcaravan service point (the only chemical disposal point is here, a long walk from many pitches). Fridge hire. Shops. Good restaurant with huge terrace and amphitheatre for daily entertainment (in season). Two large pools and paddling pool, all supervised by lifeguard in July/Aug. Two half size tennis courts (free) and two full size (charged July/Aug), large play areas with amusements such as moto-track and daily children's club, minigolf, table tennis, boules, volleyball and basketball. Doctor calls daily in high season. **Off site:** Fishing or riding 1 km.

**Charges** 2002

| Per unit incl. 2 adults | € 15.55 - € 29.70 |
| extra person | € 4.75 |
| child 7-16 yrs | free - € 3.00 |
| child under 7 yrs | free - € 1.50 |
| dog | free - € 2.80 |
| local tax | € 0.15 - € 0.30 |

**Tel:** 04 67 37 33 87. Fax: 04 67 37 44 89. E-mail: layole34@aol.com. **Reservations:** Made with deposit ( € 90 or €130) and, in high season, a fee ( € 25); contact site for form. **Open** 27 April - 21 September.

**Directions:** From A9 autoroute take Beziers Ouest exit for Valras Plage (13-14 km) and follow Casino signs. Site on left, just after sign for Vendres Plage.

## Mediterranean
# Camping Les Berges du Canal
promenade les Vernets, 34420 Villeneuve-les-Béziers

**3421**

Although most campers or caravanners will be aware of the Canal du Midi, there are surprisingly few campsites which provide an opportunity to enjoy the rather special ambience for which this famous waterway is renowned, so we were really pleased to discover this delightful campsite right alongside the canal at Villeneuve-les-Beziers. Its situation is such that not only can one savour the ambience of the canal, but it is within a few minutes drive of the beaches at Serignan Plage, Vias or Valras, the old city of Beziers, the famous resort of Cap d'Agde, or you can even cycle along the tow-path to the beach at Portiragnes-Plage (10 km). The village of Villeneuve-les-Beziers itself, with shops, restaurants, market etc., is just a few minutes walk along the 'towpath'/access road and over the canal bridge. The campsite has 75 level pitches on sandy grass of average size, mostly with 6A electrical connections (some occupied by mobile homes) in a peaceful and shady situation, separated from the canal only by an access road. There is a pleasant swimming pool complex, one of the two pools being fitted with a jacuzzi-style facility, but there are no big slides or toboggans thereby ensuring that it is relatively peaceful.

**Facilities:** A fully equipped toilet block has mainly British-style WCs and some Turkish style, and some washbasins in cabins. Facilities for disabled visitors (with key). Washing machine, laundry and dishwashing sinks, etc. Motorcaravan service point. Two swimming pools. Bar/snack-bar (serving breakfast too!) Evening entertainment during high season.

**Charges** 2002

| Per unit incl. 2 persons | € 13.00 - € 18.00 |
| with electricity | € 15.00 - € 21.00 |
| extra person (over 4 yrs) | € 2.50 - € 3.50 |
| animal | € 1.50 - € 2.00 |
| local tax | € 0.20 |

**Tel:** 04 67 39 36 09. Fax: 04 67 39 82 07. E-mail: contact@lesbergesducanal.com. **Reservations:** Contact site. **Open** 15 April - 15 September.

**Directions:** From A9 take exit 35, follow signs for Agde and at first roundabout take N112 (direction Béziers) turning. Then take first left onto D37 signed Villeneve-les-Béziers and Valras Plage. Pass traffic lights, then left at roundabout and follow site signs (take care crossing junction beside bridge).

## Hotel de Plein Air L'Oliveraie

**3406** chemin de Bedarieux, 34480 Laurens

Situated at the foot of the Cevennes, L'Oliveraie has many attractive features and is open all year. Don`t assume that the extensive range of sport and recreation available here means that it is all hectic activity - in fact it is surprisingly peaceful. Most of the 116 pitches are large (up to 150 sq.m. in some parts) and all have electrical connections (6/10A). Arranged in rows on two levels, those on the higher level are older and have more shade from mature trees (mainly olives). The ground is stony. The large leisure area is slightly apart from the pitches on the lower area, overlooked by the bar. The old village of Laurens is well worth visiting. A `Sites et Paysages` member.

**Facilities:** The main toilet block on the higher terrace has been renovated and includes washbasins in cabins, new baby bathroom, and covered dishwashing and washing machine. The second block on lower level is open for high season. All perfectly adequate and clean when seen in high season. Small, well stocked shop (1/7-31/8). Bar/restaurant serving pizzas, salads, etc. Indoor bar, also used for films and activities for younger children. Good sized pool and children`s pool (1/6-30/9). Tennis court and tennis practice wall. Volleyball, basketball, minigolf. Bicycle hire. Play area. Barbecue area. Adjoining riding stables. Good facilities for archery - a feature of the site. **Off site:** Local shops at Laurens, 1 km.

**Charges 2003**

| | |
|---|---|
| Per unit incl. 1 or 2 persons | €15.75 - € 22.50 |
| extra person | € 4.60 |
| electricity (6-10A) | € 3.05 - € 4.60 |
| dog | free - € 1.55 |

**Tel:** 04 67 90 24 36. Fax: 04 67 90 11 20. E-mail: oliveraie@free.fr. **Reservations:** Contact site. **Open** all year.

**Directions:** Site is signed 2 km. north of Laurens off the D909 (Béziers-Bédarieux) road.

# L'OLIVERAIE
★ ★ ★

Over towards the bluish outline of the Cévennes foothills, the beauty of the sky is only equalled by the purity of the air. Comfort, tranquility and cultural interests, as well as tennis, volleyball, archery, boules, various other games, cycling, walks and horse-riding, will play a large part in making your stay enjoyable.

*We extend a warm welcome to you.*

Camping-Caravaning L'OLIVERAIE
34480 Laurens
Tel: 0033 467.90.24.36
Fax: 0033 467.90.11.20
E-mail: oliveraie@free.fr

## Camping Vert & Gites La Borio de Roque

**3418** 34220 Saint-Pons de Thonières

A small peaceful site, La Borio de Roque is set in a very rural location on quiet hillside 4 km. from St Pons. It lies at the end of a 1.5 km. track (rough in places) but it is well worth the effort and is set around a typical farmhouse with the outbuildings made into four very attractive gites. The 31 large, terraced pitches have 10A electricity and some shade. Some are very private which Ted the owner will escort you to. Children are encouraged to help with feeding and grooming the goats, sheep, donkeys and horses. Riding is possible on a daily, half daily or lessons basis and the rides into the forest with a picnic are very popular. There are many walks and tracks for mountain bikes from the site. Marit and Ted, your Dutch hosts, are happy to advise on routes. La Borio is especially suited to couples and young families - not a site for teenagers who like lots of entertainment.

**Facilities:** The toilet blocks have been modernised and provide showers and washbasins en-suite, adjustable and roomy. Baby bath. Dishwashing and laundry sinks. Free use of large freezer. Small play area on grass. Bread is available all season and ices. Local wine and home produced goat`s cheese, honey and cherry jam are for sale. A set menu is cooked four times weekly (to order) and eaten with the family in the bar/barn. This is a very popular event and well subscribed. Barbecue areas. Swimming pool and small lake for fishing. The site is not suitable for American motorhomes.

**Charges 2003**

| | |
|---|---|
| Per pitch | € 7.00 |
| adult | € 3.00 |
| child (under 7 yrs) | € 2.00 |
| electricity | € 2.25 |
| vehicle | € 1.52 |

**Tel:** (0)4 67 97 10 97. Fax: (0)4 67 97 21 61. E-mail: laborio@worldonline.fr. **Reservations:** Necessary for the main season and made with booking fee ( € 15,24). **Open** 15 May - 15 September.

**Directions:** St Pons de Thomières is on the N112 northwest of Beziéres. Site is 4.5 km. north of the town on the D907 signed Salvatat, on the right on a bend; then 1.5 km. on a rough track (signed).

## Mediterranean
# Camping Le Plein Air de Chênes
route de Castelnau, RD112, 34830 Clapiers

**3423**

the **travel service**

TO BOOK

Ferry ✓
Pitch ✓
Accommodation ✓

01892 55 98 98

Situated just outside the village of Clapiers, just 3 km. from the exciting and interesting city of Montpellier, yet only 15 km. from the beach, this is one of those few campsites which really does seem to provide something for everyone, even for those who prefer to spend their holidays without ever leaving the campsite! Here there are large touring pitches (some with their own individual toilet cabin), plus chalets, bungalows and mobile homes to rent - all in a nicely shaded terraced setting - in fact you name it and Des Chênes seems to have it. The site boasts an amazing pool complex, with multi-lane toboggan, four pools and surrounding facilities such as bars, restaurants, etc. It is also open to the public and obviously very popular.

**Facilities:** Three well equipped modern toilet blocks of circular design provide washbasins in cabins and facilities for disabled people. Laundry and dishwashing sinks. Three washing machines. Restaurant open to the public, bar and pool side bar and café. Swimming pools (1/6-30/9). 4 tennis courts. Multi-sports court. Play area. Mini club and range of evening entertainment in main season.

**Charges** 2002

| | | |
|---|---|---|
| Per unit incl. 2 persons, electricity | € 19.00 - | € 30.00 |
| with water and drainage | € 25.00 - | € 37.00 |
| extra person | € 3.00 - | € 5.00 |
| child (3-10 yrs) | € 2.00 - | € 3.00 |

**Tel:** 04 67 02 02 53. Fax: 04 67 59 42 19.
**Reservations:** Made with booking fee (€ 28); contact site. **Open** all year.

**Directions:** Site is north of Montpellier, 8 km. from A9 autoroute. Take exit 28 on N113 toward Montpellier passing village of Vendargues, leaving N113 and crossing the N110 (which joins the N 113) to follow the D65 for Clapiers circling north of Montpellier. Follow signs for village then for site.

## Mediterranean
# Camping Mar I Sol
Route de la Plage, 66440 Torreilles

**6617**

the **travel service**

TO BOOK

Ferry ✓
Pitch ✗
Accommodation ✓

01892 55 98 98

Good quality sites with direct access to the beach are hard to find and Mar i Sol is a useful addition. It is a fairly large site with 377 pitches with a significant number of mobile homes but with 170 available for touring units. These are sandy grass pitches of good size with some shade and connected by hardcore roads. All have electricity (6/10amp). The new owners have renovated the pool area and continue with other improvements. This is essentially a 'holiday' site with all the popular facilities and an extensive entertainment programme and children's club throughout the main season.

**Facilities:** Three toilet blocks include mixed British and Turkish toilets, some washbasins in cabins and covered dishwashing and laundry sinks. Washing machine in each block. Shop. Bar (1/6-15/9) TV. Restaurant and takeaway. Swimming pool, water slide and children's pool. Play area. Tennis court. Archery. Fitness room. Football and volleyball. Side gate with access to path across dunes to sandy beach. Lifeguards in main season.

**Charges** 2002

| | | |
|---|---|---|
| Per unit incl. two persons | € 12.35 - | € 22.41 |
| extra person (over 6 yrs) | € 3.20 - | € 5.34 |
| electricity 3-6A | € 3.05 - | € 3.96 |

**Tel:** (0)4 68 28 04 07. Fax: (0)4 68 28 18 23. E-mail: marisol@camping-marisol.com. **Reservations:** Needed for July/Aug; made with deposit and fee. **Open** all year (no facilities out of the main season).

**Directions:** From A9 exit 41( Perpignan Nord) go towards Le Barcarès for 9 km then south on D81 for 3 km. (Canet) before turning to Torreilles Plage.

## Mediterranean
# Sunêlia Les Tropiques
Bvd. de la Méditerranée, 66440 Torreilles Plage

**6619**

the **travel service**

TO BOOK

Ferry ✓
Pitch ✓
Accommodation ✓

01892 55 98 98

Les Tropiques makes a pleasant holiday venue, only 400m from a sandy beach and also boasting 2 pools. There are 450 pitches with 200 given over to mobile homes and chalets. Pleasant pine and palm trees with other Mediterranean vegetation give shade and provides an attractive environment. Activities are provided for all including a large range of sports, caberets and shows but an identity bracelet for entry to the site is obligatory in high season.

**Facilities:** Modern, fully equipped sanitary facilities include provision for disabled people. Launderette. Bar/restaurant with takeaway and pizzeria (14/6-15/9). Shop. Two outdoor pools (1/6-30/9) Tennis, table tennis, football, volleyball and pétanque. Archery (1/7-31/8). TV and billards room (15/6-15/9). Disco (every evening from 1/7-31/8). Play area and club for 6-12 yrs in July/Aug. **Off site:** Riding 400 m. Bicycle hire 5 km, golf 15 km.

**Charges** 2002

| | |
|---|---|
| Per pitch incl. 2 persons | € 21.00 |
| with electricity | € 25.00 |
| extra person | € 5.50 |
| child (under 6 yrs) | € 2.75 |

**Tel:** 04 68 28 05 09. Fax: 04 68 28 48 90. E-mail: camping.tropiques@wanadoo.fr. **Reservations:** Contact site. **Open** 1 April - 30 September.

**Directions:** From autroute A9 take exit Perpignan Nord and follow D83 towards Le Barcarès for 9 km. Then south on D81 towards Canet for 3 km. before turning left at roundabout at Torreilles Plage. Site last but one on left.

## Mediterranean
### Camping-Club Le Trivoly
Route des Plages, 66440 Torreilles Plage

We have watched the tiny resort of Torreilles-Plage grow in popularity (but not in size) over the past 15 years from the time when the late Alan Rogers himself thought it might justify featuring one camp-site there, to the present day when we include three! The popularity of Torreilles derives mainly from its huge sandy beach and for off-site nightlife, centre commer-cial, etc. but for smarter resorts one really needs to visit Le Barcares or Canet a few kilometres distance in either direction. Our latest addition at Torreilles is Le Trivoly (a member of the Chadotel Group) which is about 500 m. gentle stroll from the beach. It has some 270 good size, well shaded and hedged pitches with electricity. It perhaps offers a rather more peaceful situ-ation than do the other sites here.

**Facilities:** Four toilet blocks, although not new, provide modern facilities, including washbasins in (rather small) cabins, and were all clean and well cared for when we visited. Small shop (May- Aug). Snack-restaurant and takeaway. Reasonably sized pool with water slide and paddling pool. Play area. Bicycle hire. Table tennis. Basketball. Entertainment programme in high season. **Off site:** Centre Commercial 300 m.

**Charges** 2002

| | |
|---|---|
| Per unit incl. 2 persons | € 13.50 - € 21.00 |
| with electricity (6/10A) | € 17.00 - € 24.50 |
| extra person | € 5.20 |
| extra child under 5 yrs | € 3.30 |

**Tel:** (0)4.68.28.20.28. Fax: (0)4.68.28.16.48.
**Reservations:** Contact Chadotel Reservations, BP 12, 85520 Jard-sur-Mer; tel: (0)2.51.33.05.05. **Open** 1 April - 30 September.

**Directions:** From autoroute A9 take exit 42 (Perpignan Nord) towards Le Barcarès for 9 km. Turn south on D81 towards Canet. After 3 km. turn left at roundabout, signed Torreilles Plage. Site is on left, after about 500 m.

## Mediterranean
### Camping Le Roussillon
Chemin de la Mer, 66750 Saint Cyprien

This a comfortable site, although perhaps somewhat lacking in character. It is part of the Chadotel Group and has a quiet situa-tion on the edge of Saint-Cyprien village, some 2 km. from the beach. A bus service runs in the main season. The site benefits from having a good sized, traditionally shaped swimming pool, with the added attraction for children of a water slide, and there is plenty of sunbathing area for adults too. Many pitches are occupied by mobile homes but there are 36 well-kept, grassy and level touring pitches. Of a good size, they all have 16A electrical connec-tions.

**Facilities:** Two toilet blocks (one older but refur-bished, one more modern) provide modern facilities including a baby bath, laundry and facilities for disabled visitors. Bar/snack-bar with entertainment in season. Children's play area on grass.

**Charges** 2002

| | |
|---|---|
| Per pitch incl. 2 adults | € 13.50 - € 21.00 |
| including electricity | € 17.00 - € 24.50 |
| extra person | € 5.20 |
| child (under 5 yrs) | € 3.30 |

**Tel:** (0)4.68.21.06.45. Fax: (0)4.68.21.06.45.
**Reservations:** Contact Chadotel Reservations, BP 12 85520 Jard-sur-Mer; tel: (0)2.51.33.05.05. **Open** 30 March - 30 September.

**Directions:** Via the D81 southwards, do not go into St Cyprien Plage, but follow signs towards Argelès. At roundabout (Aqualand signed to the left) turn right towards St Cyprien village. Bear right and site is indicated by large Chadotel sign on the right hand side of this road.

## Mediterranean
### Camping du Stade
Avenue du 8 Mai 1945, 66702 Argelès-sur-Mer

Quieter and more peaceful family orien-tated sites are about as rare as hens' teeth in this immediate area, so we were pleas-antly surprised to discover one in a shady setting midway between the village and the beach resort - less than 1 km. from both. With some 180 good sized pitches, mostly with electricity (6A), in green surroundings with plenty of shade, this could be a quieter haven for those who want to be close to all the various attractions offered by this resort but without the noisy pool and bar to be able to relax at the end of the day in a traditionally French campsite.

**Facilities:** Two good quality, part modern, part tradi-tional, well-maintained toilet blocks have good sized showers, washbasins in cabins, etc. Unit for disabled people, facilities for babies. Washing machine. Snack-bar and takeaway (high season only). Adventure-style play area. Table tennis. **Off site:** Beach within walking distance.

**Charges** 2002

| | |
|---|---|
| Per unit incl. 2 adults | € 11.45 - € 16.35 |
| extra person | € 2.00 - € 4.60 |
| electricity | € 2.20 - € 3.15 |

**Tel:** (0)4.68.81.04.40. Fax: (0)4.68.95.84.55. E-mail: info@campingdustade.com. **Reservations:** Contact site. **Open** 1 April - 30 September.

**Directions:** From autoroute A9 take exit 42 (Perpignan Sud) and follow N114 towards Argelès. Take exit 10 for Pujols, and follow signs towards Centre Plage. At first roundabout go straight on (Ave Molliere). At next (small) roundabout turn left and site is immediately on your left.

## Mediterranean
# Camping Cala Gogo

**6603** La Vigie, 66750 St Cyprien-Plage

This is an excellent large and well organised site (sister site to 6604, Le Soleil) and it is agreeably situated by a superb sandy beach where there is a beach bar and boats can be launched. The 450 pitches for touring units are on flat ground and around 100 sq.m. They are fully marked out on level grass with easy access, electrical connections (6A) everywhere and some shade. The site has a most impressive pool complex carefully laid out with palm trees in ample sunbathing areas. The large bar complex becomes very busy in season and dancing or entertainment is arranged on some evenings on a large stage recently built alongside the bar. A large Aquapark, reputed to be amongst the best in southern France, is nearby. Used by tour operators (148 pitches).

**Facilities:** All four toilet blocks have been refurbished to a high standard, including British and Turkish style toilets and washbasins in cabins. Good supermarket, small shopping mall and wine boutique. Sophisticated restaurant with excellent cuisine and service, plus a self-service restaurant with simple menu and takeaway. Bar and small bar by the beach in high season. Disco. TV. Three adult pools plus one for children, water-jets, jacuzzi and waterfall. Tennis, table tennis and a children's playground. Programme of events and sports organised in season. Torches useful. **Off site:** Fishing, riding, bicycle hire and golf within 5 km. Boat excursions and courses in skin-diving, windsurfing or sailing nearby

**Charges** 2003

| Per person (over 5 yrs) | € 7.00 |
|---|---|
| pitch (any unit) | € 10.00 |
| electricity (6A) | € 3.00 |
| dog | € 3.50 |
| local tax | € 0.30 |

**Tel:** 04 68 21 07 12. **Fax:** 04 68 21 02 19. **E-mail:** calagogo@campmed.com. **Reservations:** Made for Sat. to Sat. and necessary for Jul/Aug, with deposit ( € 81,70) and fee ( € 18,30). **Open** 17 May - 20 September, with all services.

**Directions:** Using D81 (southward) avoid St Cyprien Plage and continue towards Argeles. Turn right at roundabout signed Le Port and Aquapark and pick up site signs. Site is just past the Aquapark.

## Mediterranean
# Camping Le Soleil

**6604** route du Littoral, 66702 Argelès-sur-Mer

Le Soleil (sister site to Cala Go-Go, no. 6603), with direct access to the beach, is a busy, popular, family owned site which has grown in the last few years. A large site, more like a small village, it has over 800 individual numbered pitches of ample size, with over 200 used by tour operators, over 70 occupied by mobile homes and around 550 used for touring units. On sandy/grassy ground and with a mixture of trees and shrubs providing some shade, electricity connections (6A) are provided in all areas. Access for caravans sometimes needs care on the narrow access roads. The site has a wide range of amenities, including an impressive pool complex. Spain and the Pyrénées are near enough for excursions. English is spoken and there is a comprehensive reservation system (advised for most of July/Aug).

**Facilities:** Seven toilet blocks of the type with external access to individual units should give good coverage with showers in four of them. Two of the others have undergone major refurbishment and now offer family cabins with washbasins and showers with unusually two additional pressure water outlets at waist level in each. Washing machines. Supermarket, general shop, press, tabac and restaurant or sit down or takeaway food is centrally situated. ATM machine. Internet connection. Bar with disco (July/Aug) and beach bar. California type swimming pool complex and entertainment area. Children's adventure playground. TV room. Tennis. Riding in high season (charge). Dogs are not accepted. **Off site:** Fishing and mooring boats on the adjacent river. Golf 5 km.

**Charges** 2002

| Per person (over 5 yrs) | € 6.50 |
|---|---|
| pitch | € 9.20 |
| electricity (6A) | € 2.90 |
| local tax (adults) | € 0.40 |

**Tel:** 04 68 81 14 48. **Fax:** 04 68 81 44 34. **E-mail:** camping.lesoleil@wanadoo.fr. **Reservations:** Made from Sat or Wed (min. 1 week) with deposit (30%) and booking fee ( € 18.30). **Open** 15 May - 30 September.

**Directions:** Site is at north end of the beach about 1 km. from Argelès-Plage village.

2 Campsites
DIRECT ON THE BEACH
www.campmed.com

CALA GOGO

La Vigie • 66750 SAINT CYPRIEN
Tél. +33 4 68 21 07 12 • Fax +33 4 68 21 02 19
e-mail : calagogo@campmed.com

LE SOLEIL
★★★★

Rte du Littoral
66700 ARGELES SUR MER
Tél. +33 4 68 81 14 48
Fax +33 4 68 81 44 34
e-mail : lesoleil@campmed.com

## Mediterranean
# Camping-Caravaning Ma Prairie

route de Sainte-Nazaire, 66140 Canet-en-Roussillon

the **travel service**

TO BOOK

| Ferry | ✔ |
| Pitch | ✔ |
| Accommodation | ✔ |

01892 55 98 98

The Gil family provide a warm welcome immediately you arrive at the very pretty ivy covered reception area which boasts an impressive international collection of hats/helmets and uniform caps. Ma Prairie is an excellent site set among the vineyards some 3 km. back from the sandy Canet beaches. It has an excellent pool complex over looked by large air conditioned bar situated across a small road from the camping area. There are 260 pitches of around 100 sq.m. on flat grassy ground, separated by various trees and bushes which provide shade (possible road noise). Most have electricity, with water and drainage on 35. The Gils have produced another superb touch in their restaurant which is very much a family affair down to mother's cushion designs and grandfather's paintings on the wall. The area of the old restaurant is now used for children's entertainment. Tours of the family vineyard with supper are organised weekly (but book early) and the site owners offer wine with their own distinctive label (ask about the clever use of the family name). Used by tour operators (40 pitches). There is a lively family atmosphere. A 'Sites et Paysages' member.

**Facilities:** Three toilet blocks, two excellent new ones and one more mature, include washbasins in cabins with dividers. Baby bath. Washing machines and dryers. Dishwashing and laundry sinks. Extra provision near reception. Shop for basics only, covered snack bar and takeaway. Large air-conditioned bar and quality restaurant. Large adult pool (10 x 22 m), splendid children's pool. Children's play area. Tennis. Bicycle hire. Volleyball. Satellite TV, table tennis, billiards and amusement machines. Dancing about three times weekly and busy daily animation programme in season. Caravan storage. **Off site:** Riding 600 m, golf 6 km. Canet Village within walking distance with all amenities. Bus/tram services to the busy modern resort of Canet Plage.

**Charges** 2002

| Per unit with 2 persons | €15.00 - €24.00 |
| extra person | €3.00 - €5.20 |
| child 4-10 yrs | €2.30 - €4.00 |
| child under 4 yrs | free - €2.70 |
| electricity (10A) | €3.80 |
| water and drainage | €4.60 |

**Tel:** 04 68 73 26 17. Fax: 04 68 73 28 82. E-mail: ma.prairie@wanadoo.fr. **Reservations:** Made for any length with deposit (€ 61) and fee (€ 12,20). **Open** 5 May - 25 September.

**Directions:** Leave autoroute A9 at Perpignan North towards Barcares. Site access is from the D11 Perpignan road close to the junction with D617 in Canet-Village.

## Mediterranean
# Camping Le Haras

Domaine Sant Galdric, 66690 Palau del Vidre

the **travel service**

TO BOOK

| Ferry | ✔ |
| Pitch | ✔ |
| Accommodation | ✘ |

01892 55 98 98

A distinctly 'French' site, Le Haras is situated midway between the coast (about 8 km.) and the Pyrénées on the edge of a village, in quiet countryside removed from the bustle of the coastal resorts. Under the same family management as Ma Prairie at Canet Village (6602), they are dedicated to many improvements. Le Haras has some 72 individual pitches all with 6A electricity and drainage, arranged informally in bays of four, in the grounds of an old hunting lodge (designed by Gustave Violet on the lines of a small Italianate palace). A marvellous mixture of trees, shrubs and flowers provides colour and shade. There is an attractive pool complex and courtyard area beside the restaurant (developed in the old stables, with an excellent chef) and large function room, often used for weddings, with a distinctly Italian feel. Not to be missed are the love birds whose bright colours, along with some of the exotic plants, suit the distinctly Mediterranean feel of the site. Rail noise is possible from the line that runs beside the site, although this is screened by large trees.

**Facilities:** The unusually designed toilet block, fully equipped with mixed British and Turkish toilets, has been supplemented by a smart new block decorated in greens and terracotta in keeping with the site. It is planned that the smaller block near the pool will be renovated and heated. Covered dishwashing and laundry sinks. Washing machines. Bar. Restaurant, L'Oranger, open to the public (all year, but not every day). Swimming pool and paddling pool (May-Sept). Children's play area. **Off site:** Three bakers in the village, two butchers and a general stores. Beaches 10 minutes drive.

**Charges** 2002

| Per unit incl. 2 persons, sanitary unit and electricity | €12.10 - €25.90 |
| 3-6 persons | €13.50 - €34.55 |
| dog | €2.30 |
| local tax | €0.15 |

**Tel:** (0)4 68 22 14 50. Fax: 04 68 37 98 93. **Reservations:** Necessary for July and August. Made with €100 deposit and €16 booking fee. **Open** 20 March - 20 October.

**Directions:** To avoid possible heavy traffic around Perpignan leave autoroute at exit 43 (Le Boulou) and follow D618 in the direction of Argelés for approx. 13 km. Take left turn for Palau-del-Vidre (D11) as you bypass St André. Bear right through village still on D11 in direction of Elne. As you leave village, site is on right, entrance just before railway bridge.

## Mediterranean
# Camping-Caravaning Le Brasilia
BP 204, 66140 Canet-en-Roussillon

6607

We continue to be very impressed with La Brasilia - it is pretty, neat and well kept with an amazingly wide range of facilities and activities. It is a large site, but does not seem so, with 807 neatly hedged pitches all with electricity (6/10A).Some long pitches suitable for two families together. With a range of shade from mature pines and flowering shrubs, less on pitches near the beach, there are neat access roads (sometimes narrow for large units) and many flowers. The sandy beach here is busy, with a beach club (you can hire windsurfing boards) and a naturist section is on the beach to the west of the site. There is also a large California type pool , with sunbathing areas bounded by an attractive mosaic wall and bar. The village area of the site provides bars, a busy restaurant, entertainment (including a night club) and a range of shops. In fact you do not need to stir from the site which is almost a resort in itself also providing a cash dispenser, exchange facilities, telephone, post office, gas supplies and even weather forecasts. It does have a nice, lively atmosphere but is orderly and well run - very good for a site with beach access. A Yelloh Village member.

**Facilities:** Nine modern sanitary blocks are very well equipped and maintained, with British style WCs (some Turkish) and washbasins in cabins. One is very modern and impressive with good facilities for children (as has one other block). Facilities for disabled people. All have dishwashing and laundry sinks. Laundry room with washing machines and dryers. Special refuse areas.Hairdressing salon. Bars and restaurant. Swimming pool (heated and free). Sports field for football and a smaller games pitch (with 'Astroturf'). Tennis courts. Sporting activities such as aqua gym, aerobics, football, etc. Library, games and video room. Internet café planned. Bicycle hire. Fishing. Special dog walking area, cleaned daily. Torches useful (lighting is at knee level and sometimes lacking). No barbecues allowed. English is spoken. **Off site:** Riding 5 km, golf 12 km.

**Charges** 2002

| | |
|---|---|
| Per unit incl. 2 persons | € 16.00 - € 30.00 |
| extra person (over 3 yrs) | € 4.00 - € 6.50 |
| child (1-4 yrs) | free - € 3.50 |
| dog | free - € 3.00 |
| electricity (6/10A) | € 2.80 - € 4.00 |
| local tax (over 3 yrs) | € 0.30 |

**Tel:** 04 68 80 23 82. Fax: 04 68 73 32 97. E-mail: Camping_le_brasilia@wanadoo.fr. **Reservations:** Advised for July/Aug. **Open** 27 April - 29 September.

**Directions:** From A9 motorway take exit 41 (Perpignan Centre/Rivesalts) follow signs for Le Barcarès/Canet on D83 for 10 km, then signs for Canet (D81). Arriving at first Canet roundabout, make a full turn back on yourself (direction Sainte-Marie) and watch for Brasila sign almost immediately on right and follow.

## Mediterranean
# Camping-Caravaning Le Pujol
route du Tamariguer, 66700 Argelès-sur-Mer

6600

Argelès is a busy tourist area and in high season it doesn't matter which of the 50 or so sites you are on, there are various loud open air discos and activities which may impinge on the wrong side of midnight for a while. However, it is possible to avoid the standard hectic seaside sites in otherwise attractive Argelès, and Pujol may represent the best chance of doing so. It is a pretty and well cared for site which has been thoughtfully designed. There are 310 numbered pitches, all larger than 100 sq.m. on flat grass, nearly all with electricity. They include some 100 privately owned British mobile homes. The number of pitches has been increased (by 50) and these will be taken by mobile homes over the next few years, but in the meantime they are useful large pitches with electricity for tourers. Care is taken to ensure that the bar is a family bar rather than one overrun by youngsters, who are catered for in an attractively covered meeting area opposite which also houses animation and dances. The site's pride and joy is a delightful pool complex with semi-tropical shrubs and fountains. There is some road noise near the entrance to the site.

**Facilities:** Well kept fully equipped toilet blocks include a very smart shower block. Baby bath. Washing machines in each block with free ironing. Small supermarket (1/6-15/9). Good terraced restaurant and friendly family bar (1/6-15/9). Fairly large L-shaped swimming pool, children's pool, and spa pool (1/6-15/9). Table tennis, small multi-gym, volleyball, boules and minigolf. Children's playground. Games room. Only gas or electric barbecues are permitted. **Off site:** Fishing, bicycle hire 1 km, riding 500 m. Argelès Plage and quiet resort of Racou short distance if you want to exchange the pool for a Mediterranean beach.

**Charges** 2002

| | |
|---|---|
| Per pitch incl. 2 adults | € 20.00 |
| with electricity | € 23.00 |
| extra person | € 5.00 |
| child (under 3) | € 2.50 |
| local tax (over 10 yrs) | € 0.30 |

**Tel:** 04 68 81 00 25. Fax: 04 68 81 21 21. **Reservations:** Made with € 100 deposit. **Open** 1 June - 30 September.

**Directions:** Perpignan-Nord exit from autoroute, follow N114 from Perpignan and use exit 10 for Argelès, Cross first roundabout onto Chemin de Neguebous (avoiding town). Turn left at second roundabout and site is 200 m. on right opposite Tour de Pujol.

## Mediterranean
# Camping Le Dauphin

**6611** route de Taxo-d'Avall, 66701 Argelès-sur-Mer

Near Taxo in the quieter, northern part of Argelès (a somewhat frenzied resort in season), this site on flat, grassy parkland enjoys good views of the Pyrénées, particularly from the terrace area surrounding its excellent complex of swimming pools. There are 310 level, grassy well shaded pitches, all with 10A electricity and some with individual sanitary units. Although located some 1.5 km. from the town and beach, there is a regular connecting 'road train' service to and fro throughout the day and evening up to midnight. Used by tour operators (70 pitches).

**Facilities:** A central sanitary block, although mature, provides modern facilities including a number of showers and washbasins en-suite. One third of the pitches have a fully equipped individual sanitary unit. Shops, bar/restaurant, pizzeria with takeaway (all 1/6-15/9). Pool complex (small charge) with two large pools and a paddling pool. Small play area. Tennis courts. Minigolf boules, table tennis, multi-sport court, sports ground and games room. Entertainment programme in high season. Torches useful in some areas. **Off site:** Fishing 2 km, riding 1 km.

**Charges** 2002

| | |
|---|---|
| Per unit incl. 2 adults | € 19.00 |
| with electricity | € 21.50 |
| extra person | € 2.50 - € 4.00 |
| water and drainage | € 2.50 |
| Individual sanitation | € 6.00 |

**Tel:** (0)4 68 81 17 54. Fax: (0)4 68 95 82 60. E-mail: campingledauphin66@wanadoo.fr. **Reservations:** Made with deposit ( € 77) and booking fee (16). **Open** 1 June - 30 September.

**Directions:** Site is on north side of Argelès. From autoroute take exit Perpignan-Nord for Argelès and follow directions for Plage-Nord and Taxo d'Avall (similarly from the N114).

Camping **LE DAUPHIN** ★★★★

Chemin de taxo à la mer

66701 ARGELES SUR MER

Tel : 0033 468 811 754

Fax : 0033 468 958 260

camping.ledauphin66@wanadoo.fr

93 pitches with their own individual Sanitary Block

**310 SHADED PITCHES IN A QUIET AND RELAXING SITE**

---

## Mediterranean
# Camping-Caravaning Les Marsouins

**6620** Avenue de la Retirada, 66702 Argelès-sur-Mer

Les Marsouins is a large site situated on the beach road out of Argelès. About half the 587 pitches are taken by mobile homes, with those for tourers on grass divided by hedging. Plenty of trees provide shade and electricity (5A) is available. A large outdoor arena area with seating and a stage is located at the entrance but the lagoon style pool area (no water slides) is tucked away to one side of the site with ample space for sunbathing on the lawns surrounding it. The site is well situated for easy access to the good sandy beach, with activities like windsurfing possible.

**Facilities:** Four fully equipped toilet blocks provide facilities for the handicapped and there are dish-washing and laundry sinks, washing machine and iron. Motorhome service station. Bar and self-service restaurant near the outdoor arena, mini-market (8/6-7/9). Heated swimming pool (15/4-29/9). Large play area with children's club with organised activities (free 24/6-1/9). Range of evening entertainment (30/5-3/8). **Off site:** Beach 800 m.

**Charges** 2002

| | |
|---|---|
| Per pitch max.6 persons | € 13.00 - € 23.50 |
| extra person (over 5 yrs) | € 2.30 - € 5.00 |
| dog (high season) | € 2.00 |
| local tax | € 0.30 |

Tel: 04 68 81 14 81. Fax: 04 68 95 93 58. **Reservations:** Contact site. **Open** 1 April - 30 September.

**Directions:** Take Perpignan sud exit from A9 autoroute. Follow signs for Argelès (RN114) and take exit 10 following signs for Pujols at round about, then Plage Nord at next roundabout. Site is on left.

## Mediterranean
# Camping-Caravaning Le Romarin

**6623** Route de Sorède, Chemin des Vignes, 66702 Argelès-sur-Mer

In an area dominated by 'all-singing, all-dancing' holiday sites, we were pleased to discover almost by accident this charming little gem of a site tucked away some 2 km. behind the busy resort of Argelès. Essentially a site for families with younger children, or for adults seeking peace and quiet, it provides some 110 good sized touring pitches (and some chalets), all with electricity (6-10A) set among pine, euca-lyptus, oak and mimosas. Ideal for explor-ing this area, especially the Albères range of Pyreneen mountains and the ancient city of Perpignan, it is nevertheless within easy reach of shops, supermarket (2 km) and all the attractions of Argelès.

**Facilities:** One good large toilet block (half traditional style, half modern) provides a mix of British and Turkish WCs, showers, washbasins in cabins, dish-washing and laundry sinks and washing machine. Snackbar (mid June - mid Sept). Swimming pool. Children's play area. Table tennis. Some traditional (local) family entertainment in high season.

**Charges 2002**

| | |
|---|---|
| Per unit incl. 2 persons | € 11.00 - € 18.00 |
| extra person | € 3.00 - € 4.00 |
| child (2-5 yrs) | free - € 2.00 |
| electricity | € 2.00 - € 3.00 |

**Tel:** (0)4.68.81.02.06. **Fax:** (0)4.68.81.57.43. **E-mail:** camping.romarin@libertysurf.fr. **Reservations:** Made with 25% deposit. **Open** 15 May - 30 September.

**Directions:** From autoroute A9 take exit 42 (Perpignan Sud) on N114 towards Argelès for 25 km. to exit 11a. At roundabout follow directions to St.Andre for 300 m. then turn left to pick up the Route de Sorède. Site is 2 km. along this road.

## Mediterranean
# Mas Llinas Camping

**6618** 66160 Le Boulou

The highest terraces on this campsite have commanding views over the valley and to the surrounding mountains. The roads up to the level, terraced, hillside pitches (100) are paved to make access easy, with good places to choose from. Some are larger, some grassy and some hedged for privacy, many with outstanding views and lovely trees (electricity available 5/6A). This is a simple, peaceful and well maintained site with a relaxed feel. The beautiful original old farmhouse is near the top of the prop-erty. The reception is near the bar/café that serves a very limited range of snacks and some local produce, including the wine of the region. Explore the region of the Roussillon wines or just enjoy the views and the peace and quiet.

**Facilities:** Two clean and modern sanitary blocks are unisex, but cleverly designed for privacy. Facilities for disabled campers. Washing machine. Motorcaravan services. Limited bar/café. Bread and croissants (July/Aug). Swimming pools (mid-May - Oct. depend-ing on weather). Volleyball. Table tennis. Games room. Motorcyclists welcome. Torches necessary. Only gas barbecues are permitted.

**Charges 2002**

| | |
|---|---|
| Per adult | € 3.80 - € 4.50 |
| pitch | € 4.50 - € 5.00 |
| electricity (5-10A) | € 2.50 - € 3.10 |

**Tel:** (0)4 68 83 25 46. **E-mail:** info@camping_mas_ llinas.com. **Reservations:** Contact site. **Open** 1 February - 30 November.

**Directions:** Le Boulou is about 26 km. from the eastern side of the Spanish border. Travel south from Perpignan on the A9/E15 or N9 to Le Boulou (approx. 30 km). Site is well signed from town and is on the northern outskirts, approached through a light commercial area of town. Follow road uphill through countryside for about 2 km.

## Mediterranean
# Hotel de Plein Air L'Eau Vive

**6613** chemin de St Saturnin, 66820 Vernet-les-Bains

Enjoying dramatic views of the towering Pic du Canigou (3,000 m.), this small site is 1.5 km. from the centre of the spa town of Vernet-les-Bains in the Pyrénées. It is approached via a twisting road through a residential area. The 77 tourist pitches, all with electricity (4/10A) and water, are on a slight slope, part hedged, some terraced with tent field. Most have some shade. Although there is no swimming pool as such, the site has a very attractive, more or less natural pool (created by pumping and circulating water from the nearby stream). There is a central floating safety line across the pool but parents should keep an eye on children around the pool. English is spoken by the welcoming Dutch owners.

**Facilities:** First class toilet facilities in two modern blocks include washbasins in cabins, dishwashing under cover and facilities for disabled people. Washing machines. Bread to order in main season. Attractive open air (but under cover) snack bar with takeaway (1/6-30/9). Natural pool. Sports field. Basketball. Bicycle hire. **Off site:** Fishing 200 m.

**Charges 2002**

| | |
|---|---|
| Per unit incl. 1-3 persons, electricity | € 11.00 - € 13.00 |

**Tel:** 04 68 05 54 14. **Fax:** 04 68 05 78 14. **E-mail:** leav@club-internet.fr. **Reservations:** Contact site. **Open** all year except 12 Nov - 15 Dec.

**Directions:** Following the N116 to Andorra, 6 km. after Prades, take turning at Villefranche de Conflent for Vernet-les-Bains. Continue up hill for 5 km. and keep right avoiding town centre. Turn right over bridge in direction of Sahorre. Immediately, at one end of small block of shops, turn right into Ave de Saturnin and follow for about 1 km. past houses to more open area and site is signed.

# Mediterranean - part 2

Map 16

Part 2 covers the eastern coastal region of the Mediterranean. We have used two départements from the official French region of Provence, i.e. those that border the coast, and the official region of Côte d'Azur.

## Coastal Provence

Major city: Marseille

Départements:
13 Bouches-du-Rhône, 83 Var

## Côte d'Azur

Major cities: Nice, Cannes, Monte Carlo (Monaco)

Départements: 06 Alpes-Maritime

The mention of Provence immediately draws to mind lavender fields and olive groves; it is a sunny bright region backed by mountains, with a glittering coastline. The Romans settled in the region and their legacy remains in the great amphitheatres and monuments of Arles and Nîmes. The Rhône valley divides above Arles into two arms which encircle the marshlands of the Camargue before reaching the sea. The wild white horses which gallop, manes flying, through the shallow waters of the delta are legendary, as are the ragged black bulls and the rose and white flamingos.

The Côte d'Azur, perhaps better known as the French Riviera, is a beautiful stretch of coast studded with sophisticated towns such as Monte Carlo, Nice, and Cannes, not forgetting the other famous resort of St Tropez. The quaint harbours and fishing villages have become chic destinations, now full of pleasure yachts and crowded summertime beaches. Up in the hills are quieter tiny medieval villages of winding streets and white-walled houses with terracotta roofs, which have attracted artists and visitors for many years. In St Paul-de-Vence visitors can browse through shops and galleries set on narrow winding cobblestone streets. Grasse is the perfume capital of the world. Note: site reports are laid out by département in numerical order not by region.

## Cuisine of the region

Cuisine emphasizes seasonings, such as herbs and garlic, and fish
Aigo Bouido –garlic and sage soup with bread (or eggs and cheese)
Aïoli (ailloli) – a mayonnaise sauce with garlic and olive oil
Bouillabaisse – fish soup served safran (saffron) and aïoli (see above)
Rouille – an orange coloured sauce with peppers, garlic and saffron
Bourride – a creamy fish soup (usually made with big white fish), thickened with

aïoli and flavoured with crawfish
Brandade (de morue) à l'huile d'olive – a mousse of salt cod with cream, olive oil and garlic
Pain Bagna – bread roll with olive oil, anchovies, olives, onions, etc.
Pissaladière – Provencal bread dough with onions, anchovies, olives, etc.
Pistou (Soupe au) – vegetable soup bound with 'pommade'
Pommade – a thick paste of garlic, basil, cheese and olive oil
Ratatouille– aubergines, courgettes, onions, garlic, red peppers and tomatoes in olive oil
Salade Niçoise – tomatoes, beans, potatoes, black olives, anchovy, lettuce and olive oil and sometimes tuna fish

## Places of interest

Aix-en-Provence – old town with 17th/18th century character; Paul Cézanne and Tapestry museums
Cannes – popular for conventions and festivals, Cannes Film Festival, la Croisette, old city
Monte Carlo – main city of Monaco, casinos, gardens, Napoleon Museum. motorsport circuit

## Mediterranean
# Camping Domaine Sainte Madeleine

route de Moulinet, 06380 Sospel

Domaine Sainte Madeleine is an attractive, peaceful site, with swimming pool, in spectacular mountain scenery. It is about 28 kilometres miles inland from Menton, and very near the Italian border. The approach to this site is not for the faint-hearted although having said that, when we visited in late July, the site was very busy with touring caravans so it can't be too bad. The site itself makes the effort worthwhile - situated on a terraced hillside with mountain views towards Italy. On a fairly steep hillside, manoeuvring within the site presents no problem and the pitches themselves are on level, well drained grass. The lower ones have shade but those higher up on the hill have none. Electricity is available to 70 of the 90 pitches. There are way-marked walks for serious walkers in the surrounding hills. English is spoken.

**Facilities:** The single toilet block is of good quality, including washbasins in cabins and showers on payment. Hot water (often only warm) for dishwashing and laundry sinks drawn from single tap. Washing machines. Motorcaravan services. Gas supplies. Bread to order. Swimming pool (140 sq.m. and heated in spring and autumn). **Off site:** Sospel is only 4 km. with many restaurants, bars, cafés and shops. Tennis, riding and a centre for mountain biking. Fishing 1 km.

**Charges** 2002

| | |
|---|---|
| Per unit incl. 2 adults | € 15.00 |
| extra adult | € 3.50 |
| child (under 6 yrs) | € 1.90 |
| electricity (10A) | € 2.80 |
| local tax (over 12 yrs) | € 0.15 |

**Tel:** 04 93 04 10 48. **Fax:** 04 93 04 18 37. **E-mail:** camp@camping-sainte-madeleine.com.
**Reservations:** Necessary for July/Aug. and made with € 50 deposit. **Open** 1 April - 30 September.

**Directions:** Site is on D2566, 4 km. north of Sospel. The D2566 can be reached from either the A8 autoroute via Menton exit, or from the N7 at Menton.

## Mediterranean
# Camping-Caravaning Les Cigales

505 ave. de la Mer, 06210 Mandelieu la Napoule

It is hard to imagine that such a quiet, peaceful site could be in the middle of such a busy town and so near to Cannes - we were delighted with it. The entrance (easily missed) with reception and parking has large electronic gates that ensure that the site is very secure. There are only 115 pitches (20 used for mobile homes) so this is really quite a small, personal site. There are three pitch sizes, from small ones for tents to pitches for larger units. All are level with much needed shade in summer, although the sun will get through in winter when it is needed, and all have electricity (6A). The site is alongside the Canal de Siagne and for a fee small boats can be launched at La Napoule, then moored outside the campsite's side gate. Les Cigales is open all year so it is useful for the Monte Carlo Rally, the Cannes Film Festival and the Mimosa Festival, all held out of the main season. English is spoken.

**Facilities:** Two well appointed unisex toilet blocks are kept very clean, one heated for the winter months. Washbasins in cabins and facilities for babies and disabled visitors. Dishwashing and laundry sinks. Washing machine. Motorcaravan service point. Restaurant at entrance with takeaways (April - 30 Sept). Swimming pool (March - Oct). Small play area. Table tennis. Fishing possible in the canal (but not many fish!) **Off site:** The town is an easy walk. Centre commercial 2 km. Bus stop 10 minutes. Railway station 1 km. for trains to Cannes, Nice, Antibes and Monte Carlo. Riverside and canal walks. Two golf courses within 1 km. Beach 800 m.

**Charges** guide

| | | |
|---|---|---|
| Per adult | | € 3.50 |
| child (under 5 yrs) | | € 2.30 |
| pitch | € 10.67 - | € 22.11 |
| electricity (3-6A) | € 2.30 - | € 3.81 |

**Tel:** 04 93 49 23 53. **Fax:** 04 93 49 30 45. **E-mail:** campingcigales@wanadoo.fr. **Reservations:** Made with deposit (€ 77). **Open** all year.

**Directions:** From A8 take exit 40 and bear right. Remain in right hand lane and continue right signed Plages-Ports and Creche-Campings. New Casino supermarket is on the right. Continue under motor way to T-junction. Turn left and site is 60 m. on left opposite Chinese restaurant.

**Les Gorges du Loup**

**C★★★G**
**ampinG**

965 chemin des Vergers
06620 LE BAR DU LOUP
Pays de Grasse / Côte d'Azur
Tel / Fax: 0033 493 424 506

Email: les-gorges-du-loup@wanadoo.fr
www.lesgorgesduloup.com

## Mediterranean
## Camping La Vieille Ferme

**0605** 296 boulevard des Groules, 06270 Villeneuve-Loubet-Plage

Open all year, in a popular resort area, La Vieille Ferme is a family owned site with good facilities. It provides 131 level gravel-based pitches, 106 with electricity (6-10A), water and waste water connections and the majority separated by hedges. Some are only small, simple pitches for little tents. There is also a fully serviced pitch on tarmac for motorhomes. There are special winter rates for long stays with quite a few long stay units on site. The entrance to the site is very colourful with well tended flower beds. English is spoken at reception and the whole place has a very friendly feel to it. A one kilometre walk beside the road towards Antibes brings you to the railway station, giving access to all the towns along the coast and to the beach.

**Facilities:** Three modern, well kept toilet blocks (two heated in winter) provide washbasins all in cabins, children's toilets, baby room and two units for disabled people. Motorcaravan service point. Dishwashing and laundry sinks. Washing machines and dryer. Shop (Easter - Sept). Drinks, sweets and ices machine in the TV room for all year use. Gas, bread and milk to order when shop closed. Refrigerator hire. Swimming pool (20 x 10 m.) and children's pool, heated and covered for winter use (closed mid Nov-mid Dec) with jacuzzi. Internet point. Table tennis, basketball and boule pitch. Games and competitions organised in July/Aug. **Off site:** Fishing 1 km, golf 2 km.

**Charges** 2002

| | |
|---|---|
| Per unit incl. 2 persons | € 14.00 - € 24.00 |
| extra person | € 3.50 - € 4.50 |
| child (under 5 yrs) | € 2.30 - € 3.00 |
| electricity (2-10A) | € 2.29 - € 5.00 |
| local tax | € 0.38 |

**Tel:** 04 93 33 41 44. **Fax:** 04 93 33 37 28. E-mail: vieilleferme@bigfoot.com. **Reservations:** Advised over a long season and made with 25% deposit and € 20 fee; Sat.-Sat. only in July/Aug. and at Easter. **Open** all year.

**Directions:** From west take Antibes exit from Esterel autoroute and turn left towards Nice when joining the N7 outside Antibes. After 3.5 km. on N7 turn left for site. From east take N7 towards Antibes and turn right after Villeneuve Loubet Plage. The turning off the N7, though signed, is not easy to see particularly at busy times but, coming from Antibes, it is on the left, more or less between the Bonne Auberge and the Parc de Vaugrenier. Site is 150 m. on right. Avoid N98 Route du Bord de Mer. Site has prepared its own small, yellow site signs.

**CAMPING — CARAVANNING**
★★★★
**La Vieille Ferme**
Tel. 0033 493.33.41.44

**Riviéra**
**Côte d'azur**
**Winter Facilities**
**Heated Pools**
**06270 VILLENEUVE LOUBET PLAGE (PAR RN7)**

www.vieilleferme.com

## Camping-Caravaning Les Gorges du Loup

**0609** 965 chemin des Vergers, 06620 Le Bar sur Loup

In the hills above Grasse, Les Gorges du Loup is situated on a steep hillside. Many of the pitches are only suitable for tents and certainly not for large caravans, mainly due to the steepness of the site roads, but also because of the narrow one kilometre track which leads to the site. The 70 pitches are on level terrace areas and all have electricity (4/6A). A quiet family site, there is no organised entertainment. Bar-de-Loup with its few shops and restaurants is only a 500 m. walk. Grasse (9 km.) is surrounded by fields of lavender, mimosa and jasmine and has been famous for the manufacture of perfume since the 16th century. The Musée International de la Perfume has a garden of fragrant plants and the cathedral in the old town has three paintings by Reubens. The very friendly and enthusiastic owners will site your caravan with their 4x4 free of charge if you find the steepness of the site a little daunting. They also speak a little English.

**Facilities:** Two tiled toilet blocks are kept very clean and include washbasins mostly in cubicles. Around half the WCs are British style. Dishwashing and laundry sinks have a single hot tap to draw from. Washing machine and iron. Reception has small shop with bread daily. Small bar/restaurant and takeaway (July/Aug). Swimming pool (no Bermuda style shorts), small slide and diving board, but no pool for small children. Boules pitches, table tennis, volleyball and skittles. TV room with tables and chairs for board games, plus a library useful in early and late season. Children's climbing frame. Charcoal barbecues are not allowed.

**Charges** guide

| | |
|---|---|
| Per tent incl. 2 persons | € 12.95 -  € 19.05 |
| large tent, caravan or motorcaravan | € 14.48 -  € 23.62 |
| extra person | € 3.81 |
| child (under 5 yrs) | € 3.04 |
| dog | € 1.52 |
| electricity (4/10A) | € 2.28 -  € 3.81 |

**Tel:** 04 93 42 45 06. Fax: 04 93 42 45 06. E-mail: les-gorges-du-loup@wanadoo.fr. **Reservations:** Advised in high season. **Open** 1 April - 1 October.

**Directions:** From Grasse take D2085 Nice road. Take D3 briefly and then at Châteauneuf Pré du Lac take D2210 to Pont-de-Loup and Vence. Site is signed on right. Pass village of Bar-sur-Loup on left and then, after a very tight right turn, take 1 km. long, very narrow access road (a few passing places).

---

## Camping Les Pinèdes

**0610** route du Pont de Pierre, 06480 La Colle-sur-Loup

Les Pinèdes is seven kilometres inland from the busy coast, located at the centre of all the attractions of the Côte d'Azur, yet far enough away to be peaceful retreat at the end of a busy day sightseeing. In a terraced situation on a wooded hillside where olives and vines used to grow the site, has been in the hands of the welcoming Dugauguez family for the past 30 years. All the level pitches have electricity (3-10A), most also with water and are separated by low bushes. Due to the nature of the terrain there are no facilities for wheelchair users. The owners are keen to attract wildlife to the site and there are many varieties of birds and the odd fox to be seen. For three weeks from the end of May into June, the evenings are alive with fireflies lighting up the site. The restaurant at the site entrance (also owned by the family) has an excellent reputation. The owner is very interested in all the local art galleries and will advise on where all the famous painters have paintings hung. There are many typical Provencal villages in close proximity not to mention the towns of Grasse, Menton, Monaco and Antibes, and all are well worth a visit - the family will be only too pleased to give advice. A 'Sites et Paysages' member.

**Facilities:** Two clean and well maintained toilet blocks have both British and Turkish style toilets and large shower cubicles. One block has been refurbished, the other is due to be soon. All the usual facilities for dishwashing and laundry etc and a baby room. Small shop. Bar, restaurant and takeaway. Swimming pool. Two small play areas. Field for volleyball, basketball and archery. Boule pitch. Entertainment is organised for young and old in July/Aug. Weekly walks in the surrounding hills from June to Sept. Charcoal barbecues are not permitted. **Off site:** Fishing in Loup river (50 m). Village 1 km with tennis court, leisure park with keep fit course and antiques quarter. Golf 6 km. Riding 2 km. Bicycle hire 7 km.

**Charges** 2003

| | |
|---|---|
| Per small tent incl. 2 persons | € 13.10 -  € 16.70 |
| large tent, caravan or motorcaravan | € 14.10 -  € 21.50 |
| extra person | € 3.55 -  € 4.50 |
| child (under 5 yrs) | € 1.80 -  € 2.80 |
| dog | € 1.45 -  € 1.95 |
| electricity (3-10A) | € 2.80 -  € 4.10 |
| local tax | € 0.19 |

**Tel:** 04 93 32 98 94. Fax: 04 93 32 50 20. E-mail: camplespinedes06@aol.com. **Reservations:** Necessary for July/Aug. and made with 25% deposit and fee ( € 18,29). **Open** 15 March - 5 October.

**Directions:** From A8 take D2 towards Vence. At Colle sur Loup roundabout take D6 signed Grasse, site on right in approx. 3 km.

## Mediterranean
# Camping-Caravaning Domaine de la Bergerie
route de la Sine, 06140 Vence

La Bergerie is a quiet, family owned site, situated in the hills about 3 km. from Vence and 10 km. from the sea at Cagnes-sur-Mer. This extensive, lightly wooded site has been left very natural and is in a secluded position about 300 m. above sea level. Because of the trees most of the pitches are shaded and all are of a good size. It is a large site but because it is so extensive it does not give that impression. There are 450 pitches, 300 with electricity (2/5A) and 65 also with water and drainage. An hourly bus service runs (excl. Sundays) from the site to Vence. There are no organised activities here and definitely no groups allowed.

**Facilities:** Both toilet blocks have been refurbished and include washbasins in cabins and excellent provision for disabled people (pitches near the block are reserved for disabled people). Shop, small bar/restaurant with takeaway (all 1/5-30/9). Large swimming pool, paddling pool and spacious sunbathing area (5/6-30/9). Playground. Bicycle hire. Table tennis, tennis courts and 10 shaded boules pitches (lit at night) with competitions in season. **Off site:** Riding 6 km, fishing 10 km, golf 12 km.

**Charges 2002**

| | |
|---|---|
| Per unit incl. 2 persons | € 12.60 - € 15.80 |
| with electricity (2A) | € 15.80 - € 19.20 |
| with water, drainage, electricity (5A) | € 20.40 - € 23.60 |
| extra person | € 4.10 |
| local tax (over 10 yrs) | € 0.15 |

**Tel:** 04 93 58 09 36. **Fax:** 04 93 59 80 44.
**Reservations:** Necessary only in July/Aug. for the special pitches and made with 25% deposit and € 12,96 fee. **Open** 25 March - 15 October.

**Directions:** From autoroute A8 exit 47 take Cagnes-sur-Mer road towards Vence. Site is west of Vence - follow 'toutes directions' signs around the town to join the D2210 Grasse road. Follow this to round about (2 km), turn left and follow site signs for 1 km. Site is on right in light woodland.

Provence Alpes Côte d'Azur
# DOMAINE LA BERGERIE
★★★
Route de la Sine, 06140 Vence
Tel: 0033 493 58 09 36
Fax: 0033 493 59 80 44
Two pools ~ Tennis ~ Chalets in 13h

## Mediterranean
# Le Grand Saule
24-26 bvd. Jean Moulin, 06110 Le Cannet

This little site is in a pleasant setting and, although only 200 m. from a busy through road, the intervening wooded area seems to give it sufficient screening to make the camp itself quite peaceful. It is only 1.5 km. from the beach at La Bocca and 4 km. from Cannes town centre, so its position is unusually handy for one of the show-places of the Riviera. A bus stop is close to the entrance gate. With its situation the site obviously deals with much transit trade and many backpackers. It therefore has 'young people' areas, formally designed for tents, and a 'family area' with individual pitches separated by hedges, with electricity, water points and drainage, all with good shade (a total of 55 units). Being so close to Cannes, the site is naturally not cheap, but it is easily accessible.

**Facilities:** The small toilet block, although kept busy, is usually well kept and clean. Washbasins with cold water (some in cabins) but with hot water in dish-washing and laundry sinks. Washing machine. Motorcaravan services. Small swimming pool of irregular shape beside an attractive terrace bar serving snacks (all from 1/5). Table tennis, children's frames and sauna. Only gas barbecues are permitted. **Off site:** Shops close. Tennis club adjoining. Fishing, bicycle hire, riding 1.5 km. Golf 2.5 km.

**Charges** guide

| | |
|---|---|
| Per unit incl. 2 persons | € 17.38 - € 23.48 |
| extra person | € 6.25 |
| child (2-5 yrs) | € 3.05 |
| electricity | € 3.05 |

**Tel:** 04 93 90 55 10. **Fax:** 04 93 47 24 55. **E-mail:** le.grand.saule@wanadoo.fr. **Reservations:** Advised and made from any day with deposit equivalent to 1 weeks stay. **Open** 1 May - 30 September.

**Directions:** From A8 autoroute Cannes-Ouest exit turn towards Cannes, passing airport, left into Ave. de Coubertin, then into Ave. Jourdan; cross under autoroute, then 300 m. to camp on right. Le Grand Saule signed from main junctions in La Bocca.

### Mediterranean
# Camping-Caravaning Panoramic

1,630 Ave de la République, 06550 La Roquette-sur-Siagne

You receive a friendly welcome at this campsite and, although virtually within sight of the popular resort of Cannes, it enjoys a quiet location facing mimosa covered hillsides. The grass pitches are two levels, the upper level having a steep approach. All have electricity and some have water. There are 60 pitches, about half for touring units, the remainder for mobile homes and chalets. There is plenty of shade and as the name of the site suggests, it offers a fine view. Panoramic opens all year round and makes an ideal spot for a low season break, but becomes more lively in July/Aug. when varying ages can enjoy a discotheque and dancing twice weekly. The sandy beaches of Cannes and Mandelieu can be reached within a few minutes.

**Facilities:** Two toilet blocks are of a reasonable standard, only one fully opened in low season,walls and floors tiled, but not ultra modern. Washbasins in cabins. Dishwashing facilities, laundry sinks and a washing machine. No dedicated chemical disposal (the toilets are used). Restaurant/takeaway (July/Aug). Bar (all season). Heated swimming pool, solarium and sunbathing patio, but no paddling pool. Play area on grass. TV. No shop. **Off site:** Municipal sports complex with tennis courts, etc. 100 m.

**Charges** 2002

| | |
|---|---|
| Per pitch | € 15.50 |
| person | € 3.50 |
| child under 5 yrs | € 2.50 |
| electricity (6A) | € 3.00 |

**Tel:** (0)4.92.19.07.77. Fax: (0)4.92.19.07.77. E-mail: campingpanoramic@wanadoo.fr. **Reservations:** Advised in high season; contact site. **Open** all year.

**Directions:** Leave A8 autoroute at exit 40 onto N7 and turn north onto D109 signed Pegomas. Continue on D109 for 5 km. and site is on right.

### Mediterranean
# Camping Municipal Les Pins

rue Michelet, 13990 Fontvieille

Peace and quiet amongst the pines is the order of the day at Camping Les Pins. The pitches are all slightly sloping and are separated by hedges. Of the 163 pitches, 57 have electricity (6A), water and waste water points. Reception is bright and cheerful with ample tourist information. Try not to arrive during the lunch break as it is forbidden to go on site when reception is closed. There is no shop but the very pretty, floral village of Fontvieille is 15 minutes away on a forest track. The supermarket is small but fills a need, as the village tennis courts are open to all, as is the local swimming pool. Arles, Les Baux and St Remy are all only a short drive away if the peace and quiet get too much for you.

**Facilities:** The fully equipped toilet blocks are modern but, because the tiles are dark brown, the first impression is not favourable. They are, in fact, clean and well maintained. Plenty of laundry and dishwashing sinks with hot water are inside. A separate room houses washing machines, dryers and an ironing board. Play area. **Off site:** Village with shop, swimming pool and tennis courts.

**Charges** 2002

| | | |
|---|---|---|
| Per 2 adults and 1 child under 12 yrs | | € 10.00 |
| extra person | € 1.50 - | € 3.00 |
| electricity (6A) | | € 2.30 |

**Tel:** 04 90 54 78 69. Fax: 04 90 54 81 25. **Reservations:** Made for min. 8 nights with € 15,24 fee. **Open** 1 April - 15 October.

**Directions:** Site signed on eastern edge of Fontvieille, on D17 Arles - Les Baux road (just at end of one way system).

### Mediterranean
# Camping Municipal Les Romarins

13520 Maussane

A well kept, neat municipal site, Les Romarins has been in the guide for several years and remains popular with readers. Tarmac access roads lead to 145 good sized grassy pitches separated by hedges and bushes, all with electrical connections (4A). The municipal swimming pool (with discounts) is near and shops and restaurants are in the pleasant little town. Les Baux and St Remy-de-Provence are tourist attractions not to be missed, especially St Remy's Roman ruins. Les Romarins is popular and becomes very busy from 1 July - late August.

**Facilities:** Three good toilet blocks, especially the newly refurbished one which provides British style toilets, adjustable, roomy showers and washbasins in cubicles. Baby room, washing machine, laundry and dishwashing sinks and facilities for disabled visitors. The older style blocks have some Turkish style WCs but are kept clean and well maintained. Play area. Free tennis courts. **Off site:** Bicycle hire or golf 1 km, fishing or riding 3 km.

**Charges** 2002

| | | |
|---|---|---|
| Per unit incl. 1 or 2 adults + 1 child | | € 13.20 |
| extra person | € 1.70 - | € 3.00 |
| electricity | € 2.40 - | € 3.00 |

**Tel:** 04 90 54 33 60. Fax: 04 90 54 41 22. **Reservations:** Made for any length with fee. **Open** 15 March - 15 October.

**Directions:** Site is within the little town of Maussane on the eastern edge.

## Mediterranean
# Camping Municipal du Mas de Nicolas

avenue Plaisance du Touch, 13210 St-Rémy-de-Provence

**1305M**

St Rémy de Provence is a very popular town and this reflects on Mas de Nicolas, as this too is very popular and always reasonably busy. The site has a very spacious feel to it, due mainly to the central area of gently sloping grass, dotted with shrubs, that is kept clear of pitches and used for leisure and sunbathing. The 140 pitches are separated by hedges, 120 with 6A electricity, water and drainage, and access roads are wide. Some pitches are an irregular shape and some are sloping, but many have views and they are mostly organised into groups of two and four.

**Facilities:** Two toilet blocks have been refurbished to give excellent facilities including washbasins in cabins and a baby bathroom. The other blocks are of an older design with mainly Turkish style WCs. Dishwashing and laundry sinks, washing machines and drying lines. Swimming pool (15/5-15/9). **Off site:** Adjacent municipal gym, tennis and volleyball. Fishing 2 km, bicycle hire or riding 1 km, golf 15 km.

**Charges 2002**

| | |
|---|---|
| Per unit incl. 2 persons | € 12.96 - € 14.18 |
| extra adult | € 4.27 |
| child (under 10 yrs) | € 1.98 |
| electricity (6A) | € 2.90 |

**Tel:** 04 90 92 27 05. **Fax:** 04 90 92 36 83. **E-mail:** camping-mas-de-nicolas@wanadoo.fr.
**Reservations:** Necessary for main season and made with € 16,77 fee. **Open** 15 March - 15 October.

**Directions:** St Rémy is located where the D571 from Avignon and the D99 Tarascon - Cavaillon road join. Site signed from village centre on north side. Leave A7 at Cavaillon or Avignon-Sud.

## Mediterranean
# Sunêlia Douce Quiétude

3435 Bvd. Jaques Baudino, 83700 Saint Raphaël

**8325**

Douce Quiétude is only five kilometres from the beaches at Saint Raphaël and Agay but is quietly situated at the foot of the Estérel massif. There are 400 pitches (around half given over to mobile homes) set in pleasant pine woodland or shaded green areas. The pitches are of a comfortable size, separated by bushes and trees with electricity (6A), water, drainage and telephone/TV points provided. This mature site offers a wide range of services and facilities complete with a pool complex. It can be busy in the main season yet is relaxed and spacious.

**Facilities:** Fully equipped modern toilet blocks have changing facilities for babies and provision for disabled visitors. Launderette. Bar, restaurant, take-away and pizzeria (1/6 -3/9). Shop. Three outdoor swimming pools (two heated), water slide and jacuzzi. Play area. Children's club and activities for teenagers (July/Aug). Sports area for volleyball, basketball and petanque. Games room (July/Aug). Tennis. Table tennis and billards. Minigolf. Archery. Fitness centre and sauna (July/Aug). Evening entertainment. Mountain bike hire. **Off site:** Golf 2 km. Windsurf hire and sea fishing 4.5 km.

**Charges 2002**

| | |
|---|---|
| Per unit incl. 1-3 persons | € 30.00 - € 40.00 |
| extra person (over 9 yrs) | € 5.00 - € 7.00 |
| child (5-9 yrs) | € 3.00 - € 5.00 |
| animal | € 2.00 |

**Tel:** 04 94 44 30 00. **Fax:** 04 94 44 30 30. **E-mail:** info@douce-quietude.com. **Reservations:** Contact site. **Open** 23 March - 28 September.

**Directions:** Take exit 38 from A8 autoroute signed Fréjus/St-Raphaël. Follow directions for St Raphaël then site signs.

## Mediterranean
# Holiday Green Village Club Camping-Caravaning

Route de Bagnols-en-Forêt, 83600 Fréjus

**8360**

Holiday Green is seven kilometres inland from the busy resort of Fréjus. It is a large, modern campsite with a fantastic view of the red Estérel massif. The site has been developed on a hillside and by reception at the top of hill is a large Californian style heated swimming pool and a wide range of other facilities. This is where everything happens and it is said there are activities and entertainment from morning until closing. The rest of the site is terraced into the hillside and almost completely hidden in the 15 hectares of pine woods which absorbs about 500 large touring pitches and some 200 mobile homes. Sloping in parts, there is plenty of shade and electricity connections (3A) available.

**Facilities:** Modern toilet facilities include good hot showers. Laundry. Shopping centre. Bar, restaurant and fast food. Sound proof disco. Swimming pool. Three tennis courts. Archery. Petanque. All facilities are open all season. Excursions organised on foot, on horse-back and on mountain bikes. Entertainment programme. Playground. Children's club (July/Aug). **Off site:** Beach 7 km. Golf and riding 8 km. Free daily bus to the beach and free access to Aquatica, the biggest aqua park in the region.

**Charges 2002**

| | |
|---|---|
| Per pitch | € 34.00 |
| extra person | € 8.00 |
| child (0-5 yrs) | € 5.00 |

**Tel:** 04 94 19 88 30. **Fax:** 04 94 19 88 31. **E-mail:** info @holiday-green.com. **Reservations:** Advanced booking necessary for high season. **Open** 30 March - 30 September.

**Directions:** From A8 autoroute exit 38 follow signs for Bagnols-en-Forêt and pick up site signs.

# Camping-Caravaning de la Baume

route de Bagnols, 83618 Fréjus

8306

La Baume is large, busy site that has been well developed with much money spent on it. It lies about 5.5 km. from the long sandy beach of Fréjus-Plage, but it has such a fine and varied selection of five swimming pools on site that many people do not bother to make the trip. The pools with their palm trees are a feature of this site and were remarkable for their size and variety (water slides, etc.) even before the addition of the latest, very large 'feature' pool which is now one of the highlights. The site has nearly 500 pitches of varying but quite adequate size with electricity, water and drainaway, with another 200 larger ones with plumbing to mains sewerage to take mobile homes. Separators are being installed to divide the plots and shade is available over most of the terrain. Although tents are accepted, the site concentrates mainly on caravanning. It is likely to become full in season, but one section with unmarked pitches is not reserved, and there is plenty of space off-peak. La Baume's convenient location has its 'downside' as there is some traffic noise from the nearby autoroute - somewhat obtrusive at first but we soon failed to notice it. A popular site with tour operators. Adjoining La Baume is its sister site La Palmeraie, which contains self-catering accommodation and its own landscaped pool, providing some entertainment to supplement that at La Baume.

**Facilities:** The seven toilet blocks should be a satisfactory supply. Two have been enlarged recently, the others refurbished to provide mainly British style toilets with a few Turkish; washbasins in cabins and sinks for clothes and dishes with hot water. Supermarket and several other shops. Bar with external terrace overlooking pools and TV. Restaurant and takeaway. Five swimming pools. Fitness centre. Tennis courts. Archery (July/Aug). Organised events - sports, competitions, etc. in daytime and some evening entertainment partly in English. Amphitheatre for shows. Discos daily in season. **Off site:** A bus to Fréjus passes the gate.

**Charges** 2002

| Per unit incl. 2 persons, 6A electricity, water and drainage | € 17.53 - € 31.25 |
|---|---|
| extra person | € 3.81 - € 6.86 |
| child (under 7 yrs) | free - € 4.27 |

**Tel:** 04 94 15 88 88. Fax: 04 96 19 83 50. E-mail: reception@labaume-lapalmerie.com. **Reservations:** Essential for high season, and made for exact dates with substantial deposit and fee (€ 31,25), from 1 Jan. **Open** 22 March - 30 September, with full services.

**Directions:** Site is 3 km. up the D4 road, which leads north from N7 just west of Fréjus. From west on autoroute A8 take exit 37 for Fréjus/St Raphaël, turn towards them and after 4 km, turn left on D4. From east take exit 38 for Fréjus/St Raphaël; after exit turn right immediately on small road marked `Musée' etc. leading to D4 where right again.

**Note:** In peak season considerable traffic delays may be experienced at the D4/N7 junction if you wish to travel to Fréjus-Plage or to the nearest towns of Fréjus or St Raphaël. To avoid these it is possible to turn off the D4 on a minor road (signed 'Zoo' and 'Daniel Templon') leading past the easterly Fréjus/St Raphaël motorway entrance, which can get you reasonably quickly to the motorway or the eastern part of St Raphaël and areas east of that, but there can still be unwelcome delays in reaching Fréjus-Plage.

## Mediterranean
# Camping-Caravaning Esterel
**8302** avenue des Golf, 83700 Saint-Raphael

For caravans only, Esterel is a quality site east of St Raphaël, set among the hills at the back of Agay. It is an attractive quiet situation with good views around. The site is 3.5 km. from the sandy beach at Agay where parking is perhaps a little easier than at most places on this coast. In addition to a section for permanent caravans, it has some 250 pitches for tourists, on which caravans of any type are taken but not tents. Pitches are on shallow terraces, attractively landscaped with good shade and a variety of flowering plants, giving a feeling of spaciousness. Each pitch has an electricity connection and tap, and 18 special ones have their own individual en-suite washroom adjoining. A pleasant courtyard area contains the shop and bar, with a terrace overlooking the attractively landscaped (floodlit at night) pool complex. Wild boar come to the perimeter fence each evening to be fed by visitors. This is a good site, well run and organised in a deservedly popular area. A member of 'Les Castels' group.

**Facilities:** Two refurbished and well maintained toilet blocks, plus one smaller one adjacent to the tourist section, are very satisfactory. They can be heated and include washbasins mostly in cabins. Individual toilet units on 18 pitches. Facilities for disabled people. Laundry room. Motorcaravan service point. Shop. Takeaway. Bar/restaurant. Five heated, circular swimming pools, one large for adults, one smaller for children and three arranged as a waterfall (1/4-30/9). New disco. Archery, volleyball, minigolf, two tennis courts, pony rides, petanque and squash court. Playground. Bicycle hire. Events and entertainment are organised in season. Barbecues of any type are forbidden. **Off site:** Good golf courses very close. Trekking by foot, bicycle or by pony in the surrounding natural environment of L'Esterel forest park.

**Charges** 2002

| | |
|---|---|
| Per pitch incl. 2 persons | € 25.92 - € 29.73 |
| de-luxe pitch | € 32.78 - € 36.59 |
| extra person | € 6.86 |
| child (1-7 yrs) | € 4.57 |
| animal | € 1.52 |
| local tax | € 0.30 |

**Tel:** 04 94 82 03 28. **Fax:** 04 94 82 87 37. **E-mail:** contact@esterel-caravaning.fr. **Reservations:** Necessary for high season and made for min. 1 week with deposit (€ 80) and fee (€ 15,24). CD brochure available from site. **Open** 1 April - 30 September.

**Directions:** You can approach from St Raphaël via Valescure but easiest way is to turn off the coast road at Agay where there are good signs. From Fréjus exit from autoroute A8, follow signs for Valescure throughout, then for Agay, and site is on left. (Reader's comment: If in doubt, follow golf complex signs, or Leclerc). The road from Agay is the easiest to follow.

---

## Mediterranean
# Camping-Caravaning Domaine du Colombier
**8323** Route de Bagnols en Forêt, 83600 Fréjus

Domaine du Colombier is a busy site alongside a main road, so a few of the pitches will have some road noise. The majority however are down a hillside and pine trees help to deaden the noise. The pitches (326 for touring units out of 470) vary in size from smallish ones to quite large ones, of which 40 are fully serviced. The hillside is terraced, with all pitches level, with electricity and most with shade. The pool area with palm trees, a tiled surround and free sunbeds is in a sunny location. There are also three slides and water polo nets for competitions. A disco is underground to deaden the noise. Like the cabarets and competitions all these facilities operate in high season. This is a family site and no groups are accepted. The only downside is that the swimming pool is at the bottom of the site, giving a long pull back up to the majority of pitches.

**Facilities:** Well maintained and positioned toilet blocks are fully equipped, including baby rooms. Three blocks have en-suite units for people in wheelchairs. Two can be heated on cooler days. Well equipped laundry. Well stocked shop. Bar/restaurant with takeaway open at sometime during the day in low season and more often in busy periods. Snack bar (from 1/6). Disco. Large heated swimming pool (30 x 20 m) and paddling pool (all season). Communal barbecue areas for July/Aug. Internet terminal. Two play areas of excellent quality on rubber safety bases. Games room, mini-club room. Half court tennis, volleyball, basketball and boule. Tourist office with bookings to major attractions possible. Only gas or electric barbecues are permitted. **Off site:** Bus passes the gate.

**Charges** 2002

| | |
|---|---|
| Per unit incl. 2 or 3 persons and electricity (10A) | € 22.00 - € 37.00 |
| small tent pitch, 1 or 2 persons | € 13.50 - € 25.00 |
| extra person | € 4.80 - € 6.30 |
| child under 10 yrs | € 2.00 - € 4.70 |
| animal | € 2.00 - € 2.50 |

**Tel:** (0)4 94 51 56 01. **Fax:** (0)4 94 51 55 57. **Reservations:** Made with 25% deposit plus booking fee (€ 25). **Open** Easter - 30 September.

**Directions:** From A8 autoroute take 38 and follow D4 for Frejus. Site is on left, well signed

A SAMPLE OF YOUR HOLIDAY...

ON THE COTE D'AZUR – BETWEEN CANNES AND SAINT-TROPEZ
5 MN AWAY FROM THE SEA

Luxury mobile homes for rental and vast pitches for caravans !

The Club formula !

The children's paradise

NON STOP Animation !

*Esterel* Caravaning ★★★★

Avenue des Golfs - 83530 Agay - FRANCE
Tel : +33 4.94.82.03.28 - Fax : +33 4.94.82.87.37
www.esterel-caravaning.fr - contact@esterel-caravaning.fr

Open from 01.04 to 04.10.2003

# Camping-Caravaning Les Pins Parasol

**8301** route de Bagnols, 83600 Fréjus

Not everyone likes very big sites, and Les Pins Parasols with its 189 pitches is of a size which is quite easy to walk around. It is family owned and run. Although on very slightly undulating ground, virtually all the pitches are levelled or terraced and separated by hedges or bushes with pine trees for shade. They are around 100 sq.m. and all have electricity. What is particularly interesting, as it is the most unusual feature, is that 48 of the pitches are equipped with their own fully enclosed, tiled sanitary unit, consisting of British WC, washbasin, hot shower and washing up sink, all quite close together. These pitches naturally cost more but may well be of interest to those seeking extra comfort. The nearest beach is the once very long Fréjus-Plage (5.5 km) now reduced a little by the new marina, and adjoins St. Raphaël. (See note on La Baume entry concerning traffic delays at the D4/N7 road junction.) Used by tour operators (10%).

**Facilities:** Besides the individual units there are three toilet blocks of good average quality providing washbasins in cabins and facilities for disabled people. One block can be heated when necessary. Small shop with reasonable stocks and restaurant with takeaway (both 1/5-20/9). General room with TV. Swimming pool (200 sq.m) with attractive rock backdrop and separate long slide with landing pool and small children's pool. Half-court tennis. **Off site:** Bicycle hire or riding 2 km, fishing 6 km, golf 10 km. Bus from the gate into Fréjus 5km.

**Charges** 2002

| Per normal pitch with electricity | |
|---|---|
| incl. 2 persons | € 17.30 - € 22.00 |
| with sanitary unit incl. 2 persons | € 21.50 - € 27.00 |
| extra person | € 4.40 - € 5.50 |
| child (under 7 yrs) | € 2.90 - € 3.50 |
| dog | € 1.70 - € 2.00 |
| local tax | € 0.15 - € 0.30 |

**Tel:** 04 94 40 88 43. Fax: 04 94 40 81 99. E-mail: lespinsparasol@wanadoo.fr. **Reservations:** Necessary for July/Aug. only and made for min. 10 days for exact dates with deposit (€ 92) but no fee. **Open** Easter - 30 September.

**Directions:** From autoroute A8 take exit 38 for Fréjus Est. Turn right immediately on leaving pay booths on a small road which leads across to D4, where right again and under 1 km. to site.

**LES PINS PARASOLS** CAMPING CARAVANNING ★★★★NN
ROUTE DE BAGNOLS - F-83600 FRÉJUS
Telephone 0033 494.40.88.43
SWIMMING POOL
Supermarket - Snackbar - Individual washing cabins and hot water in all sanitary facilities - Separated pitches (80-100m2) all with electricity. Pitches with individual sanitary facilities (shower, washbasin, sink with hot water, WC) - Children's playground and solarium - Caravan pitches - Water points - Mini-tennis
SUN AND SHADE near the beaches
Fax : 0033 494.40.81.99
Email : lespinsparasols@wanadoo.fr
Internet : www.lespinsparasols.com

# Camping-Caravaning Leï Suves

**8303** Quartier du Blavet, 83520 Roquebrune-sur-Argens

This quiet, pretty site is a few kilometres inland from the coast, 2 km. north of the N7. Close to the unusual Roquebrune rock, it is within easy reach of resorts such as St Tropez, Ste Maxime, St Raphaël and Cannes. The site entrance is appealing - wide and spacious, with a large bank of well tended flowers. Mainly on a gently sloping hillside, the pitches are terraced with shade provided by the many cork trees which give the site its name. The 310 pitches are of a decent size, all with electricity and access to water.

**Facilities:** Two modern, well kept sanitary blocks include washbasins in cabins. Facilities for disabled visitors. Laundry room with washing machines. Shop. Bar and terrace, snack bar and takeaway (all 15/5-30/9). Outdoor stage for entertainment. Good sized pool. Table tennis, tennis, play area and sports area. Internet point. Only gas barbecues permitted. **Off site:** Fishing 3 km, bicycle hire 5 km, riding 1 km, golf 7 km. Beach at St Aygulf 15 km.

**Charges** 2002

| Per unit incl. 2 persons | € 18.00 - € 21.50 |
|---|---|
| 3 persons | € 18.50 - € 22.00 |
| extra adult | € 4.00 - € 5.00 |
| child (under 7 yrs) | € 2.50 - € 3.00 |
| electricity | € 2.75 |

**Tel:** 04 94 45 43 95. Fax: 04 94 81 63 13. E-mail: camping.lei.suves@wanadoo.fr. **Reservations:** Contact site. **Open** 1 April - 15 October.

**Directions:** Leave autoroute at Le Muy and take N7 towards St Raphaël. Turn left at roundabout onto D7 heading north signed La Boverie (site also signed). Site on right in 2 km.

# Camping Domaine de la Bergerie

**8317** Vallée du Fournel, 83520 Roquebrune sur Argens

This is yet another site near the Côte d'Azur which will take you away from all the bustle of the Mediterranean to total relaxation amongst the cork, oak, pine and mimosa. The 60 hectare site is quite spread out. The terrain varies from natural, rocky semi-landscaped areas for mobile homes to flat, grassy terrain with avenues of 200 separated pitches for touring caravans and tents. All pitches average over 80 sq.m. and have electrical connections, with those in one area also having water and drainage. The restaurant/bar, a converted farm building, is surrounded by shady patios, whilst inside it oozes character with high beams and archways leading to intimate corners. Tournaments and programmes are organised daily and, in the evening, shows, cabarets, discos, cinema, karaoke and dancing at the amphitheatre prove popular until very late - it can be noisy.

**Facilities:** Four sanitary blocks are kept clean and include washbasins in cubicles, facilities for disabled people and babies, plus dishwashing and laundry areas with washing machines. Well stocked supermarket. Bar/restaurant. Takeaway. New pool complex (1/4-30/9) with indoor pool to be added for 2003. Fitness centre (body building, sauna, gym, etc). Five tennis courts and two half courts. Archery, roller skating and minigolf. Volleyball and mini football. Mini-farm for children. Fishing. Only gas barbecues are permitted. **Off site:** Riding or golf 4 km, bicycle hire 7 km. Water skiing and rock climbing nearby. St Aygulf or Ste Maxime are 7 km.

**Charges** 2002

| | |
|---|---|
| Per unit incl. 2 adults, electricity | € 16.00 - € 25.00 |
| 3 persons and electricity | € 20.00 - € 33.00 |
| extra adult | € 4.00 - € 6.50 |
| child (under 7 yrs) | € 3.00 - € 5.00 |
| electricity (10A) | € 1.80 - € 2.50 |
| dog | free - € 2.50 |
| local tax (over 10 yrs) | € 0.30 |

**Tel:** 04 98 11 45 45. Fax: 04 98 11 45 46. E-mail: info@domainelabergerie.com. **Reservations:** Made with deposit (€ 200) and fee (€ 20). (Mobile homes available 15 February - 15 November). **Open** 1 June - 15 September.

**Directions:** Leave A8 at Le Muy exit on N7 towards Fréjus. Proceed for 9 km., then right onto D7 signed St Aygulf. Continue for 8 km. and then right at roundabout onto D8; site is on the right.

## Mediterranean
# Caravaning L'Etoile d'Argens
83370 St. Aygulf

the **travel service**
TO BOOK
| Ferry | ✓ |
| Pitch | ✓ |
| Accommodation | ✗ |

01892 55 98 98

First impressions of L'Etoile d'Argens are of space, cleanliness and calm. Reception staff are very friendly and English is spoken (open 24 hrs). This is a site run with families in mind and many of the activities are free, making for a good value holiday. There are 493 level grass pitches laid out in typical French style, separated by hedges. There are five sizes of pitch, ranging from 50 sq.m. (for small tents) to 100, 130, 180 or 250 sq.m. These are exceptionally large and two families could easily fit two caravans and cars or one family could have a very spacious plot with a garden like atmosphere. All pitches are fully serviced with fresh and waste water and 10A electricity, with some shade although the site is not overpowered by trees which leads to a spacious feeling. The pool and bar area is attractively land-scaped with old olive and palm trees on beautifully manicured and watered grass. The river runs along one side of the site and a free boat service (15/6-15/9) runs every 40 minutes to the beach. It is also possible to moor a boat or fish. This is a good family site for the summer but also good in low season for a quiet stay in a superb location with excellent pitches. Tour operators take 85 pitches and there are 130 mobile homes but for a large site it is usually calm and peaceful even in July.

**Facilities:** Two new toilet blocks were added in 2000, whilst some of the original small unisex blocks have been retiled making a big improvement. All are well kept and include some washbasins in cubicles. Dishwashing sinks and laundry with outside clothes line. Supermarket and gas supplies. Bar, restaurant, pizzeria, takeaway. Two adult pools, children's paddling pool and solarium. Tennis (two of the four courts are floodlit) with coaching and minigolf (both free in low season), aerobics, archery (July/Aug), football and swimming lessons. Volleyball, basket-ball, table tennis and boule. Play area with rubber safety base. Children's entertainer in July/Aug. Activity programme includes games, dances for adults and escorted walking trips to the surrounding hills. within 3 km. **Off site:** Golf, riding or bicycle hire

**Charges 2002**

| Per tent pitch (100 sq.m.) | |
|---|---|
| with electricity and 2 persons | € 20.00 - € 35.00 |
| 'comfort' pitch (100 sq.m), 3 persons | |
| with water and drainage | € 26.00 - € 40.00 |
| 'luxury' pitch, 4 persons 180 sq.m | € 37.00 - € 55.00 |
| extra person | € 5.50 - € 7.00 |
| child (under 7) | € 3.50 - € 5.00 |
| dog | € 3.00 - € 3.50 |

**Tel:** 04 94 81 01 41. Fax: 04 94 81 21 45. E-mail: letoiledargens@wanadoo.fr. **Reservations:** Made for any period with substantial deposit and fee. **Open** Easter - 30 September, with all services.

**Directions:** Leave A8 at exit 36 and take N7 to Le Muy and Fréjus. After about 8 km. at roundabout take D7 signed Roquebrune and St Aygulf. In 9.5 km. (after roundabout) turn left signed Fréjus. Watch for site sign and ignore width and height limit signs as site is 500 m. to right.

## Mediterranean
# Camping-Caravaning Moulin des Iscles
83520 Roquebrune-sur-Argens

A haven of peace and tranquillity, Moulin des Iscles is hidden down 0.5 km. of private, unmade road - an unusual find in this often quite hectic part of Provence. Based around a former mill, it is a small, pretty site beside the river Argens with access to the river in places for fishing, canoeing and swimming, with a concrete bank and fenced where deemed necessary (some sought after pitches overlook the river). The 90 grassy, level pitches with electricity (6A) and water to all, radiate out from M. Dumarcet's attractive, centrally situated home which is where the restaurant and shop are situated. A nice mixture of deciduous trees provide natural shade and colour and the old mill house rests comfortably near the entrance which has a security barrier closed at night. This is a quiet site with little on site entertainment, but with a nice little restaurant. An effort has been made to welcome handicapped visitors. It is a real campsite not a 'camp-ing village'.

**Facilities:** The toilet block is fully equipped, includ-ing ramped access for disabled visitors. Some Turkish style toilets. Washbasins have cold water, some in cubicles. Baby bath and changing facilities en-suite. Covered laundry and dishwashing sinks. Small separate unisex provision for pitches near the entrance. Washing machine. Restaurant with home cooked dish-of-the-day on a weekly rotation. Surprisingly well stocked shop. Library - some English books. TV room incl. satellite, Pool table, table tennis. Play area, minigolf and boules all outside the barrier for more peace and quiet on site. Internet terminal.

**Charges 2002**

| Per unit incl. 2 or 3 persons | € 17.60 |
|---|---|
| extra adult | € 3.20 |
| child (over 10 yrs) | € 2.20 |
| local tax | € 0.30 |
| electricity | € 2.70 |

**Tel:** 04 94 45 70 74. Fax: 04 94 45 46 09. E-mail: moulin.iscles@wanadoo.fr. **Reservations:** Contact site. **Open** 1 April - 30 September.

**Directions:** Follow as for site no. 8320, Les Pecheurs, but continue past it through the village of Roquebrune towards St Aygulf for 1 km. Site signed on left. Follow private unmade road for approx. 500 m. to site entrance in front of you.

# L'Étoile d'Argens

★★★★

TENNIS EN

GOLF FREE

LOW-SEASON

TEL : +33 4 94 81 01 41     FAX :+33 4 94 81 21 45
83370 ST AYGULF
www.provence-campings.com/frejus/etoile-argens
E-mail : letoiledargens@wanadoo.fr

## Camping-Caravaning Les Pêcheurs
83520 Roquebrune sur Argens

**8320**

Developed over three generations by the Simoncini family, this peaceful, friendly site is set in more than four ha. of mature, well shaded countryside at the foot of the Roquebrune Rock. It will appeal to families who appreciate natural surroundings together with many activities, cultural and sporting. Interspersed with a number of mobile homes, the 103 touring pitches are all of a good size with electricity (6/10A) and separated by trees or flowering bushes. The Provencal style buildings are delightful, especially the bar, restaurant and games room, with its terrace down to the river and the site's own canoe station (locked gate). Adjacent to the site and beside the lake (path under road bridge) is another restaurant, also open to the public. This is near a sandy beach, minigolf and half-court tennis. Other than the beach area (no lifeguard), the lake is used exclusively for water skiing. Activities include climbing the 'Rock' with a guide. We became intrigued with stories about the Rock, as unfolded by Sabine Simoncini. The Holy Hole, the Three Crosses and the Hermit all call for further exploration which Sabine is happy to arrange, likewise trips to Monte Carlo, Ventiniglia (Italy) and the Gorges du Verdon. Used by tour operators (75 pitches).

**Facilities:** Modern, well designed toilet facilities are in three blocks, one new and attractively designed in the local style, the other two refurbished. Overall, it is a good provision, open as required, with washbasins in cabins (warm water only), baby baths and facilities for disabled visitors. Dishwashing and laundry sinks (H&C) and washing machines. Sheltered swimming pool (25 x 10 m) with separate paddling pool (child-proof gates and lifeguard in high season) with ice cream bar. Shop. Bar, restaurant and games room. Children's play area. Fishing. Canoeing (free) and water skiing. Animation arranged in main season for children and adults, visits to local wine caves and sessions at rafting and diving schools. Charcoal barbecues are not permitted. Only one dog per pitch is accepted. **Off site:** Riding 6 km. Golf 6 km (reduced fees). Bicycle hire 1 km. The medieval village of Roquebrune is within walking distance.

**Charges** 2002

| | |
|---|---|
| Per unit incl. 2 persons | € 15.00 - € 27.00 |
| incl. 3 persons | € 17.50 - € 28.50 |
| extra person | € 3.40 - € 5.50 |
| child (under 7 yrs) | € 2.50 - € 4.20 |
| dog (max 1) | € 2.00 |
| electricity (6/10A) | € 4.00 - € 5.00 |
| local tax | € 0.30 |

**Tel:** 04 94 45 71 25. Fax: 04 94 81 65 13. E-mail: pecheurs@worldonline.fr. **Reservations:** Made for touring pitches with deposit and fee. **Open** 23 March - 29 September.

**Directions:** From A8 autoroute take Le Muy exit and follow N7 towards Frèjus for approx. 13 km. bypassing Le Muy. After crossing over the A8, turn right at roundabout towards Roquebrune sur Argens. Site is on left after 2 km. just before bridge over river (watch carefully for fairly narrow entrance).

## Mediterranean
# Parc Camping Les Cigales

**8316** 721, chemin du Jas de la Paro, 83490 Le Muy

In a natural, shady setting of 13.5 ha. this site is well tucked in 1 km. from the busy N7, although it is a little close to the very busy A8 which is noisy if the wind is in the wrong direction. The site itself offers the opportunity for a relaxing stay and it also makes an excellent base for exploring the coast or the hinterland and the Gorges du Verdon. On entering the site (electronic gate operated by card), reception is on the left. Sand based, gravel roads lead off a tarmac circuit to the 198 numbered pitches which vary in size, with some terracing. The terrain is typical of the area with rough, sloped and stony, dry ground, but pitches are mostly level. They benefit from the shade given by the abundance of trees which include cork, oak and umbrella pines, plus the sweet smelling mimosa and many shrubs that fill the air reminding us that this is Provence. A `Sites et Paysages` member.

**Facilities:** Six modern sanitary blocks of varying size include washbasins in cabins and facilities for disabled people. Dishwashing sinks outside but under cover. Laundry area with washing machines. Shop (1/5-30/8). Restaurant/bar with patio. New heated pool complex. Adventure play area. Multi-sport area (basketball, volleyball, etc). Trampoline. Riding. Canoeing and hang-gliding are organised. Entertainment organised each evening in season, with a disco twice weekly and daytime activities for children and senior citizens. Internet point. Charcoal barbecues not permitted. **Off site:** Le Muy 2 km. Fishing 2 km, riding 7 km, golf 10 km. The N7 is on a bus route or take a train at Les Arcs (8 km).

**Charges 2003**

| Per unit incl. 2 persons | € 11.00 - € 21.00 |
|---|---|
| extra person | € 3.00 - € 5.00 |
| child (under 7 yrs) | free - € 3.00 |
| electricity (6A) | € 3.00 |

**Tel:** 04 94 45 12 08. Fax: 04 94 45 92 80. E-mail: contact@les-cigales.com. **Reservations:** Advised for July/Aug. **Open** 28 March - 1 November.

**Directions:** Site is signed off approach to autoroute péage on A8 at Le Muy exit and is 2 km. west of Le Muy on N7. It is necessary to cross the dual-carriageway as you approach the toll booth from Le Muy, site is then 1 km. down small road running parallel to the autoroute.

## Mediterranean
# Au Paradis des Campeurs

**8308** La Gaillarde-Plage, 83380 Les Issambres

Having direct access to a sandy beach (via an underpass) and being so well maintained are just two of the reasons that Au Paradis is popular. Family owned and run, it now has 180 pitches, all with 6A electricity and 132 with water tap and drainaway. The original pitches vary in size and shape but all are satisfactory and most have some shade. The new pitches are all large but at present have little shade although trees and bushes have been planted and shade is developing. There is no entertainment which gives peaceful nights. The gates are surveyed by TV (especially the beach gate) and a security man patrols all day. The site has become popular and it is essential to book for June to August.

**Facilities:** Two toilet blocks, refurbished to an excellent standard with high quality fittings and well maintained, include most washbasins in cabins. Facilities for babies. Dishwashing, laundry sinks, two washing machines and dryer. Motorcaravan service point. Shop and restaurant (with takeaway) front onto main road and open all season. TV room. Two excellent play areas, catering for the under and over 5s. **Off site:** Bicycle hire 2.5 km, riding 3 km, golf 6 km.

**Charges** guide

| Per unit incl. up to 3 persons | € 12.35 - € 19.21 |
|---|---|
| extra person | € 4.88 |
| child (under 4 yrs) | € 2.74 |
| electricity (6A) | € 3.35 |

**Tel:** 04 94 96 93 55. Fax: 04 94 49 62 99. **Reservations:** Advised for main season. **Open** 20 March - 15 October.

**Directions:** Site is signed from N98 coast road at La Gaillarde, 2 km. south of St Aygulf.

## Mediterranean
# Camping de la Plage

**8310** route National 98, 83310 Grimaud

A site actually on the beach is always in great demand, and Camping de la Plage is no exception and consequently it becomes very crowded. The site is divided into two parts by the N98 although a dangerous crossing is avoided by an underpass. All pitches are numbered and can be reserved - the pitches away from the beach will be the more peaceful. They are mostly of a decent size, with the ones over the road having more grass and more shade. All pitches have electricity (2, 4, 6 or 10A) but long leads may be required. Ste Maxime is 6 km. and it is not very far to all the familiar names of the south of France - St Tropez, Port Grimaud and Fréjus.

**Facilities:** There are three toilet blocks on each side of the site. Of varying quality, but clean when we visited and, according to regulars, cleaned regularly they are fully equipped, the majority of WCs of the British type. Baby bath. Large, well stocked supermarket (all season). Bar, restaurant and takeaway (from May). Beach volleyball. Tennis. Small play area. **Off site:** Bicycle hire 2 km, golf and riding 3 km.

**Charges** guide

| | |
|---|---|
| Per unit with 2 persons | € 17.53 |
| extra person | € 4.57 |
| child (under 7 yrs) | € 2.29 |
| electricity (2-10A) | € 2.67 - € 5.95 |

**Tel:** 04 94 56 31 15. Fax: 04 94 56 49 61.
**Reservations:** Bookings taken for exact dates with booking fee from Oct.- March only. **Open** two weeks before Easter - 21 October.

**Directions:** Site is on N98 main coast road about 6 km. southwest of Ste Maxime. Take care - this road is very busy in main season.

## Mediterranean
# Camping Le Beau Vezé

**8313** route de la Moutonne, 83320 Carqueiranne

Le Beau Vezé is a quiet site, some way inland from the busy resort of Hyères. The owners try to keep it as a family site and it is a quiet position, although the superb beaches and hectic coastal areas are within easy reach. On a steep hillside it has terraced pitches and a plateau with more pitches on the top. The 150 pitches are well shaded but unfortunately some will be rather difficult to manoeuvre onto due to over-hanging trees. There is some road noise on the lower pitches. The lovely old town of Hyères is only 8 km.

**Facilities:** The three sanitary blocks are of a reasonable standard, two quite modern with heating. All have showers and some cubicles have a washbasin also, making them more roomy. Both British and Turkish style WCs. Baby room. Laundry and dishwashing sinks. Two washing machines. Bar/restaurant and takeaway. Bread to order. Medium sized pool and paddling pool. Refurbished play area. Bicycle hire. Minigolf, table tennis, volleyball, boule and tennis court. **Off site:** Riding and golf 2 km.

**Charges** 2002

| | |
|---|---|
| Per pitch | € 7.62 |
| extra person | € 6.10 |
| child (under 10 yrs) | € 4.27 |
| electricity (6A) | € 3.81 |

**Tel:** 04 94 57 65 30. Fax: 04 94 57 65 30.
**Reservations:** Made with deposit (€ 46) and fee (€ 15,24). **Open** 1 May - 15 September.

**Directions:** From D559 between Carqueiranne and Le Pradet, take D76 northwards signed La Moutonne and site is signed on right of D76.

## Mediterranean
# Castel Camping Château de L'Eouvière

**8326** Route de Tavernes, 83670 Montmeyan

This spacious new site is in the grounds of an 18th century château, close to the magnificent hill village of Montmeyan. There are 30 ha. of grounds to explore and the pool, bar and restaurant in front of the château have lovely views over the valley and hills beyond. The 80 large pitches (all for tourers) are well marked and separated on terraces, mostly behind the château . Many have magnificent views. Newly laid out, the pitches are part grassy, part stony with varying amounts of shade. The majority have water and electricity points. Some are a long way from the main facilities and your own sanitation would be an advantage. A 'portacabin' type toilet block is to be installed in the upper reaches for the high season. This is a quieter site for those seeking the 'real' France.

**Facilities:** The single toilet block has just been refurbished and includes all the necessary facilities. Disabled facilities are available though the steeply sloping roads and paths are not ideal. Laundry and dishwashing sinks, washing machine and iron. Bar, restaurant and small shop (June - Sept). Swimming pool (the hard surround is to be refurbished for 2003) with large grass sunbathing area. Small play area and paddling pool (some distance from the pool). Some entertainment and children's activities in high season. **Off site:** Montmeyan 1 km. Beach at Lake Quinson (7 km) and other lakes with watersports.

**Charges** 2002

| | |
|---|---|
| Per person | € 4.50 - € 6.00 |
| pitch | € 7.00 - € 12.50 |
| electricity | 3.50 |

**Tel:** (0)4 94 80 75 54. Fax: (0)4 94 80 75 54. E-mail: leouviere@wanadoo.fr. **Reservations:** Contact site. **Open** 15 April - 15 October.

**Directions:** Leave A8 autoroute at St Maximin on D560 to Barjols and then D71 to Montmeyan. At roundabout on entering village, take D13 southeast signed Cotignac and entrance is shortly on right.

## Camping-Caravaning Cros de Mouton

BP.116, 83240 Cavalaire-sur-Mer

**8322**

Cros de Mouton is a reasonably priced campsite in a popular area. High in the hills on a steep hillside, 1.5 km. from Cavalaire and its popular beaches, the site is a calm oasis away from the hectic coast. Unfortunately, due to the nature of the terrain, some of the site roads are very steep - the higher pitches with the best views are especially so. However, Olivier and Andre are happy to take your caravan up with their 4x4 Jeep if you are worried. There are 199 terraced pitches under cork trees which include 39 for mobile homes, 80 suitable only for tents with parking close by, and 80 for touring caravans. These have electricity (10A), some also have water. The restaurant terrace and the pools have wonderful view of Cavalaire and the bay. English is spoken.

**Facilities:** Two clean and well maintained toilet blocks have all the usual facilities including wash-basins in cubicles. Washing machine at each and a fully fitted facility for disabled customers (although site is perhaps a little steep in places for wheel-chairs). Bar/restaurant serving reasonably priced meals, plus takeaways. Swimming and paddling pools with lots of sun-beds on the terrace and small bar serving snacks and cold drinks. Small play area and games room.

**Charges** 2003

| | |
|---|---|
| Per adult | € 5.70 - € 7.00 |
| child (under 7 yrs) | € 4.00 |
| pitch | € 5.70 - € 7.00 |
| electricity (10A) | € 4.00 |
| local tax | € 0.15 - € 0.30 |
| dog | free - € 2.00 |

**Tel:** 04 94 64 10 87. Fax: 04 94 05 46 38. E-mail: campingcrosdemouton@wanadoo.fr. **Reservations:** Made with deposit (€ 84) and fee (€ 16). **Open** 15 March - 31 October.

**Directions:** Site is very well signed from the centre of Cavalaire.

# Le Cros de Mouton
## Cavalaire - Côte d'Azur

Under the Mediterranean sun, 1.6 km from the beach and the town centre, appreciate the peace, comfort, quietness and the welcome of a family camping site in the heart of a shady forest. Heated swimming pool. Bungalows and-mobile-homes for hire.

BP 116 – 83240 Cavalaire
Tel: 0033 494 64 10 87
Fax: 0033 494 05 46 38
campingcrosdemouton@wanadoo.fr
www.crosdemouton.com

**the travel service TO BOOK**

Ferry ✔
Pitch ✔
Accommodation ✔

01892 55 98 98

## The Alan Rogers' Travel Service

This unique service enables our readers to reserve their holidays as well as ferry crossings and comprehensive insurance cover at extremely competitive rates. The majority of participating sites are in France and we are able to offer a selection of some of the very best sites in this country.

Share our experience and let us help
to ensure that your holiday will be a complete success.

**Alan Rogers Travel Service 01892 55 98 98 or www.alanrogers.com**

## Mediterranean
# Camp du Domaine

**8312** La Favière BP 207, 83230 Bormes-les-Mimosas

Camp du Domaine, 3 km. south of Le Lavandou, is a large beach-side site with 1,200 pitches, although surprisingly it does not give the impression of being so big. Most pitches are reasonably level and 800 have 10A electricity. The most popular pitches are at the beach, but the ones furthest away are, on the whole, larger and have more shade amongst the trees, although many of them are more suitable for tents. The beach is the attraction, however, and everyone tries to get as near to it as they can. Despite its size, the site does not give the feeling of being busy, except perhaps around the supermarket. This is mainly because many pitches are hidden in the trees, the access roads are quite wide and it all covers quite a large area (some of the beach pitches are 600 m. from the entrance). Its popularity makes early reservation necessary over a long season (about mid June to mid Sept.) as regular clients book from season to season. English is spoken.

**Facilities:** The ten sanitary blocks are quite modern and kept clean but, due to high usage because of the popularity of the site, parts soon begin to show wear and tear. WCs are predominately of the Turkish type (management policy). All facilities have pre-mixed hot water with many washbasins in cabins. Facilities for disabled visitors (but steep steps). Block for children and baby room. Washing machines in most blocks. Fridges to hire. Well stocked supermarket. Bars and a pizzeria. Excellent children's play area. Boats and pedaloes for hire. Games and competitions arranged in July/Aug. Tennis courts, table tennis and minigolf. American motorhomes are not accepted. Barbecues are strictly forbidden. **Off site:** Bicycle hire 500 m, riding or golf 15 km.

**Charges 2003**

| | |
|---|---|
| Per unit incl. 2 persons | € 15.50 - € 21.50 |
| with electricity and water | € 23.00 - € 28.00 |
| extra person | € 4.60 - € 6.00 |
| child (under 7) | € 2.60 - € 3.00 |
| local tax (over 7 yrs) | € 0.30 |

**Tel:** 04 94 71 03 12. Fax: 04 94 15 18 67. E-mail: mail@campdudomaine.com. **Reservations:** Made with 30% deposit and fee (€ 22,87). **Open** 3 April - 31 October.

**Directions:** Just outside and to west of Le Lavandou, at new roundabout, turn off D559 towards the sea on road signed Favière. After some 2 km. turn left at camp signs.

## Mediterranean
# Camping Les Tournels

**8321** route de Camarat, 83350 Ramatuelle

Les Tournels is a large site set on a hillside and some of the pitches have wonderful panoramic views of the Gulf of St Tropez and Pampelonne beach. The whole hill is covered in parasol pines and old olive trees, so all pitches have some shade. Reasonably level, but varying in size, there is electricity on the majority (long electricity leads may be required). The rest are reserved for tents. Clean and well equipped sanitary blocks are within reasonable distance of the pitches, but the swimming pool, play area, shop and bar could turn out to be quite some distance away. The large swimming pool is of an unusual shape, the circular paddling pool has a mushroom shaped fountain, and both are surrounded by sunbathing areas with sun-beds. Competitions and shows are produced for adults and children in July/Aug. A shuttle bus runs the 500 m. to the local shopping centre and also to Pampelonne beach. Reception opens for long hours and English is spoken. The beaches are a big draw, but also who can resist a visit to St Tropez where perhaps you will see someone famous as they parade along the famous waterfront, and the floating `gin palaces` are a sight to behold.

**Facilities:** Two of the toilet blocks are of older design, the other six being very good. These include some washbasins in cubicles, mainly British style WCs (paper required), baby baths, children`s WCs and facilities for disabled visitors. Three blocks are heated in low season. Washing and drying machines at five blocks, with refrigerators to rent outside all of them. Dishwashing and laundry sinks. Bar/restaurant (1/4-15/10). Takeaway. Another bar with disco at the furthest end of the site, well away from most pitches. Large swimming pool (600 sq.m, open 1/4-20/10 and heated in low season). Large fenced play area with good quality equipment. Table tennis, volleyball, basketball and boules pitches. Archery. Mini-club for children over 5 years for sporting activities. Safety deposit boxes to rent. Only gas barbecues are permitted. **Off site:** Shopping centre 500 m. from the site entrance (owned by the family) contains supermarket, tobacconist, launderette, rotisserie and a snack bar. Beach 1.5 km.

**Charges 2003**

| | |
|---|---|
| Per unit incl. 2 persons | |
| with electricity and water | € 21.50 - € 29.50 |
| with electricity | € 18.50 - € 26.00 |
| extra adult | € 5.20 - € 7.00 |
| child (2-7 yrs) | € 2.70 - € 3.50 |
| animal | € 2.70 - € 3.30 |
| electricity (10A) | € 3.60 |
| local tax, child/adult | € 0.15 - € 0.30 |

**Tel:** 04 94 55 90 90. Fax: 04 94 55 90 99. E-mail: info@tournels.com. **Reservations:** Contact site for details. **Open** all year except 11 Jan - 25 February.

**Directions:** From A8 exit 36 take D25 to Ste Maxime, then D98 towards St Tropez. On outskirts of St Tropez, take D93 to Ramatuelle. Site is signed on left in 9 km.

# Camping Les Lacs du Verdon

Domaine de Roquelande, 83630 Régusse

**8314**

In beautiful countryside and within easy reach of the Grand Canyon du Verdon and its nearby lakes, this site is only 90 minutes from Cannes. This bustling and possible noisy campsite is suitable for active families and teenagers. The 30 acre wooded park is divided in two by a minor road. The 480 very stony, but level pitches (rock pegs advised) are marked and separated by trees and lines of stones. There are 130 pitches for tourists which are scattered amongst the trees and often have an irregular shape, although all are of average to good size. There are plenty of electricity boxes but long leads may be necessary. Water taps are few. The part across the road is used mainly for mobile homes but has some pitches for tourers, mostly at the far end. There are toilet blocks close by but the pitches are a long way from all the other site facilities. The main site is much more pleasant and closer to all the activities. Tour operators and mobile homes, for hire and privately owned, take up nearly three quarters of the site.

**Facilities:** The toilet blocks are old and much of the equipment is looking very jaded, but they are just about acceptable. They mainly have British style WCs and some washbasins in cubicles with warm water only. The block we tried had fairly hot water but campers complained they were not so lucky. All blocks have sinks for laundry and dishes. Washing machines and dryers. At the end of May very little was open and the level of cleanliness was just about adequate. Motorcaravan service point (with charge). Shop. Bar. Restaurant (recently rebuilt) and pizzeria (all 18/5-13/9). TV and teenage games. Discos, dances and theme nights. Excellent swimming pool/paddling pool complex (all season) and new artificial grass tennis courts - the highlight of this campsite. Volleyball, table tennis, archery and boules. Bicycle hire. Playground. Daily animations, for all the family, in May and June with a more extensive programme in high season. Only electric barbecues are permitted. **Off site:** Fishing, beach, sailing and windsurfing at the site's club at Saint Croix (15 km). The village of Regusse is about 2.5 km. and the small town of Aups is 7 km. Riding 10 km.

**Charges** 2002

| | |
|---|---|
| Per pitch incl. 1 or 2 persons | € 17.00 - € 20.00 |
| extra person over 7 yrs | € 5.00 - € 6.00 |
| child (3-7 yrs) | € 4.00 - € 5.00 |
| dog | € 2.00 |
| electricity 10A | € 4.00 |
| local tax | € 0.30 |

**Tel:** 04 94 70 17 95. Fax: 04 94 70 51 79. E-mail: info@lacs-verdon.com. **Reservations:** Made with 25% deposit and fee (€ 20). **Open** 27 April - 28 September.

**Directions:** Leave the A8 motorway at St Maximin and take the D560 northeast to Barjols. At Barjols turn left on D71 to Montmeyan, turn right on D30 to Regusse and follow site signs.

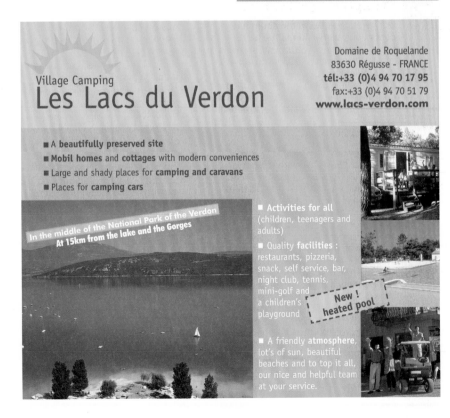

Village Camping

# Les Lacs du Verdon

Domaine de Roquelande
83630 Régusse - FRANCE
**tél:+33 (0)4 94 70 17 95**
fax:+33 (0)4 94 70 51 79
**www.lacs-verdon.com**

- A beautifully preserved site
- Mobil homes and cottages with modern conveniences
- Large and shady places for camping and caravans
- Places for camping cars

In the middle of the National Park of the Verdon
At 15km from the lake and the Gorges

- Activities for all (children, teenagers and adults)
- Quality facilities : restaurants, pizzeria, snack, self service, bar, night club, tennis, mini-golf and a children's playground
- New ! heated pool
- A friendly atmosphere, lot's of sun, beautiful beaches and to top it all, our nice and helpful team at your service.

# Corsica

Map 16

Major Cities: Ajaccio, Bastia

D partements: 2A Corse-Sud; 2B Haute-Corse

The island of Corsica is made up of two French départements: Haute Corse (upper Corsica) and Corse du Sud (south Corsica). Over the years there has been much dispute over the ownership of the island. The Phoenician Greeks, the Romans, followed by the Byzantines, Moors and Lombards have all fought over the island, creating a bloody history unparalleled for such a small area. In 1768, Genoa sold Corsica to France. The result is a fiery, lucidly intellectual and music-loving race of people, both superstitious and pious at the same time. It is also the birthplace of Napoleon Bonaparte.

Today about half of its 250,000 inhabitants live in the towns of Ajaccio and Bastia, leaving much of the 8,720 sq.km. island (the fourth largest in the Mediterranean) very thinly populated. Like a mountain in the sea, much of the island is covered with vegetation, pine trees, oaks, chestnut and the famous 'maquis', the variety of scenery is spectacular with mountains rising to 2,706 m and a coastline of 992 km. both dramatic and serenely beautiful. The highest mountains lie to the west, the gentler ranges, weathered in strange and often bizarre shapes, lie to the south and a continuous barrier forms the island's backbone. Beaches curve around scenic bays of white sand and the clear blue waters of the Mediterranean contrast with the stone pines that line the beaches and the multi coloured flowers that flourish on the sandy terrain. The entire island is ablaze with exotic flowers, aided by Corsica's excellent sunshine record.

Travel to and from Corsica by ferry is not difficult and SNCM operate a choice of routes from mainland France. On our recent visit we travelled from Nice to Bastia on a comfortable overnight sailing. The fare structure is quite complicated but a study of the ferry guide is worthwhile and can mean picking up a special offer if prepared to travel on given dates and specified sailings. There are also several services to Corsica from mainland Italy and Sardinia. Part of any stay on Corsica should include the 11 km. ferry trip from Bonifacio to Santa Teresa in Sardinia. Many make this short crossing to appreciate the incredible sight of Bonifacio from the sea. For ferry information between France and Corsica contact:

SNCM Southern Ferries, 179 Piccadilly, London WIV 9DB. Tel. 0207 491 4968.

## Cuisine of the Island

Corsican cuisine is essentially simple, with the sea providing the most dependable source of food. Freshwater fish abound in the interior and the 'maquis' is game country. Aromatic herbs and berries add a particularly piquant flavour to the meat. The extremes of the climate limit the variety of vegetables available. The Corsicans like hot and strong flavours.

*Brocchui* - sheeps' milk cheese is used much in cooking in both its soft form (savoury or sweet) or more mature and ripened.

*Capone* – local eels, cut up and grilled on a spit over a charcoal fire

*Dziminu* – fish soup, like bouillabaise but much hotter. Made with peppers and pimentos

*Figatelli* – a sausage made of dried and spiced pork with liver. Favourite between-meal snack

*Pibronata* – a highly spiced local sauce

*Prizzutu* – a peppered smoked ham; resembles the Italian prosciutto, but with chestnut flavour added

### Wine

Some of the wines are produced from grapes indigenous to the island since Phoenician times.

### Places of Interest

*Ajaccio* – a dazzling white city full of Napoleonic memorabilia

*Bastia* – historic citadel towering over the headland. The old town has preserved its streets in the form of steps connected by vaulted passages, converging on the Vieux port (the old port). The new port is the real commercial port of the island.

# Camping-Caravaning U Farniente

Pertamina Village, 20169 Bonifacio

**2000**

Irrespective of whether or not you are using the ferry to Sardinia, Bonifacio deserves a visit and it would be difficult to find a more attractive or convenient site than this one at which to pitch for a night stop or longer stay. The 120 pitches, many with electricity (3A), are partially terraced and are hedged with trees and bushes, providing reasonable shade. They are reasonably flat and vary in size, many being well over 100 sq.m. A central feature of the site is the large attractive swimming pool, surrounded by terraces and a bar and a good pizzeria/grill.

**Facilities:** Two toilet blocks include washbasins in semi-private cubicles, British and Turkish style WCs, dishwashing and washing machines plus drying and ironing facilities. Shop. Takeaway. Pizzeria/grill serving set meals and à la carte at reasonable prices (shorter opening hours in May, June and Oct). Swimming pool. Tennis, table tennis. Play area. TV room. **Off site:** Bonifacio 4 km.

**Charges** 2002

| | |
|---|---|
| Per unit incl. 2 persons, electricity | € 16.80 - € 20.75 |
| extra person | € 5.35 - € 6.40 |
| child (under 8 yrs) | € 2.75 - € 3.82 |
| electricity | € 3.51 |
| local tax | € 0.15 |

**Tel:** 04 95 73 05 47. **Fax:** 04 95 73 11 42. **E-mail:** pertamina@wanadoo.fr. **Reservations:** Contact site. Made with € 15.25 fee and 30% deposit. **Open** Easter - 15 October.

**Directions:** Site is on RN198, 4 km. north of Bonifacio to the east. Watch for the sign - you come on it quite suddenly.

# Camping-Caravaning La Vetta

route de Bastia, La Trinité, 20137 Porto-Vecchio

**2006**

In a pleasing country park setting to the north of La Trinité village, La Vetta is only 3 km. from Porto-Vecchio and its magnificent sandy beaches. This 8.5 ha. campsite enjoys a tranquil setting and is a part sloping, part terraced site, that seems to stretch endlessly. It is well maintained and has an abundance of tree varieties including cork oaks. Giving the impression of being off the beaten track, many of the delights of Corsica are only a short drive away. If you want to do no more than relax there is much on offer - a pool for hot days, plenty of trees for shade and a patio area for cool drinks. The site has 100 pitches, most with 16A electricity. The entrance is directly off the main road with security gates closed midnight - 7 am.

**Facilities:** Clean, modern, fully equipped toilet facilities are more than adequate and include dishwashing, laundry sinks and washing machine. Shop (July/Aug) with gas supplies. Patio bar (July/Aug). Swimming pool (all season), table tennis, table football, snooker table, a play area, TV and entertainment in high season. Barbecues are not permitted in certain weather conditions. **Off site:** Riding 4 km, fishing 3 km, bicycle hire 5 km, golf 7 km.

**Charges** 2002

| | |
|---|---|
| Per adult | € 5.50 - € 6.00 |
| child (under 7 yrs) | € 3.00 |
| tent or caravan | € 2.00 - € 2.50 |
| car | € 2.00 |
| motorcaravan | € 4.00 - € 4.50 |
| electricity | € 3.00 |
| local tax | € 0.15 |

**Tel:** 04 95 70 09 86. **Fax:** 04 95 70 43 21. **E-mail:** info@campinglavetta.com. **Reservations:** Made with 30% deposit. **Open** 15 May - 15 September.

**Directions:** Site is in La Trinité village, off the RN198 (east side), north of Porto-Vecchio.

# Camping Caravaning Santa Lucia

Lieudit Mulindinu, 20144 Ste-Lucie-de Porto-Vecchio

**2007**

Camping Santa Lucia is a friendly, family run site in a delightful southern Corscian setting. It is a well appointed site set in a cork oak forest just off the main road, the entrance enhanced by a huge palm tree which characterises the approach to reception. At this point you also find the restaurant and bar which overlook the pool - particularly pleasant in the evening when ornamental lamps light up the patio area. There are 160 pitches, 40 with 6A electricity. Pitches are numbered and some are in little enclosed bays which offer privacy. Chalets blend unobtrusively with the setting. Based at this site you are only minutes by car from Porto Vecchio which is surrounded by lovely beaches.

**Facilities:** Two toilet blocks include some washbasins in cubicles, dishwashing and laundry sinks, and a washing machine. Bread to order. Bar (15/6-15/9). Restaurant and takeaway (1/7-31/8). Play area. Table tennis, volleyball, and minigolf. Barbecues are only permitted in specific area. **Off site:** Fishing 5 km. Supermarket opposite site entrance and services such as a doctor, chemist and newsagent in village.

**Charges** 2002

| | |
|---|---|
| Per adult | € 4.00 - € 6.00 |
| child (2-10 yrs) | free - € 3.00 |
| pitch | € 1.80 - € 3.50 |
| with electricity | € 5.00 - € 6.00 |
| car | € 1.50 - € 2.50 |

**Tel:** 04 95 71 45 28. **Fax:** 04 95 71 45 28. **E-mail:** santalucia@wanadoo.fr. **Reservations:** Made with deposit and € 15 fee. Open 15 May - 10 October.

**Directions:** Site is at south end of Sainte-Lucie-de-Porto-Vecchio village, off N198 and well signed.

## Camping Arinella Bianca

route de la Mer, 20240 Ghisonaccia

Arinella is a lively, family oriented site situated on Corsica's east coast. It is a tribute to its owner's design and development skills as it appears to be in entirely natural glades where, in fact, these have been created from former marshland with a fresh water lake. The 300 marked pitches (164 for touring units) are on flat grass among a variety of trees and shrubs providing ample shade. They are irregularly arranged but are all of a good size with 6A electricity (long leads may be necessary). The site is right beside a beach of soft sand that extends a long way either side of the attractive central complex which, together with the swimming pool, forms the hub of this site. A large range of sport and leisure facilities is available at or adjacent to the site. Evening entertainment starts at 10 pm. and continues until past midnight and unfortunately a local disco nearby can go on until the early hours. Used by tour operators (76 pitches). A `Sites et Paysages` member.

**Facilities:** Four open plan sanitary blocks provide showers in larger than average cubicles (some with dressing area), washbasins in cabins and mainly British, some Turkish style WCs. Open air dishwashing areas. Laundry with washing machines and ironing boards. Motorcaravan service point. Shop, bar, terraced restaurant, amphitheatre and snack bar (all 10/5-15/9). Swimming pool (from 1/5)on payment. Windsurfing, canoeing, fishing, volleyball, bicycle hire, tennis, riding. Children's mini-club and play area. Disco. Entertainment programme in the main season.

**Charges** 2003

| | |
|---|---|
| Per unit incl. 2 adults | € 18.00 - € 31.00 |
| extra person | € 6.30 - € 7.90 |
| child (up to 7 yrs) | free - € 4.80 |
| animal | € 2.30 |
| electricity (6A) | € 3.05 |
| local tax | € 0.20 - € 0.50 |

**Tel:** 04 95 56 04 78. Fax: 04 95 56 12 54. E-mail: arinella@arinellabianca.com. **Reservations:** Contact site. Made with € 155 deposit and € 30.50 fee. **Open** Easter - 30 September.

**Directions:** Site is 4 km. east of Ghisonaccia. From N198 after entering Ghisonaccia look for sign 'La Plage / Li Mare' (this road is easy to miss coming from south and difficullt for caravans to turn into, so go further through town and turn in garage forecourt to approach from north). Turn east on to D144 and continue for 3.5 km. to roundabout. Turn right and site is on left in approx. 500 m.

## Aire Naturelle de Camping
La Ferme de Peridundellu, 20231 Venaco

**2009**

Just as spectacular as the coastline is Corsica's mountainous interior and by getting off the N200 this exceptional little campsite can be discovered. In a clearing among the trees are 25 pitches, many with electrical connection (20A). Whilst the panoramic view, peace and tranquillity are cause enough to be here, the enthusiastic young couple, Mathieu and Angele who run the site have already made it noteworthy. They offer visitors a restaurant service with cuisine of Corsica, prepared from their own farm produce - Mathieu works on the farm, as well as being the chef. The small restaurant is a delight with neatly laid tables, an old stone fireplace and wall hangings creating a special atmosphere.

**Facilities:** Clean fully equipped toilet block. Shop provides farm produce and bread each day Restaurant with local cheeses and wines. Around the site are picnic tables, water points, night lighting and a central rubbish point. **Off site:** Venaco (with doctor, chemist, boulangerie, etc) 4 km.

**Charges** 2002

| | |
|---|---|
| Per adult | € 4.27 |
| child (3-7 yrs) | € 2.13 |
| pitch and vehicle | € 3.20 - € 5.34 |
| electricity | € 3.51 |

**Tel:** 04 95 47 09 89. Fax: 04 95 47 09 89.
**Reservations:** Write to site but probably not necessary. **Open** 15 April - 15 October.

**Directions:** From Corte centre take N200 towards Aléria. After 15 km. turn east on the D143 and site is on left after 4 km.

## Camping-Caravaning Santa Barbara
RN 200 route d'Aleria, Aerodrome de Corte, 20250 Corte

**2010**

Santa Barbara is a developing campsite in Corsica's mountainous interior. Corte, the historical capital of the island, stands at 396 m. altitude in the central mountains where you get a feel of the real Corsica and the site is 3 km. east of the town. Already established as a restaurant/bar, the campsite is an ongoing project with, at present, 50 level touring pitches and 10 mobile homes. The pitches are separated by young shrubs and there are 32 electricity connections). An excellent pool is an established focal point and very welcome in this hot, mountainous region. The popular patio area overlooks the pool and the restaurant is outside. The owners are friendly and helpful. There could be some noise from the road or small local airport.

**Facilities:** The toilet facilities are modern and spotlessly clean units including facilities for the disabled, dishwashing, laundry sinks and washing machine. Restaurant/bar offers varied menu also pizza style hut. Swimming pool. Children's play area, table tennis and pool table. **Off site:** Corte has a full range of shops.

**Charges** 2002

| | |
|---|---|
| Per adult | € 4.50 |
| child (under 10 yrs) | € 2.60 |
| caravan | € 3.70 |
| car | € 2.50 |
| motorcaravan | € 5.40 |
| electricity | € 3.70 |
| local tax | € 0.15 |

**Tel:** 04 95 46 20 22. Fax: 04 95 61 09 44.
**Reservations:** Write to site. **Open** April - 31 October.

**Directions:** Site is 3 km. southeast of Corte by the N200 Aléria road.

## Camping Merendella
Moriani-Plage, 20230 San-Nicolao

**2003**

This attractive smaller, family run site has the advantage of direct access to a pleasant beach. It is peacefully situated on level grass with many trees and shrubs providing shade and colour. There are 133 pitches of a min. 100 sq.m. with electricity available on practically all (although long cables may be needed). The site is about 800 m. from the village but also has its own well stocked shop.

**Facilities:** Modern toilet facilities are in two main blocks, apart from a couple of individual cabin units near beach. Washbasins in private cubicles and some British style WCs plus further Turkish style ones. Washing up and laundry areas. Two washing machines. Shop. Restaurant/Pizzeria. TV and games room. No dogs or cats are accepted. **Off site:** Tennis, riding and various watersports including a diving centre nearby.

**Charges** 2002

| | |
|---|---|
| Per person | € 5.05 - € 5.85 |
| child (2-12 yrs) | € 3.15 - € 3.75 |
| pitch and vehicle | € 4.65 - € 4.90 |
| electricity (2/5A) | € 2.90 - € 3.20 |
| local tax (1/7-15/9) | € 0.15 |

**Tel:** 04 95 38 53 47. Fax: 04 95 38 44 01. E-mail: merendel@club-internet.fr. **Reservations:** Advised; write to site. **Open** 15 May - 15 October.

**Directions:** Site is to seaward side of the RN198, 800 m. south of Moriani Plage.

## Corsica
# Camping San Damiano
Lido de la Marana-Pineto, 20620 Biguglia-Bastia

**2013**

What we found pleasing about this site was the friendly reception we received and also its convenient situation only 9 km. from the port of Bastia. It makes an excellent night halt, or alternatively a suitable base for visiting Bastia, the northeast of the island or its mountainous interior. Despite being on the outskirts of a city, it enjoys an ideal location off the busy N193, situated between the Etang de Biguglia and the golden sands of Corsica`s east coast. It is divided in two by a public access road to the beach and is a sprawling site with 280 pitches, all separated by shrubsand shaded by trees. There are 180 electricity connections (10A). A security guard patrols in high season and quiet is enforced after 11 pm.

**Facilities:** Two basic toilet blocks, but clean when we visited, include washing cabins and good provision for disabled visitors. Motorcaravan service point. Well-stocked shop (1/6-20/9). Bar and restaurant (from 1/5). Launderette. TV room. Minigolf. Play area for children. Fishing. Riding. Jet-ski and Quad-bike hire. **Off site:** Golf 15 km

**Charges** 2002

| | |
|---|---|
| Per person | € 5.00 - € 6.00 |
| child (under 8 yrs) | € 3.00 - € 4.00 |
| pitch | € 4.50 - € 5.50 |
| dog | € 0.50 |
| electricity (6A) | € 3.00 |

**Tel:** 04 95 33 68 02. **Fax:** 04 95 30 84 10. **E-mail:** san-damiano@lespiedsdansleau.com. **Reservations:** Possible by phone. **Open** 1 April - 15 October.

**Directions:** From port of Bastia travel 5 km. on N193 then take D107 towards Lido de la Marana for 4 km. Site is signed on the left

## Corsica
# Camping Le Panoramic
route de Lavatoggio, Lumio, 20260 Calvi

**2012**

On the scenic route that winds inland and upwards from the coast between Calvi and L`Ile Rousse, Le Panoramic, as its name suggests, enjoys magnificent views across the Golfe d`Ambroggio. It is a simple family run site with 120 pitches laid out in named avenues (Rue Josephine, etc) and the marked places are shaded by many trees and vegetation, with quite a number having 15A electricity connections. Whilst the ground is level, the site is terraced and hard going if climbing from the bottom towards reception. It is probably best suited for small motorcaravans or tents. A recommended scenic drive is the 5 km. climb to St Antonino, a mountain village piled upon a rock face.

**Facilities:** Four sanitary blocks are housed in typical rough-cast buildings with basic decor, but appear well maintained and fully equipped. Sinks for dish-washing and two washing machines. Chemical disposal can be arranged through reception. Small shop, takeaway and bar. Swimming pool. Table football, pool table. Play area. Caravan storage. **Off site:** Bicycle hire 4 km, riding 3 km, golf 5 km.

**Charges** 2002

| | |
|---|---|
| Per adult | € 5.30 |
| child (2-7 yrs) | € 2.65 |
| pitch and vehicle | € 3.50 - € 5.20 |
| electricity | € 2.90 |
| local tax | € 0.17 |

**Tel:** 04 95 60 73 13. **Fax:** 01 40 95 16 01. **Reservations:** Phone or write. **Open** 1 June - 15 September.

**Directions:** From Calvi take N197 towards L`Ile Rousse. Proceed for 10 km. to village of Lumio, then east on D71 and site is 2 km. on the left.

## Corsica
# Camping Les Oliviers
20150 Porto

**2022**

Because of its location on this difficult to access west coast of Corsica and the steepness of the site itself, Les Oliviers is best suited for tents and small motorhomes. An attractive, family run site on the edge of this busy coastal resort, it has direct access to the river. The 190 pitches are mainly small and terraced, with 64 having electricity connections (10A). Whilst there are a number of shops and restaurants in the vicinity, the site itself has an attractive restaurant/pizzeria/bar.

**Facilities:** Toilet facilities are in four blocks spread throughout the site. Some washbasins in cubicles, British style WCs. Washing up and laundry areas. Four washing machines. Refrigerator hire. Bread supplies. Restaurant, pizzeria and bar. Children's play area. **Off site:** Supermarket 50 m. Corsican Trek organises a variety of active sports. Visits to Scandola nature reserve.

**Charges** 2002

| | |
|---|---|
| Per adult | € 5.00 - € 6.00 |
| pitch and car | € 5.00 - € 7.00 |
| electricity | € 3.00 |

**Tel:** (0)4 95 26 14 49. **Fax:** (0)4 95 26 12 49. **Reservations:** Essential for caravans and motorcaravans at all times, advised for tents in July/Aug; contact site. **Open** 28 March - 30 October.

**Directions:** When approaching Porto the road crosses a bridge over the river. Les Oliviers is on the right immediately after the bridge.

## Camping Le Sagone
route de Vico, 20118 Sagone

Situated just outside the bustling seaside resort of Sagone, this campsite is in a superb location for exploring Corsica's wild and rocky west coast or its mountainous interior. Adjacent to a mixed farm with orchards, there are 300 pitches (200 marked out) the majority with electrical connections (6A). The restaurant/bar and games room overlooking the pool are a focal point of this well managed site.

**Facilities:** Four clean, fully equipped toilet blocks include two with internal courtyard gardens. Washbasins in cubicles. Dishwashing and laundry area. Facilities for disabled people. Washing machines and dryer. Motorcaravan service point. Supermarket at entrance. Restaurant, pizzeria, bar. Games room. Swimming pool. Half court tennis, volleyball, table tennis, basketball. Play area. **Off site:** Riding, diving, windsurfing, biking, climbing.

**Charges** 2002

| | |
|---|---|
| Per unit incl. 2 persons | € 19.00 |
| electricity | € 2.30 - € 2.45 |
| dog | € 1.70 |

**Tel:** 04 95 28 04 15. Fax: 04 95 28 08 28. E-mail: sagone.camping@wanadoo.fr. **Reservations:** Made with 30% deposit and € 18,50 booking fee; write to site. **Open** April - 15 October.

**Directions:** From Ajaccio take RD81 towards Cergése and Calvilby (by coast road). In Sagone take RD70 towards Vico, Sagone Camping is on left after 1.5 km. next to Coccinelle supermarket.

# Naturist Sites

We have had very favourable feedback from readers concerning our choice of naturist sites, which we first introduced in our 1992 edition. Over the last few years we have gradually added a few more, including three in Corsica.

Apart from the need to have a 'Naturist Licence' (see below), there is no need to be a practising naturist before visiting these sites. In fact, at least as far as British visitors are concerned, many are what might be described as 'holiday naturists' as distinct from the practice of naturism at other times. The emphasis in all the sites featured in this guide at least, is on naturism as 'life in harmony with nature', and respect for oneself and others and for the environment, rather than simply on nudity. In fact nudity is really only obligatory in the area of the swimming pools.

There are a number of rules, which amount to sensible and considerate guidelines designed to ensure that no-one invades someone else's privacy, creates any nuisance, or damages the environment.

Whether as a result of these rules, the naturist philosophy generally, or the attitude of site owners and campers alike, we have been very impressed by all the naturist sites we have selected. Without exception they had a friendly and welcoming ambience, were all extremely clean and tidy and, in most cases, provided much larger than average pitches, with a wide range of activities.

The purpose of our including a number of naturist sites in our guide is to provide an introduction to naturist camping in France for British holidaymakers; we were actually surprised by the number of British campers we met on naturist sites, many of whom had `stumbled across naturism almost by accident' but had found, like us, that these sites were amongst the nicest they had encountered. You my still be required to have a Naturist Licence. These can be obtained in advance from either the British or French national naturist associations, but are also available on arrival at any recognised naturist site (a passport type photograph is required).

## Clothes-free ... the great natural way to unwind

Camping, caravanning, boating or just simply relaxing. We promote naturism as a friendly, enjoyable way to spend your free time and holidays.

**BRITISH NATURISM**
Tel 01604 620361
www.british-naturism.org.uk

# Camping Naturiste Le Colombier

85210 St-Martin-Lars-en-Ste Hermine

N8514

A countryside site for naturists near La Roche sur Yon, this site is almost akin to 'Camping a la Ferme', but with the benefit of good facilities. It provides around 160 pitches in seven very natural fields on different levels linked by informal grass tracks. There are level, terraced areas for caravans and a lovely feeling of spaciousness with pitches around the edges of fields, unmarked and with electricity (up to 16A) available at various strategic points. Goats and sheep may be watched in a central enclosure in one field. Mellow old farm buildings are pleasing and the bar/restaurant is in a converted barn beside the courtyard area where the pool is situated. For nature lovers the site's 125 acres provide many walks throughout the attractive, wooded valley and around the lake. Children are also well catered for with some unusual activities helped by volunteers. The local area is interesting, with antique 'Bocage Vendéen' and sculpture featuring prominently, and provides a very different view of the hectic coastal Vendée. Naturist licences are required.

**Facilities:** Fully equipped modern toilet blocks (one new) are good, providing some showers in cubicles. Dishwashing sinks. Motorcaravan service point. Grocer/baker calls daily. Bar/restaurant with à la carte and full menu (order before 10 am), home baked bread and pizzas. Swimming pool. Fishing. Bicycle hire. Volleyball and boules and table tennis. Children's playground. Pony and trap rides around the woods and one day a week the bread oven is lit and children can make their own bread. Ghost tours in the woods, sledging on artificial ski slope (all main season only). **Off site:** Shop 1 km.

**Charges** 2002

| | |
|---|---|
| Per person | € 6.86 |
| child 4-9 yrs | € 3.05 |
| child 10-16 yrs | € 4.27 |
| electricity | € 2.74 |
| dog | € 3.05 |

**Tel:** 02 51 27 83 84. **Fax:** 02 51 27 87 29. **E-mail:** lecolombier.nat@wanadoo.fr. **Reservations:** Not considered necessary. **Open** 1 April - 30 October.

**Directions:** From N148, La Roche sur Yon - Niort road, at St Hermine, turn onto D8 eastward for 4 km. Turn left on D10 to St Martin-Lars where there are signs to site.

# Camping Naturiste Cap Natur'

151 ave de la Faye, 85270 St Hilaire-de-Riez

N8533

the travel service
TO BOOK
Ferry ✓
Pitch ✓
Accommodation ✓
01892 55 98 98

Situated on the northern outskirts of the busy resort of St Hilaire-de-Riez, and only about 1 kilometre from the nearest beach (6 km. from the nearest official naturist beach beside Plage des 60 Bornes) this family campsite for naturists is in an area of undulating sand dunes and pine trees. The 120 touring pitches nestle among the dunes and trees and offer a wide choice to suit most tastes, including the possibility of electrical connections (4/10A), although in some cases long leads are needed. Despite the undulating terrain, some pitches are quite level and thus suitable for motorcaravans. The modern facilities are excellent and include both open air and indoor pools, and a jacuzzi. Around the pool is an ample paved sunbathing area, including a stepped 'solarium'. The whole of the indoor complex is a designated non-smoking area. In season a regular Saturday evening 'soirée' is held with a set Vendéen meal, wine and entertainment. There is an air of peace and quiet about this site which contrasts with the somewhat frenzied activity which pervades many of the resorts in this popular tourist area, with a friendly, warm welcome from the family that own it. A number of apartments, tents and mobile homes on site.

**Facilities:** Sanitary facilities are basic, but clean, consisting of one indoor and one outdoor (but roofed) block. Both blocks have open plan hot showers, British style WCs, washbasins, baby baths and children's toilets. Small shop and restaurant (menu includes some local specialities), good sized bar, with TV, pool tables and various indoor table games. Indoor and outdoor swimming pools. Children's play area on soft sand. Volleyball and archery. Torches useful.

**Charges** 2002

| | |
|---|---|
| Per unit incl. 2 adults | € 14.00 - € 25.00 |
| extra person | € 2.50 - € 5.20 |
| child (under 10 yrs) | € 1.60 - € 3.40 |
| animal | € 2.20 |
| electricity (10A) | € 4.20 |

**Tel:** 02 51 60 11 66. **Fax:** 02 51 60 17 48. **E-mail:** info@cap-natur.com. **Reservations:** Advised in high season and for French holidays. Made with 25% deposit and booking fee (€ 27,44). **Open** 24 March - 3 or 11 November.

**Directions:** Site is on the north side of St Hilaire-de-Riez. From Le Pissot roundabout go south on the D38, follow signs for St Hilaire at first roundabout you come to (first exit off roundabout), then at second roundabout (garage) turn right signed 'Terre Fort'. At third Y-shaped junction turn right again signed 'Parée Prèneau' (also site sign here). The site is 2 km along this road on the left.

# Euronat

**N3316** 33590 Grayan et l'Hopital

Euronat is really a large naturist town with extensive facilities, direct access to beach and a Thalassotherapy centre. There are various villages surrounding the commercial centre of this 335 hectare site. The caravan and camping sites are in two areas separate from the villages of chalets and mobile homes. Unfortunately many trees were lost in the storms of 99 and it will take some time before the levels of shade on the site return to the previous cover. However, there is a sense of openness and many other plants are now flourishing. A variety of fair sized fairly flat pitches, includes some suitable for large American style motorhomes. The town centre is superb with two supermarkets, an organic supermarket, cash-point, butcher, fish shop, bakery (baking on the premises), several restaurants including fish, Chinese, brasserie, pizzeria/creperie, and a large takeaway with a good selection of hot and cold dishes which you can eat in the town square at picnic tables, tabac, general store, hairdresser, electrical shop. The beach is of fine sand, 1.5 km. in length, with a special area for dogs. It is cleaned daily and there are two lifeguard stations. A bicycle is recommended as the easiest means of travelling round the 'town'. The large, modern and airy Thalassotherapy centre where a range of treatments may be found is supervised by a doctor.

**Facilities:** The large number of sanitary blocks include British style WCs, a few Turkish style WCs and communal hot showers. All blocks are well maintained with some heated in low season. Facilities for people with disabilities. Large number of dishwashing and laundry sinks (cold water). Launderette. Basic service point for motorhomes. Range of shops and restaurants. Swimming pool with children's pool. Wide range of activities and workshops (in main season) including archery, pony club, horse riding, tennis, petanque, volleyball, table tennis, special activities for children, handicrafts. Three TV rooms, video and games centre. Library. Large multi purpose hall used for dances, film nights, music evenings, sports activities. Barbecues are not permitted. Torch may be useful. English is spoken.

**Charges 2003**

| Per tent pitch incl. 2 persons | € 10.00 - € 24.00 |
|---|---|
| with electricity (10A) | € 13.00 - € 30.00 |
| caravan or motorcaravan incl. 2 persons, electricity, water and waste water | € 16.00 - € 36.00 |
| extra person | € 3.00 - € 6.00 |
| animal (sanitary bags supplied) | € 3.00 |

**Tel:** (0)5 56 09 33 33. **Fax:** (0)5 56 09 30 27. **E-mail:** info@euronat.fr. **Reservations:** Made with deposit (25%) and fee (€ 28). **Open** 23 March to 3 November.

**Directions:** from Bordeaux ring road take exit 7, then RN215 to Lesparre and Vensac, then follow (large) signposted route.

---

# Domaine Naturiste Arnaoutchot

**N4012** 40560 Vielle-St-Girons

the travel service
TO BOOK
Ferry ✓
Pitch ✓
Accommodation ✓
01892 55 98 98

'Arna' is a large naturist site with extensive facilities and direct access to the beach. Even with 500 pitches, its layout in the form of a number of sections, each with its own character, make it quite relaxing and very natural. These sections amongst the trees and bushes of the Landes provide a variety of reasonably sized pitches, most with electricity, although the hilly terrain means that only a limited number are flat enough for motorcaravans. The centrally located amenities are extensive and of excellent quality. The site has the advantage of direct access to a large, sandy naturist beach, although access from some parts of the site may involve a walk of perhaps 600-700 m. The 'Arna Club' provides more than 30 activities and workshops (in the main season). English is spoken. Chalets, mobile homes and tents for rent. The site is used by a tour operator (20 pitches). Member 'France 4 Naturisme'.

**Facilities:** Sanitary facilities include the usual naturist site type of blocks with communal hot showers, but also a number of tiny blocks with one hot shower, WC and washbasin each in an individual cabin. All blocks provide fully tiled, modern facilities, one block is heated in low season. Laundry. Motorcaravan service point. Large supermarket and a range of other shops. Bar/restaurant, pizzeria and tapita (fish) bar. Pizza delivery to pitches or to telephone point on beach. Heated indoor pool with solarium, whirlpool and slide. Outdoor pool and terraced sunbathing area. Sauna, steam, whirlpool and massage. Arna Club (main season) with riding, archery, golf practise, tennis, petanque, swimming, rambling, cycling, sailing, handicrafts, excursions and activities for children. TV, video and games rooms. Cinema. Library. Hairdresser and chiropodist. Internet point. Bicycle hire. Fishing. Barbecues are not permitted. Torches useful. **Off site:** Riding or golf 5 km.

**Charges 2002**

| Per unit incl. 2 persons | € 12.50 - € 27.50 |
|---|---|
| extra person over 3 yrs | € 3.00 - € 6.00 |
| leisure club | € 0.40 - € 1.20 |
| electricity (3A) | € 3.50 |

**Tel:** 05 58 49 11 11. **Fax:** 05 58 48 57 12. **E-mail:** contact@arna.com. **Reservations:** Made with 25% deposit and fee (€ 27,44). **Open** 1 April - 15 September.

**Directions:** Site is signed off D652 road at Vielle-Saint-Girons - follow D328 for 3-4 km.

---

# Centre Naturiste Le Couderc

**N2419** Le Couderc, 24440 Naussannes

Le Couderc is a friendly, welcoming naturist site based on an old coaching inn. It's name comes from the 12th century Occitan meaning 'gathering place' and it is set at a crossroads on the route of the Bastide (fortified) towns of the Dordogne. The original inn provides a home for the extended family of Marieke, Nico and Olivier, whilst the stables have been sensitively converted to provide a bar and clubroom complete with a large, open fire for cooler evenings. Rather than fell a large tree when connecting two buildings to provide the restaurant, the trunk grows through the dining room. There is a covered terrace, a small museum and an art display. The 180 large pitches are around the edges of three gently sloping valleys radiating from the old inn. All pitches are level and have electricity hook-ups. As with other naturist sites there is always something going on here with many leisure activities organised for adults and children. A wooded area not used for camping provides paths for walking. The famous Dordogne wines such as Bergerac and Monbazillac are waiting at the local wine châteaux! Good English is spoken by the Dutch family and the site is extremely popular with the Dutch. Cars are left outside the site in peak season.

**Facilities:** Good quality, fully equipped unisex sanitary blocks are in each valley and are kept very clean. Facilities for disabled people in some blocks. Washing machine. Small shop with local produce. Bar and snack bar open throughout the season. Restaurant (closes each Wednesday) - the Dutch chef produces excellent French dishes. Solar heated pool. New sauna (free). Small lake with sandy beach. Petanque (with competitions organised), volleyball and bicycle hire. Play areas and paddling pool with a little terrace for parents. Children's club offers painting, poetry, circus skills, etc. and adult painting and sculpture classes, a talent evening at the impressive 'podium' on Wednesdays and enjoyable themed evenings on Fridays. Small library, plus photocopying and fax service. Torches necessary. **Off site:** Fishing 5 km, riding 4 km, golf 15 km. Issigeac with its Sunday market is 8 km, Beaumont 7 km. Five castles are within walking distance and there are cave paintings at Lascaux and Padriac.

**Charges** 2002

| | |
|---|---|
| Per adult | € 4.70 |
| child (under 14 yrs) | € 3.20 |
| pitch | € 9.50 |
| dog | € 3.20 |
| electricity | € 3.20 |

**Tel:** 05 53 22 40 40. **Fax:** 05 53 23 90 98. **E-mail:** le.couderc@perigord.com. **Reservations:** Advised for 10 July-15 Aug. with deposit (€ 9,50 per night) and fee (€ 17). **Open** 1 April - 30 September.

**Directions:** 10 km. east of Bergerac on D660 Sarlat road, turn into Mouleydier and take D21 to St Aubin-de-Lanquais. In that village turn left on D19 to Faux and in Faux follow directions to Naussannes. Pass Micalie and 300 m. after second crossing to Monsac, turn left at camp sign and follow rough track for 1 km. to site.

# Centre Naturiste Deveze

**N3204** Gaudonville, 32380 Saint-Clar

This is a well established and very pleasant, Dutch owned naturist site in 50 acres of lovely Gers countryside. The 180 pitches, the majority with electricity and many terraced, are in several different areas. All are separated by mature hedges and trees, the amount of shade available varies from area to area and some pitches are flatter than others. In many respects this site would be an excellent introduction to naturist camping, being quite 'laid-back' in terms of rules and regulations, but offering a wide range of activities for those that want them without any pressure to join in if you don't want to! The ambience at Deveze is warm and friendly with the centre-piece bar and terrace in the original farm buildings somewhat reminiscent of an English country pub. Campers are encouraged to provide their own entertainment and their efforts provide much fun and enjoyment.

**Facilities:** Sanitary facilities in three blocks include hot showers (communal) and washbasins (cold water only, but hot tap nearby), all fitted out to a high standard and very well maintained. Gas available. Well stocked shop (1/7-31/8). Takeaway (1/7-31/8). Pub (all year). New restaurant. Attractive swimming pool and children's pool (1/5-15/9). Four acre lake for fishing (free) or boating and woodland area. Children's play area. Bicycle hire. Tennis, volleyball, boules, badminton, archery, film shows and a small gym. Two TV rooms, one digital, one French. Exchange facilities.

**Charges** 2002

| | |
|---|---|
| Per unit incl. 2 persons | € 8.00 - € 16.00 |
| extra adult | € 5.80 |
| child 3-10 yrs | € 3.50 |
| over 10 yrs | € 4.10 |
| electricity (5A) | € 3.51 |
| dog | 41.49 |

**Tel:** 05 62 66 43 86. **Fax:** 05 62 66 42 02. **E-mail:** camping.deveze@wanadoo.fr. **Reservations:** Made with deposit (€ 46) and fee (€ 10,67). **Open** all year (limited facilities Oct-May).

**Directions:** From Agen or Auch use N21 to Lectoure and D7 to St Clar. From St Clar take the D13 (site signed) to Gaudonville. From Montauban take D928 southwest then D27 at Beaumont de Lomagne for Gaudonville.

Bélézy is an excellent naturist site with many amenities and activities at the foot of Mt Ventoux. We continue to be impressed by its policy of annual refurbishment, its management, the French approach to naturism and the extent to which the natural environment has been managed in harmony with the Provencal countryside. The ambience is essentially relaxed and comfortable. English is spoken widely amongst staff and customers although some activities may be conducted solely in French. The site has two areas joined by a short pedestrian tunnel and the 171 marked and numbered pitches are set amongst many varieties of trees and shrubs - oaks, olives, pines, acacias, broom, lavender, etc. Electricity points (12A) are plentiful but you may need a long cable in places. The emphasis is on informality and concern for the environment and during high season cars are banned from the camping area to the supervised parking areas nearby. This not only provides an air of tranquillity, but safety for children. So far as naturism is concerned, the emphasis is on personal choice (and weather conditions!), the only stipulation being the requirement for complete nudity in the pools and pool area. The leisure park side of the site is an area of natural parkland including an orchard, fishpond and woodland (complete with red squirrels), and a good range of sports facilities including tennis courts and swimming pools. The largest pool is for swimming and relaxation (you may enjoy a musical serenade), the smaller pool (heated 25/3-30/9) is also used for watersports and aquarobics. The smallest is for children supervised by their parents. Near the pool area is the smart restaurant, with terrace, and the mellow old Mas (Provencal farmhouse) that houses many activities, as well as the library, near soundproof disco, information centre and children`s club. Unusually there is a hydrotherapy centre (1/4-30/9) to tone up and revitalise with qualified diagnosis. Treatments include steam baths, massage and seaweed packs, osteopathy and Chinese medicine (including acupuncture). A 'gardien' is on call in the Mas during the night for emergencies. The Maison d`Animation offers a restaurant booking service with certain restaurants in the scheme offering a complimentary aperitif. Member 'France 4 Naturisme'.

**Facilities:** Sanitary blocks are a little different. The newer ones are of a standard type and excellent quality, with free hot showers in cubicles with separators, and washbasins in cabins. One block has an attractive children`s section with baby baths, sinks and showers at different heights, children`s toilets and is decorated with tiles painted with animals. In the same area the adult block has hot showers in the open air, separated by natural stone dividers and washing up areas again mostly in the open air. Shop (1/4-30/9). Restaurant provides excellent food, waiter service, and takeaway meals at affordable prices. Three swimming pools. Sauna. Two tennis courts. Boules and table tennis. Adventure play area. Activities include painting and pottery courses, language lessons, archery, music (bring your own instrument) and guided walks. Children`s clubs in holiday periods. Barbecues are prohibited but there is a central barbecue area. Weekly handout 'Bélézy Scoop' outlines forthcoming events. Dogs and pets are not accepted. **Off site:** It is possible to walk into Bédoin (excellent street market - Monday mornings).

**Charges** 2002

| | |
|---|---|
| Per unit incl. 1 adult | € 13.00 - € 22.50 |
| 2 adults | € 18.30 - € 28.50 |
| 3 adults | € 25.50 - € 35.70 |
| extra adult | € 5.50 - € 8.50 |
| child (3-8 yrs) | € 4.00 - € 6.50 |
| electricity (12A) | € 3.50 |
| large pitch | € 4.00 |
| pitch with water, drainage and sink | € 5.00 |

**Tel:** 04 90 65 60 18. Fax: 04 90 65 94 45. E-mail: info@belezy.com. **Reservations:** Write with deposit (25%) and fee (€ 30) - contact site. **Open** 15 March - 4 October.

**Directions:** From A7 autoroute or RN7 at Orange, take D950 southeast to Carpentras, then northeast via D974 to Bédoin. Site is signed in Bédoin, being about 1.5 km. northeast of the village

# Domaine Naturiste L'Eglantière

Aries-Espenan, 65230 Castelnau-Magnoac

N6501

This pretty site is situated in the valley between the Pyrénées and the plain, within easy reach of Lourdes and the mountains. Alongside a small, fast flowing river, in wooded surroundings it comprises 12 ha. for camping and caravanning, with a further 32 for walking and relaxing in the woods and fields. The river is said to be suitable for swimming and canoeing, with fishing nearby. The 120 pitches are of mixed size on fairly level grass, the older ones secluded and separated by a variety of tall trees and bushes, the newer ones more open, with a natural tenting area across the river. About 100 pitches have 8A electrical connections. The site has is an attractive, central, medium sized swimming pool with sunbathing areas both on paving and grass, and a children's pool, overlooked by the attractive style clubhouse and terrace. A small health centre (massage, sauna) is being developed in the old farmhouse. A range of studios, mobile homes, chalets and tents is on site. Used by a tour operator (5 pitches). Member of France 4 Naturisme.

**Facilities:** Two main sanitary blocks at each end of the site are in typically naturist style, providing under cover, open plan, controllable hot showers, and sinks for washing up. A small centrally located sanitary block has individual cubicles. Shop (June-Sept). Clubhouse with bar, small restaurant, pizzeria and takeaway (June-mid Sept), internet access and indoor soundproofed activities/disco area, play room for younger children and table tennis for older ones. Swimming pool (April - end Sept). Play area and children's animation in season. Volleyball, badminton, table tennis, petanque and archery. Activities on the river. Canoe and mountain bike hire. Trekking and cross country cycling. Barbecues are officially forbidden. Torches useful. **Off site:** Restaurants in the nearby village.

**Charges** guide

| | |
|---|---|
| Per pitch incl. 2 persons | € 11.89 - € 21.19 |
| 'wild' pitch (July/Aug. only) | € 15.09 |
| extra person | € 3.09 - € 4.42 |
| child (3-8 yrs) | € 1.52 - € 2.74 |
| animal | € 1.22 - € 1.98 |
| electricity (10A) | € 3.81 |
| leisure card (obligatory) | € 0.38 - € 0.76 |

**Tel:** 05 62 99 83 64. Fax: 05 62 39 82 99.
**Reservations:** Made with deposit (25%) and fee (€ 27.44). **Open** Easter - October.

**Directions:** From Auch take D929 south towards Lannemezan. Just after Castelnau-Magnoac watch for signs to hamlet of Ariès-Espénan on left and follow site signs.

# Mediterranean

## Camping Naturiste Le Clapotis

11480 Lapalme

N1109

This site is very different from our other Mediterranean naturist site, Sérignan Nature (N3408). It is small and tranquil, situated between Narbonne and Perpignan in a secluded pine wood. It has direct access to a large sea lagoon which is popular with some of the campers in pursuit of the ideal conditions provided for windsurfing (this is done with appropriate clothing!). The lagoon has large, secluded sandy 'beaches' and, if you tire of that, the excellent pool (full nudity required) is directly alongside the beach. The site comprises 230 level pitches, most with electricity (4A). Some are in the pine wood on gravel, others on more open ground with trees and shrubs separating them; the pitches in the open are grassy and large. All other facilities are very natural and simple and this preserves the feeling of harmony and freedom which is exceptional here. Games and competitions develop the general convivial and enjoyable atmosphere. The Pyrénées are less than an hour away and for wine enthusiasts the Corbières valley has many interesting cellars. If you wish for peace and serenity, then Clapotis is recommended as synonymous with sun and nature.

**Facilities:** Sanitary facilities are in rustic style buildings with British and Turkish style WCs, and facilities for children and disabled campers. Washing machines. Cosy, well stocked shop selling food, hardware and general goods. Small, pretty bar and restaurant offering a menu of the day from 15 June and takeaway (evenings only), with views over the lagoon (a must at sunset). Swimming pool (open from May, weather permitting). Two half tennis courts, volleyball, basketball, petanque, table tennis and windsurfing. Torches useful.

**Charges** 2002

| | |
|---|---|
| Per pitch incl. 2 adults | € 14.60 - € 18.00 |
| extra person | € 2.90 - € 3.10 |
| child under 4 yrs | free |
| electricity | € 3.20 - € 3.40 |

**Tel:** 04 68 48 15 40. Fax: 04 68 48 54 54. E-mail: camping.leclapotis@wanadoo.fr. **Reservations:** Advisable in high season and made with deposit (€ 107) and fee (€ 17). **Open** 15 March - 31 October.

**Directions:** Exit the N9 (Narbonne - Perpignan) onto the D709 at roundabout signed La Palme and Port-la-Nouvelle. In just over 500 m. turn right to site (signed). Watch carefully for the entrance.

## Midi-Pyrénées
# Naturist Camping Millfleurs

**N0909** Le Tuilier Gudas, 09120 Varilhes

Millfleurs is peaceful naturist site in superb location for mature naturists. Owned by a Dutch couple, Gert and Annie Kos who provide a warm welcome and speak excellent English, it really is camping at a relaxed and sublime level. It is so peaceful with some 70 acres of woods and meadows to explore providing guided naturist walks in total privacy. Annie has found 16 different types of orchids and keeps a picture record in the 'salle de reunion'. The long drive leads to a traditional farmhouse housing the campsite office. The site has 40 large flat pitches (26 with 4/6A electricity) on well spaced terraces, but there are also very secluded pitches in wooded areas with shade, or you can pitch a tent in the meadows if you prefer. Long leads are required if you decide to pitch off the terraces. There are few of the normal leisure facilities here and the site is definitely aimed at the more mature naturist camper. Transport is required as there is no bus service. Explore the nearby mediaeval town of Foix with its castle towering over the busy centre, and investigate the history of the Cathares and the region with its underground rivers and caves.

**Facilities:** An excellent central unisex toilet block, well thought out, includes great facilities for disabled campers, inside and outside showers and cheerful flowers and potted plants. Bread available to order in high season. Guests dine together in the 'salle de reunion' within the farmhouse two nights a week (Sat/Wed) or you just relax and meet friends for a drink. Refrigerator with drinks operated on an honesty system. Petanque court and guide book for walks and cycle rides in local area. Torches essential at night. Pick ups from airports and stations can be arranged. **Off site:** The coast is approximately 1.5 hours.

**Charges** 2002

| | |
|---|---|
| Per pitch | € 3.80 - € 4.57 |
| person (all ages) | € 4.20 |
| dog | € 1.50 |
| electricity | € 2.30 |

**Tel:** 05 61 60 77 56. **E-mail:** ag.kos@wanadoo.fr.
**Reservations:** Not necessary. **Open** 1 April - 15 October.

**Directions:** One can find the site very easily from the village of Varilhes which is 8 km. south of Pamiers on D624 (parallel to N20). Take D13 for Dalou and Gudas cross railway and N20. The site is 2 km. past Gudas, pass small road to left and site drive is further on right.

## Mediterranean
# Camping Naturiste Le Mas de Lignières

**N3405** Cesseras-en-Minervois, 34210 Olonzac

A naturist site hidden in the hills of the Minervois, this is a delightful find, only 3 km. from the medieval town of Minerve with its Cathar connections. Parts of this site enjoy some marvellous views to the Pyrénées, the Corbières and the coast at Narbonne. We recommend that you watch at least one wonderful sunrise over the Pyrénées. The owners Jeanne and Gilles, offer a warm welcome and promote a most enjoyable family atmosphere. The site provides 50 large (200 sq.m.) pitches, all with electricity (6A), with 25 with water and waste water connections. Mainly level grass, they are separated by mature hedges that give considerable privacy. Some smaller pitches (100 sq.m.) are available for tents, with cars parked elsewhere. There is natural shade and a variety of fauna and flora including four types of orchid. Within the confines of the seven hectare site there are some good walks with superb views and, although the camping area is actually quite small, the very large pitches create a very relaxing ambience and a nice introduction to naturist camping. The owners are proud that the site has been awarded the coveted 'Clef Vert' award for environmental awareness.

**Facilities:** The pleasant, clean toilet block has open washbasins and semi-open showers. Dishwashing and laundry sinks. En-suite facilities for disabled people. Washing machine. The décor is tasteful with attractive potted plants and pictures on the walls. Simple shop for essentials and local specialities. Bread can be ordered (15/06 -15/09). Bar and snack bar (15/7-15/8). Swimming pool with sliding cover which ensures it can be used early and late in season. Paddling pool. Comfortable room for general use with TV, library and tourist information and separate provision for young people. Playground. Tennis, volleyball and boules (all free). Torch useful. Only gas barbecues are permitted. **Off site:** Sailing, riding and canoeing nearby - Lac de Jouarres. Canal du Midi.

**Charges** 2002

| | |
|---|---|
| Per large pitch, incl. 2 persons and electricity (6A), water and drainage | € 22.00 |
| smaller pitch excl. electricity | € 16.00 |
| extra person | € 3.50 |
| child (2-7 yrs) | € 2.50 |
| dog | € 1.50 |
| supplement for 10A electricity | € 1.30 |

**Tel:** 04 68 91 24 86. **Fax:** 04 68 91 24 86. **E-mail:** mas.lignieres@mageos.com. **Reservations:** Made until 25/6 with deposit (25%) and fee (€ 10). **Open** April - 31 October.

**Directions:** From A61 autoroute take Lézignan-Corbières exit, through the town via the D611 to Homps, then via the D910 to Olonzac. Go through the village following the signs to Minerve (D10). Follow road for approx. 4 km. taking left hand turn to Cesseras (D168). At Cesseras follow signs to Fauzan for approx another 4 km. Site is signed to the right where there is a climb up a winding road, which can be a little narrow in places.

## Mediterranean
# Camping Naturiste de la Sablière

Domaine de la Sablière, St Privat de Champclos, 30430 Barjac

Spectacularly situated in the Cèze Gorges, this naturist site occupies a much larger area than its 250 pitches might suggest. It offers a wide variety of facilities, all within a really peaceful, wooded and dramatic setting. Pitches are grouped in areas - 'Mesange' (mainly for tents with cars banned in high season and parking provided 200 m. away) and 'Fauvette' at the bottom of the gorge alongside the river at some points close to the main access road, which is well surfaced but steep and winding. A newer area, 'Pinson', is near the top of the hill, the side of which forms part of the site. The pitches themselves are mainly flat on terraces, attractively situated among a variety of trees and shrubs. Some with low overhang. Many are of a good size and have electricity. A pool complex provides a children's pool and two large pools, one of which can be covered by a sliding glass dome, bar, sauna, TV room and disco. This is essentially a family run and orientated site and Gaby Cespedes, and her team provide a personal touch that is unusual in a large site. This no doubt contributes to the relaxed and very informal atmosphere - first time naturists would find this a gentle introduction into naturism without any pressure. You must expect some fairly steep walking between pitches, pool complex, restaurant and supermarket, although there is a minibus service in high season. Member of France 4 Naturisme.

**Facilities:** Six good unisex sanitary blocks (two new in 2001) have excellent free hot showers in typical open plan, naturist site style, washbasins (cold water), baby baths and facilities for people with disabilities. Washing up and laundry sinks. Laundry. Supermarket and charcuterie. Open air, covered restaurant (all season) with good value waiter service meals and a takeaway in an attractive setting. Swimming pool complex. Small café/crêperie. Varied and numerous activities include walking, climbing, swimming, canoeing, fitness trail, fishing (permit required), archery, tennis, minigolf and volleyball, book binding, pottery, yoga etc. Entertainment programme for adults and children (mid June - end Aug). Torch useful. **Off site:** Barjac with its Antiques Fair at Easter and mid-August. Alès, Chemin de Fer des Cevennes.

**Charges** 2003

| | |
|---|---|
| Per pitch incl. 2 persons | € 11.00 - € 28.00 |
| extra person | € 3.00 - € 6.10 |
| child under 8 yrs | free - € 5.60 |
| electricity | € 3.60 |
| dog | € 1.00 - € 2.50 |

**Tel:** 04 66 24 51 16. Fax: 04 66 24 58 69. E-mail: sabliere@club-internet.fr. **Reservations:** Made with deposit (25%) and fee (€ 30)- contact site. **Open** Easter - end September.

**Directions:** From Barjac take D901 east for 3 km. Site is signed just before St Privat-de-Champclos and is approx. 3 km. on narrow roads following camp signs.

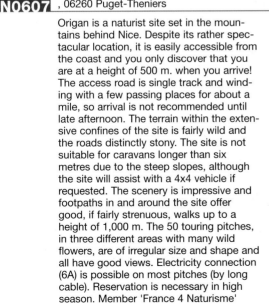

## Mediterranean
# Domaine Naturiste Club Origan

, 06260 Puget-Theniers

Origan is a naturist site set in the mountains behind Nice. Despite its rather spectacular location, it is easily accessible from the coast and you only discover that you are at a height of 500 m. when you arrive! The access road is single track and winding with a few passing places for about a mile, so arrival is not recommended until late afternoon. The terrain within the extensive confines of the site is fairly wild and the roads distinctly stony. The site is not suitable for caravans longer than six metres due to the steep slopes, although the site will assist with a 4x4 vehicle if requested. The scenery is impressive and footpaths in and around the site offer good, if fairly strenuous, walks up to a height of 1,000 m. The 50 touring pitches, in three different areas with many wild flowers, are of irregular size and shape and all have good views. Electricity connection (6A) is possible on most pitches (by long cable). Reservation is necessary in high season. Member 'France 4 Naturisme'

**Facilities:** Sanitary facilities, exceptionally clean when we visited, are of a standard and type associated with most good naturist sites - mainly British type WCs, mostly open plan hot showers and ample washbasins with hot and cold water. Laundry facilities. Shop (15/6-21/8). Bar/restaurant (all season). Takeaway. Heated swimming pools, one for children (1/5-31/8). Jacuzzi and sauna. Disco in cellars. Tennis. Fishing. Bicycle hire. Organised activities for adults and children (high season). Individual barbecues are not permitted. Torches advised. **Off site:** The nearby small town of Puget-Theniers is very pleasant and offers choice of bars, cafés, shops, etc. Steam train. Eco-museum of the Roudoule.

**Charges** 2002

| | |
|---|---|
| Per unit incl. 1 person | € 12.00 - € 17.00 |
| incl. 2 persons | € 14.00 - € 24.00 |
| incl. 3 persons | € 17.00 - € 29.00 |
| extra person | € 5.00 - € 8.00 |
| child (4-10 yrs) | free - € 5.00 |
| electricity | € 4.00 |
| leisure package | € 0.46 - € 0.92 |

**Tel:** 04 93 05 06 00. Fax: 04 93 05 09 34. E-mail: info@club-origan.com. **Reservations:** Made with 25% deposit and fee (€ 30). **Open** 12 April - 30 September.

**Directions:** Heading west on the N202, just past the town of Puget-Theniers, turn right at camp sign at level crossing; site is 1.5 km.

## Mediterranean
# Camping Le Sérignan Plage Nature
34410 Sérignan

the travel service
TO BOOK
Ferry ✓
Pitch ✓
Accommodation ✓
01892 55 98 98

Sérignan Plage Nature is a very comfortable and distinctly characterful naturist site beside a large sandy beach. It was for many years run as a private club but in recent years the charming, English speaking owner, Jean Guy Amat, has improved facilities here to make the site a comfortable, relaxed and friendly naturist campsite. Jean Guy also owns Sérignan Plage next door. The site has 260 touring pitches (out of 500) on level grass and all with 5A electricity. The pitches vary in size (80-120 sq.m), the smaller ones nearest to the beach with less shade and sandy, whilst many of the larger grassy ones further back are of a comfortable size with varying shade from the varieties of trees that have been encouraged to grow to a good size (utilising waste water for irrigation). A new area away from the beach and this has younger saplings only. The Romanesque architectural style of several of the buildings (one is called the Forum) has been preserved. There is a warm and friendly ambience at the bar and restaurant and evening entertainment is provided. This atmosphere is helped in no small measure by the enthusiasm of the managers. This is a well equipped family oriented campsite, with many facilities and good entertainment in season. It has direct access to a superb, safe and virtually private naturist beach of fine sand (with lifeguard in high season). Member 'France 4 Naturisme'.

**Facilities:** The toilet blocks of differing design have all been refurbished, and all offer modern facilities with some washbasins in cabins and both British and Turkish style WCs. All is clean and well maintained. Dishwashing under cover. Washing machines. Large supermarket, market for fresh fruit and vegetables, newsagent/souvenir shop and ice cream kiosk. Bar, restaurant with reasonably priced menu. Evening entertainment. Children's disco. **Off site:** Riding 2 km.

**Charges 2002**

| | |
|---|---|
| Per unit incl. 1 or 2 persons | € 13.00 - € 26.00 |
| extra person | € 3.50 - € 4.00 |
| electricity (5A) | € 3.00 |
| dog | € 3.00 |

**Tel:** 04 67 32 09 61. **Fax:** 04 67 32 26 36. **E-mail:** info@serignsnnaturisme.com. **Reservations:** Made from 1 Feb. with deposit (€ 61), fee (€ 15,24) and cancellation insurance (€ 70). **Open** 1 May - 30 September.

**Directions:** From A9 exit 35 (Béziers Est) follow signs for Sérignan on D64 (9 km). Prior to Sérignan, take road to Sérignan Plage. At small multi sign (blue) turn right onto one-way single carriageway (poorly surfaced) for 500 m. At T-junction turn left over small bridge and site is 75 m. on right immediately after left hand bend (not the first, but the second naturist site).

## Mediterranean
# Domaine Naturiste La Clapère
route de Las Illas, 66480 Maureillas

This very attractive naturist site is situated in the rural lower ranges of the Pyrénées, in a wooded valley in the Albères. It occupies a large natural area (50 hectares) that includes a fast flowing small river and offers a choice of 200 good sized pitches on no less than eight separate terraces, all very natural. They are all slightly different in character; two for example are alongside the river, one is among fruit trees, another among vines. Electricity is available on five terraces, the others being more suitable for tents. The river provides an attractive waterfall and a deep pool for non-serious fishing (but you may not remove the crayfish). This is one of a small number of very attractive, unspoilt naturist sites located in beautiful, wild countryside. It is little wonder that more and more campers and caravanners are turning to naturist sites for their holidays in these more environmentally conscious times.

**Facilities:** Three modern sanitary blocks of unusual design provide good facilities. The first block is heated by solar panels, so if the weather is not so good, the water is cooler. Toilets are both British and Turkish style, showers open plan. Dishwashing and laundry sinks. Washing machines in one block. The shop although small, is well stocked. Bar and terrace with views of the Pyrénées. Restaurant and takeaway (all 15/5 -15/9). Large swimming pool, smaller children's pool, and ample paved sunbathing areas. Good playground. Table tennis, boules and volleyball. Fishing. Organised rambles. **Off site:** Nearby town of Céret has a Saturday morning market.

**Charges 2002**

| | |
|---|---|
| Per person | € 4.00 - € 6.50 |
| child (0-14 yrs) | € 2.50 - € 4.50 |
| pitch | € 4.00 - € 6.50 |
| electricity (3A) | € 3.20 |
| local tax | € 0.12 - € 0.25 |

**Tel:** 04 68 83 36 04. **Fax:** 04 68 83 34 44. **E-mail:** clapere@aol.fr. **Reservations:** Made with deposit (30%). **Open** 1 April - 31 October.

**Directions:** Take last autoroute (A9) exit before Spain (Boulou exit). Leave Boulou on N9 in the direction of Le Perthus for 3 km. Turn right onto N618 to Maureillas-las-Illas, then D13 (Las Illas/Riunoguès) to site (2 km). Uphill winding road little narrow in parts. Site entrance on right.

## Domaine Naturiste Riva Bella

BP 21, 20270 Alèria

A relaxed, informal naturist site beside a glorious beach, Riva Bella is arguably camping and caravanning at its very best. Although offering a large number and variety of pitches, they are situated in such a huge area of varied and beautiful countryside and seaside that it is difficult to believe it could ever become overcrowded. The site is divided into several distinct areas - pitches and bungalows, alongside the sandy beach, in a wooded glade with ample shade, behind the beach, or beside the lake/lagoon which is a feature of this site. The ground is undulating, so getting an absolutely level pitch could be a problem in the main season. Although electric hook-ups are available in most parts, a long cable is probably a necessity. There is an interesting evening entertainment programme. A recent addition is a therapy centre with treatments based on marine products. Noël Pasqual is fully proud of his site and the fairly unobtrusive rules are designed to ensure that everyone is able to relax, whilst preserving the natural beauty of the environment. There is, for example, a restriction on the movement of cars in certain areas (but ample free parking). Generally the ambience is relaxed and informal with nudity only obligatory on the beach itself. Member 'France 4 Naturisme'.

**Facilities:** Toilet facilities in several blocks have been completely refurbished. Whilst fairly typical in design for naturist sites, they are fitted and decorated to the highest standards facilities for disabled people and babies. Large well stocked shop (15/5-30/9). Fridge hire. Excellent restaurant (all season) with reasonable prices overlooks the lagoon. Snack bar beside the beach during the main season (1/6-30/9). Watersports including sailing school, fishing, sub-aqua etc. Therapy centre. Sauna. Volleyball, aerobics, table tennis, giant draughts and archery. Fishing. Mountain bike hire. Half-court tennis. Herd of llamas to watch. The police/fire service ban barbecues during the summer as a safety precaution. **Off site:** Riding 5 km.

**Charges** 2003

| | |
|---|---|
| Per unit incl. 2 persons | € 17.00 - € 29.00 |
| 1 person | € 13.00 - € 21.00 |
| extra person | € 4.00 - € 8.00 |
| child (0-8 yrs) | € 2.00 - € 4.50 |
| electricity | € 3.50 |
| dog | € 2.50 - € 3.00 |
| local tax | € 0.15 |

**Tel:** 04 95 38 81 10. Fax: 04 95 38 91 29. E-mail: riva-bella@wanadoo.fr. **Reservations:** Made with deposit and fee/cancellation insurance. **Open** 12 April - 11 October.

**Directions:** Site is approx. 8 km. north of Aleria on N198 (Bastia) road. Watch for signs and unmade road to it and follow for 4 km.

## Camping Naturiste Club La Chiappa

20137 Porto-Vecchio

This holiday paradise stands in a magnificent setting on the Chiappa peninsula, which juts out into the bluest of seas. It is an extensive naturist site with 3 km. of private beach. There are 220 pitches for caravans and tents, plus 430 bungalows to rent. Even when full, there should be lots of space and something to suit all tastes - in fact, here you can be as private and relaxed or as convivial as you wish. There are three beaches where you are sure to find a quiet spot and where it is safe to swim, or alternatively enjoy the pool. There are also extensive grounds and gardens. The pitches are large, part shaded and mainly level, and some have 6A electrical connections (long leads necessary).

**Facilities:** There are more than enough sanitary blocks and open plan facilities, which are clean and modern. Dishwashing sinks. Washing machines. Motorcaravan services. Well stocked shop. Three bars, restaurant meals and snacks. Baby sitting service. Swimming pool. Play area and mini club for children. Riding, tennis, fishing, diving, keep fit and much more (some at extra cost). Torches useful.

**Charges** 2002

| | |
|---|---|
| Per pitch incl. electricity | € 10.00 - € 12.00 |
| adult | € 7.00 - € 9.00 |
| child (5-13 yrs) | € 3.50 - € 4.50 |
| tent pitch | € 6.50 - € 8.00 |

**Tel:** 04 95 70 00 31. Fax: 04 95 70 07 70. E-mail: chiappa@wanadoo.fr. **Reservations:** Contact site. **Open** 18 May - 5 October.

**Directions:** From Bastia on N198 heading south, continue through Porto-Vecchio for 2 km. Turn left onto unclassified road signed 'Pointe de la Chiappa' and follow camp signs.

# Camping Naturist U Furu

Route de Muratello, 20137 Porto-Vecchio

The contrast between the busy coastal resorts and the peace and tranquility of U Furu makes it difficult to believe this site is barely eight kilometres from the busy beaches, port and town of Porto Vecchio. This small, 50 pitch site, is set in 30 hectares of rocky, wooded mountain country alongside a river. The pitches vary in size and are arranged on one bank of the river or on terraces above. Long electricity leads are required. The single traditional toilet block is centrally located, as are the pool which is overlooked by the bar and open air restaurant terrace. A small shop is open in high season. The main attraction of this site is the six kilometres of walks alongside the river leading to rock pools big enough to swim in and to waterfalls. Good shoes are needed for the river walks.

**Facilities:** Traditional toilet block with washbasins, hot and cold showers, toilets and a washing machine. Shop, bar and restaurant in high season. Outdoor swimming pool (98 sq.m). Table tennis, volleyball, badminton, tennis. Small children's play area. River walk and swimming. Torches useful.

**Charges** 2002

| | |
|---|---|
| Per adult | € 4.50 - € 5.50 |
| child | € 2.00 - € 2.50 |
| pitch | € 2.50 - € 3.50 |
| vehicle | € 0.70 - € 0.80 |
| motorcaravan | € 1.50 - € 1.80 |
| caravan | € 0.70 - € 0.90 |
| electricity | € 2.50 - € 2.80 |

**Tel:** 04 95 70 10 83. Fax: 04 95 70 63 47.
**Reservations:** Advised for July/Aug; contact centre. Single men are not accepted unless they have a naturist card. **Open** 15 May - 15 October.

**Directions:** Using by-pass at Porto-Vecchio, take exit marked Muratello - U Furu is signed from this exit and along the winding minor road to the site.

# The Regions and Départements of France

# Open All Year

The following sites are understood to accept caravanners and campers all year round, **although the list also includes some sites open for at least 10 months.** For sites marked with a star (*) please check our report for dates and other restrictions. In any case, it is always wise to phone as, for example, facilities available may be reduced.

**Brittany**
2910 Pen-ar-Steir
4401M Petit Port
**Normandy**
6101M La Campière
7609M Etennemare
7610M Cany-Barville
**Northern France**
5905M Mauberge
8003 Port de Plaisance
**Paris / Ile de France**
7502 Bois de Boulogne
7804M Etang d'Or
**Eastern France**
0802M Lac des Vieilles-Forges
0803M Lac de Bairon
6801 Ile du Rhin*
8802 Belle Hutte*
8804 Lac de Bouzey
**Burgundy**
2104M Fouché
2106 Les Bouleaux

**Loire Valley**
3605M Les Vieux Chênes
4106 Dugny
4908 Ile d'Offard *
5309M Gué St-Léonard
8604 Le Futuriste
**Savoy-Dauphiny Alpes**
7401 Les Deux Glaciers
7407 Escale *
7413 La Plage*
3807 La Chabannerie
3808 Au Joyeux Réveil *
3811 Champ du Moulin *
7302 Le Versoyen*
7303 Les Lanchettes*
**Atlantic Coast**
3320M L'Eyre
4009M Lou Broustaricq
6404 Les Gaves
**Dordogne / Aveyron**
2415 Les Deux Vallées
2428 Barnabé
4607 La Plage
**Limousin / Auvergne**
6306 Le Clos Auroy

**Rhône Valley**
6901M Porte de Lyon
**Provence**
8408 La Simioune
**Midi-Pyrénées**
0903 Le Montagnou
0905M La Prade
0908 Du Lac
3204N Naturiste Deveze
6503 Pyrénées *
6507 Le Rioumajou
6508 Le Lavedan
6509 Soleil du Pibeste
8101 Entre Deux Lacs
**Mediterranean**
0605 La Vieille Ferme
0608 Les Cigales
0611 Panoramic
1111 Val d'Aleth
3406 L'Oliveraie
3423 De Chênes
6613 L'Eau Vive*
6617 Mar I Sol
6618 Mas Llinas *
8321 Les Tournels *

# Dogs

Since the introduction in 2000 of the Passports for Pets scheme many British campers and caravanners have been encouraged to take their pets with them on holiday, but not only are the Pet Travel conditions understandably strict, the procedure is quite lengthy and complicated, and may be modified again - you can check the current situation via the Passports for Pets web site: http://freespace.virgin.net/passports.forpets

For the benefit of those who want to take their dogs to France, we list here the sites which have indicated to us that they do not accept dogs. The sites shown in italics do not accept dogs at certain times. We do advise that phoning the site first to check – there may be limits on numbers, breeds, or times of the year when they are excluded.

**Brittany**
2201 Les Capucines
2914 Kerlann
2921M Bois de la Palud
3503M Fougères
4410 Le Patisseau
**Normandy**
1409 Brévedent
**Paris / Ile de France**
7701 Davy Crockett Ranch
**Eastern France**
*6808 Clair Vacances*
**Vendée / Charente**
1701 Bois Soleil
1702 Puits de L'Auture
1704 Bonne Anse Plage
8502 du Jard
8503 La Loubine
8506 Le Pas Opton

8510 Le Bois Dormant
8515 La Yole
8521 Les Ecureuils
**Burgundy**
7104M Val d'Arroux
**Atlantic Coast**
3320M L'Eyre
4004 La Paillotte
6406 Pavillon Royal
**Dordogne / Aveyron**
1602 Gorges du Chambon
2404 Moulin du Roch
2405 Hauts de Ratebout
4604 Moulin de Laborde
**Rhône Valley**
*2609 Les Truffières*
**Provence**
8402 Naturiste de Bélézy

**Mediterranean**
0608 Les Cigales
3007 Boisson
3414 La Carabasse
6604 Le Soleil
**Corsica**
2003 Merendella

**Sites that accept dogs but with certain restrictions - check with site::**
5003 Lez-Eaux
4005 Le Col-Vert
1602 Gorges du Chambon
2429 Moulin du Bleufond
2301 Poinsouze
2603 Le Grand Lierne
3413 Le Neptune
8320 Les Pêcheurs
4012N Naturiste Arnaoutchot

# Bicycle Hire

We understand that the following sites have bicycles to hire **on site**. Where bicycle hire facilities are within easy reach of the site (and we have been given details), we include this information in the individual site reports. However, if this facility is important to you, we would recommend that you contact the site to check as the situation can change.

| | | | | | | | |
|---|---|---|---|---|---|---|---|
| 2200 | Des Vallées | 8513 | Pong | 3301 | La Dune | 0703 | Soleil Vivarais |
| 2201 | Les Capucines | 8520M | Petite Boulogne | 3306 | Palace | 0704 | Rouveyrolle |
| 2205 | Le Vieux Moulin | 8521 | Les Ecureuils | 3308 | Barbanne | 0709 | Plantas |
| 2213 | Port l'Epine | 8524M | Jarny-Ocean | 3311 | Côte d'Argent | 0711 | Pommier |
| 2901 | Ty-Nadan | 8526 | Guyonnière | 3313 | Grands Pins | 0713 | Coudoulets |
| 2905 | Orangerie | 8527 | Oceano d'Or | 3320M | Eyre | 2602 | Senaud |
| 2908 | Le Panoramic | 8528 | Places Dorées | 3324 | Océan | 2603 | Grand Lierne |
| 2909 | Raguénèz-Plage | 8530 | Grand' Métairie | 4002 | Les Chênes | 2604 | Couspeau |
| 2911 | La Plage | 8531 | La Trévillière | 4003 | Pins du Soleil | 2612 | Gervanne |
| 2912 | Manoir de Kerlut | 8532 | Val de Vie | 4004 | Paillotte | 4201M | Charlieu |
| 2914 | Kerlann | 8536 | La Forêt | 4005 | Col-Vert | 0401 | Hippocampe |
| 2916 | Genets d'Or | 8543 | Bolée D'Air | 4006 | Eurosol | 0402 | Verdon |
| 2920M | Bois de Pleuven | 8544 | Les Brunelles | 4007 | Lous Seurrots | 0502 | Serre-Chevalier |
| 2925 | Bois Ecureuils | 8545 | Les Roses | 4010 | La Rive | 8405 | Sorguette |
| 2929 | Grand Large | 8546 | Dune des Sables | 4011 | Sen Yan | 8407 | Carpe Diem |
| 2931 | Roche Percée | 8547 | Les Pirons | 4014 | Lou P'tit Poun | 8409 | Pont d'Avignon |
| 2932 | Pendruc | 8548 | Le Chaponnet | 4015 | Les Ecureuils | 8412 | Sources |
| 3502 | Des Ormes | 8549 | Beaulieu | 4016 | Les Vignes | 0902 | Arize |
| 4401M | Petit Port | 8550 | Bahamas Beach | 4017 | La Réserve | 0906 | Pré Lombard |
| 4404 | Sainte-Brigitte | 8551 | Le Bois Joli | 4020 | Sylvamar | 3201 | Florence |
| 4409 | Deffay | 8553 | Parée Préneau | 6407 | Le Ruisseau | 3206 | Trois Vallées |
| 4413 | Hermitage | 7901M | Noron | 6411 | Col d'Ibardin | 3208 | Talouch |
| 4417 | Ajoncs d'Or | 2811M | Bonneval | 6414 | Bérrua | 6509 | Soleil du Pibeste |
| 5601 | Grande Métairie | 3607M | Les Chênes | 1207 | Monteillac | 8101 | Entre Deux Lacs |
| 5602 | La Plage | 3701 | Mignardière | 1208 | Les Genêts | 8103M | Gourjade |
| 5612 | Les Iles | 3706 | Arada Parc | 1209 | Boissiere | 8201 | Trois Cantons |
| 5613 | Mané Guernehué | 4501 | Bois du Bardelet | 1214 | Soleil-Levant | 0603 | Bergerie |
| 1403 | Martragny | 4101 | Val de Loire | 1215 | Marmotel | 1101 | Eden II |
| 1405 | Le Colombier | 4102 | Grenouillière | 1602 | Gorges-Ch'bon | 1106 | Arnauteille |
| 1406 | Hautes Coutures | 4103 | Alicourts | 1603M | Le Champion | 1107 | Mimosas |
| 1407 | La Vallée | 4104 | Marais | 2400 | La Tuilière | 1108 | Nautique |
| 1409 | Brévedent | 4106 | Dugny | 2401 | Le Verdoyer | 1111 | Val d'Aleth |
| 5000 | Etang-Haizes | 4107 | Grande Tortue | 2402 | Les Granges | 3002 | Petite Camargue |
| 5003 | Lez-Eaux | 4900M | Lac de Maine | 2406 | Le Paradis | 3005 | Eden |
| 5005 | Le Cormoran | 4901 | Etang-Brèche | 2408 | Moulin de David | 3011 | Mas de Rey |
| 5007 | Anse du Brick | 4902 | Chantepie | 2410 | Le Moulinal | 3012 | Ile des Papes |
| 0200 | Vivier-Carpes | 4904 | Etang | 2411 | Aqua Viva | 3014 | Soubeyranne |
| 6201 | La Bien-Assise | 4906 | Montsabert | 2415 | Deux Vallées | 3403 | Napoléon |
| 8001 | Drancourt | 4907 | Vallée Vignes | 2417 | Port de Limeuil | 3404 | Lou Village |
| 8004 | Le Royon | 4908 | Ile d'Offard | 2418 | St Avit Loisirs | 3406 | Oliveraie |
| 8006 | Val de Trie | 4909 | Isle Verte | 2422 | Chênes Verts | 3407 | Sérignan Plage |
| 8009 | Val d'Authie | 5301M | Loisirs de Vaux | 2423 | Moulin Paulhiac | 3409 | La Yole |
| 7701 | Davy Crockett | 7203 | Chanteloup | 2432 | Les Peneyrals | 3411 | Farret |
| 7703M | Jablines | 8601 | Petit Trianon | 4604 | Moulin Laborde | 3413 | Neptune |
| 0802M | Vieilles-Forges | 8603 | Relais du Miel | 4605 | Le Rêve | 3417 | Mimosas |
| 5202 | Forge Ste Marie | 2100 | Lac de Panthier | 4607 | La Plage | 3420 | Californie Plage |
| 6807 | Les Sources | 2105 | Grappe d'Or | 4608 | Lacomté | 3421 | Berges du Canal |
| 8804 | Lac de Bouzey | 7105 | Moulin Collonge | 4610M | Le Soulhol | 6602 | Ma Prairie |
| 8808 | Des Bans | 7106 | Montrouant | 4701 | Moulin du Périé | 6605 | Le Haras |
| 1701 | Bois Soleil | 7107 | Epervière | 4703 | Fonrives | 6607 | Brasilia |
| 1702 | Puits de L'Auture | 7109 | Lac de St-Point | 4707 | Fontaine du Roc | 6613 | Eau Vive |
| 1704 | Bonne Anse | 7111 | du Lac | 0301 | Filature | 6621 | Roussillon |
| 1705 | Orée du Bois | 8903M | Coullemières | 0305 | Petite Valette | 6624 | Trivoly |
| 1711 | Monplaisir | 2500 | Val de Bonnal | 0306 | Deneuvre | 8302 | Esterel |
| 1714 | Sequoia Parc | 2503 | Bois de Reveuge | 0317M | Municipal | 8306 | La Baume |
| 1717 | Les Charmilles | 3901 | Plage Blanche | 1905 | La Rivière | 8313 | Beau Vezé |
| 1719 | Logis du Breuil | 3903 | Chalain | 1906 | Le Mialaret | 8314 | Lacs du Verdon |
| 8502 | Du Jard | 7403M | Belvédère | 2301 | Poinsouze | 8317 | Bergerie |
| 8503 | La Loubine | 7406 | Colombière | 4303 | Vaubarlet | 8321 | Tournels |
| 8504 | La Garangeoire | 7408 | Les Rosières | 8702 | Leychoisier | 2419N | Le Couderc |
| 8506 | Le Pas Opton | 7410 | Europa | 6304 | Grange Fort | 3204N | Deveze |
| 8507 | Les Biches | 7411 | Le Taillefer | 6306 | Clos Auroy | 3316N | Euronat |
| 8508 | Puerta del Sol | 7412 | Écureuil | 0101 | Plaine Tonique | 2004N | Riva Bella |
| 8509 | Abri des Pins | 3801 | Coin Tranquille | 0102 | Ile Chambod | 3408N | Sérignan Nature |
| 8510 | Bois Dormant | 3803 | La Cascade | 0702 | Ardéchois | 4012N | Arnaoutchot |

# Fishing

We are pleased to include details of sites which provide facilities for fishing on the site. Many other sites are near rivers or are in popular fishing areas and have facilities within easy reach. Where we have been given details, we have included this information in the individual site reports. It is always best to contact individual sites to check that they provide for your individual requirements.

| | | | | | | | |
|---|---|---|---|---|---|---|---|
| 2204 | Le Châtelet | 1711 | Monplaisir | 4017 | La Réserve | 2602 | Senaud |
| 2209 | Galinée | 1720 | Au Fil de l'Eau | 4019 | Saint Martin | 2612 | Gervanne |
| 2213 | Port l'Epine | 8504 | Garangeoire | 6404 | Les Gaves | 2613 | Hirondelle |
| 2214 | Port La Chaine | 8506 | Pas Opton | 6406 | Pavillon Royal | 4201M | Charlieu |
| 2901 | Ty-Nadan | 8513 | Pong | 6407 | Le Ruisseau | 0401 | Hippocampe |
| 2902 | St-Laurent | 8519 | Marais Braud | 6409 | La Chêneraie | 0402 | Verdon |
| 2903 | Letty | 8526 | Guyonnière | 1200 | Peyrelade | 0403 | Moulin de Ventre |
| 2905 | Orangerie | 8535 | La Ningle | 1202 | Les Rivages | 0406 | Haut-Verdon |
| 2906 | Pil-Koad | 8551 | Bois Joli | 1204 | Les Tours | 0502 | Serre-Chevalier |
| 2909 | Raguénèz-Plage | 7901M | Noron | 1205 | Terrasses du Lac | 8405 | La Sorguette |
| 2911 | La Plage | 2811M | Bonneval | 1208 | Les Genêts | 0902 | Arize |
| 2913 | Des Abers | 3607M | Les Chênes | 1209 | La Boissiere | 0903 | Montagnou |
| 2927 | Ddes Dunes | 3711M | Bord du Cher | 1210M | Lauradiol | 0906 | Pré Lombard |
| 3500 | Vieux Chêne | 4501 | Bois du Bardelet | 1214 | Soleil-Levant | 0908 | Du Lac |
| 3502 | Des Ormes | 4103 | Alicourts | 1215 | Marmotel | 3206 | Trois Vallées |
| 4402M | Du Moulin | 4104 | Marais | 1216 | Les Peupliers | 6506 | Pyrenees Natura |
| 4404 | Sainte-Brigitte | 4105M | Grands Prés | 1601M | Bourgines | 8102 | Moulin de Julien |
| 4409 | Deffay | 4106 | Dugny | 1603M | Le Champion | 8104M | Auzerals |
| 4416 | Armor-Héol | 4901 | Etang-Brèche | 1605M | Cognac | 0608 | Cigales |
| 5601 | Grande Métairie | 4902 | Chantepie | 1606 | Marco Bignac | 1101 | Eden II |
| 5608M | Le Pâtis | 4904 | Etang | 2400 | La Tuilière | 1104 | Martinet Rouge |
| 5612 | Les Iles | 4907 | Vallée-Vignes | 2401 | Verdoyer | 1111 | Val d'Aleth |
| 5613 | Mané-G'hué | 4909 | Isle Verte | 2404 | Moulin du Roch | 3000 | Gaujac |
| 5616 | Vallée-Ninian | 5301M | Vaux | 2406 | Le Paradis | 3006 | Fumades |
| 1403 | Martragny | 5309M | Gué St-Léonard | 2407 | Lestaubière | 3007 | Boisson |
| 1405 | Colombier | 7203 | Chanteloup | 2409 | Soleil Plage | 3012 | Ile des Papes |
| 1406 | Hautes Coutures | 7206M | Val de Sarthe | 2410 | Le Moulinal | 3411 | Farret |
| 1408 | Le Puits | 8603 | Relais du Miel | 2411 | Aqua Viva | 3413 | Neptune |
| 1409 | Brévedent | 8604 | Le Futuriste | 2414 | Bel Ombrage | 3415 | Nouvelle Floride |
| 1410M | Château | 8605M | Le Riveau | 2415 | Deux Vallées | 3416 | Charlemagne |
| 5000 | Etang-Haizes | 8608 | Les Peupliers | 2417 | Port de Limeuil | 3418 | Borio de Roque |
| 5002M | J-L Bougourd | 8609 | Saint Cyr | 2421M | Repaire | 3420 | Californie Plage |
| 5003 | Lez-Eaux | 2100 | Lac de Panthier | 2423 | Paulhiac | 6603 | Cala Gogo |
| 5005 | Cormoran | 2104M | Fouché | 2428 | Barnabé | 6604 | Soleil |
| 5006 | Grand Large | 5803 | Bezolle | 2429 | Bleufond | 6607 | Brasilia |
| 5007 | Anse du Brick | 7104M | Val d'Arroux | 2432 | Les Peneyrals | 8307 | Etoile d'Argens |
| 5008 | Haliotis | 7105 | Collonge | 4604 | Laborde | 8308 | Paradis |
| 5009 | Gerfleur | 7106 | Montrouant | 4607 | La Plage | 8310 | La Plage |
| 6101M | Campière | 7107 | Epervière | 4610M | Le Soulhol | 8312 | Domaine |
| 7604 | Source | 7108 | Etang Neuf | 4703 | Fonrives | 8317 | Bergerie |
| 0200 | Vivier-Carpes | 7109 | Lac St-Point | 4705 | Campech | 8318 | Rives de l'Agay |
| 0206M | Cany-Barville | 7110M | Port d'Arciat | 0301 | Filature | 8320 | Pêcheurs |
| 5901 | La Chaumière | 7111 | Du Lac | 0305 | Petite Valette | 8324 | Moulin-Iscles |
| 6206 | Orée du Bois | 8903M | Coullemières | 0306 | Deneuvre | 2001 | Arinella Bianca |
| 8001 | Drancourt | 2500 | Val de Bonnal | 0317M | Municipal | 2003 | Merendella |
| 8003 | Port-Plaisance | 2503 | Bois de Reveuge | 0320M | Neris Les Bains | 0607N | Origan |
| 8006 | Val de Trie | 2505M | St Point-Lac | 1905 | Rivière | 1109N | Clapotis |
| 7703M | Jablines | 7002M | Lac Vesoul | 1906 | Mialaret | 3010N | Sablière |
| 7708M | Les Prés | 3901 | Plage Blanche | 2301 | Poinsouze | 3204N | Deveze |
| 9500 | Etang | 3903 | Chalain | 4303 | Vaubarlet | 2004N | Riva Bella |
| 7801 | International | 3904 | La Pergola | 8702 | Leychoisier | 4012N | Arnaoutchot |
| 7804M | Etang d'Or | 3905 | Fayolan | 6304 | Grange Fort | 6612N | Clapère |
| 0802M | Vieilles-Forges | 7407 | Escale | 6305 | La Ribeyre | 8514N | Colombier |
| 0803M | Lac de Bairon | 3803 | Cascade | 6307 | Le Pré Bas | | |
| 6703 | Du Ried | 3806 | Trois Lacs | 0101 | Plaine Tonique | | |
| 5201M | Champaubert | 7303 | Lanchettes | 0702 | Ardéchois | | |
| 5202 | Forge-Ste Marie | 3302 | Fontaine-Vieille | 0703 | Soleil Vivarais | | |
| 6803M | Masevaux | 3308 | Barbanne | 0704 | Rouveyrolle | | |
| 5102M | Châlons | 3309 | Le Pressoir | 0705 | Ranc Davaine | | |
| 5501 | Les Breuils | 3320M | L'Eyre | 0707 | Ranchisses | | |
| 8801 | Deux Ballons | 3331 | Panorama | 0708 | Bastide | | |
| 8802 | Belle Hutte | 4004 | Paillotte | 0709 | Plantas | | |
| 8804 | Lac de Bouzey | 4005 | Col-Vert | 0711 | Pommier | | |
| 8807 | Messires | 4007 | Lous Seurrots | 0712 | Ardéchois | | |
| 8808 | Des Bans | 4010 | La Rive | 0713 | Coudoulets | | |

# Riding

We understand that the following sites offer horse riding on site for at least part of the year. However, we would recommend that you contact the site to check that the facility meets your requirements. It is worth bearing in mind that French attitudes to safety may differ from your own (for example, take your own hard hat).

| | | | | | |
|---|---|---|---|---|---|
| 2901 | Ty-Nadan | 4902 | Chantepie | 0410 | International |
| 3500 | Vieux Chêne | 4904 | Etang | 8408 | Simioune |
| 3502 | Des Ormes | 5301M | Loisirs de Vaux | 0902 | Arize |
| 4409 | Deffay | 5803 | Bezolle | 1106 | Arnauteille |
| 5612 | Les Iles | 2503 | Bois de Reveuge | 3002 | Petite Camargue |
| 5005 | Le Cormoran | 3803 | La Cascade | 3406 | Oliveraie |
| 7608M | Colombier | 3311 | Côte d'Argent | 3418 | Borio de Roque |
| 8001 | Drancourt | 4005 | Col-Vert | 3421 | Berges du Canal |
| 7701 | Davy Crockett | 4006 | Eurosol | 3422 | La Creole |
| 7703M | Jablines | 2425 | Tourterelles | 6604 | Le Soleil |
| 6807 | Les Sources | 0301 | La Filature | 8302 | Esterel |
| 8804 | Lac de Bouzey | 6305 | La Ribeyre | 8316 | Les Cigales |
| 1714 | Sequoia Parc | 0703 | Soleil Vivarais | 2001 | Arinella Bianca |
| 8504 | Garangeoire | 0402 | Verdon | 2005N | La Chiappa |
| | | | | 3316N | Euronat |

# Golf

We understand that the following sites have facilities for playing golf. However, we would recommend that you contact the site to check that the facility meets your requirements.

| | | | |
|---|---|---|---|
| 2602 | Château de Senaud | 8609 | Saint Cyr |
| 2930 | Grand Large | 4103 | Parc des Alicourts |
| 3502 | Des Ormes | 8001 | Château de Drancourt |

The following sites inform us that there are golf courses within a short distance (under 4 km). Where facilities are within easy reach but slighly further away, we have included this information in the site reports.

| | | | | | |
|---|---|---|---|---|---|
| 0608 | Les Cigales | 1702 | Puits de L'Auture | 4414M | Henri Dubourg |
| 1110 | La Cité | 2204 | Châtelet | 6406 | Pavillon Royal |
| 1202 | Les Rivages | 2910 | Pen-ar-Steir | 7409 | Plan du Fernuy |
| 1301M | Les Romarins | 2924 | Kéranterec | 8004 | Le Royon |
| 1407 | La Vallée | 4002 | Les Chênes | 8302 | Esterel |

## Public Holidays in France 2003

| | |
|---|---|
| 1 January | New Year's Day |
| 18 April | Good Friday |
| 21 April | Easter Monday |
| 1 May | Labour Day |
| 8 May | VE Day |
| 29 May | Ascension Day |
| 8 June | Whit Monday |
| 14 July | Bastille Day |
| 15 August | Assumption |
| 1 November | All Saints' Day |
| 11 November | Rememberance |
| 25/26 December | Christmas |

Note: The months of July and August are traditionally when the French take their holidays. For this reason, the less touristic parts of France are quiet during these months, while coastal resorts, especially in the south, are very crowded.

## Electrical Connections

The Voltage on most sites in France varies from 220V to 240V AC, which presents no problem for most British appliances. However, the amperage available will vary considerably and may be anything from 2A to 16A, depending on the site, and within the site itself, depending on what supply you wish to pay for. You will probably need a Continental Adapter (rather than the UK CEE 17 one) to plug into the sites' supply.

These can be purchased in the UK, at specialist caravan accessory shops, or in many French hypermarkets, or occasionally they can be borrowed from the site itself. For the sake of safety you should also carry a Polarity Tester, to check that you have connected up correctly.

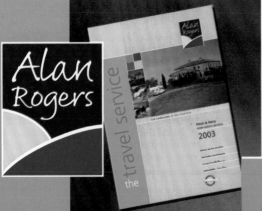

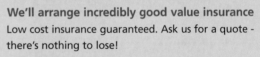

# Travelling in France

Before you set off for a holiday abroad it's worth making yourself a checklist of things to do, and what to pack - We've been travelling abroad several times a year for more than thirty years and we still don't rely on our memory for this, so here is a shortlist of essentials to start you off:

- ❏ Passports
- ❏ Tickets
- ❏ Motor Insurance Certificate, Green Card or Continental Cover clause
- ❏ V5 Registration Document and/or (if not your vehicle) the owners authority
- ❏ Breakdown Insurance Certificate
- ❏ Driving Licence
- ❏ Form E1-11 (to extend NHS Insurance to European destinations)
- ❏ Foreign Currency (euros) and/or Travellers Cheques
- ❏ Credit Card(s)
- ❏ Campsite and Tourist Guide(s)
- ❏ Maps/Road Atlas
- ❏ GB Stickers on car & caravan/trailer
- ❏ Beam deflectors to ensure headlights dip towards the right hand side

- ❏ Red Warning Triangle
- ❏ Spare vehicle/caravan driving light bulbs
- ❏ Torch
- ❏ First-Aid Kit (incl. mosquito repellent)
- ❏ Fire extinguisher
- ❏ Basic tool kit (eg screwdriver, pliers)
- ❏ Continental mains connector/ adaptor, and long cable
- ❏ Polarity tester
- ❏ Spare fuses for car and caravan
- ❏ Spare fan/alternator belt

Remember – it is well worth having your car and caravan serviced before you go, and do check that your outfit is properly 'trimmed'.

# On the Road in France

### The Law

You must be aged eighteen or over to drive a car in France, but a UK national driving licence is sufficient - only non-EU nationals require an International Driving Permit. You should carry your Registration Document, and your Insurance (valid for use on the Continent) and you must display a GB plate. You must carry a warning triangle, and a spare set of light bulbs and your headlights must be adjusted to dip to the right. A first-aid kit and fire extinguisher are recommended but not compulsory.

Drive on the right-hand-side of the road, and remember to look left when turning onto a another road.

### Conditions and Conventions

'A' roads are Autoroutes, usually toll roads
'N' roads are Routes Nationale, the equivalent of our A roads
'D' roads are Routes Departemental, the equivalent of our B roads
'C' roads are Routes Communale, unclassified minor roads

'Prioité a Droite' means 'Give way to traffic coming from your right' (even if you think you are on a more main road and have the right of way - you don't, so give way.

On roundabouts (rounded anti-clockwise of course) traffic already IN the roundabout has priority.

### Traffic Lights

Lights in France turn from Red to Green without going through an amber period. Flashing amber means you can proceed with caution

Most traffic lights have small repeater lights at shoulder height adjacent to the line where you must stop - these are very useful as many traffic lights don't have a set of lights on the far side of the junction.

Watch for 'right filters' - a slowly flashing amber light/arrow which allows you to filter right, with care.

### Pedestrian Crossings

There are lots of pedestrian crossings, even more than in the UK, but they are more often than not ignored by motorists (except those from abroad). Don't be surprised if you're honked at for stopping for pedestrians!

### Autoroutes

Mostly these are toll roads, and you must pay to use them. You will either have to pay at the toll (Péage) where you join, or you must take a ticket from the machine at the Péage and surrender this, with your money or credit card, at the Péage where you leave the Autoroute. There are service areas (Aires de Service) with full facilities every 40 km. on Autoroutes, and rest areas (Aires de Repos) also at regular intervals. Both have

# the travel service

# New for 2003

## ALAN ROGERS' MOBILE HOME AND CAMPING HOLIDAYS

**INSPECTED CAMPSITES & SELECTED**

Superb campsites, ideal for families and couples, offering state-of-the-art fully equipped tents and mobile homes. Just turn up and move in!

- ✓ 70 top sites in France, Italy, Holland
- ✓ All selected and inspected
- ✓ Spacious mobile homes
- ✓ Luxury, ready erected family tents
- ✓ Free children's clubs on many sites
- ✓ Superb facilities on all sites
- ✓ Premium locations (next to stunning beaches or tucked away in beautiful surroundings)
- ✓ Great destinations including Brittany, Mediterranean, Dordogne, Venice, Lake Garda
- ✓ Helpful, friendly couriers on many sites
- ✓ Comprehensive travel pack supplied

# On the Road in France

warning signs well in advance, indicating the facilities and even the price of fuel.

## Signposting

Is better than in the past but the positioning and angling of signposts is something one just gets used to.

## Navigating

Michelin Maps are the most popular, particularly the Michelin 1: 200,000 scale Atlas, but for more detailed maps you can buy IGN Maps, which are the French equivalent of our Ordnance Survey maps, but often even more expensive.

Tips for Navigators: Siitting in the 'hot seat' on the off-side of the car, with a better view ahead, you'll almost certainly be asked to help your driver with advice on when it is safe to overtake - be ultra cautious.

When giving your driver advice at junctions use the word 'OK' if it is safe to go, and 'Wait' if it is not, rather than 'Go, No or Alright', all of which can lead to confusion.

Remember that you go round roundabouts ANTIclockwise so if you use the words 'Second Exit' that's the second one you come to going round anticlockwise!

## Breakdowns

You should have breakdown insurance, towing in France can involve long distances and hefty charges. If you do break down you are required to display your warning triangle 30 m. behind your car (or car and caravan) and it should be visible for at least 100 m. if possible. Don't forget to turn on hazard lights as well. There are emergency phones every 2 km. on Autoroutes.

## Security

Take sensible precautions against theft of, or from, your vehicle and/or caravan - be particularly vigilant in car parks and Aires de Service where thieves are often active.

# On the Road in France - Speed

Most of Europe has a bewildering range of speed limits, but in France it is simple and logical. One set of limits covers motor caravans, solo cars and cars towing trailers or caravans. These are the limits:

In built-up areas 50 kph (31 mph)
Outside built-up areas 90 kph (56 mph)
Motorways 130 kph (81 mph)

There is also a requirement that no vehicle may use a French motorway unless it can cruise at 80 kph (50 mph).

When it is raining the maximum speed outside built-up areas is automatically reduced to 80 kph (50 mph) and on motorways to 110 kph (68 mph). The definition of rain is any time you have to put wipers on, so reduce speed even if it has stopped raining but roads are wet.

On non-charged sections of motorway, speed limits may be reduced to 110 kph (68 mph) and there may be signs on any road reducing the maximum speed allowed because of road conditions or oher factors.

The French do not tend to use a sign on the outskirts of a town or village to tell you a speed limit applies. A name post is sufficient to indicate that built-up area limits apply. On the exit from the town you will see the name post again, but with the name crossed out. That means the built-up area speed limits no longer apply.

Speed limits are rigidly enforced. 110 kph means exactly that - not 111 kph. The French have adopted the Gatso automatic speed recording and photographing machine and holidaymakers have returned home to find a speeding summons waiting.

Under French Law the summons for speeding cannot be enforced unless the driver of the vehicle is clearly identifiable in the photograph. However the majority of speeding motorists are caught by a following Police vehicle or Police speed camera. French Police don't wear reflective jackets and do hide behind hedges.

During the summer months French magistrates escape from stuffy court rooms and set up court in a tent by the road. Motorists caught speeding are escorted there and given on-the-spot fines. In some circumstances the Police can themselves impose an on-the-spot fine. On-the-spot means just that. If you can't pay there and then they'll escort you to a cash machine or bank to draw out money.

Since 2001 laws have come into effect so that anyone caught exceeding the speed limit by more than 40kph will LOSE THEIR LICENCE ON THE SPOT - this means you won't be able to complete your journey without a substitute driver, to say nothing of the standard £900 fine! If you really cannot pay, magistrates have the power to confiscate your vehicle until you do. Anyone caught for a second offence faces a three month jail sentence plus a £2,200 fine.

So although French speed limits are more generous than ours, exceeding the limit can be a seriously expensive pastime!

# Insurance

There is probably no subject which causes campers, caravanners and motor-caravanners venturing abroad more worries than insurance. The problem is that there is an overlap, so that sometimes one problem is apparently covered on two insurance policies. To avoid confusion let's cut through the hype and take a clear look at insurance.

If you are planning on camping, caravanning or motorcaravanning abroad, this is what you will need.

### Road traffic insurance

Under European Law your ordinary car or motorcaravan road insurance will cover you anywhere in the EU. But many policies only provide minimum cover. So if you have an accident your insurance may only cover the cost of damage to the other person's property.

To maintain the same level of cover abroad as you enjoy at home you need to tell your vehicle insurer. Some will automatically cover you abroad with no extra cost and no extra paperwork. Some will say you need a Green Card – which is neither green or on card – but won't charge for it. Some will charge extra for the green card.

Ideally you should contact your vehicle insurer 3-4 weeks before you set off, and confirm your conversation with them in writing.

A good insurance company will provide a European recognised accident report form. On this you mark details of damage to yours and the other party's property and draw a little diagram showing where the vehicles were in relation to each other. You give a copy of your form to the other motorist, he gives you a copy of his. It prevents all the shouting which often accompanies accidents in this country.

### Holiday insurance

This is a multi-part insurance. One part covers your vehicles. If they breakdown or are involved in an accident they can be repaired or returned to this country. The best will even arrange to bring your vehicle home if the driver is unable to proceed.

Many new vehicles come with a free breakdown and recovery insurance which extends into Europe. Some professional motoring journalists have reported that the actual service this provides can be patchy and may not cover the recovery of a caravan or trailer. Our advice is to buy the motoring section of your holiday insurance.

The second section of holiday insurance covers people. It will include the cost of doctor, ambulance and hospital treatment if needed. If needed the better companies will even pay for English language speaking doctors and nurses and will bring a sick or injured holidaymaker home by air ambulance.

The third part of a good holiday insurance policy covers things. If someone breaks in to your motorhome and steals your passports and money, one phone call to the insurance company will have everything sorted out. If you manage to drive over your camera, it's covered.

One part of the insurance which is often ignored is the cancellation section. Few things are as heartbreaking as having to cancel a holiday because a member of the family falls ill. Cancellation insurance cannot take away the disappointment, but it makes sure you don't suffer financially as well.

Ideally you should arrange travel insurance when you book your ferry. If you are using the Alan Rogers' Travel Service they will be able to take care of all your travel insurance requirements.

For those travelling independently, we have arranged special terms with Insure4Europe run in association with Green Flag (and which imposes no restriction on the age of your vehicle). Full details are shown opposite.

### Form E111

By arrangement between the British Government and rest of the European Community Governments, British holiday-makers can enjoy the same health care as that Government offers its own citizens. The form which shows you are entitled to take advantage of this arrangement is called E111.

E111 doesn't replace holiday insurance, but is in addition to. The form is available from all main UK Post Offices. Fill out one for every member of your family. Get it stamped by the counter staff and take it on holiday with you.

In theory one Form E111 lasts you for ever. But we have had reports that in some rural areas in Europe they may not understand that, so our advice is to get a new E111 every year. It is free.

And that is all you need to know about insurance. You know what they say about insurance, don't you? You'll only need it if you haven't got it.

Mike Cazalet

# www.insure④europe.com

## Taking your own tent, caravan or motorhome abroad?

## Looking for the best cover at the best rates?

Our prices considerably undercut most high street prices and the 'in-house insurance' of many tour operators whilst offering equivalent (or higher) levels of cover.

Our annual multi-trip policies offer superb value, covering you not only for your european camping holiday but also subsequent trips abroad for the next 12 months.

### Total Peace of Mind

To give you total peace of mind during your holiday our insurance policies have been specifically tailored to cover most potential eventualities on a self-drive camping holiday. Each is organised through Voyager Insurance Services Ltd who specialize in travel insurance for Europe and for camping in particular. All policies are underwritten by UK Insurance, part of the Green Flag Group.

### 24 Hour Assistance

Our personal insurance provides access to the services of International Medical Rescue (IMR), one of the UK's largest assistance companies. Experienced multi-lingual personnel provide a caring and efficient service 24 hours a day.

European vehicle assistance cover is provided by Green Flag who provide assistance to over 3 million people each year. With a Europe-wide network of over 7,500 garages and agents you know you're in very safe hands.

Both IMR and green flag are very used to looking after the needs of campsite-based holidaymakers and are very familiar with the location of most European campsites, with contacts at garages, doctors and hospitals nearby.

### Save with an Annual policy

If you are likely to make more than one trip to Europe over the next 12 months then our annual multi-trip policies could save you a fortune. Personal cover for a couple starts at just £90 and the whole family can be covered for just £110.
Cover for up to 17 days wintersports participation is included.

**Low Cost Annual multi-trip insurance**

**Premier Annual Europe self-drive**
including 17 days wintersports

### £90 per couple

**Premier Annual Europe self-drive**
including 17 days wintersports

### £110 per family

### Low Cost Combined Personal and Vehicle Assistance Insurance

**Premier Family Package**
10 days cover for vehicle, 2 adults plus dependent children under 16.

### £71-50*

**Premier Couples Package**
10 days cover for vehicle and 2 adults

### £57-75*

\* Motorhomes, cars towing trailers and caravans, all vehicles over 4 years old and holidays longer than 10 days attract supplements – ask us for details. See leaflet for full terms and conditions.

# Money

From January 2002 the French unit of currency has been the EURO ( ) Given that most European countries have now changed to the Euro, one immediate benefit is that you no longer need to change currency every time you cross a border between any of the countries within the Euro Zone (Austria, Belgium, Finland, France, Holland, Germany, Greece, Ireland, Italy, Luxembourg, Portugal and Spain). This has certainly made life easier for all our Irish readers visiting France! For UK residents the benefits are not so obvious, but if for example you're travelling to France via Dover-Ostend or Harwich-Hook of Holland you'll only need one foreign currency you will no longer need to buy Belgian Francs or Dutch Guilders for use en-route.

So how much is a Euro worth? In exactly the same way as previously with the Franc the value of the Euro depends on the daily exchange rate between the pound and the Euro.

Euro notes and coins have been in circulation throughout the Euro Zone countries from 1st January 2002, in the following denominations:

Notes: 5, 10, 20, 50, 100, 200, 500

A 500 note is likely to be worth about £305.00, so be careful not to lose them!

The Euro is sub-divided into Cents (100 Cents = 1 Euro) in the same way that UK pounds are divided into pence, or the old French Franc was divided into Centimes.

Coins: 1 Cent, 2 Cents, 5 Cents, 10 Cents, 20 Cents, 50 Cents, 1, and 2

France is one European country where many transactions are still done with cash. We advise all readers to have some cash with them when they land. Major credit cards (Visa and MasterCard) are accepted in most restaurants, cafes and petrol stations, and can also be used to pay for motorway tolls.

In some of the more rural parts of France they may not be familiar with British issue credit cards as French cards incorporate a computer chip rather than just a magnetic strip. If your card is refused by a trader showing the Visa/MasterCard sign you should say:

*"Les cartes Britanniques ne sont pas des cartes a puce, mais a pistes magnetiques. Ma carte est valable et je vous serais reconnaissant d'en demander la confirmation aupres de votre banque ou de votre centre de traitement."* If you cannot pronounce this don't worry. Just point out this phrase.

Charge cards like American Express and Diners don't seem to be as widely used as they are in the UK.

Eurocheques - these were useful and popular as a means of paying for goods and services, and for obtaining cash. However, they have now been phased out as a result of most European countries having adopted a uniform currency (the Euro).

Travellers cheques are widely accepted but in some places, and small country banks, there is a surcharge for cashing them. We have found that most sites are happy to accept travellers cheques as payment for site fees.

The British Switch card, under the Cirrus name, is widely accepted. French cash machines with the Cirrus symbol will accept British Switch cards with the Cirrus symbol but we suggest not using them if the loss of a card would disrupt your holiday. You can't argue with a machine that just swallowed your card.

Our advice to holidaymakers is to take holiday money in a mixture of cash, travellers cheques and credit card.

# Car Ferry Services

The number of different services from the UK to France provides a wide choice of sailings to meet most needs. The actual choice is a matter of personal preference, influenced by factors such as where you live, your actual destination in France, cost and whether you see the channel crossing as a potentially enjoyable part of your holiday or, (if you are prone to sea-sickness) as something to be endured!

You will find a summary of the services likely to be operating in the year 2002, based on information available at the time of going to press (Oct 2001), together with a number of reports on those services which we have used ourselves during the last two years.

Detailed, up-to-date information and bookings for any of these services, and for campsite pitch reservations, travel insurance etc. can be made through the Alan Rogers Travel Service, telephone 01892 55 98 98.

| Route | Frequency | Crossing Time |
| --- | --- | --- |
| **Brittany Ferries (Tel: 08705 360360)** | | |
| Portsmouth - Caen | Up to 3 daily | 6 hours |
| Portsmouth - St. Malo | Daily | 8.75 hours |
| Poole - Cherbourg (jointly with Condor) | Daily | 2.25 hours |
| Poole - Cherbourg (conventional ferry) | Up to 2 daily | 4.25 hours |
| Plymouth - Roscoff | Up to 3 daily | 6 hours |
| **Condor Ferries (Tel 01305 761551)** | | |
| Poole - St. Malo | Daily | 4.5 hours |
| **Eurotunnel (Tel 08705 353535)** | | |
| Folkestone - Calais | Up to 4 hourly | 35 minutes |
| **Hoverspeed (Tel 08705 240241)** | | |
| Dover - Calais | Up to 12 daily | 45 minutes |
| Folkestone - Boulogne | Up to 6 daily | 55 minutes |
| Newhaven - Dieppe | Up to 3 daily | 2 hours |
| **P&O Portsmouth (Tel 0870 2424999)** | | |
| Portsmouth - Cherbourg (ferry) | Up to 4 daily | 5 hours |
| Portsmouth - Cherbourg (Fast Craft) | Up to 3 daily | 2.75 hours |
| Portsmouth - Le Havre | 3 daily | 5.5 hours |
| **P&O Stena Line (Tel 0870 6000600)** | | |
| Dover - Calais | Up to 2 hourly | 1.25 hours |
| **Sea France (Tel 0870 5711711)** | | |
| Dover - Calais | 15 daily | 1.5 hours |
| **Norfolk Line (Tel 0870 8701020)** | | |
| Dover - Dunkerque | up to 6 daily | 2 hours |

# Ferry Reports

## Brittany Ferries/Condor Fast Ferries
Poole/St Malo

Introduced in 2001, this service has the potential to save a lot of time for those holidaying in Normandy or Brittany especially if, like us, they live in the south or southwest. To be honest, I am a little wary of super-fast ferry services, whether they be hovercraft, hydrofoils or catamarans as in the past they have so often been heavily 'weather dependent', but I must say that the Poole-St Malo service operated by Condor 10 was a real eye-opener. With a capacity for over 700 passengers and around 200 cars and with a cruising speed of around 40 knots, the journey from Poole to St Malo takes a little over two hours - impressive stuff! The on-board facilities include aircraft-style seats for all, a bar, cafeteria and duty-free shop. Loading and unloading at Poole and St Malo is fast and efficient. Congratulations to Brittany and Condor on introducing genuinely innovative services. We used this service ourselves in 2001 taking advantage of the Club Class seating which certainly enhanced our experience.

## SeaFrance
Dover / Calais

SeaFrance operates thirty departures a day on the Dover - Calais route, using four ferries: the 'Cèzanne' (550 cars), 'Manet' and 'Renoir' (each 330 cars) and the new Flagship 'Rodin', which we used in June 2002. Rodin can carry 1,900 passengers, 700 cars and 120 trucks and, at 185 metres in length, she is the largest ship on this route. Travelling at 25 knots she takes just one hour to make the crossing. Most noticeable is the increased width of each lane on the car decks, making door opening much easier. The ship is quieter and the passenger accommodation more luxurious and spacious, than the rest of the fleet.
Generally the staff are efficient and friendly, the ships are clean, and the decor modern and reasonably comfortable. Each ship has a 'Les Relais Gourmet' self-service restaurant, 'La Brasserie' waiter service, 'La Parisien Café' and 'Le Pub' bars. Cèzanne and Renoir have private lounges ( at and extra charge) and all have a bureau de change. We have always found SeaFrance to be fairly flexible about bookings and, if you return to Calais early, they may be able to offer an alternative crossing (certainly possible in low season). We thoroughly enjoy our crossings with SeaFrance and look forward to using them again.

## P&O Irish Sea
Dublin/Cherbourg

A new route and a new ferry from Dublin to Cherbourg is what P&O Irish Sea introduced in 2002. It compliments the already popular Rosslare/Cherbourg route. This service is scheduled to operate every weekend from June to early Sept. and we were lucky enough to be amongst its first passengers. Being able to travel from Dublin direct to France is a great boost for Irish caravanners, for the port of Dublin is easily accessible whether coming from the north or south of the country. We found the crossing was excellent, the fare included all meals and combined with the feel and freshness of this new well equipped ferry, means you enjoy more of a pre-holiday cruise. The European Ambassador is a state-of-the-art vessel providing a first class onboard experience. You find the Fables restaurant, Poets bar, a video lounge, gift shop and outside viewing deck. For young children there is an excellent play room. Accommodation ranges from two to four berth brightly furnished ensuite cabins, a Club Class lounge and Club Cabins with a TV/Video, plus a minibar if wanted. The crossing time is about 18 hours.

## Brittany Ferries
Portsmouth/St Malo or Portsmouth/Caen

We have used these two services on several occasions this year. Both are very comfortable and the choice will normally be determined by your onward destination, St Malo being ideal for Brittany, whereas Caen is probably more convenient for those travelling south or east on arrival in France. The timing of the night sailings on these two services is somewhat different - for comfort and relaxation we prefer the St Malo service, which provides the opportunity to dine in some style (but at a reasonable cost) in the Bretagne's very attractive on-board restaurant before getting a good night's sleep in the comfortable cabins, followed by a fairly leisurely breakfast prior to disembarkation around 08.00. The Caen night service, operated by the luxury super-ferry the 'Normandie' and the older (but nevertheless very comfortable 'Duc de Normandie' is arguably more convenient in terms of timing (it leaves later and arrives earlier) than the St Malo service. These modern ferries are all very well equipped, with a choice of restaurants, well-stocked duty-free shops, boutiques, cinemas for insomniacs or those who don't want to make use of the choice of comfortable cabins, and an excellent standard of service throughout.

# WE GO
# THERE !

Offering more destination ports than any other UK ferry port, Portsmouth provides you with the best connections to France, Spain and the Channel Islands:

- ☑ **Direct access to the UK motorway network.**
- ☑ **Quicker access from the Midlands, North of England and Wales with the completion of the A34 Newbury bypass.**
- ☑ **Continental destination ports well placed for autoroutes and main links.**
- ☑ **A fast ferry service taking just 2 hours 40 minutes to Cherbourg, from April to September.**

So wherever you want to go for short breaks or longer holidays, go via Portsmouth. We put the continent within easy reach!

**PORTSMOUTH**

**BRITAIN'S BEST CONNECTED FERRY PORT**
**www.portsmouth-port.co.uk**

**Brittany Ferries**     **P&O PORTSMOUTH**     **CONDOR Ferries**

**08705 360 360**     **0870 2424 999**     **01305 761551**

CHERBOURG *◢* CAEN *◢* LE HAVRE *◢* ST. MALO *◢* GUERNSEY *◢* JERSEY *◢* BILBAO

# BILBAO, CHERBOURG, AND LE HAVRE: TWINNED WITH P&ORTSMOUTH

Sail with P&O Portsmouth and you'll enjoy easier access to your ferry. And disembark in the heart of France or northern Spain miles closer to your destination. On your crossing, you can relax as you enjoy not only our on board facilities but also the knowledge that you'll be pitching your tent or uncoupling your caravan far faster when you arrive. There can't be a better way to start your holiday. For a brochure call **0870 9000 212** (quoting AR). To book, call **0870 2424 999**, visit poportsmouth.com or see your local travel agent.

**P&O**
**PORTSMOUTH**

BILBAO    CHERBOURG    LE HAVRE

# Can you cross The Channel in a different style?

## Yes you Can Can.

Not only does SeaFrance guarantee you the lowest possible fares between Dover and Calais it also serves up that famous French style. With SeaFrance you can enjoy delicious Gallic cuisine and make great savings on a huge selection of wines, beers, spirits and gifts in our on board shops. Next time you're travelling to France travel in unique style.

**08705 711 711**
www.seafrance.com

SEE THE DIFFERENCE WITH

 SEAFRANCE
DOVER · CALAIS · FERRIES

# Less driving,
## more holiday

Why spend your holiday driving hundreds of unnecessary miles through France when we can take you and your car closer to your holiday destination? Not only do we offer the best choice of routes, you can also enjoy the finest on-board experience. And all for less than you'd expect.

**Call 0870 908 1284** or visit **brittanyferries.com**

CORK

PLYMOUTH POOLE PORTSMOUTH

CHERBOURG

CAEN

ROSCOFF ST MALO

SANTANDER

# Jersey, Guernsey and St. Malo

## The fast car ferry service

If you're travelling to the Channel Islands
or Western France for your holiday next year, the first thing
you need is your copy of a Condor 2002 Car Ferries Brochure.

With services up to 3 times daily from Weymouth or Poole
you can be in Jersey in 3 hours, Guernsey in 2 hours
or St. Malo in as little as 4¹/₂ hours.

**Information & Booking 0845 345 2000**

ONLY WE DUTY FREE

**CONDOR** *Ferries*

www.condorferries.co.uk          *JERSEY • GUERNSEY • ST. MALO*

# Press enquiries this way

## by Mike Cazelet

After years of receiving accolades in the specialist camping and caravanning magazines, but only a very occasional mention in the national press, about two years ago the Alan Rogers team decided to make a major effort to promote camping and caravanning by sending press releases, copies of their guides, etc. and an invitation to sample a camping-caravanning holiday to a carefully targeted group of non-specialist journalists - albeit more in hope than anticipation.

To their surprise and delight this initiative prompted several replies including one from Cassandra Jardine of *The Daily Telegraph*.

Cassandra fancied trying camping. Her editors thought it would make a good article, but who could she turn to for help? It was Alan Rogers. The opportunity to promote camping and caravanning generally, and the Alan Rogers Guides and the Alan Rogers Travel Service by means of well-written accurate copy in a major newspaper was irresistible. So with almost no budget and precious little time they put together a package which allowed Cassandra, her husband William and five children, to try trailer tent camping in France.

Site operators in those parts of Europe where she wanted to visit readily offered pitches, and to be on hand to answer any questions she might have. The ferry operators never hesitated in offering a crossing. Camping International at Horsham could see a positive publicity opportunity and did more than we could ever have expected to help by providing their demonstration model for Cassandra's use.

The result was three pages in The Daily Telegraph. Partly about Cassandra's trip. Partly good sound advice for anyone who fancied trying camping. If the industry were to book the same space as advertising the bill would have run to tens of thousands of pounds.

Fast forward now to the beginning of 2002. Again Cassandra was on the telephone, but this time wanting to know if the Alan Rogers people could help her try caravanning. The Alan Rogers' Travel Service made the travel arrangements, but help was still needed to acquire the loan of a suitably large caravan, and something suitable to tow it. And it was readily given.

This time caravan manufacturer Avondale said "please use one of our caravans." Bear in mind they were lending a brand new caravan to a family that had never towed a caravan. Chrysler loaned just about the only vehicle which would carry Cassandra and family, and still have the power and weight to safely pull a big family caravan.

The result of this trip? Well it rained – a lot – when the Jardine family were away, but it's hoped the editorial when it appears in print in 2003 will be another piece of accurate reporting explaining why more and more people are taking to caravanning and camping.

Working with The Daily Telegraph has created all sorts of other opportunities. For example when a news article appeared which pointed out that many (so-called) independent travel guides weren't that independent, Clive Edwards wrote to the newspaper and pointed out that the Alan Rogers Guides have always been both independent and objective, quoting exactly the same words which Alan Rogers used in 1968, and which have been reiterated every year in their introduction. And The Daily Telegraph published this letter almost word for word.

Yes, it was good publicity for Alan Rogers. But hopefully it also emphasised some-thing we believe to be true. Namely that the camping, caravanning and motor caravan industry is incredibly honest. In general the people who run the industry are themselves campers and caravanners. What they want for their customers - that means you and us - is what they want for themselves.

Along with the increased awareness of Alan Rogers in the national media, there has been even more publicity in the specialist press. One article in particular I'd like to mention. It appeared in the trade only magazine Caravan Industry, and was written by our good friend Dennis Needham. At the time Dennis and his wife and photographer Elizabeth visited the Guides editorial office in Dorset, Dennis knew he was terminally ill. But Dennis, being Dennis, was totally professional and produced an article which combined total accuracy with his trademark sense of humour. Like all the campers, caravanners, motor caravanners and boat-owners who've enjoyed Dennis Needham's articles in many consumer publications, we will miss him greatly.

In the early months of 2003 you may catch a BBC2 television programme about an English couple buying a French campsite. And about their efforts to develop it as a good quality site. The BBC decided that the mark of a good quality site was an entry in the Alan Rogers French guide, so the BBC got in touch with Lois, the Alan Rogers Guides Sites Director and asked how the site could join the list of Alan Rogers inspected and recommended sites.

As it happens they'd already inspected the site when the previous owners were in place, but it didn't meet the Alan Rogers' standards. Even for the BBC they wouldn't compromise their standards, but they did agree to bring forward their next site inspection to see if the site had been improved to meet their requirements. It had been, and you'll find Etang Bleu in this 2003 edition.

Yes, it will be (hopefully) good publicity for Alan Rogers. But I hope the message which goes out will be more general than that. I hope it will say to those in the industry and those thinking of coming into it, that campers, caravanners and motor caravanners demand exceptionally high standards.

Perhaps this television programme brings us back to where the guides started. When Alan Rogers started the series of guides which carry his name, he had two objectives. One was to advise fellow campers which were high quality sites, and the other was to encourage all sites to aim for the highest possible standard.

High standards doesn't mean four star status. It means doing what you do as well as you can do it. With this BBC2 programme, and indeed all the national publicity that's been generated, they are still sending out the same message. Those sites which work hard and do the best they can do get rewarded with an entry in an Alan Rogers guide and nowadays, perhaps a bit of national publicity as well.

# Tourist Attractions in France

We have undertaken some research this year into tourist attractions in France. Included below are some details about these increasingly popular attractions, featured by region. We hope that you find it useful and interesting.

## Normandy

### Manche (département 50)

Although La Cité de la Mer at Cherbourg (50100 Cherbourg, telephone 02 33 20 26 26) includes a large aquarium, its principal attraction is the submarine 'Redoubtable' the first French nuclear submarine open to visitors. Open every day from 9.30am to 7.00pm from 1 May to mid September (shorter hours in winter) the actual tour of the submarine lasts 45 minutes, but there's a lot else to see here as well.

The Musée de la Liberté (50310 Quineville, tel 02 33 21 40 44) is a museum which illustrates the lives of the French people during the occupation. Not a war museum as such, more a museum of social history under the occupying German forces. Open daily March-November.

### Calvados (département 14)

A most impressive and moving attraction is the Memorial de Caen (14066 Caen, telephone 02 31 06 06 48) which is a 35 hectare park devoted to the two world wars, and the Cold War, but particularly to the Second World War, the Normandy landings and the Occupation - there are interactive displays, huge artefacts and even a bit of the Berlin Wall! Allow about six hours to see everything! Open all year except 1-15 January.

For aspiring racing or rally drivers, or powerboat racers there's The Driver's Club (14800 Deauville, tel 02 31 81 31 31) which is a 30 hectare park incorporating kart circuits, quad bikes, jet skis etc - just the thing for junior 'petrol heads', and it's open all year too.

The 70 m. long Bayeux Tapestry (14400 Bayeux, tel 02 31 51 25 50) is arguably the best known tourist attraction in Normandy and of course tells the story of the Norman Conquest from the perspective of the 11th century in great beauty and detail. Open daily most of the year.

The Musée du Debarquement (14117 Arromanches, tel 02 31 22 34 31) is actually built on the very spot where the artificial port (The Mulberry Harbour) was laid for the invasion in 1944. Working models, bits of the original harbour, film archives and videos illustrate the enormity of the undertaking to liberate Europe from the Nazis. Open daily all year except January.

### Seine-Maritime (département 76)

L'Estra cité de la mer (76200 Dieppe, tel 02 35 06 93 20) is both a maritime museum, with an emphasis on boat-building, and an aquarium. Open all year.

### Eure (département 27)

Les Oiseaux (27300 Plasnes, tel 02 32 43 21 22) is a fun park specifically aimed at children between the ages of 2 and 12, with over 40 attractions to choose from - should keep them amused for hours! Opening hours vary, but daily except Sundays during the main season.

### Orne (département 61)

The Château Carrouges (61320 Carrouges, tel 02 33 27 20 32) is a very impressive castle, and a national monument. Open most days.

# Northern France

### Pas de Calais (département 62)

Bagatelle in the Pas de Calais (62155 Merlimont, tel 03 21 89 09 91) is reckoned to be France's oldest theme park, its 26 hectares offering a range of over forty activities and things to see, including rafting, train rides, an animal park, fun-fair style rides, even a small circus It therefore appeals to a wide age-range, and there's enough here to keep the whole family amused. Open April-September inclusive.

Nausicaa, Centre National de la Mer, (62203 Boulogne-sur-Mer, tel 03 21 30 99 99) is a centre devoted exclusively to the sea and the creatures that live in it. To call it an aquarium would be an under-statement. Although arguably of more interest to families with older children, there is a 'touchy-feely' zone aimed specifically at younger children. Open every day all year except Christmas Day and from 6-24 January.

La Coupole (62504 Saint-Omer, tel 03 21 12 27 27) is an enormous underground bunker, built by the Nazis during the occupation as a base for the V2 rockets aimed at the UK! There are two cinemas regularly showing films about the war and the German occupation. Open daily all

year except for the first two weeks of January.

The Forum des Sciences (59650 Villeneuve d'Ascq, tel 03 20 19 36 36) is said to appeal to everyone aged from 9 to 99! It's a combination of a science museum and a planetarium, with a dedicated multimedia area where kids can teach their parents the latest about the World Wide Web and Internet! Open Tuesday-Friday, but hours vary depending on whether it's term time or not in France.

### Somme (département 80)

Associations with the First World War are so strong, and the area is so dominated by war cemeteries that it seems almost frivolous to be identifying attractions such as fun-parks - not that there are many in this area, and none worth mentioning.

# Ile de France

First and foremost nowadays of course is Disneyland Paris and the Disney Studios, both of which need to be booked in advance, and both of which are sufficiently well known not to require any detailed description in this short summary of theme parks and attractions. For bookings in France for Disneyland Paris or for the Walt Disney Studios (7777 Marne-la-Vallée) you should telephone 01 60 30 60 30.

Almost as well-known is Park Asterix (60128 Plailly, tel 03 44 62 30 30) which is a 'must' for all fans of 'Asterix the Gaul' but even for those that are not Asterix Addicts this huge 70 hectare park has a lot to offer in terms of exciting and scary looking rides, and no less than six separate zones with circus acts, sword fighting displays, acrobats etc as well as the famous Gallic Village itself.

# Eastern France

### Aube (département 10)

Nigloland - 10200 Dolancourt, (tel 03 25 27 94 52) An 18 hectare family-oriented theme park whose success they say derives from the integration of its many attractions with the natural environment which abounds in forests and lakes. Lots of rides, etc. for youngsters. Open daily April-August inclusive, and weekends in September.

Domaine Raid Decouverte, 10210 Chaource (tel 03 25 40 01 25) certainly offers something different to the normal run of attractions - quad bikes, jet-skis, archery, rafting, mountain-bikes - almost every type of 'go-for-it' activity seems to

be catered for here. Open daily throughout the year, but pre-booking is advisable.

Moselle (département 57)

Parc Walibi Schtroumpf (57280 Maizieres les Metz, tel 03 87 51 90 52) Well known in France, but less so in the UK, probably because of its unpronounceable name! This is a huge (150 hectare) family fun-park with lots of attractions to keep children of all ages amused for hours. Open weekends April-October inclusive, daily in main season

Haut-Rhin (département 68)

EcoMusée d'Alsace (68190 Ungersheim, tel 03 89 74 44 74) is an unusual attraction where we spent a very interesting evening some years ago. It's more of a theme park than a museum really, with the emphasis on 're-creating the working environment that existed in this region years ago' so there's an ancient farm, rural craft workshops, an old mining train, houses of the period, etc, etc. Open all year, but hours vary with the seasons.

The Collection Schlumpf (68051 Mulhouse, tel 03 89 33 23 23) The French National Motor Museum, with over 400 historic vehicles, including a motorsports section with some 80 or so racing and rally cars. This museum is recognised as home to one of Europe's premier vehicle

collections, including a hugely rare Bugatti Royale Coupe. Open daily all year, except Christmas and New Year's days.

Bas-Rhin (département 67)

The Parc des Cigognes et de Loisirs (67600 Kintzheim, 03 88 92 05. 94) an animal park, specialising in storks, but with lots of other species too, audio-visual presentations and displays, all coupled with a range of leisure facilities, mainly for younger children - open March-October

# Vendée - Charente

Charente-Maritime (département 17)

With some 1600 different species in 14 hectares of park, the Zoo de la Palmyre (17570 Les Mathes, tel 05 46 22 46 06) is a major attraction, and one should allow for a visit of at least four hours to see everything. Open daily throughout the year.

The Vendée (département 85)

Le Grand Parc du Puy du Fou (85590 Les Epresses, tel 02 51 64 11 11) is without question the major attraction in this département. In fact it is said to be Europe's leading historical theme park, and the fourth most important park in France after Disneyland, Futuroscope and

Parc Asterix. Its 35 hectares, with its historical reconstructions, spectacular re-enactments of battles, 1,500 fountains, falconry etc really warrant a full day visit. It's open daily from 1 June - mid September, and at weekends in May.

## Loire Valley

### Eure et Loir, département 28

The Parc de Loisirs de Cloyes (28220 Cloyes, tel 02 37 98 50 53) is essentially a children's fun park, with the emphasis on 'water activities' aimed particularly at younger children with heated paddling pools, slides, a little train, trampolines, pony rides etc. Open daily July and August, but only on Sundays in May/June and September

### Indre-et-Loire, département 37

Les Châteaux Miniatures (37403 Amboise, tel 02 47 23 44 44) For those without the necessary time to visit all or many of the real châteaux for which this region is so famous, the 'Châteaux Miniatures' provides a means of seeing miniature reproductions of many of the best-known in less than a day! Open daily from 1 April to early November.

### Loir et Cher, département 41

Zoo Parc de Beauval (41110 Saint-Aignan-sur-Cher, tel 02 54 75 50 00) is a somewhat unusual zoo highly dedicated to the preservation and protection of a variety of endangered species, and their way of life. Open daily all year.

### La Sarthe, département 72

To motorsports enthusiasts La Sarthe means just one thing - the Le Mans 24 hour race, held every year in June.

However the département of La Sarthe is home to more than just the 24 Heures du Mans, and for those who are not so interested in motorsports (or for those enthusiasts who are staying in the area for longer than the race) there is:

Papea City, (72530 Yvre-L'Eveque, tel 02 43 89 61 05) which is a family oriented park with an overhead railway, a special kiddies train, mini-ranch, goats, sheep etc should keep the younger ones occupied, plus there is a swimming pool complex, complete with toboggans. Open daily July-August, weekends at other times, but hours vary.

### Vienne, département 86

Without doubt the most important attraction in this département is the Parc du Futuroscope, (86130 Jaunay-Clan, tel 05 49 49 30 00) - see advert on page 143.

Futuroscope offers something for everyone, of whatever age, particularly for those with even a passing interest in science fiction. It offers a range of 'formulae' so far as prices are concerned too, thereby catering for a range of budgets, including one for those who just want to visit for the evening when there are several hugely popular 'night-time spectaculars'. Open all year, 0900-1800 hours, and longer (0900-2200 hours) from April to August.

## Franche Comté

### Doubs, département 25

La Citadelle (25000 Besancon, tel 03 81 65 07 50) is difficult to describe in so far as it was originally built, as a citadel, at the end of the 17th century as part of the fortifications of Vauban, and it's therefore of significant historical interest. More recently La Citadelle has been partially restored or converted to include a zoo and an aquarium and even an 'insectarium'. Open daily all year except Christmas and New Year.

## Savoy/Dauphiny Alpes

### Isère, département 38

Parc Walibi Rhone-Alpes (38630 Les Avenieres, tel 04 74 33 71 80) is a 35 hectare fun park with more than 30 attractions of various types, including quite a few pretty scary rides etc., but also catering for the less adventurous and younger children too. Open weekends in May, June and September, daily in July and August.

## Atlantic Coast

### Gironde, département 33

Aqualand de Gujan-Mestras (33470 Gujan-Mestras, tel 05 56 66 39 39) is one of several Aqualand Parks in France, where they're considered to be the premier 'waterparks' of Europe. There's a large range of slides, toboggans and other watersports all in a shady setting in the Landes forest. Open daily early June to early September.

### Landes, département 40

EcoMusée de la Grande Lande (40630 Sabres, tel 05 58 08 31 31) is a 3-centre park dedicated to the portrayal of the culture and history of the region, and it even includes a steam railway as well as traditional horse-drawn transport, re-constructed houses etc. The French seem to do these 'ecoMusées' particularly well. Open daily April-October.

## Dordogne/Aveyron

### Dordogne, département 24

Le Village du Bournat (24260 Le Bugue-sur-Vezere, tel 05 53 08 41 99) is a fascinating reconstruction of a 19th century Perigordian village and its lifestyle, complete with actors, craftsmen etc. Open daily at least April-October inclusive, but times vary.

### Lot et Garonne, département 47

Walibi Aquitaine, (47310 Roquefort, tel 05 53 96 58 32) is a 30 hectare park and a 18th century chateau with 16 separate attractions, including rides, rafting etc for the more adventurous, a small theatre and in 'Walibiland' itself plenty to amuse younger children too. Open daily mid April - August, and weekends during September.

## Limousin/Auvergne

### Puy-de-Dome, département 63

Opened only in February 2002, Vulcania near Clermont-Ferrand, (tel 0820 827 828) is a unique attraction, set perhaps to become one of France's leading theme parks. Vulcania is, as its name suggests, devoted to 'earth science' and in particular the scientific exploration, history, cultural and economic impact and general study of the world of volcanoes. Set in a volcanic region of course, Vulcania really needs to be visited to be appreciated - it's open daily, but the hours vary according to season.

### Allier, département 03

Le Pal (03290 Dompierre-sur-Bresbre, tel 04 70 42 68 10) with over 320,000 visitors is one of the biggest theme parks in the Auvergne, offering a wide range oif attractions, including exciting rides, a 'theatre of parrots' a zoo-park with 500 animals etc. Open daily July-August, less often during April, May, June and September.

## Rhône Valley

### Ardèche, département 07

Safari Parc de Peaugres (07340 Peaugres, tel 04 75 33 00 32) is an 80 hectare safari park with over 800 animals, set in natural surroundings. You can explore by car or on foot, take a trip into the labyrinth of mirrors, or explore the crocodile area beneath the chateau. At least a half-day is needed to see everything, probably more. Open daily throughout the year except Christmas day, but hours vary according to the season.

Aerocity (07202 Aubenas, tel 04 75 35 00 00) is, as its name suggests, a park dedicated to aviation, and indeed it's situated next to an airfield. Its 10 hectares aren't entirely devoted to aircraft as there's swimming pools, animals etc as well, aimed particularly at keeping younger members of the family happy while the older ones look at the many aeronautical exhibits. Open early May to the end of September - daily during July/August, less frequently at other times.

Ain, département 01

Le Parc des Oiseaux de Villars-les-Dombes (01330 Villars-les-Dombes, tel 04 74 98 05 54) is a large bird sanctuary situated among canals and lakes, featuring more than 2,000 birds and 400 different species. Open daily March - October inclusive, but times vary considerable according to season.

## Provence (inland)

Hautes-Alpes, département 05

Adventure Parc (05240 La Salle les Alpes) This is a genuine adventure park, rather on the lines of 'outward-bound' with a range of activities with differing degrees of difficulty, offering a variety of challenges. Perhaps not for the faint-hearted, but there are experienced staff on hand. This is one of a number of similar adventure parks in France. Opening times vary - for further information telephone 04 92 24 90 57

## Midi-Pyrénées

Haute-Garonne, département 31

City de l'Espace (31506Toulouse, tel 05 62 71 48 71) is more than just a space-museum, as its 300,000 visitors annually will testify. There really is a lot to see, and to do in terms of interactive displays etc., and our own four hour visit didn't really allow time for us to do it justice. There's even some of the original 'kit' here, and lots of full size reproductions, such as the Ariane rocket, space station Mir, the Soyouz capsule etc. Open daily all year, apart from Mondays during the low season.

## Mediterranean
### (Provence and Côte d'Azur)

Bouches du Rhone, département 13

El Dorado City (13820 Ensues-la-Redonne) situated between Marseilles and Fos is essentially a recreation of a 19th Century Wild West town embracing four distinct themes - Western, Red Indian, Mexican and Canadian. Although mainly orientated towards 'family outings' it will appeal to anyone with an interest in the Wild West and North/Central American culture. It's open for a long season (mid March- early November) For further information telephone 04 42 79 86 90.

On a similar 'Western' theme the OK Corral (13780 Cuges-les-Pins) is another park devoted to the conquest of the American West, with Rodeo's, wagon-trains, Cowboy and Indian encounters etc. Aimed especially at families, and open for a long season, from early March until late October - For further information telephone 04 42 73 80 05.

Var, département 83

Home to Le Village des Tortues (83590 Gonfaron, Telephone 04 94 78 26 41) which is a 3 hectare park devoted to tortoises! It's open from March to October (we presume that even in Provence they hibernate during the winter!)

## Côte d'Azur

Alpes Maritime, département 06

Boasts of having the premier aquarium in the whole of France - Marineland, 06600 Antibes (telephone 04 93 33 49 49) which is open all year and is indeed much more than 'just another aquarium'. Opened in 1970 this park has become bigger year by year and now welcomes over a million visitors a year, and the variety of its attractions have grown beyond just fish, and even include golf, a small Provencal farm, and butterflies.

Strictly speaking not in France at all of course, but nevertheless included in the general scope of the Côte d'Azur is the Musée Oceanographique at Monaco, which is perhaps more of an aquatic life museum than a spectacular aquarium, and may therefore appeal more to those with a serious interest in marine life than to those wondering what to do with the kids if the weather's not nice enough for the beach! Of course Monte Carlo is well worth a visit at any time (apart from Grand Prix weekend unless you're a motor racing fan of course!)

# THE HEART OF RURAL SOUTH-WEST FRANCE

Wake up to the fresh air of the wide open spaces of the Aveyron and the lush, meandering valleys of the Lot. Live the outdoor life at sites where everything has been done to ensure a perfect break from routine. Relax in pavement cafés in exquisite mediaeval towns where time seems to have stood still, and where history lives. Let names like Quercy, Conques, Rocamadour, Armagnac, Roquefort stimulate your imagination. Explore countryside where man has barely left an imprint. Welcome to the Midi-Pyrénées.
Choose from 700 campsites. There'll be one just right for you.

To get your FREE copy of our Camping Guide and the Introductory Brochure («Discovering Midi-Pyrénées»), contact :
Comité Régional du Tourisme
54 boulevard de l'Embouchure - BP 2166
31022 TOULOUSE CEDEX 2 - France
Tel. 33 (0)5 61 13 55 48
Fax. 33 (0)5 61 47 17 16
E-mail : information@crtmp.com
www.tourisme-midi-pyrenees.com

MIDI-PYRÉNÉES

Comité
Régional du
Tourisme

# WARM, WELCOMING, WONDERFUL

Called «Midi» after the noonday sun, the Midi-Pyrénées' delightful climate is reflected in the spirit of its welcoming people. With 700 sites to choose from, you can set your own pace. Leisurely sightseeing. A day's hill walking in the Pyrenees. Cycling along country lanes without a car in sight. Bustling street markets groaning with fresh produce. A picnic by an unhurried river or in shaded woods. White water rafting. Horse riding. Maybe a spot of fishing. Checking out local delicacies - from foie gras and truffles, cassoulet to pink garlic and Roquefort cheese, with a glass of Gaillac or Madiran wine. We promise enchantment.

**To get your FREE copy of our Camping Guide and the Intro-ductory Brochure («Discovering Midi-Pyrénées»), contact :**
Comité Régional du Tourisme
54 boulevard de l'Embouchure - BP 2166
31022 TOULOUSE CEDEX 2 - France
Tel. 33 (0)5 61 13 55 48
Fax. 33 (0)5 61 47 17 16
E-mail : information@crtmp.com
www.tourisme-midi-pyrenees.com

MIDI-PYRÉNÉES

Comité Régional du Tourisme

# Vendée

## Let yourself go...

NANTES ○

CHOLET ○

ST-JEAN-DE-MONTS ○

LA-ROCHE-SUR-YON ○

LES SABLES-D'OLONNE ○          FONTENAY-LE-COMTE ○

JARD-SUR-MER ○

LA ROCHELLE ○

## Call today for your free brochure

## 01892 55 98 05

**VENDÉE**
TRAVEL SERVICE

- Long sandy shores, clear blue skies, brillian sunshine and historical towns. With an enviable sunshine record, watersports galore and the warm Atlantic waves, it's easy to see why the Vendée is one of the most popular areas of France for couples and families alike.

- Beach lovers will discover 140 kilometres o sandy shores backed by fragrant pine forests running alongside and, as a change, Le Puy du Fou spectacle is a must.

- You'll find a superb selection of accommodation to suit all tastes, ranging from hotels, châteaux, holiday apartments, villages and campsites. All with on site amenities to keep everyone happily occupied.

- And with so much to see, you'll be pleased that the Vendée is a comfortable drive from the port of St Malo.

**Why not let yourself go?**

# www.vendee.org.uk

SITES
&
PAYSAGES
de
FRANCE

# Fifty-two good reasons for coming to France

*SITES & LANSCAPES of FRANCE, 52 quality campsites covering the rich diversity of the French regions.*

SITES & PAYSAGES of France offers campers and caravanners a carefully chosen selection of high quality, 3- and 4-star comfortable campsites across the country. Our 52 campsites are situated in attractively landscaped, tree-shaded environments, with all the amenities for tents, caravans, camping-cars, mobile homes or chalet accommodation. All are laid out with 'room to breathe' and located in areas of great natural beauty, with masses to do and see, from on-site sport and leisure activities, to nearby heritage visits... not forgetting the sublime joys of authentic local French cuisine.

**SITES & PAYSAGES**
Chemin des Bosses - Orouet
85160 - St Jean de Monts - FRANCE
Fax 00 33 251 590 535

**Ask us for your FREE 2003 guide**

**Information & reservations in English**
## 00 33 228 114 036

INCONITO - Photos : Dorian Shaw - Scorpius - Wallis - Hoa-Qui.

**www.sites-et-paysages.com**
E.mail us at: **contact@sites-et-paysages.com**

# Grand Prix Racing

**JUST TICKETS**

As the largest suppliers of **Formula One** and **Le Mans 24 Hour** spectator tickets **we provide the best range of seats in this country**.

Our **TICKET ONLY** service covers general admission, grandstand seats and parking at F.1 circuits and Le Mans.

At **MONACO** we offer some of the **best viewing of all from private apartment terraces** located at the most advantageous points, and seats and hospitality at a trackside restaurant.

For **SILVERSTONE** we can book seats, hospitality marquees, adjoining private parking and helicopters.

**JUST MOTORING**

Offers inclusive self-drive arrangements with hotels at **European Formula One** events, plus for **Le Mans**, ferry bookings, parking, camping and hospitality marquees.

**CAMPING**

We hae made arrangements with camping areas at several circuits, also nearby sites at most of the others.

**Just Tickets**
1 Charter House
Camden Crescent
Dover, Kent
CT16 1LE
Tel: 01304 228866
Fax: 01304 242550
www.justtickets.co.uk

- - - - - - - - - - - - - - - - - - - - - - - - - - - - - - - - - - - - - - - - - - - - - - - - - - - - - - - - - - - - -

Mr/Mrs/Ms

Address

Postcode

Event

Ref GCG/03

# Don't leave home without at least one of these in your car

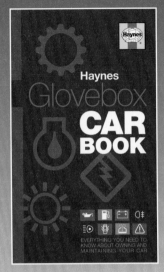

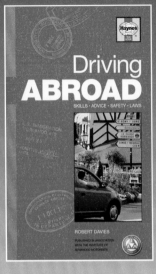

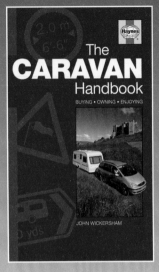

**Haynes Glovebox Car Book**
*BY Steve Rendle*
A compilation of material from the best-selling *Car Book*, reformatted to fit the glovebox and with additional information on practical aspects of driving both at home and abroad. Aimed at the car owner or driver who does not have wide-ranging technical knowledge but who would welcome concise instructions on what to do when a dashboard warning light comes on or a flat tyre has to be changed.
*Paperback, 220 x 130mm, 216pp, Full colour throughout*
ISBN: 1 85960 792 6 **£9.99** RRP

**Driving Abroad:**
**Skills, advice, safety, laws**
*BY Robert Davies*
This handbook, published in association with the Institute of Advanced Motorists, contains all the information a driver will need when travelling abroad. Presented in a colourful, easy-to-follow format, with details on driving techniques, dealing with extreme weather conditions, car preparation, documents and safety procedures. There are also specific details for each country in Europe, North America and Australasia and general information for Asia, Africa and Central America.
*Paperback, 220 x 130mm, 208pp, Full colour throughout*
ISBN: 1 85960 803 5 **£12.99** RRP

**The Caravan Handbook**
**Owning, Enjoying, Improving**
*BY John Wickersham*
This handbook contains all the information a caravanner will need when preparing for a journey and is also an essential glovebox companion for use en route and on site. Presented in a colourful, easy-to-follow format, with details on buying, towing, accessories and site procedures, this guide will answer all the questions raised when using and maintaining a caravan. There are detailed chapters on electricity, gas, sanitation and refrigeration, and information on servicing and laying up for winter.
*Paperback, 220 x 130mm, 304pp, Full colour throughout*
ISBN: 1 85960 801 9 **£12.99** RRP

## Also from Haynes...

**The Caravan Manual**
**(3rd Edition)**
*380 colour illustrations*
ISBN: 1 85960 333 5
**£14.99** RRP

**The Motorcaravan**
**Manual**
*Full colour throughout*
ISBN: 1 85960 322 X
**£14.99** RRP

**Haynes** Publishing
Sparkford, Yeovil, Somerset BA22 7JJ
**T** 01963 442030 • **F** 01963 440001
**E** sales@haynes-manuals.co.uk • **W** www.haynes.co.uk

# Alan Rogers PASSPORT 2003

Take this form along to any inspected and selected campsite featured in the 2003 editions of the Alan Rogers guides. Ask Reception to stamp and validate it for you.

When you have collected four 'stamps' cut out and return the form to the address below. In return we'll send you an Alan Rogers baseball cap with our compliments, to wear with pride on your travels!

---

**Warranted that:**

Mr/Mrs/Miss . . . . . . . . . . . . . . . . . . . . . . . . .

**Stayed at this Alan Rogers selected campsite**

From: . . . . . . . . . . . . . . . . . . . . . . . . . . . .

To: . . . . . . . . . . . . . . . . . . . . . . . . . . . . .

Signed on behalf of Camping

. . . . . . . . . . . . . . . . . . . . . . . . . . . . . . .

INSPECTED CAMPSITES & SELECTED — *Alan Rogers* — Name/Stamp of campsite and authorised signature

---

**Warranted that:**

Mr/Mrs/Miss . . . . . . . . . . . . . . . . . . . . . . . . .

**Stayed at this Alan Rogers selected campsite**

From: . . . . . . . . . . . . . . . . . . . . . . . . . . . .

To: . . . . . . . . . . . . . . . . . . . . . . . . . . . . .

Signed on behalf of Camping

. . . . . . . . . . . . . . . . . . . . . . . . . . . . . . .

INSPECTED CAMPSITES & SELECTED — *Alan Rogers* — Name/Stamp of campsite and authorised signature

---

**Warranted that:**

Mr/Mrs/Miss . . . . . . . . . . . . . . . . . . . . . . . . .

**Stayed at this Alan Rogers selected campsite**

From: . . . . . . . . . . . . . . . . . . . . . . . . . . . .

To: . . . . . . . . . . . . . . . . . . . . . . . . . . . . .

Signed on behalf of Camping

. . . . . . . . . . . . . . . . . . . . . . . . . . . . . . .

INSPECTED CAMPSITES & SELECTED — *Alan Rogers* — Name/Stamp of campsite and authorised signature

---

**Warranted that:**

Mr/Mrs/Miss . . . . . . . . . . . . . . . . . . . . . . . . .

**Stayed at this Alan Rogers selected campsite**

From: . . . . . . . . . . . . . . . . . . . . . . . . . . . .

To: . . . . . . . . . . . . . . . . . . . . . . . . . . . . .

Signed on behalf of Camping

. . . . . . . . . . . . . . . . . . . . . . . . . . . . . . .

INSPECTED CAMPSITES & SELECTED — *Alan Rogers* — Name/Stamp of campsite and authorised signature

---

Send to: **Alan Rogers Guides, 96 High Street, Tunbridge Wells, Kent TN1 1YF**
**Your details:**

Name: (Mr/Mrs/Miss) . . . . . . . . . . . . . . . . . . . . . . . . . . . . . . . . . . . . . . . . . . . . . . . . . . .

Address: . . . . . . . . . . . . . . . . . . . . . . . . . . . . . . . . . . . . . . . . . . . . . . . . . . . . . . . . . . .

Post code: . . . . . . . . . . . . . . . . . Tel: . . . . . . . . . . . . . . . . . . . . . . . . . . . . . . . . . . .

*Please make sure all forms are returned by 30 September 2003 at the latest.*
*You must stay at least one night at each of the campsites.*

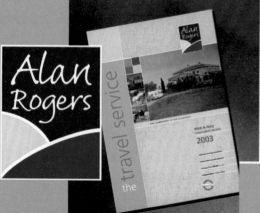

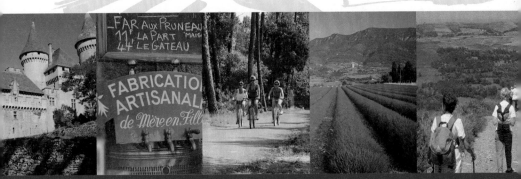

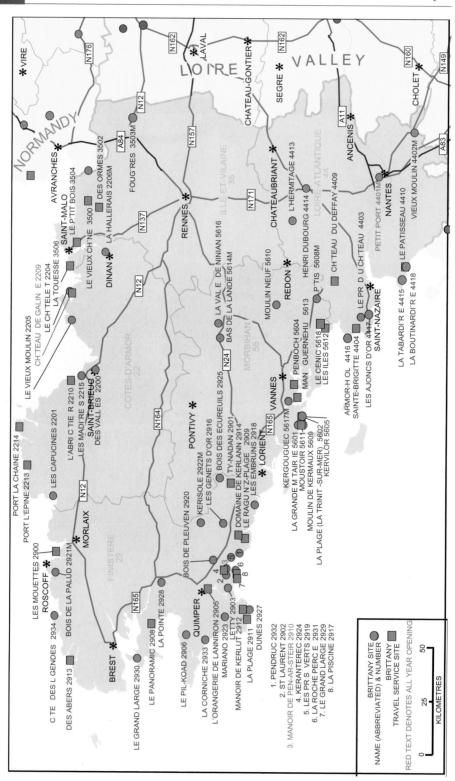

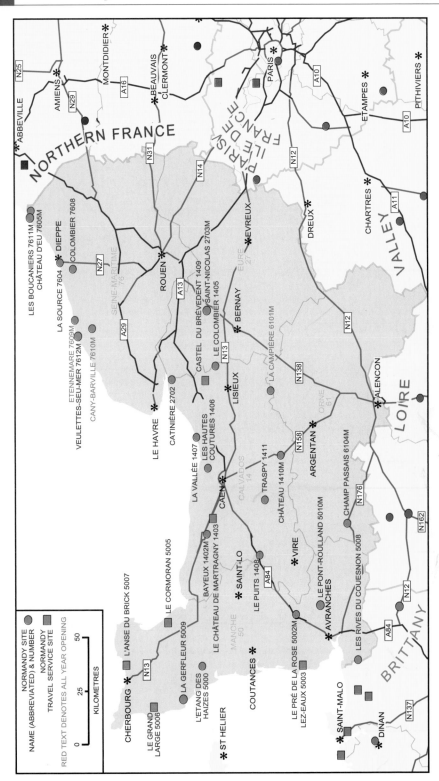

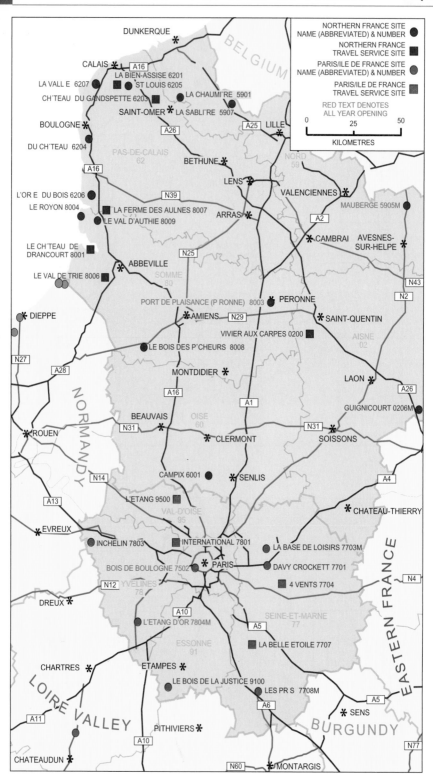

DUNKERQUE

BELGIUM

CALAIS

A16

LA BIEN-ASSISE 6201
LA VALL E 6207    ST LOUIS 6205
CH'TEAU DU GANDSPETTE 6203    LA CHAUMI'RE 5901
SAINT-OMER    LA SABLI'RE 5907
A26    A25    LILLE

BOULOGNE

DU CH'TEAU 6204

PAS-DE-CALAIS
62

BETHUNE

A16    NORD
59

LENS

L'OR E DU BOIS 6206    N39    VALENCIENNES
LE ROYON 8004    LA FERME DES AULNES 8007    MAUBERGE 5905M
LE VAL D'AUTHIE 8009    ARRAS
A2

CAMBRAI    AVESNES-
SUR-HELPE

LE CH'TEAU DE    N25
DRANCOURT 8001    ABBEVILLE    N43

LE VAL DE TRIE 8006    SOMME    N2
80

PORT DE PLAISANCE (P RONNE) 8003    PERONNE
DIEPPE    AMIENS    N29    SAINT-QUENTIN

VIVIER AUX CARPES 0200    AISNE
02

N27    LE BOIS DES P'CHEURS 8008

A28    MONTDIDIER    LAON

A26

A16    GUIGNICOURT 0206M

BEAUVAIS    OISE    A1
N31    60    N31
ROUEN    CLERMONT    SOISSONS

N14    CAMPIX 6001    SENLIS    A4

A13    L'ETANG 9500    CHATEAU-THIERRY
VAL-D'OISE
95

EVREUX    INCHELIN 7803    INTERNATIONAL 7801    LA BASE DE LOISIRS 7703M    FRANCE

BOIS DE BOULOGNE 7502    PARIS    DAVY CROCKETT 7701    N4
N12    YVELINES
78    4 VENTS 7704

DREUX    A10
L'ETANG D'OR 7804M    SEINE-ET-MARNE
77    A5
ESSONNE    LA BELLE ETOILE 7707
91

CHARTRES    ETAMPES
LE BOIS DE LA JUSTICE 9100    EASTERN FRANCE
A11    LES PR S 7708M    A5
LOIRE    A6    SENS
PITHIVIERS    BURGUNDY
VALLEY
A10    N77
CHATEAUDUN    N60    MONTARGIS

NORMANDY

### Legend

NORTHERN FRANCE SITE
NAME (ABBREVIATED) & NUMBER ●
NORTHERN FRANCE
TRAVEL SERVICE SITE ■
PARIS/ILE DE FRANCE SITE
NAME (ABBREVIATED) & NUMBER ●
PARIS/ILE DE FRANCE
TRAVEL SERVICE SITE ■
RED TEXT DENOTES
ALL YEAR OPENING

0    25    50

KILOMETRES

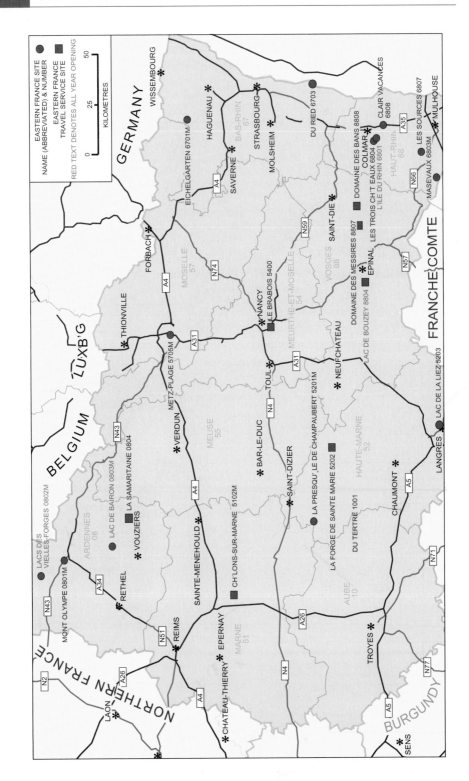

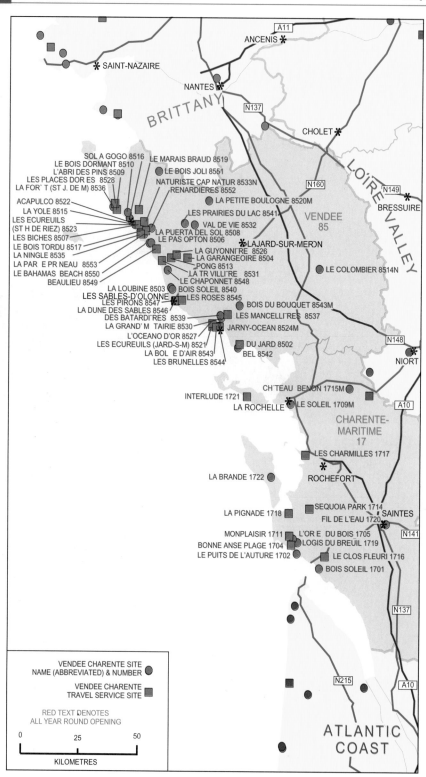

ANCENIS ✱

SAINT-NAZAIRE ✱

NANTES ✱

BRITTANY

A11

N137

CHOLET ✱

LOIRE VALLEY

N160

N149

BRESSUIRE ✱

VENDEE
85

SOL A GOGO 8516
LE BOIS DORMANT 8510        LE MARAIS BRAUD 8519
L'ABRI DES PINS 8509        LE BOIS JOLI 8551
LES PLACES DOR ES  8528     NATURISTE CAP NATUR 8533N
LA FOR' T (ST J. DE M) 8536   RENARDIERES 8552

ACAPULCO 8522                    LA PETITE BOULOGNE 8520M
LA YOLE 8515
LES ECUREUILS               LES PRAIRIES DU LAC 8541
(ST H DE RIEZ) 8523              VAL DE VIE 8532
LES BICHES 8507            LA PUERTA DEL SOL 8508
LE BOIS TORDU 8517          LE PAS OPTON 8506   ✱ LAJARD-SUR-MER)N
LA NINGLE 8535                LA GUYONNI'RE  8526
LA PAR  E PR NEAU  8553       LA GARANGEOIRE 8504
LE BAHAMAS  BEACH 8550        PONG 8513
BEAULIEU 8549                 LA TR VILLI'RE  8531
                             LE CHAPONNET 8548
LA LOUBINE 8503    BOIS SOLEIL 8540
LES SABLES-D'OLONNE  LES ROSES 8545
LES PIRONS 8547               BOIS DU BOUQUET 8543M
LA DUNE DES SABLES 8546
DES BATARDI'RES  8539        LES MANCELLI'RES  8537
LA GRAND' M  TAIRIE 8530
L'OCEANO D'OR 8527           JARNY-OCEAN 8524M
LES ECUREUILS (JARD-S-M) 8521
LA BOL  E D'AIR 8543         DU JARD 8502
LES BRUNELLES 8544           BEL 8542

LE COLOMBIER 8514N

N148

NIORT ✱

CH'TEAU  BENON 1715M
INTERLUDE 1721              LE SOLEIL 1709M
LA ROCHELLE ✱

A10

CHARENTE-
MARITIME
17

LES CHARMILLES 1717
✱
LA BRANDE 1722              ROCHEFORT

SEQUOIA PARK 1714
LA PIGNADE 1718            FIL DE L'EAU 1720      SAINTES ✱

MONPLAISIR 1711      L'OR E  DU BOIS 1705       N141
BONNE ANSE PLAGE 1704   LOGIS DU BREUIL 1719
LE PUITS DE L'AUTURE 1702    LE CLOS FLEURI 1716

BOIS SOLEIL 1701

N137

N215

A10

ATLANTIC
COAST

VENDEE CHARENTE SITE
NAME (ABBREVIATED) & NUMBER ●

VENDEE CHARENTE
TRAVEL SERVICE SITE ■

RED TEXT DENOTES
ALL YEAR ROUND OPENING

0            25            50

KILOMETRES

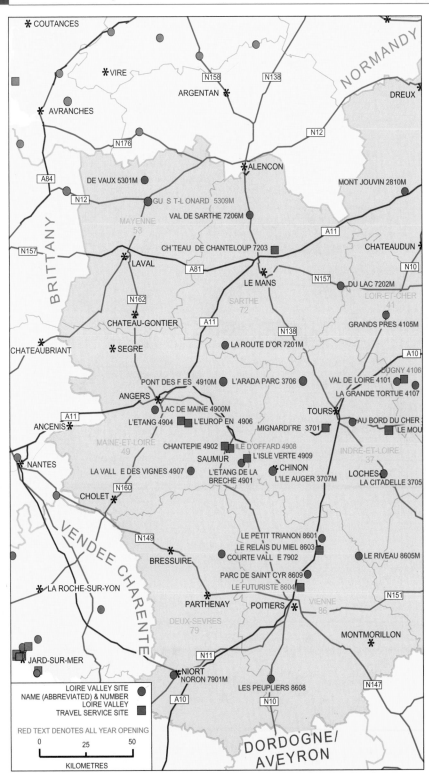

* COUTANCES

* VIRE

N158   N138

NORMANDY

ARGENTAN *

DREUX *

* AVRANCHES

N176

A84

N12

ALENCON *

MONT JOUVIN 2810M

DE VAUX 5301M ●

GU S T-L ONARD 5309M ●

VAL DE SARTHE 7206M ●

MAYENNE
53

A11

CHATEAUDUN *

N157

CH'TEAU DE CHANTELOUP 7203 ■

LAVAL *

A81

N157   DU LAC 7202M ●

N10

N162

LE MANS *

SARTHE
72

LOIR-ET-CHER
41

BRITTANY

CHATEAU-GONTIER *

A11

GRANDS PRES 4105M ●

CHATEAUBRIANT *

* SEGRE

N138

LA ROUTE D'OR 7201M ●

A10

VAL DE LOIRE 4101 ■

DUGNY 4106

PONT DES F ES 4910M ●   L'ARADA PARC 3706 ●

LA GRANDE TORTUE 4107

ANGERS *

LAC DE MAINE 4900M ●

TOURS *

A11

ANCENIS *

L'ETANG 4904 ■ ■ L'EUROP EN 4906

MIGNARDI'RE 3701 ■

AU BORD DU CHER
LE MOU

CHANTEPIE 4902 ■ ILE D'OFFARD 4908

MAINE-ET-LOIRE
49

L'ISLE VERTE 4909

INDRE-ET-LOIRE
37

* NANTES

LA VALL E DES VIGNES 4907 ●

SAUMUR

L'ETANG DE LA
BRECHE 4901 ■

● CHINON

L'ILE AUGER 3707M ■

LOCHES *

LA CITADELLE 3705

N160

CHOLET *

N149

LE PETIT TRIANON 8601 ●

LE RELAIS DU MIEL 8603 ■

VENDEE   CHARENTE

* BRESSUIRE

COURTE VALL E 7902 ●

LE RIVEAU 8605M ●

PARC DE SAINT CYR 8609 ●

LE FUTURISTE 8604 ■

N151

* LA ROCHE-SUR-YON

PARTHENAY *

POITIERS *

VIENNE
86

MONTMORILLON *

DEUX-SEVRES
79

* JARD-SUR-MER

N11

NIORT *
NORON 7901M ●

LES PEUPLIERS 8608 ●

N147

A10

N10

DORDOGNE/
AVEYRON

**Legend:**

● LOIRE VALLEY SITE
NAME (ABBREVIATED) & NUMBER
LOIRE VALLEY
■ TRAVEL SERVICE SITE

RED TEXT DENOTES ALL YEAR OPENING

0    25    50

KILOMETRES

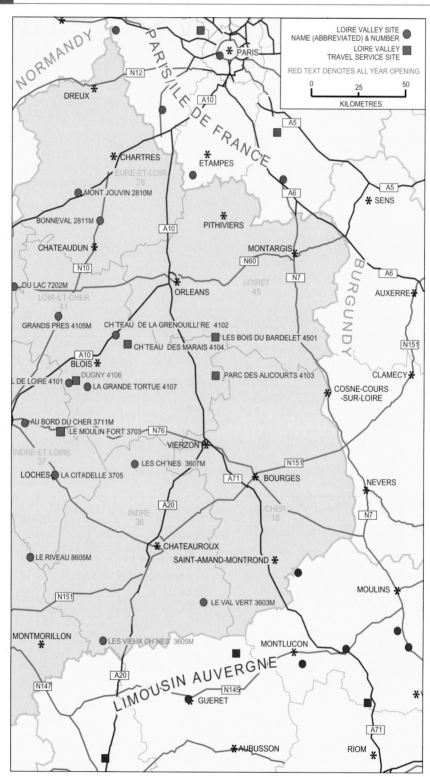

**LOIRE VALLEY SITE**
NAME (ABBREVIATED) & NUMBER
**LOIRE VALLEY**
TRAVEL SERVICE SITE

RED TEXT DENOTES ALL YEAR OPENING

0      25      50

KILOMETRES

NORMANDY

PARIS / ILE DE FRANCE

PARIS

N12

DREUX

A10

A5

CHARTRES

ETAMPES

EURE-ET-LOIR
28

MONT JOUVIN 2810M

A6

A5

SENS

BONNEVAL 2811M

A10

PITHIVIERS

CHATEAUDUN

MONTARGIS

N10

N60

N7

A6

DU LAC 7202M

ORLEANS

LOIRET
45

AUXERRE

LOIR-ET-CHER
41

BURGUNDY

GRANDS PRES 4105M

CH'TEAU DE LA GRENOUILLI'RE 4102

LES BOIS DU BARDELET 4501

N151

CH'TEAU DES MARAIS 4104

A10

BLOIS

CLAMECY

DUGNY 4106

PARC DES ALICOURTS 4103

DE LOIRE 4101

LA GRANDE TORTUE 4107

COSNE-COURS
-SUR-LOIRE

AU BORD DU CHER 3711M

LE MOULIN FORT 3703

N76

VIERZON

INDRE-ET-LOIRE
37

LES CH'NES 3607M

N151

LOCHES

LA CITADELLE 3705

A71

BOURGES

NEVERS

A20

INDRE
36

CHER
18

N7

CHATEAUROUX

LE RIVEAU 8605M

SAINT-AMAND-MONTROND

MOULINS

N151

LE VAL VERT 3603M

MONTMORILLON

LES VIEUX CH'NES 3605M

MONTLUCON

A20

N147

LIMOUSIN AUVERGNE

N145

A71

GUERET

AUBUSSON

RIOM

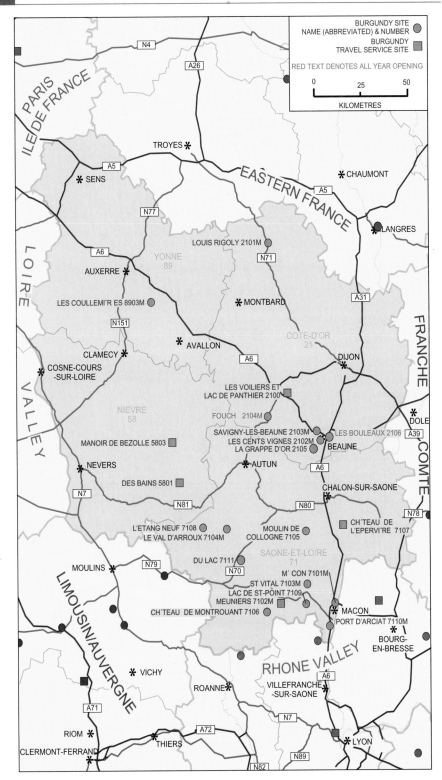

BURGUNDY SITE
NAME (ABBREVIATED) & NUMBER
BURGUNDY
TRAVEL SERVICE SITE

RED TEXT DENOTES ALL YEAR OPENING

0          25          50

KILOMETRES

N4

A26

PARIS
ILE DE FRANCE

TROYES

EASTERN FRANCE

CHAUMONT

A5

SENS

A5

N77

LANGRES

LOIRE

LOUIS RIGOLY 2101M

N71

A6

YONNE
89

AUXERRE

A31

LES COULLEMI'R ES 8903M

MONTBARD

N151

AVALLON

COTE-D'OR
21

CLAMECY

AVALLON

A6

DIJON

COSNE-COURS
-SUR-LOIRE

FRANCHE

DOLE

LES VOILIERS ET
LAC DE PANTHIER 2100

VALLEY

NIEVRE
58

FOUCH   2104M

A39

SAVIGNY-LES-BEAUNE 2103M    LES BOULEAUX 2106
LES CENTS VIGNES 2102M
LA GRAPPE D'OR 2105    BEAUNE

MANOIR DE BEZOLLE 5803

AUTUN

NEVERS

A6

N7

DES BAINS 5801

CHALON-SUR-SAONE

N81

N80

N78

COMTE

L'ETANG NEUF 7108
LE VAL D'ARROUX 7104M

MOULIN DE
COLLOGNE 7105

CH'TEAU DE
L'EPERVI'RE 7107

SAONE-ET-LOIRE
71

DU LAC 7111

MOULINS

N79

N70

LIMOUSIN/AUVERGNE

M' CON 7101M

ST VITAL 7103M
LAC DE ST-PÔINT 7109
MEUNIERS 7102M

CH'TEAU  DE MONTROUANT 7106

MACON
PORT D'ARCIAT 7110M

BOURG-
EN-BRESSE

VICHY

RHONE VALLEY

ROANNE

VILLEFRANCHE
-SUR-SAONE

A6

A71

N7

RIOM

A72

THIERS

LYON

CLERMONT-FERRAND

N89

N82

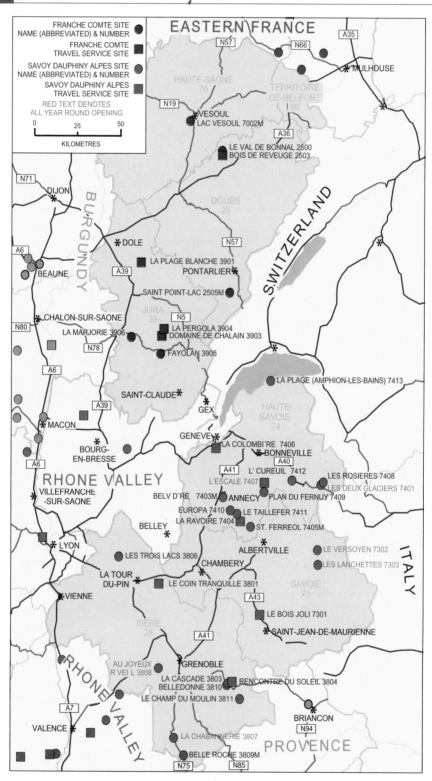

FRANCHE COMTE SITE NAME (ABBREVIATED) & NUMBER ●
FRANCHE COMTE TRAVEL SERVICE SITE ■
SAVOY DAUPHINY ALPES SITE NAME (ABBREVIATED) & NUMBER ●
SAVOY DAUPHINY ALPES TRAVEL SERVICE SITE ■
RED TEXT DENOTES ALL YEAR ROUND OPENING

0    25    50
KILOMETRES

EASTERN FRANCE

N57
N66
A35
✳ MULHOUSE
HAUTE-SAONE 70
TERRITOIRE -DE-BELFORT 90
N19
✳ VESOUL
LAC VESOUL 7002M
A36
LE VAL DE BONNAL 2500
BOIS DE REVEUGE 2503

N71
DIJON ✳
BURGUNDY
DOUBS 25
SWITZERLAND

A6
BEAUNE
✳ DOLE
N57
A39
LA PLAGE BLANCHE 3901
PONTARLIER ✳
SAINT POINT-LAC 2505M

✳ CHALON-SUR-SAONE
N80
LA MARJORIE 3906
N78
JURA 39
N5
LA PERGOLA 3904
DOMAINE DE CHALAIN 3903
FAYOLAN 3905

A6
LA PLAGE (AMPHION-LES-BAINS) 7413
SAINT-CLAUDE ✳
A39
GEX ✳
HAUTE-SAVOIE 74
✳ MACON
A6
GENEVE ✳
LA COLOMBI'RE 7406
BOURG-EN-BRESSE
✳ BONNEVILLE
A40
L' CUREUIL 7412
A41
LES ROSIERES 7408
L'ESCALE 7407
LES DEUX GLACIERS 7401
RHONE VALLEY
VILLEFRANCHE -SUR-SAONE
BELV D"RE  7403M
ANNECY
PLAN DU FERNUY 7409
EUROPA 7410
LE TAILLEFER 7411
LA RAVOIRE 7404
ST. FERREOL 7405M
BELLEY ✳
✳ LYON
LES TROIS LACS 3806
ALBERTVILLE
LE VERSOYEN 7302
CHAMBERY
LES LANCHETTES 7303
LA TOUR DU-PIN ✳
LE COIN TRANQUILLE 3801
SAVOIE 73
ITALY
✳ VIENNE
A43
LE BOIS JOLI 7301
ISERE 38
A41
✳ SAINT-JEAN-DE-MAURIENNE
RHONE VALLEY
AU JOYEUX R VEI L 3808
✳ GRENOBLE
LA CASCADE 3803
RENCONTRE DU SOLEIL 3804
BELLEDONNE 3810
A7
LE CHAMP DU MOULIN 3811
BRIANCON
N94
VALENCE ✳
LA CHABANNERIE 3807
PROVENCE
BELLE ROCHE 3809M
N75
N85

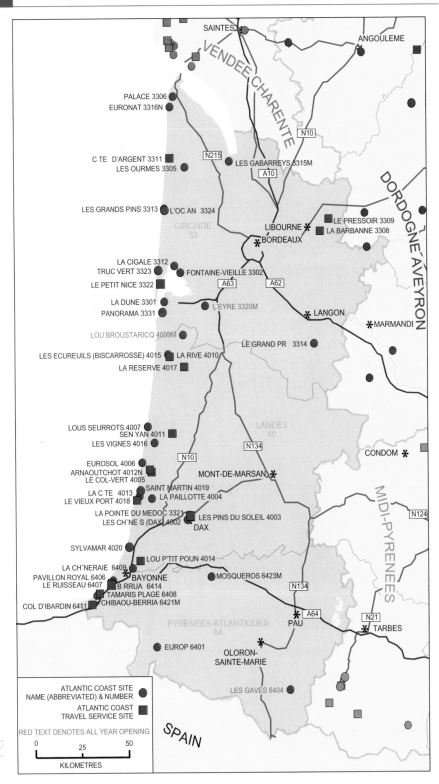

SAINTES

ANGOULEME

VENDEE
CHARENTE

PALACE 3306
EURONAT 3316N

N10

C TE D'ARGENT 3311
LES OURMES 3305

N215
LES GABARREYS 3315M
A10

LES GRANDS PINS 3313    L'OC AN 3324

LE PRESSOIR 3309
LIBOURNE ✶    LA BARBANNE 3308
✶BORDEAUX

GIRONDE
33

LA CIGALE 3312
TRUC VERT 3323    FONTAINE-VIEILLE 3302
LE PETIT NICE 3322    A63    A62

LA DUNE 3301
PANORAMA 3331    L'EYRE 3320M    ✶ LANGON

✶MARMANDE

LOU BROUSTARICQ 4009M

LE GRAND PR  3314

LES ECUREUILS (BISCARROSSE) 4015    LA RIVE 4010
LA RESERVE 4017

LOUS SEURROTS 4007
SEN YAN 4011    LANDES
LES VIGNES 4016    40

N134

EUROSOL 4006    CONDOM ✶
ARNAOUTCHOT 4012N    N10
LE COL-VERT 4005    MONT-DE-MARSAN ✶

SAINT MARTIN 4019
LA C TE  4013    LA PAILLOTTE 4004
LE VIEUX PORT 4018    N124

LA POINTE DU MEDOC 3321    LES PINS DU SOLEIL 4003
LES CH'NE S (DAX) 4002    DAX

MIDI-PYRENEES

SYLVAMAR 4020

LOU P'TIT POUN 4014
LA CH'NERAIE 6409
PAVILLON ROYAL 6406    ✶BAYONNE
LE RUISSEAU 6407    B RRUA  6414    MOSQUEROS 6423M    N134
TAMARIS PLAGE 6408
COL D'IBARDIN 6411    CHIBAOU-BERRIA 6421M

✶ A64    N21
PAU    ✶ TARBES

PYRENEES-ATLANTIQUES
64

EUROP 6401    OLORON-
SAINTE-MARIE

ATLANTIC COAST SITE
NAME (ABBREVIATED) & NUMBER
ATLANTIC COAST
TRAVEL SERVICE SITE    LES GAVES 6404

RED TEXT DENOTES ALL YEAR OPENING

0    25    50

KILOMETRES

SPAIN

DORDOGNE-AVEYRON

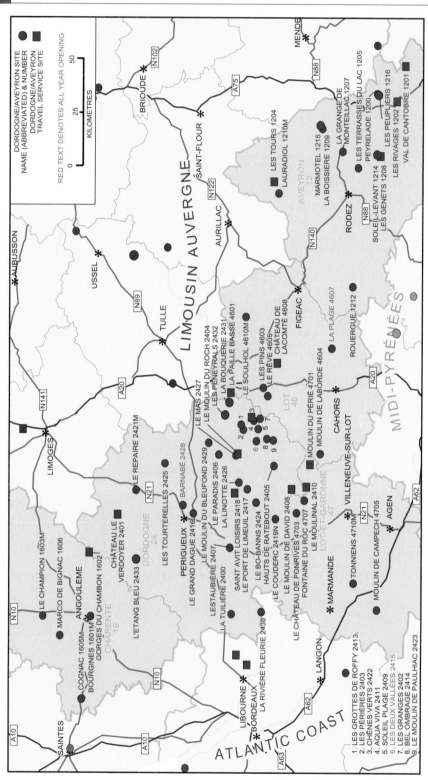

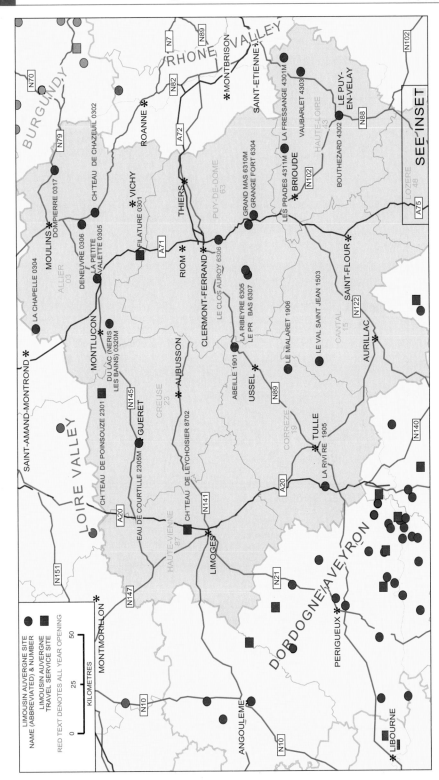

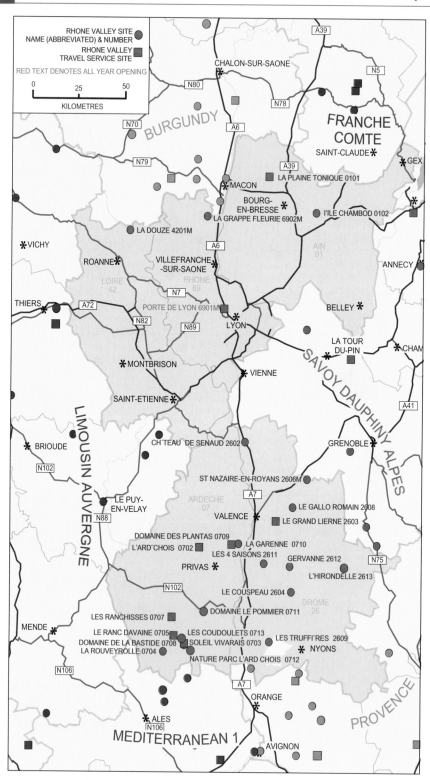

RHONE VALLEY SITE
NAME (ABBREVIATED) & NUMBER
RHONE VALLEY
TRAVEL SERVICE SITE
RED TEXT DENOTES ALL YEAR OPENING

0          25          50
KILOMETRES

CHALON-SUR-SAONE

A39

N5

N80

N78

FRANCHE COMTE

SAINT-CLAUDE

N70

BURGUNDY

A6

N79

GEX

A39

LA PLAINE TONIQUE 0101

MACON

BOURG-EN-BRESSE

I'ILE CHAMBOD 0102

LA GRAPPE FLEURIE 6902M

LA DOUZE 4201M

A6

AIN 01

VICHY

ROANNE

VILLEFRANCHE-SUR-SAONE

ANNECY

LOIRE 42

RHONE 69

N7

BELLEY

THIERS

A72

PORTE DE LYON 6901M

N82

N89

LYON

LA TOUR DU-PIN

SAVOY DAUPHINY ALPES

CHAM

MONTBRISON

VIENNE

A41

SAINT-ETIENNE

BRIOUDE

CH'TEAU DE SENAUD 2602

GRENOBLE

N102

LIMOUSIN AUVERGNE

ST NAZAIRE-EN-ROYANS 2606M

LE PUY-EN-VELAY

ARDECHE 07

A7

LE GALLO ROMAIN 2608

N88

VALENCE

LE GRAND LIERNE 2603

DOMAINE DES PLANTAS 0709

L'ARD¨CHOIS 0702

LA GARENNE 0710

LES 4 SAISONS 2611

GERVANNE 2612

N75

PRIVAS

L'HIRONDELLE 2613

N102

LE COUSPEAU 2604

DROME 26

LES RANCHISSES 0707

DOMAINE LE POMMIER 0711

MENDE

LE RANC DAVAINE 0705

LES COUDOULETS 0713

DOMAINE DE LA BASTIDE 0708

SOLEIL VIVARAIS 0703

LES TRUFFI`RES 2609

LA ROUVEYROLLE 0704

NYONS

NATURE PARC L'ARD CHOIS 0712

N106

A7

PROVENCE

ORANGE

ALES

N106

MEDITERRANEAN 1

AVIGNON

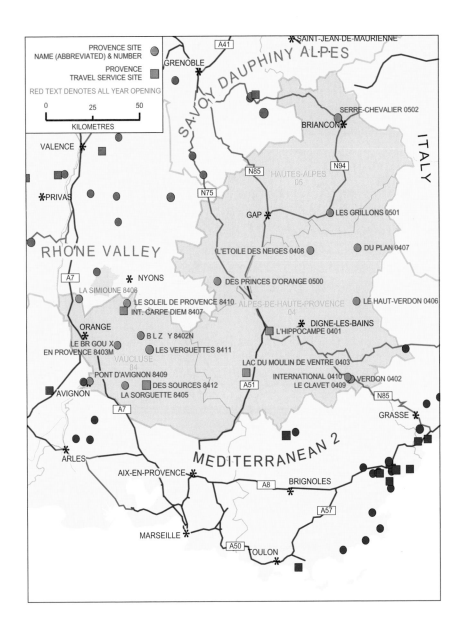

SAINT-JEAN-DE-MAURIENNE

PROVENCE SITE
NAME (ABBREVIATED) & NUMBER

PROVENCE
TRAVEL SERVICE SITE

RED TEXT DENOTES ALL YEAR OPENING

0    25    50

KILOMETRES

SAVOY DAUPHINY ALPES

A41

GRENOBLE

ITALY

SERRE-CHEVALIER 0502

BRIANCON

VALENCE

N85    HAUTES-ALPES
05    N94

PRIVAS

N75

GAP    LES GRILLONS 0501

L'ETOILE DES NEIGES 0408    DU PLAN 0407

RHONE VALLEY

A7    NYONS

LA SIMIOUNE 8406

DES PRINCES D'ORANGE 0500

LE SOLEIL DE PROVENCE 8410    ALPES-DE-HAUTE-PROVENCE    LE HAUT-VERDON 0406
INT. CARPE DIEM 8407    04

ORANGE    DIGNE-LES-BAINS

LE BR GOU X    B L Z  Y 8402N    L'HIPPOCAMPE 0401
EN PROVENCE 8403M    LES VERGUETTES 8411

VAUCLUSE
84    LAC DU MOULIN DE VENTRE 0403

PONT D'AVIGNON 8409    INTERNATIONAL 0410    VERDON 0402
DES SOURCES 8412    A51    LE CLAVET 0409
AVIGNON    LA SORGUETTE 8405    N85

A7    GRASSE

ARLES    MEDITERRANEAN 2

AIX-EN-PROVENCE    BRIGNOLES
A8

A57

MARSEILLE

A50    TOULON

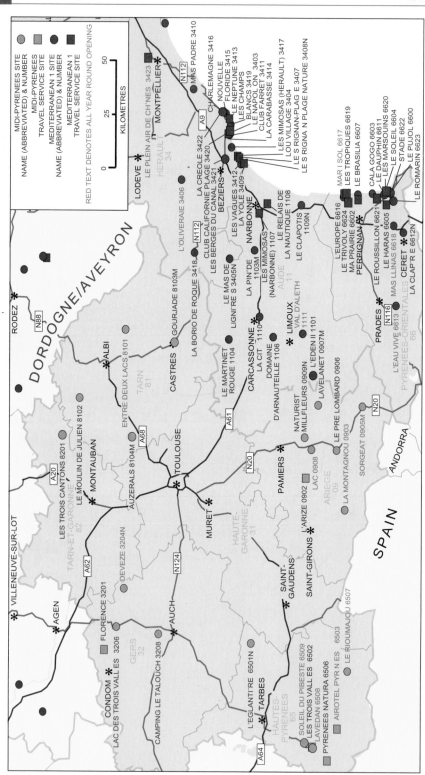

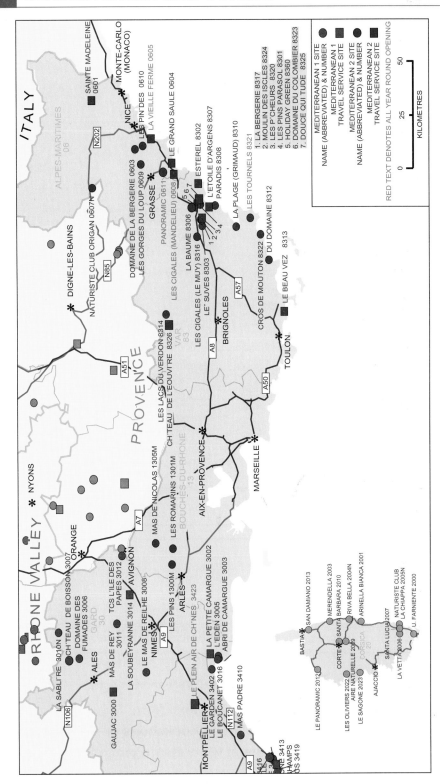

Map showing the Regions and Départements of France, including inset maps of Paris & Île-de-France and Corsica.

**PARIS & ILE-DE-FRANCE**
- VAL-D'OISE 95
- YVELINES 78
- SEINE-ET-MARNE 77
- PARIS 75
- ESSONNE 91

**NORTHERN FRANCE**
- PAS-DE-CALAIS 82
- NORD 59
- SOMME 80
- SEINE-MARITIME 76
- AISNE 02
- ARDENNES 08
- OISE 60

**EASTERN FRANCE**
- MEUSE 55
- MOSELLE 57
- BAS-RHIN 67
- MARNE 51
- MEURTHE-ET-MOSELLE 54
- AUBE 10
- HAUTE-MARNE 52
- VOSGES 88
- HAUT-RHIN 68

**NORMANDY**
- MANCHE 50
- CALVADOS 14
- EURE 27
- ORNE 61

**PARIS ILE DE FRANCE**
- EURE-ET-LOIR 28

**BRITTANY**
- FINISTERE 29
- COTES-D'ARMOR 22
- ILLE-ET-VILAINE 35
- MORBIHAN 56
- LOIRE-ATLANTIQUE 44

**LOIRE VALLEY**
- MAYENNE 53
- SARTHE 72
- MAINE-ET-LOIRE 49
- INDRE-ET-LOIRE 37
- LOIR-ET-CHER 41
- LOIRET 45
- CHER 18

**BURGUNDY**
- YONNE 89
- COTE-D'OR 21
- NIEVRE 58
- SAONE-ET-LOIRE 71

**JURA/ALPES**
- HAUTE-SAONE 70
- TERRITOIRE-DE-BELFORT 90
- DOUBS 25
- JURA 39
- AIN 01
- HAUTE-SAVOIE 74
- SAVOIE 73
- ISERE 38

**VENDEE CHARENTE**
- VENDEE 85
- DEUX-SEVRES 79
- CHARENTE-MARITIME 17
- CHARENTE 16
- VIENNE 86

**LIMOUSIN/AUVERGNE**
- INDRE 36
- ALLIER 03
- CREUSE 23
- HAUTE-VIENNE 87
- PUY-DE-DOME 63
- LOIRE 42
- RHONE 69
- CORREZE 19
- CANTAL 15
- HAUTE-LOIRE 43

**RHONE VALLEY**
- ARDECHE 07
- DROME 26

**DORDOGNE/AVEYRON**
- DORDOGNE 24
- LOT 46
- AVEYRON 12
- LOZERE 48

**PROVENCE**
- HAUTES-ALPES 05
- ALPES-DE-HAUTE-PROVENCE 04
- VAUCLUSE 84
- ALPES-MARITIMES 06

**ATLANTIC COAST**
- GIRONDE 33
- LOT-ET-GARONNE 47
- LANDES 40

**MIDI-PYRENEES**
- TARN-ET-GARONNE 82
- GERS 32
- TARN 81
- HAUTE-GARONNE 31
- PYRENEES-ATLANTIQUES 64
- HAUTES-PYRENEES 65
- ARIEGE 09

**MEDITERRANEAN**
- GARD 30
- HERAULT 34
- BOUCHES-DU-RHONE 13
- VAR 83
- AUDE 11
- PYRENEES-ORIENTALES 66

**CORSICA**
- CORSICA 20

---

# Town and Village Index

# Town and Village Index

## Town and Village Index

## Town and Village Index

## Index of Advertisers

# Campsite Index by Number

# Campsite Index by Number

# Campsite Index by Region

## Northern France

## Paris / Ile de France

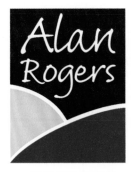

## Eastern France

## Vendée/Charente

## Loire Valley

## Burgundy

There are three indexes in this guide:

On pages 401-404 is an index of towns where the campsites are situated.

On pages 405-409 each campsite indexed by its Number.

On pages 410-416 each campsite indexed by its Region.

Sites that are new to the guide this year are highlighted in bold text.

Municipal sites are marked 'M', Naturist sites are marked 'N'

# THIS CARD WILL
## save you money!

TO QUALIFY FOR SOME MONEY SAVING OFFERS, AND
USEFUL INFORMATION, SIMPLY RETURN THE CARD -
**NO STAMP REQUIRED.**

## Register Me For Savings - Today

### ○ Ferry Savings
Please keep me posted with the latest ferry savings,
special offers and up to date news

### ○ Discounts on Alan Rogers' Guides
Please offer me discounts on future editions of the
Alan Rogers' Guides plus other camping and
caravanning publications

Mr/Mrs/Ms          Initial          Surname
_____

Address
_____

_____

                                  Postcode
_____

Telephone                         Email
_____

**Brickbats and Bouquets**
Tell us what you think of the Alan Rogers' Guides
_____

_____

_____

_____

**THANK YOU AND HAPPY TRAVELLING!**

www.**alanrogers**.com

INSPECTED
CAMPSITES
& SELECTED

W1610